Die Grundlehren der mathematischen Wissenschaften

in Einzeldarstellungen
mit besonderer Berücksichtigung
der Anwendungsgebiete

Band 157

Herausgegeben von

J. L. Doob · A. Grothendieck · E. Heinz · F. Hirzebruch
E. Hopf · H. Hopf · W. Maak · S. MacLane · W. Magnus
M. M. Postnikov · F. K. Schmidt · D. S. Scott · K. Stein

Geschäftsführende Herausgeber

B. Eckmann und B. L. van der Waerden

Yu. V. Prohorov · Yu. A. Rozanov

Probability Theory

Basic Concepts · Limit Theorems
Random Processes

Translated by
K. Krickeberg and H. Urmitzer

Springer-Verlag New York · Heidelberg · Berlin 1969

Prof. Yu. V. Prohorov and Prof. Yu. A. Rozanov

Steklov-Institute for Mathematics, Akad. Nauk SSSR, Moscow/USSR

Geschäftsführende Herausgeber:

Prof. Dr. B. Eckmann

Eidgenössische Technische Hochschule Zürich

Prof. Dr. B. L. van der Waerden

Mathematisches Institut der Universität Zürich

Translation of

"Teorija Verojatnostej" Moscow 1967

Preface

The aim of this book is to serve as a reference text to provide an orientation in the enormous material which probability theory has accumulated so far. The book mainly treats such topics like the foundations of probability theory, limit theorems and random processes.

The bibliography gives a list of the main textbooks on probability theory and its applications. By way of exception some references are planted into the text to recent papers which in our opinion did not find in monographs the attention they deserved (in this connection we do not at all want to attribute any priority to one or the other author). Some references indicate the immediate use of the material taken from the paper in question.

In the following we recommend some selected literature, together with indications of the corresponding sections of the present reference book.

The textbook by *B. V. Gnedenko*, „Lehrbuch der Wahrscheinlichkeitstheorie", Akademie-Verlag, Berlin 1957, and the book by *W. Feller*, "Introduction to Probability Theory and its Applications", Wiley, 2. ed., New York 1960 (Chapter I, § 1 of Chapter V) may serve as a first introduction to the various problems of probability theory. A large complex of problems is treated in *M. Loéve's* monograph "Probability Theory", Van Nostrand, 2. ed., Princeton, N. J.; Toronto, New York, London 1963 (Chapters II, III, § 2 Chapter VI). The foundations of probability theory are given in *A. N. Kolmogorov's* book „Grundbegriffe der Wahrscheinlichkeitsrechnung", Springer, Berlin 1933. Some special problems are the subject of *E. B. Dynkin's* „Die Grundlagen der Theorie der Markoffschen Prozesse", Springer, Berlin, Göttingen, Heidelberg 1961 (§§ 1.2, 2.4 of Chapter III). The books "Limit Distributions for Sums of Independent Random Variables, Addison-Wesley, Cambridge 1954 by *B. V. Gnedenko* and *A. N. Kolmogorov*, and "Independent Stationarily Connected Variables", Nauka, Moscow 1965 (in Russian) by *I. A. Ibragimov* and *Yu. V. Linnik* are dedicated to limit theorems. A basic monograph on random processes is *J. L. Doob's* "Stochastic Processes", Wiley, New York 1953 (§§ 1.2, 1.3, 2.3 of Chapter III; § 2.2 of Chapter VI); a detailed study of basic classes of random processes was presented by *I. I. Gichman* and *A. V. Skorochod* in their "Introduction to the Theory of Random Processes", Nauka, Moscow 1965 (in Russian) (§§ 1.4, 2, 3, 4, 5 of Chapter V; § 1 of Chapter VI). Particular classes of random processes are the subject of the following monographs: *K. L. Chung*, "Markov Chains with Stationary Transition Probabilities", Springer, Berlin, Göttingen, Heidelberg 1960; *T. Harris*, "Theory of Branching Processes", Springer, Berlin, Göttingen, Heidelberg 1963, *A. V. Skorochod*, "Studies in the Theory of Random Processes", Addison-Wesley, Cambridge 1954; *E. B. Dynkin*, "Markov Processes", Springer, Berlin, Göttingen, Heidelberg 1965; *Y. A. Rozanov*, "Stationary Random Processes", Fizmatgiz, Moscow 1963 (in Russian). Problems of the general theory of measure and integration are considered in the books of *P. Halmos*, "Measure Theory", Van Nostrand, Princeton, N. J.; Toronto, New York, London 1959, and *N. Dunford, D. Schwartz*, "Linear Operators", Wiley and Sons, New York - London 1964 (Part I), 2. ed., (Part II) 1964, 2. ed.

The text contains relatively few numbered references and formulas. Among them for example § 2.3 means point 3 of paragraph 2 of the current chapter. If there is any reference to another chapter its number will be indicated. The formulas are numbered separately in each chapter: for example (1.2) means the 2-nd formula of § 1.

When writting this book we had useful contacts with many specialists in probability theory. We therefore take the occasion to express our gratitude to *R. L. Dobrushin, V. M. Zolotariev, V. V. Sazonov, R. Z. Chasminsky, N. N. Čencov, A. N. Shiryaev* and especially to *L. N. Bolshev* who undertook the difficult task of redactorial work.

Yu. V. Prohorov
Yu. A. Rozanov

Annotation

The book gives a survey of the most important results, methods and trends of modern probability theory. The basic concepts of probability theory, the most important theoretical probability models, some methods of optimal control, linear filtration, elements of the theory of transmission of stationary informations through communication channels – this is by far not a complete list of the sections in which readers dealing with probability theory without being specialists might be interested. The book also contains sections for those who are working in probability theory or similar directions; thus there are the foundations of probability theory, some aspects of the general theory of random processes, limit theorems etc.

The book is intended for engineers, physicists and mathematicians as well as for candidates and advanced students specializing in these subjects.

Contents

CHAPTER III
Basic Concepts of Probability Theory

CHAPTER IV
Limit Theorems in Probability Theory

CHAPTER V

Markov Processes

CHAPTER VI

Stationary Processes

CHAPTER I

Basic Concepts of Elementary Probability Theory

§ 1. Experiments with Equally Probable Outcomes

1. Experiments with a Finite Number of Equally Probable Outcomes

Frequency and Probability. We consider a simple experiment such as coin tossing which has two outcomes excluding each other: the outcome of "head" or "tail", denoted by "H" or "T", correspondingly. It is impossible to the observer to analyze and take into account all factors which influence the result of our experiment: coin tossing is a random game and therefore no certain forecast of whether "H" or "T" will come out can be made. Despite the randomness of the outcome we can observe a remarkable regularity when the trials are repeated many times. After n tossings the number of "heads" $n(H)$ is such that the ratio $n(H)/n$ is approximately $1/2$. Below in Table 1 the results from a trial series of 10,000 coin tossings are given. Here, series of 100 trials each were selected

Table 1

The number of heads $n(H)$ in series of $n = 100$ trials each										The total number of heads in a series of 1000 trials
54	46	53	55	46	54	41	48	51	53	501
48	46	40	53	49	49	48	54	53	45	485
43	52	58	51	51	50	52	50	53	49	509
58	60	54	55	50	48	47	57	52	55	536
48	51	51	49	44	52	50	46	53	41	485
49	50	45	52	52	48	47	47	47	51	488
45	47	41	51	49	59	60	55	53	50	500
53	52	46	52	44	51	48	51	46	54	497
45	47	46	52	47	48	59	57	45	48	494
47	41	51	59	51	52	55	39	41	48	484

and in each of them the corresponding number $n(H)$ of outcomes "head" was registered [1].

The number $\mathbb{P}(H) = 1/2$ is the probability that any single trial will result in "head". This probability can be defined without prolonged trial series, by the fact that under the conditions of the experiment, H and T are equivalent outcomes or, in other words, they have the same probability: $\mathbb{P}(H) = \mathbb{P}(T) = 1/2$. What is meant by *probability*? Which sense can be ascribed to this concept? The large number of observations performed in practice permits to characterize probability as follows: Suppose we consider an experiment or a phenomenon where the random event A the observer is interested in takes place or not. Suppose that the conditions of the experiment (those under which the considered phenomenon may take place) can be restored so many times that in principle series of identical and independent trials can be made, where in each of them, depending on chance, the random event A occurs or not. We denote by n the number of trials and by $n(A)$ the number of those which have resulted in the occurrence of the event A. The ratio $n(A)/n$ is called the *frequency* of A in the given series of trials. As was shown by practice, for large n the frequency $n(A)/n$ in various trial series turns out to be almost identical. There exists a value $\mathbb{P}(A)$ called the *probability* of the event A near which the aforementioned frequencies $\dfrac{n(A)}{n}$ are gathering:

$$\mathbb{P}(A) \approx \frac{n(A)}{n}. \tag{1.1}$$

Calculation of Probabilities. If the experiments considered have equally probable outcomes, then the probability $\mathbb{P}(A)$ of the event A which we obtained from our experiment can be calculated by the simple formula

$$\mathbb{P}(A) = \frac{N(A)}{N}, \tag{1.2}$$

where N is the number of mutually exclusive outcomes of equal probability, and $N(A)$ the number of those outcomes which result in the occurrence of the event A.

Example. Suppose an experiment consists in throwing two dice whose faces are numbered from one to six. What is the probability that both dice will show the same number of spots? We describe each outcome of our trials by a pair of numbers (a, b): the first die shows a and the second one b spots. Obviously, the outcomes are equally probable, and there are $N = 36$ of them. The event A: "same number of spots"

---

[1] *Feller, W.*: Introduction to Probability Theory and its Applications. 2. ed. New York: Wiley 1960.

occurs if and only if we obtain one of the outcomes (a, b) where $a = b$. There are $N(A) = 6$ such outcomes. Hence the probability of A is $\mathbb{P}(A) = 6/36 = 1/6$.

We remark that it is an independent task of the observer to establish a relation between some event and the one or the other outcome of the corresponding experiment. What do we consider as outcomes of the experiment, which may or may not result in the event A in question? This problem is usually not at all easily to be solved and requires a careful analysis of the conditions of the problem as well as of the experiment.

Exampel. *Méré's Paradox.* The frenchman *de Méré* who had attended many games of dice found out that when three dice are thrown at the same time a combination which adds up to 11 spots will occur more frequently than a combination with 12 spots, although in his opinion both were equally probable. *De Méré* argued like this: one can get 11 spots in six various combinations (6-4-1, 6-3-2, 5-5-1, 5-4-2, 5-3-3, 4-4-3), and also six combinations with 12 spots (6-5-1, 6-4-2, 6-3-3, 5-5-2, 5-4-3, 4-4-4), and the equality of the number of outcomes inducing the occurrence of events A_1 and A_2 means that their probabilities $\mathbb{P}(A_1)$ and $\mathbb{P}(A_2)$ ought to be equal. The famous mathematician *B. Pascal* revealed *de Méré's* error by explaining that the outcomes considered by *de Méré* were not equally probable, for one had to consider not only the spots but also the dice on which they appear. If, for example, we number the dice and write down the spots as they turn up in corresponding order we see that 6-4-1 appears in six different outcomes $(6, 4, 1)$, $(6, 1, 4)$, $(4, 6, 1)$, $(4, 1, 6)$, $(1, 6, 4)$, $(1, 4, 6)$, whereas the combination 4-4-4 occurs only at the outcome $(4, 4, 4)$. Equally probable outsomes are those which can be described by three numbers (a, b, c), where a is the number of spots on the first, b the number of spots on the second, and c the number of spots on the third die. It is easy to compute that there are $N = 216$ equally probable outcomes. Among them the event A_1: "the sum of the spots which appeared equals 11" is favored by $N = (A_1) = 27$ outcomes, whereas the event A_2: "12 spots turning up" is favored by $N(A_2) = 25$ outcomes only. This explains why *de Méré* noticed that there is a tendency of 11 spots coming up more frequently [2].

2. Some Combinatorial Formulas

Examples of the Calculation of Probabilities. The study of theoretical probability schemes with a finite number of equally probable outcomes

---

[2] See *Borel, E.:* Probabilité, certitude et application aux nombres premiers. Paris: Gauthier-Villars 1952.

usually leads to the solution of mere combinatorial problems. Below we present the most customary formulas.

Combinations of Elements from Various Groups; Ordered Sampling with Replacement. Suppose there are r groups of elements: the first group consists of n_1 elements $a_{11}, ..., a_{1n_1}$, the second one of n_2 elements $a_{21}, ..., a_{2n_2}$ etc., the last one, the r-th group, contains n_r elements $a_{r1}, ..., a_{rn_r}$. We combine r elements in such a way that only one element from each group is contained in the combination. Then $N = n_1 n_2 ... n_r$ is the number of all combinations $a_{1i_1}, a_{2i_2}, ..., a_{ri_r}$ of this type.

Consider an ordered sample taken from some set which consists of elements $a_1, ..., a_n$, where successively an element a_i is selected (which then returns into the set), such that after r steps a sample of $a_{i_1}, a_{i_2}, ..., a_{i_r}$ is registered. $N = n^r$ is the number of all possible samples $a_{i_1}, a_{i_2}, ..., a_{i_r}$, where each element a_{i_k} is selected from the corresponding "group" – the given set at the k-th step.

The Number of Ordered Samples without Replacement. Let there be given n elements $a_1, ..., a_n$. We form all possible combinations of r different elements of the type $a_{i_1}, ..., a_{i_r}$ taking into account their order, in other words, r of the n elements are distributed over r places. The number of all these samples is

$$N = \frac{n!}{(n-r)!} = n(n-1) ... (n-r+1).$$

The same combinations are obtained, e. g. by successively selecting without replacement elements $a_{i_1}, ..., a_{i_r}$ from some set $a_1, ..., a_n$.

Number of Unordered Samples without Replacement. Suppose we disregard the order of the elements in the combinations $a_{i_1}, ..., a_{i_r}$ which are taken from the set of n elements $a_1, ..., a_n$; thus combinations of the same elements are considered to be equal. Then

$$N = C_n^r = \frac{n!}{(n-r)!r!}$$

is the number of these unordered samples without replacement of r elements from n, and is called the binomial coefficient of n over r.

Distributions over Cells. Let there be given n different elements which are distributed over r different cells. Each distribution can be described by the combination $(i_1, i_2, ..., i_n)$, where i_k denotes the cell which is occupied by the k-th object. Therefore $N = r^n$ is the number of all possible distributions. If the distributions satisfy the requirement that precisely n_i elements occupy cell i ($i = 1, ..., r$ and $n_1 + ... + n_r = n$), the number of all distributions is

$$N = \frac{n!}{n_1! \, n_2! \ldots n_r!}.$$

Distribution of Indistinguishable Objects over Cells. When in-distinguishable elements are distributed over cells, each distribution is defined by the numbers of elements which occupy the various cells, and may be described by the combination $(n_1, n_2, \ldots, n_r)$, where n_i is the number of the elements in the i-th cell.

$$N = \frac{(n+r-1)!}{n!(r-1)!} = C_{n+1-1}^{r-1}$$

is the number of all possible distributions.

If we require in addition that none of the cells should remain empty (it is then supposed that $n \geq r$), the number of all possible distributions equals

$$N = \frac{(n-1)!}{(r-1)!\,(n-r)!} = C_{n-1}^{r-1}.$$

Stirling's Formula. In all formulas above the expression $n! = n(n-1)\ldots 1$ occurs. The direct computation of this product for large n is extremely difficult. There exists a relatively simple formula which renders an approximate value for $n!$, called Stirling's formula:

$$n! \sim \sqrt{2\pi n} \cdot n^n e^{-n}$$

for large n.

Here and in the sequel the relation $\alpha_n \sim \beta_n$ between the quantities α_n and β_n means that $\dfrac{\alpha_n}{\beta_n} \to 1$ for $n \to \infty$. The relative error in *Stirling's* formula for all $n \geq 1$ can be estimated by the inequalities

$$0 < \frac{n!}{\sqrt{2\pi n}\, n^n e^{-n}} - 1 < e^{\frac{1}{12n}} - 1.$$

For a sharpening of *Stirling's* formula see § 5.2.

Example. A lot of 100 items is examined by a tester who, at random, takes out 10 pieces and checks their quality. If among these 10 items no defective piece is found the whole lot is accepted; otherwise it will undergo an additional examination. What is the probability that a lot which contains 10 defective pieces will be accepted by the tester?

The number of all possible ways of taking out 10 items from a lot of 100 equals the number of possibilities to select 10 elements from 100, e.g. $N = \dfrac{100!}{10!\,90!}$. It is natural to assume that the outcomes of this selection are equally probable [3]. The event A: "The lot of items is accepted by the tester" occurs when all the 10 pieces taken out at random form a sample from the set of items of high quality, the total number of which is 90. Therefore the number of outcomes leading to the event A equals the number of possibilities to select 10 pieces from 90 which is $N(A) = \dfrac{90!}{10!\,80!}$.

The lot is accepted if one of $N(A)$ equally probable outcomes occurs, the total number of outcomes being N. Therefore

$$\mathbb{P}(A) = \frac{81 \cdot 82 \dots 90}{91 \cdot 92 \dots 100} \approx \left(1 - \frac{1}{10}\right)^{10} \approx 0.349$$

is the probability that the tester will accept the lot [actually up to the 3-rd decimal, $\mathbb{P}(A) = 0.331$].

Example. We consider a préférence game, where 32 court cards of a block are dealt out at random between three players who get 10 cards each, and two cards are left "in stock". What is the probability that two "aces" turn out to be "in stock"? The number of the various assignment of the two cards into the "stock" equals the number of possibilities to select 2 cards out of 32 which is $N = \dfrac{32!}{2!\,30!} = 496$. There are 4 aces in a block of cards, and the number of the various assignments which yield two "aces" equals the number of possibilities to select 2 cards out of 4, that is, $N(A) = \dfrac{4!}{2!\,2!} = 6$. Thus the probability sought for is $\mathbb{P}(A) = 6/496 \approx 0.012$.

Suppose that one of the players, "the one whose turn it is", has 5 court cards of one color (5 hearts, say) except the queen. When announcing the rank of the game the player has to consider the possibility that one of his opponents might be able to get a combination which includes the three hearts being left (such a combination is called "third queen"). What is the probability of this event?

There are $N = C_{20}^{10} = \dfrac{20!}{10!\,10!}$ equally probable distributions of 20 cards into the two equal groups of 10 cards which are given to the two opponents. If the whole combination "third queen of hearts" is in the hands of any specific opponent, the number of the distributions compatible

---

[3] Strictly spoken, this is the very sense of the assumption that the tester takes out items at random.

with this constellation equals the number of selecting 7 cards out of the 17 being left, that is, $N(A) = \dfrac{17!}{7!\,10!}$. Thus the probability that the combination "third queen of hearts" appears at a given opponent is $\mathbb{P}(A) = \dfrac{8 \cdot\ 9 \cdot 10}{18 \cdot 19 \cdot 20} = 2/19 \approx 0.105$. Therefore, the probability of the "third queen of hearts" occuring at any one of the two "opponents" (regardless who gets it) is obviously twice larger.

3. "Geometric" Probabilities

In the case of an experiment with a finite number of equally probable outcomes the probability $\mathbb{P}(A)$ that the event A occurs at the given experiment is defined as the "share" taken up by those outcomes which lead to the occurence of this event [see formula (1.2)]. Analogously, the probability in more complicated experiments is calculated when an infinite number of equivalent outcomes is given.

We consider some examples where so-called "geometric" probabilites are calculated.

Example. Suppose that a point ξ is thrown at random onto a segment of length L of the real line in such a way that the probability to hit some subsegment is the same for all subsegments of equal length. What is the probability that its distance from the center of the segment will not exceed l (see Fig. 1)?

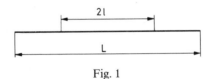

Fig. 1

Here we have an infinite number of possible outcomes, for ξ may fall down anywhere into the given segment of length L. Besides, the conditions of the experiment are such that, with equal probability, ξ can fall down at any point x of the segment. The event A: "the distance of ξ from the center does not exceed l" occurs when ξ falls onto a point x whose distance from the center is not larger than l. The "fraction" taken by the points x in the whole segment can be defined as the ratio $L(A)/L$, where L is the length of the entire interval, and $L(A) = 2l$ the length of the interval which leads to the occurrence of the event A. Thus the probability $\mathbb{P}(A)$ sought for equals

$$\mathbb{P}(A) = \frac{L(A)}{L} = \begin{cases} 2l/L & \text{if } 2l < L, \\ 1 & \text{if } 2l \geq L. \end{cases}$$

Example. Suppose two different points are thrown at random and independently from each other onto a segment of length L in such a way that for each point the probability to hit some subsegment is the same for all subsegments of equal length. What is the probability that the distance between them will not exceed l?

In order to answer this question we consider the following model. We draw the coordinate of the point ξ_1 in the interval $(0, L)$ on the x_1-axis and the coordinate of the point ξ_2 on the x_2-axis (Fig. 2). We can

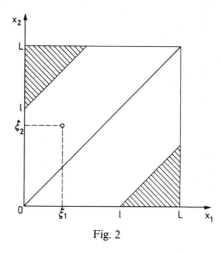

Fig. 2

make the assumption that the point (ξ_1, ξ_2) is thrown at random into a square with sidelength L. The probability sought for coincides with the probability that the following event A occurs: the point (ξ_1, ξ_2) falls into the part of the square which is bounded by the straight lines given by the equations $x_2 = x_1 \pm l$. On Fig. 2 this domain has been left unmarked. The "fraction" of outcomes which induce the event $A = \{|\xi_1 - \xi_2| \leq l\}$ can be defined as the ratio $S(A)/S$ where S is the area of the whole square, and $S(A)$ the area of the domain where the event A occurs [$S(A)$ is the area of the unmarked figure]:

$$\mathbb{P}(A) = \frac{S(A)}{S} = \frac{L^2(L-l)^2}{L^2} = 1 - \left(1 - \frac{l}{L}\right)^2.$$

Example. *The Needle Problem.* Suppose that a needle of length *l* is thrown onto a plane (*x*, *y*) which is marked by lines parallel to the *x*-axis at a distance *L* from each other (Fig. 3). What is the probability that the needle will intersect one of these lines?

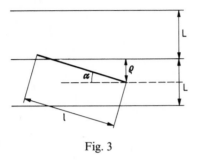

Fig. 3

We consider the needle as a segment of length *l*. By α we denote the angle of inclination between this segment and the *x*-axis, and by ϱ the distance between its lower point and the nearest upper line (see Fig. 3). It is intuitively obvious that α and ϱ can take anyone of the possible values within the limits $0 \le \alpha \le \pi$ and $0 \le \varrho \le L$ with equal probability and independently of each other. Geometrically, the set of all possible

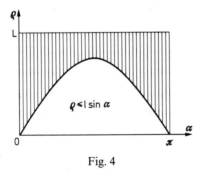

Fig. 4

outcomes (α, ϱ) forms a rectangle (Fig. 4). The event A: "the needle intersects one of the lines" occurs if and only if the values α and ϱ are such that $\varrho \le l \sin \alpha$. The "fraction" of outcomes (α, ϱ) which lead to the occurrence of A can be defined as the ratio $S(A)/S$, where S is the area of the whole rectangle and $S(A)$ the area below the curve $\varrho = l \sin \alpha$, that is, the area of the domain of all values (α, ϱ) which result in the occurrence of the event A. Therefore, the probability $\mathbb{P}(A)$ sought for is given by the formula

$$\mathbb{P}(A) = \frac{S(A)}{S},$$

where $S = \pi L$, $S(A) = l \int_0^\pi \sin \alpha \, d\alpha = 2l$, that is, $\mathbb{P}(A) = 2l/(\pi L)$.

In all examples studied so far we departed from purely intuitive considerations about the conditions of the experiment which we described briefly as "throwing at random". The first example was in fact based on the assumption that the probability of the point ξ falling onto an interval Δ does not depend on where this interval is located in the segment of length L in question. The second and third example were based on the assumption that the probability of the points with coordinates (ξ_1, ξ_2) or (α, ϱ) falling into a certain figure Δ in the square $0 \leq \xi_1, \leq L, 0 \leq \xi_2 \leq L$ or in the rectangle $0 \leq \alpha \leq \pi, 0 \leq \varrho \leq L$, does not depend on its position. It is sufficiently obvious that these conditions on the experiment which we have now already formulated exactly are satisfied.

It should be mentioned that the expression $\mathbb{P}(A) = \dfrac{2l}{\pi L}$ for the probability that the needle will intersect any line in the plane, has been used for the determination of π by random trials. In fact, a prolonged series of trials was made, and the corresponding frequency $n(A)/n$ was set equal to the probability $\mathbb{P}(A)$ [here, n is the number of trials, $n(A)$ the number of those among them where the needle intersected some lines]. For $l = L$ and at $n = 10,000$ trials the corresponding value $\pi \approx \dfrac{2l}{L} \cdot \dfrac{n}{n(A)}$ turned out to be 3.15.

§ 2. The Space of Elementary Events and the Law of Composition of Probabilities

1. Combination of Events

The events A_1 and A_2 are called equal if the occurrence of the event A_1 induces the occurrence of the event A_2 and vice versa. A_1 and A_2 are called *incompatible* or *disjoint* if the occurrence of one of them excludes the occurrence of the other, in other words, if A_1 and A_2 cannot occur at the same time.

Example. When two dice are thrown the events A_1: "an even sum of spots turns up" and A_2: "the numbers on the two sides appearing have the same parity" turn out to be equal. The analogous events at another experiment where not two, but three dice are thrown are no longer equal.

The event A which consists in the occurrence of at least one of the events A_1 and A_2 is called the *union* or the *sum* of the events A_1 and A_2, written as $A = A_1 \cup A_2$, where $\cup$ is a special symbol for union. The union of several events $A_1, A_2, \ldots$ is defined analogously, and is written as $A = \bigcup_k A_k$.

The event A which means the occurrence of A_1 as well as A_2 is called the *intersection* or the *product* of A_1 and A_2, and is written as $A = A_1 \cap A_2$, where $\cap$ is a special symbol for intersection. The product of several events $A_1, A_2, \ldots$, is defined analogously, and is denoted by $A = \bigcap_k A_k$ or $A = A_1 \cdot A_2 \cdot \ldots$. By the *difference* of A_1 and A_2 we mean the event A which occurs if and only if A_1 occurs whereas A_2 does not: $A = A_1 \setminus A_2$. The event $\bar{A}$ which occurs if and only if A does not occur is called the *complement* of A.

Example. We consider an experiment where two dice are cast. The event A: "an even sum of spots come up" is the union of the disjoint events A_1: "even number on each side" and A_2: "uneven number on each side". Then $A_1 = A \setminus A_2$ and $A_2 = A \setminus A_1$. The complement of A is the event $\bar{A}$: "uneven number of spots". The complement of A_1 is the event $\bar{A}_1$: "an uneven number on at least one side", and the complement of A_2 is the event $\bar{A}_2$: "an even number on at least one side". Then $\bar{A}_1 \setminus \bar{A} = \bar{A}_1 \cdot A = A_2$ and $\bar{A}_2 \setminus A = \bar{A}_2 \cdot A = A_1$.

2. The Space of Elementary Events

Suppose that among all possible events A which at random may or may not occur in the given experiment, a set of so-called *elementary events* or *elementary outcomes* with the following properties can be selected. First, they exclude each other – they are disjoint – and one of these elementary outcomes is bound to occur at the experiment, secondly, whatever the event A may be, the occuring elementary outcome permits to decide whether this event takes place or not. The elementary outcomes are usually denoted by the Greek letter ω and the set Ω of all them is called the *space of elementary events*.

Example. When casting two dice the pair of numbers $\omega = (a, b)$ where a is the number of spots on the first die and b the number of spots on the second die, $1 \leq a, b \leq 6$, can be regarded as the elementary outcome. When throwing a needle onto a ruled plane the elementary outcome is described by the point $\omega = (\alpha, \varrho)$ where α is the angle of inclination of the needle and ϱ the distance between its lower end and the next upper line. In this case the space Ω is geometrically represented by a rectangle $0 \leq \alpha \leq \pi; 0 \leq \varrho \leq L$ in the plane of the variables (α, ϱ).

Let Ω be the space of the elementary outcomes ω of the considered experiment or phenomenon. Given any event A connected with this experiment we can form the set of the elementary outcomes ω the occurrence of which induces the event A. We denote the set of these outcomes by the same symbol A as the corresponding event. Obviously the event A occurs if and only if one of the elementary outcomes ω contained in the

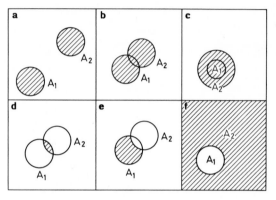

Fig. 5

set A occurs. In other words, the event A is equal to the event which consists in the occurrence of any elementary outcome belonging to the set A (symbolically, we write $\omega \in A$ to express that ω belongs to A). The event A can be identified with the corresponding set A of elementary outcomes.

The certain event A which occurs with every elementary outcome ω equals the entire space Ω, when events and sets are identified: $A = \Omega$. *The impossible event* A which does not occur with any elementary outcome ω, coincides with the empty set which is usually denoted by the symbol $0: A = 0$.

The concepts of union, intersection etc., introduced above now become very descriptive: $A_1 \cup A_1$ is the union of the sets A_1 and A_2, $A_1 \cap A_2$ their intersection, $\bar{A} = \Omega \backslash A$ the set of the elementary outcomes which completes the set A to the entire space of elementary events Ω. The event A_1 implies the occurrence of the event A_2 if and only if A_1 is contained in A_2 which we write as $A_1 \subseteq A_2$ or $A_2 \supseteq A_1$.

To elucidate relations among various events it often turns out to be convenient to represent the space of the elementary events Ω by a domain in the plane. Then the elementary events ω are described by points of the plane lying within Ω and the events (certain sets of points ω) are represented by certain domains included in Ω. Fig. 5 illustrates various relations between the events A_1 and A_2 which are represented as domains in the plane contained in the rectangle Ω which represents the space of elementary events. The shaded area represents the event A, where in Fig. a and b we have $A = A_1 \cup A_2$, in c $A = A_1 \cup A_2$, in d $A = A_1 \cap A_2$, and in e $A = A_2 = \overline{A}_1$.

Looking at these domains we see that the following general connections exist among the various relations between events. If $A_1 \subseteq A_2$, then $\overline{A}_1 \supseteq \overline{A}_2$; if $A = A_1 \cup A_2$, then $\overline{A} = \overline{A}_1 \cap \overline{A}_2$, and if $A = A_1 \cap A_2$, then $\overline{A} = \overline{A}_1 \cup \overline{A}_2$. In general, if a certain relation among events is true, then the relation which we obtain by passing to the complementary events and by replacing the sign of union $\cup$, the sign of intersection $\cap$, and the sign of inclusion $\subseteq$, by the sign $\cap$, $\cup$, and $\supseteq$, respectively (the equality signs "$=$" remain unchanged), is also true. For example the following relations are equivalent:

$$\bigcup_k A_k = B \subseteq \overline{\bigcap_k C_k^k}; \quad \bigcap_k \overline{A}_k = \overline{B} \supseteq \bigcap_k C_k; \quad \bigcup_k A_k = B \subseteq \bigcup_k \overline{C}_k.$$

3. The Law of Composition of Probabilities

We consider incompatible events A_1, A_2 and their union $A = A_1 \cup A_2$. We imagine a series of identical and mutually independent experiments being performed which can result in the occurrence of the events A, A_1 or A_2. Let n be the number of all experiments, $n(A)$, $n(A_1)$, $n(A_2)$ the number of those which lead to the occurrence of the events A, A_1 and A_2, respectively. If a certain experiment resulted in the event A, then either the event A_1 or A_2 occurred (A_1 and A_2 cannot occur at the same time, since they are incompatible). Therefore, the numbers $n(A)$, $n(A_1)$ and $n(A_2)$ are connected by the equation

$$n(A) = n(A_1) + n(A_2).$$

Thus, the frequencies of the events in question satisfy the relation

$$n(A)/n = n(A_1)/n + n(A_2)/n.$$

Given a large number of experiments n the frequency practically equals the corresponding probabilities (see § 1.1). Hence the probabilities of the experiments A, A_1 and A_2 ought to be connected by the equation

$$\mathbb{P}(A) = \mathbb{P}(A_1) + \mathbb{P}(A_2).$$

This formula is a particular case of the law of composition of probabilities, according to which the probability of the union of incompatible events (in finite or countable infinite number) equals the sum of their probabilities:

$$\mathbb{P}\left\{\bigcup_k A_k\right\} = \sum_k \mathbb{P}(A_k). \tag{2.1}$$

Probabilities of Various Combinations of Events. If the relations between various events are visually described by relations between the corresponding domains in the plane (see Fig. 5), then the properties of probabilities are completely analogous to the properties of the areas of these domains. In particular,

$$\left.\begin{aligned}
\mathbb{P}(A_1 \backslash A_2) &= \mathbb{P}(A_1) - \mathbb{P}(A_1 \cap A_2), \\
\mathbb{P}(A_2 \backslash A_1) &= \mathbb{P}(A_2) - \mathbb{P}(A_1 \cap A_2), \\
\mathbb{P}(A_1 \cup A_2) &= \mathbb{P}(A_1) + \mathbb{P}(A_2) - \mathbb{P}(A_1 \cap A_2).
\end{aligned}\right\}$$

Let $A_1, A_2, \dots, A_n$ be some events and

$$p_i = \mathbb{P}(A_i), \qquad p_{ij} = \mathbb{P}(A_i A_j), \qquad p_{ijk} = \mathbb{P}(A_i A_j A_k), \dots$$

We set

$$S_0 = 1, \qquad S_1 = \Sigma\, p_i, \qquad S_2 = \Sigma\, p_{ij}, \qquad S_3 = \Sigma\, p_{ijk}, \dots,$$

where we sum over all different sets of indices (all different sets of events). Then the following formula holds:

$$Q_1 = \mathbb{P}\left(\bigcup_{i=1}^{n} A_i\right) = S_1 - S_2 + S_3 - \cdots - (-1)^n S_n. \tag{2.2}$$

The probability P_0 that none of the events $A_1, A_2, \dots, A_n$ occurs is

$$P_0 = 1 - Q_1 = S_0 - S_1 + S_2 - S_3 + \cdots + (-1)^n S_n.$$

In general, the probability P_m that exactly m of the events $A_1, A_2, \dots, A_n$ $(0 \le m \le n)$ happen can be evaluated by the formula

$$P_m = S_m - C_{m+1}^1 S_{m+1} + C_{m+2}^2 S_{m+2} - \cdots + (-1)^{n-m} C_n^{n-m} S_n. \tag{2.3}$$

The probability Q_m that at least m of the events $A_1, A_2, \dots, A_n$ $(0 \le m \le n)$ occur is expressed in terms of the sums $S_m, S_{m+1}, \dots, S_n$ by the formula

$$Q_m = S_m - C_m^1 S_{m+1} + C_{m+1}^2 S_{m+2} - \cdots + (-1)^{n-m} C_{n-1}^{n-m} S_n \tag{2.4}$$

(here as everywhere C_m^k denotes the binomial coefficient of m over k, where $C_m^k = 0$ if $k > m$).

Example. *A Coincidence Problem.* Suppose n cells and n elements are given; each cell and each element is labelled with a corresponding number i $(1 \le i \le n)$. The elements are distributed at random over the cells such that each cell contains exactly one element; all these distributions are assumed to be equally probable. By a coincidence we mean any of the events A_i which consists in the element i falling into the cell i with the same number. What is the probability Q_1 of at least one coincidence? The probability P_m of exactly m coincidences? How do these probabilities change when the number of elements n increases?

The event A_i is favored by $(n-1)!$ distributions of $n-1$ elements over $n-1$ places, the cell i being occupied by the element with the same number; the event $A_i A_j$ occurs at $(n-2)!$ distributions, the cells with the number i and j being occupied by the elements i and j, etc. There are $n!$ possible distributions altogether, hence

$$p_i = \frac{(n-1)!}{n!}, \qquad p_{ij} = \frac{(n-2)!}{n!}, \qquad p_{ijk} = \frac{(n-3)!}{n!}, \ldots$$

The sum S_k contains exactly $\dfrac{n!}{k!(n-k)!}$ identical terms, each of them being equal to $\dfrac{(n-k)!}{n!}$, and therefore $S_k = \dfrac{1}{k!}$. Consequently, the probability that at least one of the events $A_1, A_2, \ldots, A_n$ occurs (in other words the probability of at least one coincidence) is

$$Q_1 = 1 - \frac{1}{2!} + \frac{1}{3!} - \cdots - (-1)^n \frac{1}{n!}.$$

This expression is the partial sum of the $n+1$ first terms of the series for $1 - e^{-1}$:

$$1 - e^{-1} = 1 - \frac{1}{2!} + \frac{1}{3!} - \cdots \quad (e = 2.718 \ldots).$$

Thus, $\lim\limits_{n \to \infty} Q_1 = 1 - e^{-1} = 0.632 \ldots$ Analogously, we have for $m \geq 1$

$$\lim_{n \to \infty} P_m = \frac{1}{m!} e^{-1}, \quad \text{that is,} \quad P_m \approx \frac{1}{m!} e^{-1}.$$

The Borel-Cantelli Lemma. Let $A_1, A_2, \ldots, A_n, \ldots$ be a sequence of events and Q_m the probability that at least m of the events $A_1, A_2, \ldots, A_n, \ldots$ occur. The probabilities Q_m $(m = 1, 2, \ldots)$ are monotone decreasing, and

$$\lim_{n \to \infty} Q_m = Q$$

is the probability that an infinite number of the events $A_1, A_2, \ldots, A_n, \ldots$ occurs; if

$$S_1 = \sum_{i=1}^{\infty} P(A_i) < \infty,$$

then $Q = 0$.

§ 3. The Relation between Various Events

1. Conditional Probabilities

When analyzing the one or the other phenomenon the observer is often met by the question how the occurrence of an event A may be influenced by the occurrence of another event B. A very simple example is given by the following two extreme cases of connections between A and B: the occurrence of B is bound to induce the event A or, on the contrary, B excludes the possibility of the occurrence of A. In probability theory characteristic relations between A and B are described by the so-called conditional probability $\mathbb{P}(A|B)$ of the event A under the condition B. This conditional probability is defined as the ratio

$$\mathbb{P}(A|B) = \frac{\mathbb{P}(AB)}{\mathbb{P}(B)} \tag{3.1}$$

(it is assumed that the probability of B is positive).

The quantity $\mathbb{P}(A|B)$ can be considered as the probability of the occurrence of A under new conditions, namely, the occurrence of B. We will explain this by an example of an experiment with a finite number of equally probable elementary outcomes ω. Let N be the number of all elementary outcomes, $N(B)$ the number of those which lead to the occurrence of B, and $N(AB)$ the number of elementary outcomes which induce the occurrence of A and B. In this case the probabilities of B and AB are $\mathbb{P}(B) = \dfrac{N(B)}{N}$ and $\mathbb{P}(AB) = \dfrac{N(AB)}{N}$ so that the conditional probability $\mathbb{P}(A|B)$ is expressed by the formula

$$\mathbb{P}(A|B) = \frac{N(AB)}{N(B)}. \tag{3.2}$$

Here $N(B)$ is the number of all elementary outcomes ω which are still possible under the condition that B occurs, and $N(AB)$ is the number of those among them which lead to the occurrence of the event A. In correspondance with the general formula (1.2) the Eq. (3.2) defines the probability of the event A under the new condition which arise if the event B occurs.

Conditional probabilities have all the properties of ordinary probabilities. In fact,

$$0 \leqq \mathbb{P}(A|B) \leqq 1;$$

if the event B entails the occurrence of the event $A : B \subseteq A$, then

$$\mathbb{P}(A|B) = 1;$$

if B excludes the possibility of the occurrence of A: $A \cdot B = \emptyset$, then

$$\mathbb{P}(A|B) = 0;$$

if A is the union of the disjoint events $A_1, A_2, \ldots : A = \bigcup_k A_k$, then

$$\mathbb{P}(A|B) = \sum_k \mathbb{P}(A_k|B).$$

The Formula of the Complete Probability. In order to find the probability of one or the other event A it is often appropriate to choose first in a convenient way some event B and determine the conditional probability $\mathbb{P}(A|B)$ as the probability of the event A under the new condition that the occurrence of B is known. If there is a *complete system of incompatible events* $B = B_1, B_2, \ldots$ (that is, a system of disjoint events, one of which must occur), then the probability $\mathbb{P}(A)$ of the event A is expressed in terms of the corresponding conditional probabilities $\mathbb{P}(A|B)$ by the so-called *formula of the complete probability:*

$$\mathbb{P}(A) = \sum_k \mathbb{P}(A|B_k) \mathbb{P}(B_k). \tag{3.3}$$

Example. Imagine a wanderer departing from a point 0 and choosing at random one of the possible ways leading off from the cross-roads. The scheme of ways is given on Fig. 6. On this figure some point A and

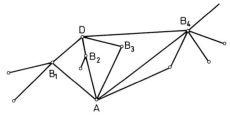

Fig. 6

ways leading to it are shown. What is the probability that the wanderer will reach this point? As is shown by the figure the wanderer must pass through one of the intermediate points B_1, B_2, B_3, B_4. By B_k we denote the event that he moves through the point B_k. The events B_1, B_2, B_3, B_4 form a complete system. Obviously, these events are equally probable, since the wanderer chooses one of the ways $0B_1, 0B_2, 0B_3, 0B_4$ at random. Thus, we have $\mathbb{P}(B_k) = 1/4$. If the wanderer comes to B_1 he can reach A only in one of the three possible directions departing from B_1 so that the conditional probability of reaching A under the condition of B_1 is 1/3. If we denote by A the event that the wanderer reaches the point A, then $\mathbb{P}(A\,|\,B_1) = 1/3$. According to Fig. 6 we have analogously

$$\mathbb{P}(A\,|\,B_2) = 1/2, \qquad \mathbb{P}(A\,|\,B_3) = 1, \qquad \mathbb{P}(A\,|\,B_4) = 2/5\,,$$

and by the formula of the complete probability

$$\mathbb{P}(A) = 1/4\,(1/3 + 1/2 + 1 + 2/5) = 61/120.$$

Example. *The Problem of Best Choice.* Suppose that we are given a collection of m objects. By comparing any two of them an observer can decide which of the two is better or worse. The problem is now to choose the best possible object. We assume that this problem is complicated by the fact that after an object had been tried and rejected one cannot return to it any more. In particular, by bad luck the absolutely best object can be rejected in the hope that further examination will bring a still better one. Imagine for instance a girl particular in her choice of a husband who either accepts the proposal of marriage of the wooing bridegroom and then her choice terminates, or she rejects his proposal and the bridegroom is lost forever to her.

We adopt one natural rule of choice: not to stop at an object which is worse than some of the objects which had already been tried and rejected before. We suppose that the observer procedes according to this rule so that when trying the given objects successively he can choose the first one at once, and thus terminate the process. If he did not, then the examination will be continued until at some step the best of all objects tried so far is found. The observer can choose this best object from the objects he had tried (and thus terminate the process), or go on seeking a still better one etc. Of course, it may happen that actually the absolutely best object is rejected, and then nothing at all is chosen. If the number of the given objects is large, then hardly anyone would agree to choose the first object coming up without taking the chance of getting some better one.

Suppose that following this rule the observer made his choice at the k-th object, e.g. the last one of these k objects turned out to be better than all former ones, and was then chosen. What is the probability that this object is the best among the set of the objects tried as well as of those which were not tried?

The event that among the k objects observed the last one was found to be the best will be denoted by B. The observer knows that B has occurred. The event that the k-th element is the best of all objects will be denoted by A. We are interested in the conditional probability $\mathbb{P}(A\,|\,B)$ of the event A under the condition that the event B occurred. This probability is expressed by the formula (3.2); therefore in order to evaluate $\mathbb{P}(A\,|\,B)$ we have to find the probabilities of the events B and $A\,B$.

Obviously, the event A is contained in B so that the intersection AB coincides with the event A. Under the conditions of choice described above it is reasonable to assume that all possible arrangements of the objects are equally probable. The probability of the event B coincides with the probability that under a random permutation of k distinguishable elements (they differ in quality) the best of them is found at the fixed k-th place. This probability is equal to $\dfrac{(k-1)}{k!}$ where k is the number of all permutations of k elements, and $(k-1)!$ the number of the permutations of $k-1$ elements which are still possible under the condition that the best element is fixed at the k-th place. Thus

$$\mathbb{P}(B) = \frac{(k-1)!}{k!} = \frac{1}{k}.$$

The probability of the event A is evaluated analogously. It coincides with the probability that under a random permutation of m distinguishable elements a given element, in fact the best object of the set of m objects in question, is found at the k-th place. Thus

$$\mathbb{P}(A) = \mathbb{P}(AB) = \frac{(m-1)!}{m!} = \frac{1}{m},$$

and the conditional probability sought for is $\mathbb{P}(A|B) = k/m$.

Example. *The Problem of the Gambler's Ruin.* We consider a game of so-called "heads" or "tails" where the player chooses "head" or "tail", and then tosses a coin. If the side turns up which the player had named then he wins and gets, say, one ruble, in the opposite case he looses this amount. Suppose that the gambler's initial capital equals x rubles and his aim is to increase it to a rubles. The game continues until the player has the sum a he aimed at, or until he is ruined having lost his entire capital. What is the probability that the player finally gets ruined without having obtained the sum of a rubles?

It is evident that this probability depends from the initial capital x and the final sum a. We denote by $p(x)$ the probability that having had x rubles, the gambler nevertheless gets ruined. In this notation, under the condition of winning at the first step the probability of ruin equals $p(x+1)$, since then the gambler's capital after the first step is $x+1$. Analogously, under the condition of loosing at the first step the probability of ruin equals $p(x-1)$, since then the capital after the first step is $x-1$. Let B_1 be the event that the player wins at the first step and B_2 the event that he looses. Finally, let the event A stand for the gambler's ruin.

In terms of the notation adopted above the conditional probabilities of ruin are given by the formulas

$$\mathbb{P}(A|B_1) = p(x+1), \quad \mathbb{P}(A|B_2) = p(x-1).$$

The events B_1 and B_2 form a complete system since at the first step the player either wins or looses; moreover, obviously,

$$\mathbb{P}(B_1) = \mathbb{P}(B_2) = \frac{1}{2}.$$

The formula of complete probability yields the following equation for the probabilities $p(x)$:

$$p(x) = \frac{1}{2}[p(x+1) + p(x-1)] \quad (0 \leq x \leq a),$$

where $p(0) = 1$, $p(a) = 0$. The solution of this equation is given by the linear function

$$p(x) = C_1 + C_2 x,$$

whose coefficients are determined by the boundary conditions:

$$p(0) = C_1 = 1, \quad p(a) = C_1 + C_2 a = 0.$$

From this we finally obtain the following expression for the desired probability of ruin $p(x)$ if the initial capital was x:

$$p(x) = 1 - \frac{x}{a} \quad (0 \leq x \leq a).$$

Urn Model. We consider an urn with white and black balls. At the beginning the urn contains a white and b black balls. One ball is drawn at random, and then c balls of the same color as the one that had been drawn, and d balls of the opposite color are placed into the urn. The parameters c and d may be negative which corresponds to an additional decrease of the number of balls of a certain color. Under the condition that a white ball is drawn, the probability of drawing a ball of the same color at the next trial equals $\dfrac{a+c}{a+b+c+d}$, and the probability of drawing a black ball equals $\dfrac{b+d}{a+b+c+d}$. Under the condition that a black ball is drawn the probability of drawing a white ball at the next trial is $\dfrac{a+d}{a+b+c+d}$ and the probability of drawing a black ball is $\dfrac{b+c}{a+b+c+d}$.

Example. *Diffusion Model.* Suppose we are given two boxes A and B filled with "white" and "black" molecules, respectively. The molecules are wandering at random from one box into the other. It is assumed that a transition of two or more molecules at the same time is impossible and that at each step the transition from A to B or from B to A takes place with a probability proportional to the number of molecules in A and B. We then have an urn model with parameters $c = -1$ and $d = 1$. Under the condition that at the present moment there are a molecules in box A and $b = N - a$ molecules in box B, box A will contain at the next step $a - 1$ molecules with probability a/N and $a + 1$ molecules with probability b/N.

2. Independent Events

We consider two independent experiments. By this we mean that no outcome of an experiment has any influence on the outcomes of the other. If the event A_1 is connected only with the first experiment and the event A_2 only with the second experiment, the occurrence of A_1 does not influence the possibility of A_2 happening, and conversely, the event A_2 does not influence A_1. In this sense we may say that the events A_1 and A_2 are *independent* of each other. What is the probability that these events occur both?

In order to answer this question we refer to the empirical fact according to which in a large series of independent experiments the frequency of any event equals approximately its probability (see § 1.1). We imagine a long series of independent trials in each of which both experiments are carried out. If n is the number of all trials and $n(A_1 A_2)$ the number of those which result in the occurrence of both A_1 and A_2, the probability $\mathbb{P}(A_1, A_2)$ sought for can be evaluated approximately by the formula

$$\mathbb{P}(A_1 A_2) \approx n(A_1 A_2)/n .$$

Next we consider only those trials at which the event A_2 occurs. Let $n(A_2)$ be the number of these trials. Then the approximation

$$\mathbb{P}(A_2) \approx n(A_2)/n$$

holds. For sufficiently large n the number of the trials where A_2 happens is large, too. However the event A_2 occurs only in connection with the second experiment which is performed independently of the first one and its corresponding event A_1. We consider the results of the first experiments in the series of the $n(A_2)$ trials which lead to the occurrence of the event A_2 in the second experiment. The number of these trials which result in the occurrence of A_1 equals the numbers $n(A_1 A_2)$ introduced above, so that

$$\mathbb{P}(A_1) \approx n(A_1 A_2)/n(A_2).$$

These relations allow to express the probability of the simultaneous occurrence of the independent events A_1 and A_2 through their probabilities $\mathbb{P}(A_1)$ and $\mathbb{P}(A_2)$:

$$\mathbb{P}(A_1 A_2) \approx \frac{n(A_1 A_2)}{n} = \frac{n(A_1 A_2)}{n(A_2)} \cdot \frac{n(A_2)}{n}.$$

But $n(A_2)/n \approx \mathbb{P}(A_2)$, and therefore

$$\mathbb{P}(A_1 A_2) = \mathbb{P}(A_1) \cdot \mathbb{P}(A_2). \tag{3.4}$$

In probability theory any two events A_1 and A_2 for which the Eq. (3.4) holds are called *independent*, disregarding physical conditions on such or such experiment.

This definition agrees well with the concept of conditional probability introduced formerly. For, the event A_1 is independent of the event A_2 if and only if the occurrence of A_2 does not influence the probability that A_1 will occur; more precisely, if the conditional probability $\mathbb{P}(A_1 | A_2)$ of A_1 under the condition that A_2 occurs equals the unconditional probability of this event:

$$\mathbb{P}(A_1 | A_2) = \mathbb{P}(A_2)$$

(here, the events A_1 and A_2 can be interchanged).

Example. We consider the following experiment. One card is drawn at random from a block of 36 cards. Let A_1 be the event that a "pique" is drawn and A_2 the event that a "queen" appears. Are these events independent? Here an intuitive answer is hard to give. Elementary calculations, however, show that the probability $\mathbb{P}(A_1)$ of drawing one of the cards from the block of 9 "piques" is $9/36 = 1/4$, the probability $\mathbb{P}(A_2)$ of getting one of the four "queens" is $4/36 = 1/9$, and the probability $\mathbb{P}(A_1 A_2)$ of drawing "pique" and "queen" is $1/36$, that is, $\mathbb{P}(A_1 A_2) = \mathbb{P}(A_1) \cdot \mathbb{P}(A_2)$. Thus, the events A_1 and A_2 are independent in this case.

Example. Suppose that two dice are cast. Let A_1 be the event that the first die shows an uneven number, A_2 the event that the second die shows an uneven number, and A_3 the event that the sum of all spots together is uneven. It is natural to assume that the result of throwing one die has no influence on the result of throwing the other die; hence the events A_1 and A_2 are independent of each other, and $\mathbb{P}(A_1) = \mathbb{P}(A_2) = 1/2$. Under one of the conditions A_1 or A_2 the event A_3 occurs if and only if an even number of spots turns up on the second or the first die, respectively, and it is easy to see that

$$\mathbb{P}(A_3 \mid A_1) = \mathbb{P}(A_3 \mid A_2) = \mathbb{P}(A_3) = \frac{1}{2}.$$

Thus, A_1 and A_2, A_2 and A_3, A_3 and A_1 are pairs of independent events. At the same time it is impossible that A_3 occurs if A_1 and A_2 occur both; therefore, we cannot claim that A_3 is independent from the *collection* of events A_1 and A_2.

Events $A_1, A_2, \ldots$ are said to be *mutually independent* if the probability of the intersection of the events $A_{i_1}, \ldots, A_{i_n}$ for any set of different subscripts $i_1, \ldots, i_n$ equals the product of the probabilities of the single events:

$$\mathbb{P}(A_{i_1}, \ldots, A_{i_n}) = \mathbb{P}(A_{i_1}) \ldots \mathbb{P}(A_{i_n}).$$

The $0-1$ Law. Let $A_1, A_2, \ldots$ be a sequence of mutually independent events and B any event the occurrence of which depends only on the outcomes of the "infinitely remote" events $A_n, A_{n+1}, \ldots$, where n can be chosen as large as desired. The probability $\mathbb{P}(B)$ of any such event is 0 or 1.

Example. Let B mean that an infinite number of events among $A_1, A_2, \ldots$ occurs. According to the $0-1$ law the probability $\mathbb{P}(B)$ of B equals 0 or 1. If the series of probabilities of the considered events $\sum_{i=0}^{\infty} \mathbb{P}(A_i)$ diverges, then $\mathbb{P}(B) = 1$, whereas if this series converges, $\mathbb{P}(B) = 0$. This result is known as Borel-Cantelli lemma.

3. The Amount of Information

How can we estimate the amount of some information? If we are dealing with information given in a written text, then it can presumably be measured roughly by the length of the text. To this end it is obviously necessary to chose some suitable way of writing, that is, some suitable rule of codifying information.

Let N objects be given. In order to name them we use the so-called binary code under which to each object there corresponds a code combination of the form $(a_1, \ldots, a_d)$ where the symbols a_i take only one of the two possible values 0 or 1, and the length d of all code combinations remains unchanged. There are 2^d different code combinations of this type. Therefore, in order to distinguish the N objects, the length d of the code combinations has to be chosen in such a way that the inequality

$N \leq 2^d$ is true. The smallest d for which this inequality holds is the natural number which satisfies the relation

$$0 \leq d - \log_2 N < 1 .$$

Obviously, the number

$$I = \log_2 N$$

characterizes the length of the most economical code combinations by means of which the N different objects can be described.

We consider an experiment which may result in one of the N incompatible events $A_1, \ldots, A_N$ with probabilities

$$p_1 = \mathbb{P}(A_1), \ldots, p_N = \mathbb{P}(A_N),$$

where $p_1 + \cdots + p_N = 1$. Suppose that n independent and identical trials are made, where in each of them one of the considered events $A_1, \ldots, A_N$ occurs. The outcome of the n trials is usually reported by way of the sequence $(A_{i_1}, A_{i_2}, \ldots, A_{i_n})$, where A_{i_k} denotes the event among $A_1, \ldots, A_N$ which occured at the k-th trial. Since in a large series of trials the frequency $n(A)/n$ of an event A practically equals its probability $\mathbb{P}(A)$, we will meet the event A_1 in the "report" $(A_{i_1}, A_{i_2}, \ldots, A_{i_n})$ practically $n_1 \approx p_1 \cdot n$ times, the event A_2 about $n_2 \approx p_2 \cdot n$ times, $\ldots$, and A_N about $n_N \approx p_N \cdot n$ times. Below only such outcomes are considered.

The number of all outcomes where A_1 occurs exactly n_1 times, A_2 occurs n_2 times, $\ldots$, and A_N occurs exactly n_N times $(n_1 + n_2 + \cdots + n_N = n)$ equals

$$N_n = \frac{n!}{n_1 ! n_2 ! \ldots n_N !} .$$

Using *Stirling's* formula we obtain for $n \to \infty$ and $n_1 \approx p_1 n$, $n_2 \approx p_2 n, \ldots, n_N \approx p_N n$:

$$\log_2 N_n \approx n \log_2 n - \sum_{i=1}^{N} n p_i \log_2 (n p_i) + \left(\log_2 \sqrt{2\pi n} - \sum_{i=1}^{N} \log_2 \sqrt{2\pi n_i} \right),$$

$$\log_2 N_n \approx - n \sum_{i=1}^{N} p_i \log_2 p_i .$$

If we use the binary code in order to describe the "reports" $(A_{i_1}, A_{i_2}, \ldots, A_{i_n})$, then as shown above, the length of the most economical code combinations is approximately equal to

$$d_n \approx \log_2 N_n \approx - n \sum_{i=1}^{n} p_i \log_2 p_i .$$

On the average this renders the value

$$I(p_1, ..., p_N) = - \sum_{i=1}^{N} p_i \log_2 p_i \qquad (3.5)$$

per trial for any of the n trials. In probability theory the value I defined by the formula (3.5) is conceived of as the *amount of information* carried on the average by the report about the events $A_1, ..., A_N$ occurring at each single trial. In the case of equally probable events this is equal to

$$I = - \sum_{1}^{N} \frac{1}{N} \log_2 \frac{1}{N} = \log_2 N .$$

The expression (3.5) for the amount of information $I(p_1, ..., p_N)$ can also be found by another method which is based on some requirements that can naturally be imposed on the values of the estimates of the information. First, the function $I(p_1, ..., p_N)$ should not change under any permutation of the arguments $p_1, ..., p_N$ since then the system of events $A_1, ..., A_N$ remains unchanged. Secondly, if it is already known that the event $B_1 = \bigcup_{k=1}^{m} A_k$ occurred (that is, if one of the outcomes $A_1, ..., A_m$ turned up) then, using the notations introduced above, the amount of information should be given by the formula

$$I_1 = I(p_1/q_1, ..., p_m/q_1, 0, ..., 0) ,$$

where $q_1 = \sum_{k=1}^{m} p_k = \mathbb{P}(B_1)$, and $p_i/q_1 = \mathbb{P}(A_i | B_1)$ are the conditional probabilities of the outcomes A_i $(i = 1, ..., m)$ under the hypothesis B_1. Similarly, under the condition that the event $B_2 = \bigcup_{k=m+1}^{N} A_k$ occurred the amount of information should be expressed by

$$I_2 = I(0, ..., 0, p_{m+1}/q_2, ..., p_N/q_2) ,$$

where $q_2 = \sum_{k=m+1}^{N} p_k = \mathbb{P}(B_2)$. It is natural to demand that the average amount of information $I(p_1, ..., p_N)$ is connected with the quantities I_1 and I_2 by the relation

$$I(p_1, ..., p_N) = q_1 \cdot I(p_1/q_1, ..., p_m/q_1, 0, ..., 0)$$
$$+ q_2 \cdot I(0, ..., 0, p_{m+1}/q_2, ..., p_N/q_2) .$$

If we assume that $I(p_1, ..., p_N)$ is a continuous function of the arguments $p_1, ..., p_N$, then these requirements define $I(p_1, ..., p_N)$ uniquely up to a constant factor. In fact the function $I(p_1, \ldots, p_N)$ necessarily has the form

$$I(p_1, \ldots, p_N) = -c \sum_{k=1}^{N} p_k \log p_k$$

where c is a constant (the basis of the system of logarithms can be chosen arbitrarily).

An experimental confirmation that the definition of the amount of information is adequate has been obtained from a sufficiently large practical experiment. In particular it turned out that when information is transmitted in a living organism the time of transmission is proportional to the amount of information computed from formula (3.5). As a similar example may serve one of the very simple experiments for determining the mean time of psychic reactions. The experiment looks like this: in front of the person being tested one of N lamps is lighted which he then has to name[4]. A large series of trials is made where the i-th lamp is lighted with a given probability p_i $(i = 1, \ldots, N)$. It turns out that the mean time the person being tested needs for a right answer is proportional to the quantity $I = - \sum_{i=1}^{N} p_i \log p_i$ (and not to the number of lamps N as might be expected).

In general, the amount of information on the events $A_1, A_2, \ldots$, which is carried by the report on the occurrence of one of the events B_1, B_2 is defined by the formula

$$I = \sum_{i,j} \mathbb{P}(A_i B_j) \log \frac{\mathbb{P}(A_i B_j)}{\mathbb{P}(A_i) \mathbb{P}(B_j)}; \tag{3.6}$$

here, $A_1, A_2, \ldots$, and $B_1, B_2, \ldots$, are complete systems of disjoint events.

Example. Suppose that at some time after the spring-summer season rain will normally fall on one out of five days, whereas the other days the weather will be fine. We assume that on the eve of every day a weather forecast is given. Naturally, this forecast may turn out to be wrong. We suppose that the prediction of rain turns out to be wrong in approximately half the cases (it is extremely difficult to give a right prediction of a little probable event like rain), whereas the prediction of fine weather works better and is wrong only in one out of ten cases.

What is the amount of information contained on the average in a single weather forecast?

---

[4] See *Yaglom, A. M.*, and *J. M. Yaglom: Probability and Information.* 2. ed. Moscow: Fizmatgiz 1960 (Russian).

We introduce the following notations: A_1: rain, A_2: fine weather, B_1: prediction of rain, B_2: prediction of fine weather. We have to put

$$\mathbb{P}(A_1) = \frac{1}{5}, \qquad \mathbb{P}(A_2) = \frac{4}{5},$$

$$\mathbb{P}(A_1|B_1) = \frac{1}{2}, \quad \mathbb{P}(A_1|B_2) = \frac{1}{10}.$$

According to the formula of complete probability

$$\mathbb{P}(A_1) = \mathbb{P}(A_1|B_1)\,\mathbb{P}(B_1) + \mathbb{P}(A_1|B_2)\,\mathbb{P}(B_2)$$

we find that

$$\mathbb{P}(B_1) = \frac{1}{4}, \qquad \mathbb{P}(B_2) = \frac{3}{4},$$

$$\mathbb{P}(A_1 B_1) = \frac{1}{8}, \qquad \mathbb{P}(A_1 B_2) = \frac{3}{40},$$

$$\mathbb{P}(A_2 B_1) = \frac{1}{8}, \qquad \mathbb{P}(A_2 B_2) = \frac{27}{40},$$

hence, according to (3.6) the amount of information sought for equals

$$I = \frac{1}{8}\log_2\frac{5}{2} + \frac{3}{40}\log_2\frac{1}{2} + \frac{1}{8}\log_2\frac{5}{8} + \frac{27}{40}\log_2\frac{9}{8} \approx 0.120$$

$$\text{(binary units)}.$$

How much more informations does an absolutely true forecast render? To answer this question we have to set $B_1 = A_1, B_2 = A_2$ and obtain from formula (3.5):

$$I = -\frac{1}{5}\log\frac{1}{5} - \frac{4}{5}\log\frac{4}{5} \approx 0.722 \quad \text{(binary units)}.$$

§ 4. Random Variables

1. Random Variables and their Probability Distributions

A real-valued variable ξ whose value depends on chance is called a *random variable*. In the framework of general probability theory where some space Ω of elementary outcomes ω is assumed, we mean by a random variable a function of the elementary outcomes:

$$\xi = \xi(\omega), \qquad \omega \in \Omega.$$

There are two basic types of random variables: *discretely* and *continuously distributed variables*. A discrete variable $\xi = \xi(\omega)$ as a function of ω takes only a finite or denumerable number of different values x with corresponding probabilities

$$P_\xi(x) = \mathbb{P}\{\xi = x\};$$

here $\{\xi = x\}$ stands for the event that the random variable ξ takes the value x, that is, $\{\xi = x\} = \{\omega : \xi(\omega) = x\}$. The probability of the event $x' \leq \xi \leq x''$ that ξ takes one of the values x lying in $x' \leq x \leq x''$ is

$$\mathbb{P}\{x' \leq \xi \leq x''\} = \sum_{x'}^{x''} P_\xi(x)$$

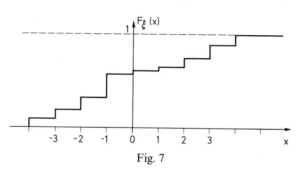

Fig. 7

where the summation is extended over the finite or denumerable number of values x which the discrete random variable ξ may take. $P_\xi(x)$ as a function of all possible values x of the random variable ξ is called the *probability distribution* of this variable.

Let ξ be an arbitrary random variable. The function $F_\xi(x)$ which is defined for all x on the real line by

$$F_\xi(x) = \mathbb{P}\{\xi \leq x\} \quad (-\infty < x < \infty)$$

is called the *distribution function* of the random variable ξ. For any x' and x'' where $x' < x''$ we have

$$\mathbb{P}\{x' < \xi \leq x''\} = F_\xi(x'') - F_\xi(x').$$

The distribution function $F_\xi(x)$ of a discrete random variable ξ is piece-wise constant (Fig. 7).

If the distribution function $F_\xi(x)$ of the random variable ξ is continuous, then the variable ξ takes any single value x only with probability 0. If the distribution function $F_\xi(x)$ is not only continuous but also differentiable, then $p_\xi(x) = \dfrac{d}{dx} F_\xi(x)$ is called the *density of the probability distribution* (or shortly, *probability density*), and ξ is called a *continuously distributed* random variable. The probability density is a non-negative function $p_\xi(x)$ such that for any x' and x'' with $x' < x''$:

$$\mathbb{P}\{x' \leqq \xi \leqq x''\} = \int_{x'}^{x''} p_\xi(x)\, dx .$$

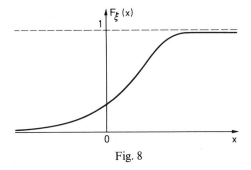

Fig. 8

In the notation of the distribution function and the probability density we often omit the index ξ and simply write $F(x)$ and $p(x)$. On Fig. 8 a graph of a continuous distribution function $F_\xi(x)$ is presented. Every monotone continuous function $F(x)$ such that $\lim\limits_{x \to -\infty} F(x) = 0$ and $\lim\limits_{x \to \infty} F(x) = 1$ can act as a distribution function.

Example. Suppose that a point ξ is thrown at random onto an interval $[a, b]$ of the real line. The probability of falling into the given interval $[x', x'']$ equals

$$\mathbb{P}\{x' \leqq \xi \leqq x''\} = \frac{x'' - x'}{b - a} = \int_{x'}^{x''} \frac{dx}{b - a} \quad (a \leqq x' \leqq x'' \leqq b).$$

It is obvious that the random variable ξ has a probability density $p(x)$ of the form

$$p(x) = \begin{cases} \dfrac{1}{b - a} & \text{for} \quad a \leqq x \leqq b, \\ 0 & \text{for} \quad x < a,\ x > b. \end{cases}$$

This probability distribution is called the uniform distribution on $[a, b]$.

Joint Probability Distributions. Let $\xi = (\xi_1, \dots, \xi_n)$ be a family of some random variables or in other words, a *random vector*, where

$\xi_1, \ldots, \xi_n$ are discrete variables. The event $\{\xi_1 = x_1, \ldots, \xi_n = x_n\}$ that the random variables $\xi_1, \ldots, \xi_n$ take the values $x_1, \ldots, x_n$, respectively, has a well-determined probability

$$P(x_1, \ldots, x_n) = \mathbb{P}\{\xi_1 = x_1, \ldots, \xi_n = x_n\} .$$

The probabilities $P(x_1, \ldots, x_n)$ where the variables $x_1, \ldots, x_n$ take all possible values of the random variables $\xi_1, \ldots, \xi_n$ form the so-called *joint probability distribution* of these variables. The probability of the event $\{x_1' \leq \xi_1 \leq x_1'', \ldots, x_n' \leq \xi_n \leq x_n''\}$ that the random variables $\xi_1, \ldots, \xi_n$ are lying within the boundaries $x_1' \leq \xi_1 \leq x_1'', \ldots, x_n' \leq \xi_n \leq x_n''$ equals

$$\mathbb{P}\{x_1' \leq \xi_1 \leq x_1'', \ldots, x_n' \leq \xi_n \leq x_n''\} = \sum_{x_1'}^{x_1} \cdots \sum_{x_n'}^{x_n''} P(x_1, \ldots, x_n) .$$

Suppose that the random variables $\xi_1, \ldots, \xi_n$ are continuously distributed. If there exists a non-negative function $p(x_1, \ldots, x_n)$ of $x_1, \ldots, x_n$ such that for all $x_1' \leq x_1'', \ldots, x_n' \leq x_n''$ we have

$$\mathbb{P}\{x_1' \leq \xi_1 \leq x_1'', \ldots, x_n' \leq \xi_n \leq x_n''\} = \int_{x_1'}^{x_1''} \cdots \int_{x_n'}^{x_n''} p(x_1, \ldots, x_n)\, dx_1, \ldots, dx_n ,$$

then it is called the *probability density of the joint distribution* of the variables $\xi_1, \ldots, \xi_n$.

Let the random variable η be a function of $\xi_1, \ldots, \xi_n : \eta = \varphi(\xi_1, \ldots, \xi_n)$. The for discrete variables $\xi_1, \ldots, \xi_n$:

$$\mathbb{P}\{y' \leq \eta \leq y''\} = \sum_{y' \leq \varphi(x_1, \ldots, x_n) \leq y''} \cdots \sum P(x_1, \ldots, x_n)$$

where the summation is extended over all $x_1, \ldots, x_n$ which satisfy the inequality $y' \leq \varphi(x_1, \ldots, x_n) \leq y''$, and for continuous $\xi_1, \ldots, \xi_n$:

$$\mathbb{P}\{y' \leq \eta \leq y''\} = \int_{y' \leq \varphi(x_1, \ldots, x_n) \leq y''} \cdots \int p(x_1, \ldots, x_n)\, dx_1, \ldots, dx_n ,$$

where the integration is extended over the domain of all $x_1, \ldots, x_n$ such that $y' \leq \varphi(x_1, \ldots, x_n) \leq y''$.

Independent Variables. The random variables $\xi_1, \ldots, \xi_n$ are called *independent* if all possible events of the form $\{x_1' \leq \xi_1 \leq x_1''\}, \ldots, \{x_n' \leq \xi_n \leq x_n''\}$ are mutually independent. Discrete random variables $\xi_1, \ldots, \xi_n$ are independent if and only if their joint distribution is given by

$$P_\xi(x_1, \ldots, x_n) = P_{\xi_1}(x_1) \ldots P_{\xi_n}(x_n)$$

where $P_{\xi_k}(x_k)$ denotes the distribution of the single variable ξ_k, $k = 1, \ldots, n$. Continuous random variables are independent if and only if the density of their joint distribution equals

$$p_\xi(x_1, \ldots, x_n) = p_{\xi_1}(x_1) \ldots p_{\xi_n}(x_n)$$

where $p_{\xi_k}(x_k)$ is the density of the distribution of the single variable ξ_k, $k = 1, \ldots, n$,

Example. Let ξ_1 and ξ_2 be independet random variables with densities $p_1(x)$ and $p_2(x)$. What is the probability distribution of the random variable $\eta = \xi_1 + \xi_2$?

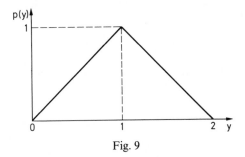

Fig. 9

The joint density of the distribution of the random variables ξ_1 and ξ_2 equals $p_1(x_1) \cdot p_2(x_2)$. We have:

$$\mathbb{P}\{y' \leq \eta \leq y''\} = \iint\limits_{y' \leq x_1 + x_2 \leq y''} p_1(x_1) \, p_2(x_2) \, dx_1 \, dx_2$$

$$= \int_{y'}^{y''} \left[\int_{-\infty}^{\infty} p_1(y - x) \, p_2(x) \, dx \right] dy \,.$$

It is now obvious that the random variable η has the density $p(y)$ given by

$$p(y) = \int_{-\infty}^{\infty} p_1(y - x) \, p_2(x) \, dx \,.$$

Thus the density $p(y)$ is the *convolution* of the original densities $p_1(x)$ and $p_2(x)$.

For example, if ξ_1 and ξ_2 are uniformly distributed in the interval $[0, 1]$, then the density $p(y)$ of the variable $\eta = \xi_1 + \xi_2$ equals (Fig. 9)

$$p(y) = \begin{cases} y & \text{for} \quad 0 \leq y \leq 1, \\ 2 - y & \text{for} \quad 1 \leq y \leq 2. \end{cases}$$

2. Mathematical Expectation, Variance and Correlation Coefficient

The number $M\xi$ defined by the equation

$$M\xi = \begin{cases} \sum_{-\infty}^{\infty} x P_\xi(x) & \text{for discrete } \xi, \\[2ex] \int_{-\infty}^{\infty} x p_\xi(x)\, dx & \text{for continuous } \xi \end{cases}$$

is called the *mathematical expectation* or the *mean value* of the random variable ξ.

Example. Let ξ take any of the N possible values $x = x_1, \ldots, x_N$ with the same probability. Then its mean value equals

$$M\xi = \frac{1}{N} \sum_{k=1}^{N} x_k.$$

If the random variable ξ is uniformly distributed in the interval $[a, b]$, then its mean value equals

$$M\xi = \int_a^b \frac{x}{a-b}\, dx = \frac{a+b}{2}.$$

Consider a random variable η which is a function of $\xi_1, \ldots, \xi_n$, say $\eta = \varphi(\xi_1, \ldots, \xi_n)$. Then

$$M\xi = \begin{cases} \sum_{-\infty}^{\infty} \cdots \sum_{-\infty}^{\infty} \varphi(x_1, \ldots, x_n)\, P_\xi(x_1, \ldots, x_n) \\[1ex] \qquad\qquad\qquad\qquad \text{for discrete } \xi_1, \ldots, \xi_n, \\[2ex] \int_{-\infty}^{\infty} \int_{-\infty}^{\infty} \varphi(x_1, \ldots, x_n)\, p_\xi(x_1, \ldots, x_n)\, dx_1, \ldots, dx_n \\[1ex] \qquad\qquad\qquad\qquad \text{for continuous } \xi_1, \ldots, \xi_n. \end{cases}$$

The simplest properties of the expectation:
a) $M1 = 1$;
b) for any constant c

$$M(c\,\xi) = c\,M\xi;$$

c) for any ξ_1 and ξ_2 which have expectations $M\xi_1$ and $M\xi_2$:

$$M(\xi_1 + \xi_2) = M\xi_1 + M\xi_2;$$

d) if the random variables $\xi_1 = \xi_1(\omega)$ and $\xi_2 = \xi_2(\omega)$ are such that $\xi_1(\omega) \leq \xi_2(\omega)$ for all elementary outcomes ω, then

$$M\xi_1 \leq M\xi_2;$$

e) if ξ_1 and ξ_2 are independent random variables, then

$$\mathbb{M}(\xi_1 \cdot \xi_2) = \mathbb{M}\xi_1 \cdot \mathbb{M}\xi_2.$$

The number $\mathbb{D}\xi$ defined by the equation

$$\mathbb{D}\xi = \mathbb{M}(\xi - a)^2, \qquad a = \mathbb{M}\xi$$

is called the *variance* of the random variable ξ.

The simplest properties of the variance:

a) $\mathbb{D}1 = 0$;

b) for any constant c

$$\mathbb{D}(c\,\xi) = c^2\,\mathbb{D}\xi;$$

c) if ξ_1 and ξ_2 are independent random variables, then

$$\mathbb{D}(\xi_1 + \xi_2) = \mathbb{D}\xi_1 + \mathbb{D}\xi_2.$$

Čebyšev's Inequality. If the random variable ξ takes only non-negative values and the expectation $\mathbb{M}\xi$ exists, then for every $\varepsilon > 0$

$$\mathbb{P}\{\xi \geq \varepsilon\} \leq \frac{1}{\varepsilon}\,\mathbb{M}\xi.$$

This inequality is often called the *first Čebyšev inequality*. The *second inequality* follows from the first one. Namely if the variance $\mathbb{D}\xi$ exists, then for every $\varepsilon > 0$

$$\mathbb{P}\{|\xi - a| \geq \varepsilon\} \leq \frac{1}{\varepsilon^2}\mathbb{D}\xi$$

where $a = \mathbb{M}\xi$. The second Čebyšev inequality shows that if the variance is sufficiently small, say $\mathbb{D}\xi \leq \delta\varepsilon^2$, then with probability not smaller than $1 - \delta$ the random variable $\xi = \xi(\omega)$ differs from its mean value $a = \mathbb{M}\xi$ by not more than ε, that is,

$$\mathbb{P}\{a - \varepsilon \leq \xi \leq a + \varepsilon\} \geq 1 - \delta.$$

The Law of Large Numbers. Let $\xi_1, \ldots, \xi_n$ be independent random variables with identical probability distributions, in particular with the same expectation $a = \mathbb{M}\xi_k$ and variance $\sigma^2 = \mathbb{D}\xi_k$, $k = 1, \ldots, n$. Given any $\varepsilon > 0$ and $\delta > 0$ the arithmetic mean $\dfrac{1}{n} \sum_{k=1}^{n} \xi(\omega)$ which itself depends on chance, differs for sufficiently large n from the mathematical expectation a at most by ε with probability not smaller than $1 - \delta$.

This fact follows from the second Čebyšev inequality according to which

$$\mathbb{P}\left\{\left|\frac{1}{n}\sum_{k=1}^{n}\xi_k - a\right| \le \varepsilon\right\} \ge 1 - \frac{\sigma^2}{n\varepsilon^2}.$$

In other words, if $n \ge \dfrac{\sigma^2}{\delta\varepsilon^2}$, then with probability at least $1 - \delta$ the inequalities

$$a - \varepsilon \le \frac{1}{n}\sum_{k=1}^{n}\xi_k \le a + \varepsilon$$

hold.

If for practical purposes we disregard the possibility of events occurring with probability less than δ and do not distinguish between variables differing by not more than ε, then we may take it for granted that for sufficiently large n $\left(\text{e.g. } n \ge \dfrac{\sigma^2}{\delta\varepsilon^2}\right)$ the arithmetic mean $\dfrac{1}{n}\sum_{k=1}^{n}\xi_k$ of the random variable $\xi_1, \ldots, \xi_n$ under consideration practically coincides with their mathematical expectation:

$$\frac{1}{n}\sum_{k=1}^{n}\xi_k \approx a.$$

This fact is known as the *law of large numbers*.

Frequency and Probability. Suppose a series of identical and mutually independent trials is made, where any of them either results in the outcome of A or of $\bar{A}$. We define random variables ξ_k by putting $\xi_k = 1$ if A occurs at the k-th trial and $\xi_k = 0$ if $\bar{A}$ occurs. Then in a series of n trials the frequency $n(A)/n$ of A coincides with the arithmetic mean of the variables ξ_k:

$$\frac{n(A)}{n} = \frac{1}{n}\sum_{k=1}^{n}\xi_k.$$

The probability of the event A equals the mathematical expectation $\mathbb{M}\xi_k$ of any of the summands: $\mathbb{P}(A) = \mathbb{M}\xi_k$. Therefore, according to the law of large numbers

$$n(A)/n \approx \mathbb{P}(A)$$

when the number of trials n is sufficiently large.

A Connection Between Different Random Variables. Correlation Coefficient. The so-called *correlation coefficient* which is defined by the formula

$$r = \frac{\mathbb{M}(\xi_1 - a_1)(\xi_2 - a_2)}{\sigma_1\sigma_2},$$

where

$$a_1 = \mathbb{M}\xi_1, \quad a_2 = \mathbb{M}\xi_2, \quad \sigma_1^2 = \mathbb{D}\xi_1, \quad \sigma_2^2 = \mathbb{D}\xi_2,$$

characterizes in a very simple way a connection between the random variables ξ_1 and ξ_2.

For independent variables ξ_1 and ξ_2 the correlation coefficient is equal to 0. In the general case it lies within the boundaries $-1 \leq r \leq 1$. If $r = -1$ or $r = 1$, then ξ_2 is a linear function of ξ_1:

$$\xi_2 = r \frac{\sigma_2}{\sigma_1} (\xi_1 - a_1) + a_2.$$

For any value of the correlation coefficient the variable $\hat{\xi}_2 = r \frac{\sigma_2}{\sigma_1} (\xi_1 - a_1) + a_2$ gives the *best linear approximation* of the random variable ξ_2 in the sense that

$$\mathbb{M}(\xi_2 - \hat{\xi}_2)^2 = \min_{c_1, c_2} \mathbb{M}(\xi_2 - c_1 \xi_1 - c_2)^2,$$

where min is taken over all possible constants c_1 and c_2. Analogously, the variable $\hat{\xi}_1 = r \frac{\sigma_1}{\sigma_2} (\xi_2 - a_2) + a_1$ is the best linear approximation of ξ_1.

The random variables ξ_1 and ξ_2 are called *uncorrelated* if their correlation coefficient is equal to 0. For example the best linear approximation $\hat{\xi}_2$ and the difference $\xi_2 - \hat{\xi}_2$ are uncorrelated.

Roughly speaking the correlation coefficient of the random variables ξ_1 and ξ_2 characterizes only the "degree of linear dependence" of ξ_1 and ξ_2. Suppose that for instance ξ_1 is a symmetrically distributed variable with a density $p_\xi(x)$ such that $p_\xi(-x) = p_\xi(x)$, and let $\xi_2 = |\xi_1|$. Then, although the variable ξ_2 is even a function of ξ_1, the correlation coefficient of the ξ_1 and ξ_2 is equal to 0, since

$$\mathbb{M}\xi_1 = \int_{-\infty}^{\infty} x p_\xi(x) \, dx = 0,$$

$$\mathbb{M}\xi_1 \xi_2 = \int_{-\infty}^{\infty} x |x| p_\xi(x) \, dx = 0.$$

3. Integral-Valued Variables and Generating Functions

Let ξ be an integral-valued variable which at random takes one of the values $k = 0, 1, 2, \ldots$ with corresponding probabilities $P_\xi(k)$. The function $\varphi_\xi(z)$ of the variable z, $|z| \leq 1$, defined by the formula

$$\varphi_\xi(z) = \sum_{k=0}^{\infty} P_\xi(k) z^k,$$

is called the *generating function* of the distribution of the random variable ξ. It is an analytic function of z for $|z| < 1$, and the formula given above represents its expansion into a power series. The probability distribution $P_\xi(k)$ is uniquely determined by its generating function:

$$P_\xi(k) = \frac{1}{k!}\,\varphi_\xi^{(k)}(0) \quad (k = 0, 1, 2, \ldots),$$

where $\varphi_\xi^{(k)}(0)$ is the value of the derivative $\dfrac{d^k\,\varphi_\xi(z)}{dz^k}$ at the point $z = 0$.

For fixed z the generating function $\varphi_\xi(z)$ is equal to the mathematical expectation of the random variable $\eta = z^\xi$:

$$\varphi_\xi(z) = \mathbf{M}\,z^\xi.$$

If the random variable ξ has expectation $\mathbf{M}\xi$ and variance $\mathbf{D}\xi$, then

$$\mathbf{M}\xi = \varphi_\xi'(1),$$
$$\mathbf{D}\xi = \varphi_\xi''(1) + \varphi_\xi'(1) - [\varphi_\xi'(1)]^2.$$

Let $\xi_1, \ldots, \xi_n$ be independent variables with generating functions $\varphi_{\xi_1}(z), \ldots, \varphi_{\xi_n}(z)$, and let $\xi = \xi_1 + \cdots + \xi_n$. Then the following formula holds:

$$\varphi_\xi(z) = \varphi_{\xi_1}(z) \ldots \varphi_{\xi_n}(z).$$

Let $\xi_1, \xi_2, \ldots$ be independent random variables which have an identical probability distribution with generating function $\varphi(z)$, and let $\xi = \xi_1 + \cdots + \xi_v$ be the sum of a certain number of these variables where the number v of the terms is a random variable which does not depend on $\xi_1, \xi_2, \ldots$, and has a probability distribution with generating function $\psi(z)$. Then the generating function $\varphi_\xi(z)$ of the sum ξ can be obtained by the formula

$$\varphi_\xi(z) = \psi[\varphi(z)];$$

for example if $v \equiv n$ then $\psi(z) = z^n$ and $\varphi_\xi(z) = \varphi(z)^n$.

Convergence of Distributions. Let ξ_n be a sequence of random variables, $P_n(k)$ the probability distribution and $\varphi_n(z)$ the generating function [5] of $\xi_n (n = 0, 1, 2, \ldots)$. The probability distribution $P(k)$ is called the limit of $P_n(k)$ for $n \to \infty$ if

$$\lim_{n \to \infty} P_n(k) = P(k) \quad (k = 0, 1, 2, \ldots).$$

---

[5] The notations $P_n(k)$ and $\varphi_n(z)$ present a simpler way of writing the probability distribution $P_{\xi_n}(k)$ and the generating function $\varphi_{\xi_n}(z)$.

The convergence $P_n(k) \to P(k)$ holds if and only if

$$\lim_{n \to \infty} \varphi_n(z) = \varphi(z)$$

uniformly with respect to z in any circle $|z| \le r < 1$, where $\varphi(z)$ is the generating function of the limit distribution.

§ 5. Some Probability Distributions

1. Probability Distributions Connected with the Poisson Law

The Poisson distribution is defined to be the probability distribution of the form

$$P(k) = \frac{a^k}{k!} e^{-a} \quad (k = 0, 1, 2, \ldots).$$

It is determined by a unique positive parameter a. If ξ is a random variable with a Poisson distribution, then the corresponding parameter a is the mean value of this variable:

$$a = \mathbb{M}\xi = \sum_{k=0}^{\infty} k P(k).$$

The generating function $\varphi(z)$ of the Poisson distribution has the form

$$\varphi(z) = e^{a(z-1)}.$$

The distribution function of Poisson type $F(x)$ is given in the points $x = 0, 1, 2, \ldots$ by the formula

$$F(x) = \sum_{k=0}^{x} \frac{a^k}{k} e^{-a} = \frac{1}{(x+1)!} \int_a^{\infty} y^x e^{-y} \, dy.$$

Uniform Flow of Events. Suppose that within a time interval of duration t the occurrence of some events is registered. For example, demands which are being made successively on a certain service system are registered (say, inquiries directed to an information office, or cars driving into a gas station).

Suppose that the flow of events under consideration has the following properties:

a) The probability of a single event within a short time interval of duration Δt equals $\lambda \cdot \Delta t + 0(\Delta t)$, where λ is a positive constant and $0(\Delta t)$ tends to 0 faster than Δt;

b) the probability that more than one event occurs during this interval is $0(\Delta t)$;

c) the numbers of events $\xi(\varDelta_1), ..., \xi(\varDelta_n)$ which occur in non-over-lapping time intervals $\varDelta_1, ..., \varDelta_n$ are mutually independent random variables.

We consider a fixed time interval $(0, t)$. If we decompose it into n equal parts of lengths $\varDelta_1, ..., \varDelta_n$, then the total number $\xi(t)$ of the events which occur during the time t can be represented in the form

$$\xi(t) = \sum_{k=1}^{n} \xi_k(\varDelta_k),$$

where the random variables $\xi_k(\varDelta_k)$ $(k = 1, ..., n)$ are independent and identically distributed. The generating function $\varphi_n(z)$ of the variables $\xi_k(\varDelta_k)$ is, up to terms which are small of higher order than $1/n$, given by

$$\varphi_n(z) = \left(1 - \frac{\lambda t}{n}\right) + \frac{\lambda t}{n} z + 0\left(\frac{1}{n}\right) = 1 + \frac{\lambda t(z-1)}{n} + 0\left(\frac{1}{n}\right).$$

Hence the generating function $\varphi(z)$ of $\xi(t)$ equals

$$\varphi(z) = [\varphi_n(z)]^n = \left[1 + \frac{\lambda t(z-1)}{n} + 0\left(\frac{1}{n}\right)\right]^n.$$

Passing to the limit for $n \to \infty$ we obtain the final formula:

$$\varphi(z) = \lim_{n \to \infty} \left[1 + \frac{\lambda t(z-1)}{n}\right]^n = e^{\lambda t(z-1)}.$$

Therefore, $\varphi(z)$ is the generating function of a Poisson distribution with parameter $a = \lambda t$. Thus, the total number of events occuring during the time t is a random variable which obeys *Poisson's* law:

$$\mathbb{P}\{\xi(t) = k\} = \frac{(\lambda t)^k}{k!} e^{-\lambda t} \quad (k = 0, 1, 2, ...),$$

where the constant λ introduced above equals the mean value of the number of events which occur during one unit of time: $\lambda t = \mathbb{M}\xi(t)$.

Exponential Distribution. In the flow of events considered above, for example the demands made upon a service system, the waiting time for the first demand is random. We denote it by τ. The probability distribution of the random variable τ is determined by

$$\mathbb{P}\{\tau > t\} = \mathbb{P}\{\xi(t) = 0\} = e^{-\lambda t} \quad (t \geq 0).$$

This distribution is called the *exponential* distribution. It has a density of the form

$$p(t) = \begin{cases} \lambda e^{-\lambda t} & \text{for } t \geq 0 \\ 0 & \text{for } t < 0. \end{cases}$$

The mean value of the random variable τ, that is, the mean waiting time, is equal to

$$\mathbb{M}\tau = \int\limits_0^\infty t\, p(t)\, dt = \frac{1}{\lambda}\,.$$

Compound Poisson Distribution. Suppose that we are given an integral-valued random variable v which obeys the Poisson law with parameter $a = \mathbb{M}v$, and a sequence $\xi_1, \xi_2, \ldots$ of identically distributed integral-valued random variables which are mutually independent and independent of v. The probability distribution of the sum $\xi = \xi_1 + \cdots + \xi_v$ of the random number of terms $\xi_1, \ldots, \xi_v$ is called a *compound Poisson distribution.* The generating function $\psi(z)$ of this distribution is given by the formula

$$\psi(z) = e^{a[\varphi(z)-1]},$$

where $\varphi(z)$ is the generating function of distribution of the single terms; for example if $\xi_k \equiv 1$ then $\varphi(z) = z$ and $\psi(z) = e^{a(z-1)}$.

2. Probability Distributions Connected with the Normal Law

Normal Distribution. Let $\xi_1, \ldots, \xi_n$ be independent and identically distributed random variables, and $\xi = \xi_1 + \cdots + \xi_n$. If the terms $\xi_1, \ldots, \xi_n$ are sufficiently small and their total number n sufficiently large, more precisely, if for $n \to \infty$ the expectation $\mathbb{M}\xi$ and variance $\mathbb{D}\xi$ of the variable $\xi = \xi_1 + \cdots + \xi_n$ are such that $\mathbb{M}\xi \sim a$, $\mathbb{D}\xi \sim \sigma^2$, then

$$\mathbb{P}\{x' \leqq \xi \leqq x''\} \sim \frac{1}{\sqrt{2\pi}\,\sigma} \int\limits_{x'}^{x''} e^{-\frac{(x-a)^2}{2\sigma^2}}\, dx$$

for any x' and x'' with $x' < x''$. This limit probability distribution is described by the density of the form

$$p(x) = \frac{1}{\sqrt{2\pi}\,\sigma}\, e^{-\frac{(x-a)^2}{2}} \qquad (-\infty < x < \infty),$$

and is called a *normal or Gaussian distribution.* It is determined by two parameters a and σ. If ξ is a normally distributed random variable with parameters a and σ, then $a = \mathbb{M}\xi$ is the mean value of this variable and $\sigma^2 = D\xi$ its variance:

$$a = \frac{1}{\sqrt{2\pi}\,\sigma} \int_{-\infty}^{\infty} x e^{-\frac{(x-a)^2}{2\sigma^2}} \, dx,$$

$$\sigma^2 = \frac{1}{\sqrt{2\pi}\,\sigma} \int_{-\infty}^{\infty} (x-a)^2 e^{-\frac{(x-a)^2}{2\sigma^2}} \, dx.$$

The transformation $u = \dfrac{x-a}{\sigma}$ carries the normal distribution with parameters a and σ into the normal standard law with parameters $a = 0$, $\sigma = 1$ and density

$$\frac{1}{\sqrt{2\pi}} e^{-\frac{u^2}{2}} \quad (-\infty < u < \infty),$$

the graph of which is shown in Fig. 10.

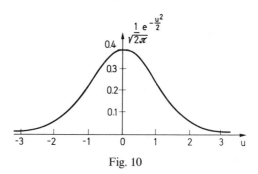

Fig. 10

There exist tables of the normal distribution function[6]

$$\Phi(x) = \frac{1}{\sqrt{2\pi}} \int_{-\infty}^{x} e^{-\frac{1}{2}} \, du \quad (-\infty < x < \infty).$$

[6] Bolshev, L. N., and N. V. Smirnov: Tables of math. statistics, Nauka, Moscow 1965. The book "Tables of probabilistic functions", Vol. II, V. C. AN SSSR (Computing Center of the Academy of Sciences of the USSR), Moscow 1959, gives the values of the function $2\Phi(x) - 1$ up to 15 decimals. Tables with eight decimals of the inverse function of $\Phi(x)$ are contained in the "statistical tables" by T. L. Kelly, V. C. (Computing Center of the Academy of Sciences of the USSR), Moscow 1966. (Translation.)

The function $\Phi(x)$ satisfies the identity

$$\Phi(x) + \Phi(-x) \equiv 1 .$$

If $x \to \infty$, then the asymptotic formula

$$1 - \Phi(x) \sim \frac{1}{x\sqrt{2\pi}} e^{-\frac{x^2}{2}} \left(1 - \frac{1}{x^2} + \frac{1 \cdot 3}{x^4} - \frac{1 \cdot 3 \cdot 5}{x^6} + \cdots\right)$$

holds. For finite values of x the absolute error in this formula does not surpass the first omitted term. If for example $x \geq 4$, then

$$0 < \frac{1}{x\sqrt{2\pi}} e^{-\frac{x^2}{2}} \left(1 - \frac{1}{x^2} + \frac{1 \cdot 3}{x^4}\right)$$

$$- [1 - \Phi(x)] < \frac{15}{x^7\sqrt{2\pi}} e^{-\frac{x^2}{2}} \leq 2 \cdot 10^{-7} .$$

If ξ is a normally distributed random variable with parameters a and σ, then

$$\mathbb{P}\{a + \sigma x' \leq \xi \leq a + \sigma x''\} = \Phi(x'') - \Phi(x')$$

for any x' and x'' such that $x' < x''$. In particular, we have for $x'' = -x' = x$

$$\mathbb{P}\{a - \sigma x \leq \xi \leq a + \sigma x\} = 2\Phi(x) - 1 .$$

Numerical values of these probabilities are given in Table 2.

Logarithmic Normal Distribution. By this we mean the probability distribution of a non-negative random variable ξ whose logarithm $\log \xi$ is normally distributed. The density of the logarithmic normal distribution has the form

$$p(x) = \frac{\log e}{\sqrt{2\pi}\sigma x} e^{-\frac{(\log x - a)^2}{2\sigma^2}} \qquad (0 < x < \infty)$$

where the parameters a und σ are $a = \mathbb{M}\log \xi$, $\sigma^2 = \mathbb{D}\log \xi$. Fig. 11 shows the graphs of the densities $p(x)$ which correspond to the values $a = 1$, $\sigma = 0.1$. 0.3 and 0.5.

The moments of a random variable ξ which follows the logarithmic normal distribution with parameters a and σ are expressed by the formula

$$\mathbb{M}\xi^n = e^{na + \frac{n^2\sigma^2}{2}} .$$

Table 2

x	00	01	02	03	04	05	06	07	08	09
0.0	0.000	008	016	024	032	040	048	056	064	072
1	080	088	096	103	111	119	127	135	143	151
2	159	166	174	182	190	197	205	213	221	228
3	236	243	251	259	266	274	281	289	296	303
4	311	318	326	333	340	347	354	362	369	376
0.5	0.383	390	397	404	411	418	425	431	438	445
6	451	458	465	471	478	484	491	497	503	510
7	516	522	528	535	541	547	553	559	565	570
8	576	582	588	593	599	605	610	616	621	627
9	632	637	642	648	653	658	663	668	673	678
1.0	0.683	688	692	697	702	706	711	715	720	724
1	729	733	737	742	746	750	754	758	762	766
2	770	774	778	781	785	789	792	796	799	803
3	806	810	813	816	820	823	826	829	832	835
4	838	841	844	847	850	853	856	858	861	864
1.5	0.866	869	871	874	876	879	881	884	886	888
6	0.890	893	895	897	899	011	031	051	070	090
7	0.9 109	127	146	164	181	199	216	233	249	265
8	281	297	312	328	342	357	371	385	399	412
9	426	439	451	464	476	488	500	512	523	534
2.0	0.9 545	556	566	576	586	596	606	615	625	634
1	643	651	660	668	676	684	692	700	707	715
2	722	729	736	743	749	756	762	768	774	780
3	786	791	797	802	807	812	917	822	827	832
4	836	840	845	849	853	857	861	865	869	872
2.5	0.9 876	897	883	886	889	892	895	898	012	040
6	0.99 068	095	121	146	171	195	219	241	264	285
7	307	327	347	367	386	404	422	439	456	473
8	489	505	520	535	549	563	576	590	602	615
9	627	639	650	661	672	682	692	702	712	721
3.0	0.99 730	739	747	755	763	771	779	786	793	800
1	806	813	819	825	831	837	842	848	853	858
2	0.99 863	867	872	867	880	885	889	892	896	900
3	0.999 033	067	100	132	162	192	221	248	275	301
4	326	350	374	396	418	439	460	480	499	517
3.5	0.999 535	552	568	584	600	615	629	643	656	669
6	682	694	705	717	727	738	748	757	767	776
7	784	793	801	809	816	823	830	837	843	849
8	0.999 855	861	867	872	877	882	887	891	896	900
9	0.9999 038	077	115	151	185	218	251	281	311	339
4.0	0.9999 367									

In the table the values of the integral $2\Phi(x) - 1 = \dfrac{1}{\sqrt{2\pi}} \displaystyle\int\limits_{-x}^{x} e^{-\frac{1}{2}u^2} du$ are given by three significant figures. If for example $x = 2.58$, then at the intersection of the line 2.5 and the column 08 we find the number 012. Since the first three decimals in the column 00 of the corresponding "zone" are 0.99, the value of the integral for $x = 2.58$ equals 0.99012.

χ^2-*distribution ("χ-square") and γ-distribution.* By the χ^2-distribution we mean the probability distribution of a random variable χ^2 of the form

$$\chi^2 = \xi_1^2 + \cdots + \xi_n^2$$

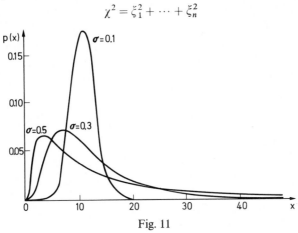

Fig. 11

where $\xi_1, \ldots, \xi_n$ are independent random variables which have identical normal distributions with parameters $a = 0$ and $\sigma = 1$. The number n is called the degree of freedom of the χ^2-distribution. The corresponding density (Fig. 12) is given by the formula:

$$p(x) = \frac{1}{2^{\frac{n}{2}} \Gamma\left(\dfrac{n}{2}\right)} x^{\frac{n}{2}-1} e^{-\frac{x}{2}} \qquad (0 < x < \infty).$$

The χ^2-distribution is a particular case of the so-called γ-*distribution,* the density of which is expressed by the formula [7]

$$p(x) = \begin{cases} 0, & \text{if } x \leq 0, \\[2mm] \dfrac{\beta^{\alpha}}{\Gamma(\alpha)} x^{\alpha-1} e^{-\beta x} & \text{if } x > 0 \end{cases}$$

---

[7] Tables with 5 decimals of the χ^2 distribution function are given in the book by L. N. *Bolshev* and N. V. *Smirnov* referred to before. The values of the γ-distribution with 7 decimals for arbitrary positive α and β can be computed with the help of the tables: V. I. *Pagurova:* "Tables of the incomplete gamma-function", V. C. (Computing Center of The Academy of Sciences of the USSR), Moscow 1963.

where α and β are positive parameters and Γ is the Gamma-Function:

$$\Gamma(\alpha) = \int_0^\infty y^{\alpha-1}\, e^{-y}\, dy\,.$$

The equation

$$\Gamma(\alpha + 1) = \alpha\, \Gamma(\alpha)$$

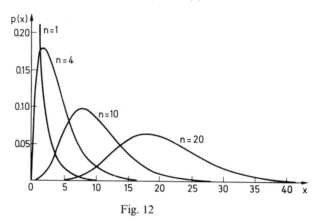

Fig. 12

holds for any positive α, hence

$$\Gamma(\alpha) = (\alpha - 1)!$$

if α is an integer. Since $\Gamma(1/2) = \sqrt{\pi}$, we can write in the formula for the density of the χ^2-distribution:

$$\Gamma\left(\frac{n}{2}\right) = \begin{cases} \left(\dfrac{n}{2} - 1\right)! & \text{if } n \text{ is even,} \\[2ex] \left(\dfrac{n}{2} - 1\right)\left(\dfrac{n}{2} - 2\right)\cdots\dfrac{3}{2}\cdot\dfrac{1}{2}\sqrt{\pi} & \text{if } n \text{ is odd.} \end{cases}$$

For $\alpha \to \infty$ the asymptotic *Stirling formula* holds where all logarithms are to the basis e:

$$\log\Gamma(\alpha) \sim \left(\alpha - \frac{1}{2}\right)\log\alpha - \alpha + \frac{1}{2}\log(2\pi) + \sum_{k=1}^{s} \frac{B_{2k}}{2k(2k-1)}\cdot\frac{1}{\alpha^{2k-1}}\,.$$

Here, the B_r's are the Bernoulli number ($B_2 = 1/6$, $B_4 = -1/30$, $B_6 = 1/42$, ...), the values of which are determined from the identity

$$\sum_{r=0}^{\infty} B_r \frac{z^r}{r!} = \frac{z}{e^z - 1}\,.$$

The inequality

$$\left| \log \Gamma(\alpha) - \left(\alpha - \frac{1}{2} \right) \log \alpha + \alpha - \frac{1}{2} \log(2\pi) - \sum_{k=1}^{s} \frac{B_{2k}}{2k(2k-1)} \cdot \frac{1}{\alpha^{2k-1}} \right|$$

$$< \frac{|B_{2(s+1)}|}{2(s+1)(2s+1)\alpha^{2s+1}}$$

holds for all positive α.

The χ-Distribution. This is the distribution of the square root

$$\sqrt{\chi^2} = \sqrt{\xi_1^2 + \cdots + \xi_n^2}$$

where $\xi_1, \ldots, \xi_n$ are independent random variables subject to the normal law with parameters $a = 0$ and $\sigma = 1$. The density of the χ-distribution is given by the formula

$$p(x) = \begin{cases} 0 & \text{if } x \le 0, \\ \dfrac{1}{2^{\frac{n}{2}-1} \Gamma\left(\dfrac{n}{2}\right)} x^{n-1} e^{-\frac{x^2}{2}} & \text{if } x > 0. \end{cases}$$

The moments of the random variable χ can be calculated by the formula

$$\mathbf{M}\chi^m = \frac{1}{2^{\frac{n}{2}-1} \Gamma\left(\dfrac{n}{2}\right)} \int_0^\infty x^{n+m-1} e^{-\frac{x^2}{2}} dx = 2^{\frac{m}{2}} \frac{\Gamma\left(\dfrac{n+m}{2}\right)}{\Gamma\left(\dfrac{n}{2}\right)} \quad (n+m>0).$$

Example. *The reflected normal distribution* is the probability distribution of the absolute value $|\xi|$ of a random variable ξ which follows the symmetric normal law with parameters $a = 0$ and $\sigma > 0$. The density of the reflected normal distribution is given by the formula

$$p(x) = \frac{1}{\sigma} \sqrt{\frac{2}{\pi}} e^{-\frac{x^2}{2}} \quad (0 < x < \infty),$$

moreover

$$\mathbf{M}|\xi|^m = {}^m\mathbf{M}\chi^m = \sigma^m 2^{\frac{m}{2}} \frac{\Gamma\left(\dfrac{m+1}{2}\right)}{\sqrt{\pi}}.$$

The Cauchy distribution is the distribution with the density

$$p(x) = \frac{1}{\pi(1+x^2)} \quad (-\infty < x < \infty),$$

whose graph is shown in Fig. 13. It coincides with the probability distribution of the ratio ξ_1/ξ_2 of identically and normally distributed independent variables ξ_1 and ξ_2 with parameters $a = 0$, $\sigma = 1$. The same probability distribution appears as the distribution of the tangent $\tan\alpha$ of a random variable α which is uniformly distributed in the interval $[-\pi/2, \pi/2]$.

The β-Distribution. By this we mean the probability distribution with the density

$$p(x) = \frac{1}{B(a, b)} x^{a-1}(1 - x)^{b-1} \qquad (0 < x < 1).$$

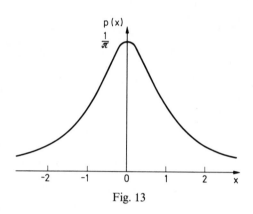

Fig. 13

The β-distribution depends on two positive parameters a and b. The normalizing factor $B(a, b)$, the so-called β-function, is defined by the formula

$$B(a, b) = \int_0^1 y^{a-1}(1 - y)^{b-1}\, dy = \frac{\Gamma(a)\,\Gamma(b)}{\Gamma(a + b)}$$

where $\Gamma(\alpha)$ is the γ-function defined above. If a and b are positive integers, then

$$B(a, b) = \frac{(a - 1)!\,(b - 1)!}{(a + b - 1)!}.$$

The distribution function of the β-distribution [8] is given by the integral:

$$F(x; a, b) = \frac{1}{B(a, b)} \int_0^x y^{a-1}(1 - y)^{b-1}\, dy \qquad (0 < x < 1).$$

---

[8] For the computation of the β-distribution function see L. N. Bolshev, N. V. Smirnov: Tables of math. Statistics. Nauka, Moscow 1965, and also K. Pearson: Tables of incomplete β-distribution function. Biometric Lab., London 1934.

If the random variable ξ follows the β-distribution, then its mathematical expectation and variance are expressed by the formulas:

$$M\xi = \frac{a}{a+b}, \quad D\xi = \frac{ab}{(a+b)^2\,(a+b+1)}.$$

3. Probability Distributions Connected with Bernoulli Trials

Bernoulli trials are identical and mutually independent trials in each of which a certain event A is considered which occurs with positive probability $p = \mathbb{P}(A)$. The event A is usually called "success" and its complementary event $\overline{A}$ "failure".

Binomial Distribution. Let ξ be the number of successes in n Bernoulli trials. The probability distribution of ξ has the form

$$P(k) = C_n^k p^k (1-p)^{n-k} \quad (k = 0, \ldots, n),$$

and is called the *Bernoulli distribution* or *binomial distribution*[9]. Here, p stand for the probability of a single success, n for the number of trials and $C_n^k = \dfrac{n!}{k!(n-k)!}$ for the binomial coefficient. The binomial distribution is determined by the two parameters p an n. Moreover, $M\xi = np$, $D\xi = np(1-p)$, $M(\xi - np)^3 = np(1-p)(1-2p)$, and the generating function $\varphi(z)$ of ξ equals

$$\varphi(z) = [1 + p(z-1)]^n.$$

The binomial distribution function is given by the formula

$$F(m) = \mathbb{P}\{\xi \leq m\} = \sum_{k=0}^{m} P(k)$$

$$= \frac{1}{B(m+1, n-m)} \int_p^1 x^m (1-x)^{n-m-1}\,dx, \quad m = 0, 1, 2, \ldots, n.$$

In other words: if $F(x; m+1, n-m)$ is the β-distribution function with parameters $a = m+1$ and $b = n-m$, then $F(m) = 1 - F(p; m+1, n-m) = F(1-p; n-m, m+1)$.

For $n \to \infty$ and $np \to \infty$ the following asymptotic formulas hold:

1) $P(k) = C_n^k p^k (1-p)^{n-k} \sim \dfrac{1}{\sqrt{2\pi}} e^{-\frac{x^2}{2}} \Delta x$

---

[9] The following tables of the binomial distributions are common: "Tables of the binomial probability distribution". Washington, N.B.S., 1950; *Romig, H. G.*: "50–100 binomial tables". New York: Wiley 1953.

where

$$x = \frac{k - np}{\sqrt{np(1-p)}}, \qquad \varDelta x = \frac{1}{\sqrt{np(1-p)}} \qquad (-\infty < x < \infty),$$

and

2) $$\mathbb{P}\left\{ x' \leqq \frac{\xi - np}{\sqrt{np(1-p)}} \leqq x'' \right\} \sim \frac{1}{\sqrt{2\pi}} \int_{x'}^{x''} e^{-\frac{x^2}{2}} dx.$$

This is the so-called *normal approximation* to the binomial law.

For $n \to \infty$ and $np \sim a$ we have $P(k) = C_n^k p^k (1-p)^{n-k} \dfrac{a^k}{k!} e^{-a}$

$(k = 0, 1, 2, \ldots)$. This is the so-called *Poisson approximation* which applies when each single "success" is little probable and represents a rare event in the corresponding scheme of Bernoulli trials.

Example. *The Raisin Problem.* Consider an amount of dough V of which rolls with raisins in them are being baked. An amount n of raisins is added to the dough which is then carefully mixed and cut into equal portions. Let any single roll contain the amount v of dough so that altogether $N = V/v$ rolls with raisins are baked. It is obvious that although each roll contains a definite average quantity $a = n/N$ of raisins the amount of raisins is not the same in all rolls. What is the probability that in a roll singled out there will be at least one raisin?

It is natural to assume that the amount of raisins is much smaller than the amount of dough so that when mixing the dough many times the raisins finally move independently of each other. In particular, they occur independently of each other in the sampled roll. After careful mixing the raisins are, of course, approximately uniformly distributed in the dough, and the probability that a given raisin will occur in a given roll is always the same, namely $p = 1/N$. The occurrence of a single raisin in a certain roll can be considered as the "success" at a single trial; the probability of this success equals $p = 1/N$. The independence of the movements of the raisins during the mixing leads to the assumption that we have n Bernoulli trials with probability of "success" p where n is the total number of raisins. This probability is comparatively small if a sufficiently large quantity of rolls is baked. At the same time the number of raisins n is then comparatively large. Therefore, the random number of raisins in a single roll which is equal to the number of "successes" is distributed approximately according to the Poisson law: the probability $P(k)$ that a roll contains exactly k raisins equals

$$P(k) \approx \frac{a^k}{k!} e^{-a} \qquad (k = 0, 1, \ldots, n)$$

where $a = \dfrac{n}{N} = n\dfrac{v}{V}$ is the mean number of raisins in one roll. The probability P that a roll contains at least one raisin is equal to

$$P = 1 - P(0) \approx 1 - e^{-a} = 1 - e^{-\frac{nv}{V}}.$$

Example. *A Model of Radioactive Disintegration.* As is known radium Ra is converted into radion Rn in the course of time. The disintegrating nucleus of the radium atom "emits" the so-called α-particle which is the nucleus of the helium atom He. In this process of emission of α-particles from radium we note some regularities.

The distance between the atoms is comparatively large and it is natural to assume that the disintegration of an individual radium atom takes place independently of the state of the other atoms. We also assume that the probability of disintegration of a single atom during a period of time merely depends on the length of this period. By $p(t)$ we denote the probability of disintegration during a time interval of length t. If there are n radium atoms altogether (one gram is supposed to contain approximately 10^{22} atoms), then the mean number of α-particles emitted during the time t will be $a = n\,p(t)$. As was shown by numerous experiments this number is of the order of magnitude 10^{10} for $t = 1$ sec so that the probability $p(t)$ is indeed very small; for $t = 1$ sec the probability $p(t)$ is of the order of magnitude 10^{-12}.

If we consider the disintegration of any of the radium atoms as a "success", then the number of α-particles emitted during the time t equals the number of "successes" in the n "Bernoulli trials" with probability of "success" $p = p(t)$. The parameters n and p are such that the probability distribution of the random variable $\xi(t)$, the number of α-particles emitted during the time t, is practically the Poisson distribution with parameter $a = n\,p(t)$:

$$\mathbb{P}\{\xi(t) = k\} = \frac{a^k}{k!}\,e^{-a} \quad (k = 0, 1, 2, \ldots).$$

Here, the "Bernoulli trials" represent a formal scheme by which the actual distribution of the random variable $\xi(t)$ can be found.

The Geometric Distribution. We consider unlimited Bernoulli trials. We denote by ξ the number of trials preceding the occurrence of the first "success". If we assume that each trial takes one unit of time, then ξ can be looked upon as the waiting time for the first "success". The probability distribution of the random variable ξ has the form

$$P(k) = p(1 - p)^k \quad (k = 0, 1, 2, \ldots),$$

and is called the *geometric distribution*. It is determinated by one parameter $p > 0$. This is the probability of a single "success" in the corresponding scheme of Bernoulli trials. The expectation, variance, and generating
function of ξ are given by

$$\mathbb{M}\xi = \frac{1-p}{p}, \quad \mathbb{D}\xi = \frac{1-p}{p^2}, \quad \varphi(z) = \frac{p}{1-(1-p)z}.$$

The Pascal Distribution. In an unlimited scheme of Bernoulli trials
let ξ denote the total number of "failures" which precede the occurrence
of the r-th "success". The probability distribution of the random variable ξ
has the form

$$P(k) = C_{r+k-1}^{r-1} p^r (1-p)^k \quad (k = 0, 1, 2, \ldots)$$

and is called the *Pascal distribution*. It coincides with the distribution
of the sum $\xi = \xi_1 + \cdots + \xi_r$, where $\xi_1, \ldots, \xi_r$ are independent random
variables which have the same geometric distribution with parameter p.
The expectation, the variance and the generating function of ξ have the
form:

$$\mathbb{M}\xi = r\frac{1-p}{p}, \quad \mathbb{D}\xi = r\frac{1-p}{p^2}, \quad \varphi(z) = \left[\frac{p}{1-(1-p)z}\right]^r.$$

The distribution function of the Pascal distribution is expressed
by the formula ($m = 0, 1, 2, \ldots$)

$$F(m) = \mathbb{P}\{\xi \leq m\} = \sum_{k=0}^{m} C_{r+k-1}^{r-1} p^r (1-p)^k$$

$$= \sum_{l=r}^{r+m} C_{r+m}^{l} p^l (1-p)^{r+m-l} = \frac{1}{B(r, m+1)} \int_{0}^{p} x^{r-1}(1-x)^m dx.$$

In other words, if m is a non-negative integer, then the value $F(m)$
of the Pascal distribution function in the point m equals the value of the
binomial distribution function [10] with parameters $n = r + m$ and $p' = 1 - p$
in the same point m.

The representation of $F(m)$ as a β-distribution function allows to
define $F(m)$ in a natural way for all real non-positive values of the parameter r. In this wide sense the Pascal distribution is called the *negative
binomial distribution*.

---

[10] There exist tables which allow to compute the values $F(m)$ directly without
recourse to tables of the binomial distribution: E. *Williamson* and M. H. *Bretherton*:
Tables of the negative binomial probability distribution. London-New York:
Wiley 1963.

The Hypergeometric Distribution. Let there be given a set of n elements of one type and $n - m$ elements of some other type. Suppose that a group of r elements is sampled at random from this set. The number of the elements of the first type contained in this sample of r elements is a random variable. The probability distribution of the random variable ξ has the form

$$P(k) = \frac{C_m^k \, C_{n-m}^{r-k}}{C_n^r} \quad [\max(0, m + r - n) \leq k \leq \min(m, r)]$$

where k is an integer. It is called the *hypergeometric distribution*[11]. The corresponding expectation and variance are given by

$$\mathbb{M}\xi = \frac{mr}{n},$$

$$\mathbb{D}\xi = \frac{mr(n-m)(n-r)}{n^2(n-1)}.$$

For $n \to \infty$ and $m/n \sim p$ the *"binomial approximation"* holds:

$$P(k) = \frac{C_m^k \, C_{n-m}^{r-k}}{C_n^r} \sim C_r^k p^k (1-p)^{r-k} \quad (k = 0, \ldots, r).$$

4. Some Probability Distributions Arising in the Scheme of the Symmetric Random Walk [12]

We consider a particle which moves at random through the integers on the real axis: at any unit of time a Bernoulli trial is being performed, and in the case of "success" the particle takes one step of length 1 to the right, whereas in the case of "failure" it moves by one step of length 1 to the left. The paths of the particle can be graphically represented by a broken line $\xi = \xi(t)$ whose vertices have integral-valued coordinates (Fig. 14).

We shall assume that "success" and "failure" are equally probable so that the particle moves with probability $1/2$ by $+1$ and with probability $1/2$ by -1. In this case all paths are equally probable.

Return Times. Let τ be the moment of the first return to the origin $x = 0$. The particle can return only in an even number of steps so that the random variable τ takes only even values. Its probability distribu-

---

[11] Tables of the hypergeometric distributions are contained in the book by *D. B. Owen:* Handbook of statistical tables. London: Addison-Wesley 1962.

[12] *Feller, W.:* Introduction to Probability Theory and its Applications. 2. ed. New York: Wiley 1960.

tion has the following form:

$$P(2n) = \frac{1}{2n} C_{2n-2}^{n-1} \frac{1}{2^{2n+2}} \quad (n = 1, 2, \ldots).$$

The return time τ is finite with probability 1:

$$\mathbb{P}\{\tau < \infty\} = \sum_{n=1}^{\infty} P(2n) = 1,$$

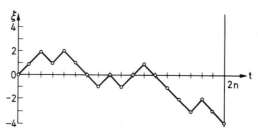

Fig. 14

whereas its mean value is infinite:

$$\mathbb{M}\tau = \sum_{n=1}^{\infty} 2n \, P(2n) = \infty.$$

Let τ_k be the moment of the k-th return to the origin $x = 0$, $\tau_0 = 0$, and $\Delta_k = \tau_k - \tau_{k-1}$ the time between the $(k-1)$-st and the k-th return; thus $\tau_n = \sum_{k=1}^{n} \Delta_k$. The variables $\Delta_1, \Delta_2, \ldots$ are mutually independent and identically distributed; moreover, $\Delta_1 = \tau$ is the time of the first return.

The sequence Δ_1, Δ_2, satisfies the law of large numbers, that is, *with probability 1*

$$\lim_{n \to \infty} \frac{1}{n} \tau_n = \lim_{n \to \infty} \frac{1}{n} \sum_{k=1}^{n} \Delta_k = \infty.$$

Also

$$\mathbb{P}\left\{ \frac{1}{n^2} \tau_n \leq t \right\} \sim 1 - \sqrt{\frac{2}{\pi}} \int_0^{1/\sqrt{t}} e^{-\frac{u^2}{2}} \, du$$

if $n \to \infty$.

It turns out that the time until the n-th return increases approximately as n^2. The limit probability distribution of the normalized random variables $n^{-2}\tau_n$ appears to be the so-called positive stable law with parameter $\alpha = 1/2$. The density of this continuous distribution has the form (Fig. 15)

$$p(t) = \begin{cases} \dfrac{1}{\sqrt{2\pi}} t^{-\frac{3}{2}} e^{-\frac{1}{2t}} & \text{for } t > 0, \\ 0 & \text{for } t < 0. \end{cases}$$

The Time of First Arrival. Let $x > 0$ be an integer and $\tau(x)$ the moment when the moving particle reaches this point first. The random variable

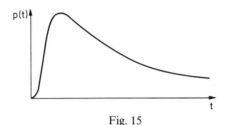

p(t)

Fig. 15

$\tau(x)$ can take only values of the form $2n - x$, where $n = x$, $x + 1, \ldots$ Its probability distribution is determined by the following formula:

$$P(2n - x) = \frac{x}{2n - x} C^n_{2n-x} \frac{1}{2^{2n-x}} \qquad (n = x, \ x + 1, \ldots).$$

If x increases the values of the variable $\tau(x)$ are likely to increase approximately as x^2; in fact

$$\mathbb{P}\left\{ \frac{1}{x^2} \tau(x) \le t \right\} \sim 1 - \sqrt{\frac{2}{\pi}} \int_0^{1/\sqrt{t}} e^{-\frac{u^2}{2}} \, du$$

for $x \to \infty$. The limit distribution is the same as for the time of the n-th return, that is, the *positive stable* law with parameter $\alpha = 1/2$.

The Number of Returns. We denote by v the number of returns to the origin $x = 0$ during $2n$ steps. The probability distribution of the random variable v has the following form:

$$P(k) = C^n_{2n-k} \frac{1}{2^{2n-k}} \qquad (k = 0, 1, \ldots, n).$$

For $n \to \infty$ we obtain

$$\mathbb{P}\left\{ \frac{1}{\sqrt{2n}} v \le x \right\} \sim \sqrt{\frac{2}{\pi}} \int_0^x e^{-\frac{u^2}{2}} \, du.$$

The limit distribution of the normalized random variable $\dfrac{1}{\sqrt{2n}}$ turns out to be the reflected normal distribution. It appears that for $n\to\infty$ the number of returns to the origin $x = 0$ in n steps increases proportionally to $\sqrt{n}$ (and not proportionally to n, as might be expected).

The Time Spent on the Positive Side of the x-Axis. Let T_{2n} be the total time which the moving particle spends on the positive side of the x-axis during the interval $0\leq t\leq 2n$. The random variable T_{2n} takes only even values $2k$ $(k = 0, ..., n)$. Its probability distribution has the form

$$P(2k) = C_{2k}^{k} \cdot C_{2n-2k}^{n-k} \cdot \frac{1}{2^{2n}} \qquad (k = 0, ..., n).$$

Despite the symmetry of the walk the event that the time T_{2n} spent on the positive side of the x-axis equals half of the entire length of time $2n$ is least probable. The variable T_{2n} takes the extreme values 0 or $2n$ with greatest probability.

Let $\alpha = \dfrac{T_{2n}}{2n}$ be the fraction taken by the time which the particle spends on the positive side of the x-axis during the interval $0\leq t\leq 2n$. For $n\to\infty$ we have

$$\mathbb{P}\left\{\frac{1}{2n} T_{2n}\leq x\right\} \sim \frac{2}{\pi} \arcsin\sqrt{\alpha} \qquad (0\leq\alpha\leq 1).$$

The limit distribution here is called the *arc-sine law*. Its density has the form

$$p(\alpha) = \begin{cases} \dfrac{1}{\pi\sqrt{\alpha(1-\alpha)}} & \text{for} \quad 0\leq\alpha\leq 1, \\ 0 & \text{for} \quad \alpha<0,\ \alpha>1. \end{cases}$$

The graph of the function $p(\alpha)$ is shown in Fig. 16.

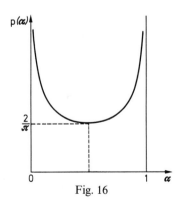

Fig. 16

The Location of the Maximum. We consider the path of the particle during the time interval $0 \le t \le 2n$ (see Fig. 14). The function $\xi = \xi(t)$, $0 \le t \le 2n$ which describes the motion of the particle depends on chance. We denote by τ^* the point where the random function $\xi = \xi(t)$ takes its absolute maximum in the interval $0 \le t \le 2n$ under consideration. The probability distribution of the random variable τ^*, which takes the values $t = 0, 1, \ldots, 2n$, has the form

$$P(t) = \begin{cases} C_{2n}^{n} \dfrac{1}{2^{2n}} & \text{for} \quad t = 0, \\[2ex] \dfrac{1}{2} C_{2k}^{k} C_{2(n-k)}^{n-k} \dfrac{1}{2^{2n}}, \quad k = \left[\dfrac{t}{2} \right] & \text{for} \quad t = 1, 2, \ldots, 2n, \end{cases}$$

where $\left[\dfrac{t}{2} \right]$ is the largest integer less than or equal to $\dfrac{t}{2}$. The boundaries $t = 0$ or $t = 2n$ are the most probable points of the maximum of the path $\xi(t)$, $0 \le t \le 2n$. For $n \to \infty$ we obtain

$$\mathbb{P} \left\{ \frac{1}{2n} \tau^* \le \alpha \right\} \sim \frac{2}{\pi} \arcsin \sqrt{\alpha} \quad (0 \le \alpha \le 1).$$

Here, the limit distribution is the same as for the time spent on the positive side of the x-axis, that is, the *arc-sine law*.

CHAPTER II

Spaces and Measures

§ 1. Some Facts about Measurable and Topological Spaces

1. Measurable and Topological Spaces

Sets. A set is a collection of certain elements. The formulas $x \in A$, or $x \notin A$, mean that x is or is not an element of the set A, respectively. Sometimes the symbol $\bar{\in}$ is used instead of $\notin$. The relations $A_1 \subseteq A_2$ or $A_2 \supseteq A_1$ signify that the set A_1 is contained in the set A_2, that is, each element x of A_1 is also an element of A_2.

We will call a certain set X of elements x a *space*, its elements x *points of the space* X, and the sets A of points x, where $A \subseteq X$, *sets of the space* X. The sets A_1 and A_2 will be called equal: $A_1 = A_2$, if $A_1 \subseteq A_2$ and $A_2 \subseteq A_1$.

The set $A_1 \cup A_2$ which consists of all points x belonging to at least one of the sets A_1 or A_2 is called the *sum* or the *union* of A_1 and A_2. The union $\bigcup_\alpha A_\alpha$ of an arbitrary number of sets A consists of all points x which are contained in at least one of the sets A_α.

The set $A_1 \setminus A_2$ which consists of all points x belonging to A_1 but not to A_2 is called the *difference* of the sets A_1 and A_2.

The set $A_1 \circ A_2$ which is defined by the formula $A_1 \circ A_2 = (A_1 \setminus A_2) \cup (A_2 \setminus A_1)$ is called the *symmetric difference* of A_1 and A_2, and the set $\bar{A} = X \setminus A$ the *complement* of A.

By the *intersection* or *product* of two sets A_1 and A_2, written as $A_1 \cap A_2$, $A_1 \cdot A_2$ or $A_1 A_2$, we mean the set of all points x which belong both to A_1 and A_2; the intersection $\bigcap_\alpha A_\alpha$ of an arbitrary number of sets A_α consists of all points x which belong to every set A_α. The sets A_1 and A_2 are called *disjoint* if their intersection $A_1 \cap A_2$ contains no point x, in other words, if it is the empty set. The empty set is denoted by 0.

Systems of Sets. A collection (or system) of sets $\mathfrak{S}$ of the space X is called a *semi-ring* if it has the following properties: together with arbitrary sets A and A_1 in $\mathfrak{S}$ it contains their intersection; if in addition $A_1 \subseteq A$, then the set A can be written as the union of a finite number of disjoint sets $A_1, A_2, \ldots, A_n$ which also belong to $\mathfrak{S}$:

$$A = \bigcup_{k=1}^{n} A_k;$$

the space X itself can be written as the union of a countable number of disjoint sets $A_1, A_2, \ldots$ of $\mathfrak{S}$:

$$X = \bigcup_{k} A_k.$$

Example. Let the space X be the set of all points x of the real line. The system of all semi-intervals $(x', x'']$, which are open on the left and closed on the right is a semi-ring.

The semi-ring of sets $\mathfrak{S}$ is called a *ring* if together with arbitrary sets A_1 and A_2 in $\mathfrak{S}$ it contains their sum $A_1 \cup A_2$.

Let $\mathfrak{S}$ be an arbitrary semi-ring. Then the system of all sets $A \subseteq X$ which can be represented as the union of a finite number of disjoint sets $A_1, \ldots, A_n$ of $\mathfrak{S}$:

$$A = \bigcup_{k=1}^{n} A_k,$$

is a ring. If a ring $\mathfrak{S}$ contains the entire space X it is called an *algebra*.

An algebra $\mathfrak{A}$ of sets includes with any set A its complement $\bar{A}$, and with any sets $A_1, A_2, \ldots, A_n$ in $\mathfrak{A}$ it contains the union $A = \bigcup_{k=1}^{n} A_k$. The algebra $\mathfrak{A}$ is called a *σ-algebra* if with every countable number of sets $A_1, A_2, \ldots$ in $\mathfrak{A}$ it also contains their union $A = \bigcup_{k=1}^{\infty} A_k$.

The intersection of an arbitrary number of σ-algebras is again a σ-algebra of sets of the space X. For any system of sets $\mathfrak{S}$ there exists a σ-algebra $\mathfrak{A}$ which contains this system $\mathfrak{S}$. The *smallest σ-algebra* $\mathfrak{A}$ containing the system of sets $\mathfrak{S}$ (this is the intersection of all σ-algebras with this property) is called the *σ-algebra generated by the system* $\mathfrak{S}$.

Measurable and Topological Spaces. The space X is called measurable and denoted by $(X, \mathfrak{A})$ if a certain σ-algebra of sets $\mathfrak{A}$ is distinguished. The space X is *topological* if a system $\mathfrak{S}$ of so-called *open sets* is distinguished in it with the properties: $\mathfrak{S}$ contains the empty set 0 and the space X; the intersection $A_1 \cap A_2$ of two sets A_1 and A_2 of $\mathfrak{S}$ belongs to $\mathfrak{S}$; the union $\cup A_\alpha$ of an arbitrary number of sets A_α of $\mathfrak{S}$ belongs to $\mathfrak{S}$. Moreover it is usually assumed that the system $\mathfrak{S}$ separates the points of X, that is, for any $x_1, x_2 \in X$ there exist disjoint sets $A_1, A_2 \in \mathfrak{S}$ such that $x_1 \in A_1$, $x_2 \in A_2$.

A system $\mathfrak{S}$ of open sets of the topological space X is called a *basis* of this space if every open set is the union of open sets of $\mathfrak{S}$.

By a *measurable topological space* we usually mean a measurable space $(X, \mathfrak{A})$ where the distinguished σ-algebra $\mathfrak{A}$ is generated by some basis of open sets of the topological space X. The minimal σ-algebra which contains all open sets is called the *Borel σ-algebra* of the space X; the sets $A \in \mathfrak{A}$ are called Borel sets.

In general, the system of all open sets is not a semi ring. The complements of the open sets of the topological space X are called *closed* sets. The union of a finite and and the intersection of an arbitrary number of closed sets are closed sets, too. Any single point of the space X is a "one point" closed set.

The topological space X is called *regular* if for any closed set F and any point $x \notin F$ there exist disjoint open sets G_1 and G_2 such that $F \subseteq G_1$ and $x \in G_2$.

Let A be an arbitrary set of the space X. The smallest closed set F containing A (F coincides with the intersection of all closed sets containing A) is called the closure of the set A and is denoted by $[A]$.

The intersection of a countable number of open sets is called a *set of type G_δ*; the sum of a countable number of closed sets is called a *set of type F_σ*; the sum of a countable number of sets of type G_δ is called a *set of type $G_{\delta\sigma}$*; the intersection of a countable number of sets of type F_σ is called a *set of type $F_{\sigma\delta}$* etc.

The measurable space $(X, \mathfrak{A})$ is called *separable* if there exists a countable system of sets $\mathfrak{S}$ which separates the points of the space X and generates the corresponding σ-algebra $\mathfrak{A}$. The topological space X is called *separable* if there exists some countable basis of open sets which separates the points of this space.

Example. Let X be an arbitrary space. The system of all "one-point" sets $x \subseteq X$ can be chosen as a basis of the open sets.

Then any set A of the space X is open and closed at the same time. This space X is separable if and only if it contains only denumerably many points x.

Example. Let X be the real line. The system of all open intervals (x', x'') can be taken as a basis of the open sets. A set G is open if and only if with any of its points x it contains also some neighborhood $(x - \delta, x + \delta)$ of this point. Every open set is a sum of countably many disjoint open intervals. Every open set is a set of type F_σ, and every closed set is a set of type G_δ. The space X is separable; the system of all open intervals (x', x'') with rational endpoints can be taken as a basis separating points.

In some sense every measurable separable space $(Y, \mathfrak{B})$ is a "part" of the space $(X, \mathfrak{A})$ where X is the real line and $\mathfrak{A}$ the σ-algebra of the Borel sets. In fact there exists a one-to-one correspondance $x \leftrightarrow y$ between the points x of some set A_Y on the real line and the points y of the space Y such that to every set $B \in \mathfrak{B}$ there corresponds some set of the type A_Y. $A, A \in \mathfrak{A}$ and to every such set on the real line there corresponds some set $B \in \mathfrak{B}$. (Here it is understood that $A_Y \cdot A \leftrightarrow B$ if $x \leftrightarrow y$ for all $x \in A_Y \cdot A$, $y \in B$). Such a correspondance of the spaces $(Y, \mathfrak{B})$ and $(A_Y, \mathfrak{A}_Y)$ where $\mathfrak{A}_Y$ is the σ-algebra of all sets of the new space A_Y which can be presented in the form $A_Y \cdot A, A \in \mathfrak{A}$, is given for instance by the following relation:

$$x = \sum_k \frac{2}{3^k} \, \varphi_{B_k}(y).$$

Here $B_1, B_2, \ldots$ stands for a denumerable system of sets which separates the points of the space Y and generates the σ-algebra $\mathfrak{B}$ and $\varphi_{B_k}(y)$ are the indicator functions of the sets B_k $(k = 1, 2, \ldots)$:

$$\varphi_B(y) = \begin{cases} 1 & \text{for} \quad y \in B, \\ 0 & \text{for} \quad y \notin B. \end{cases}$$

The corresponding set A_Y is a subset of the well-known Cantor set on the real line.

   Products of Spaces. The product of the spaces X_1 and X_2 is defined as the space X whose points are all possible ordered pairs (x_1, x_2) where $x_1 \in X_1, x_2 \in X_2$. It is denoted by $X = X_1 \times X_2$.

   The set $A \in X$ is called *rectangular* if it can be written in the form $A_1 \times A_2$, or more precisely, if it consists of all points $x = (x_1, x_2)$ where $x_1 \in A_1, x_2 \in A_2$. If $\mathfrak{S}_1$ and $\mathfrak{S}_2$ are systems of sets in the spaces X_1 and X_2, respectively, and if each of them is a semi-ring, then the collection of all rectangular sets of the form $A = A_1 \times A_2$, where $A_1 \in \mathfrak{S}_1$ and $A_2 \in \mathfrak{S}_2$, is also a semi-ring.

   Example. Let the space X be the real plane. Then X is the product of two real lines X_1 and X_2. The system of all rectangles $(x_1', x_1''] \times (x_2', x_2'']$ forms a semi-ring of sets in the plane; recall that the system of all semi-intervals $(x', x'']$ forms a semi-ring of sets on the line.

   By the *product of two measurable spaces* $(X_1, \mathfrak{A}_1)$ and $(X_2, \mathfrak{A}_2)$ we mean the measurable space $(X, \mathfrak{A})$ where $X = X_1 \times X_2$, and where the σ-algebra $\mathfrak{A}$ is *the product* of the σ-algebras $\mathfrak{A}_1$ and $\mathfrak{A}_2$, that is, the σ-algebra generated by the semi-ring $\mathfrak{A}_1 \times \mathfrak{A}_2$ of all rectangular sets of the form $A = A_1 \times A_2$ with $A_1 \in \mathfrak{A}_1$ and $A_2 \in \mathfrak{A}_2$.

   By the *product of two topological spaces* X_1 and X_2 we mean the topological space $X = X_1 \times X_2$ in which we use as a basis of the open sets the class of all rectangular sets of the form $A = A_1 \times A_2$ with $A_1 \in \mathfrak{S}_1$ and

$A_2 \in \mathfrak{S}_2$, where $\mathfrak{S}_1$ and $\mathfrak{S}_2$ are bases of the open sets in the spaces X_1 and X_2, respectively.

Let $(E, \mathfrak{B})$ be a measurable space and T a finite set of indices $t = 1, \ldots, n$. The measurable space $(X, \mathfrak{A})$, where $X = E^T$ is the n-fold product of the space E with itself, and the σ-algebra $\mathfrak{A} = \mathfrak{B}^T$ the n-fold product of the corresponding σ-algebras $\mathfrak{B}$, is called a *measurable coordinate space*. The points $x = \{x(1), \ldots, x(n)\}$ of this space $X = E^T$ are determined by the coordinates $x(t)$, $t \in T$. If T is an arbitrary set of indices, the coordinate space $X = E^T$ is defined to be the set of all function $x = x(t)$ on the set T with values in the space E. The single values $x(t)$ can again be interpreted as the coordinates of the point $x = x(t)$ which belongs to the space $X = E^T$.

Let $t_1, \ldots, t_n$ be arbitrary points of the set T in a finite number n, and $B_1, \ldots, B_n$ be arbitrary sets from the space E. The set of the form

$$\{x(t_1) \in B_1, \ldots, x(t_n) \in B_n\}$$

which is contained in the space X is called a *cylinder set* in $X = E^T$. In other words, the cylinder set consists of all points $x = x(t)$ whose coordinates $x(t_1), \ldots, x(t_n)$ belong to the corresponding sets $B_1, \ldots, B_n$. The system of all cylinder sets where the corresponding sets $B_1, \ldots, B_n$ belong to the σ-algebra $\mathfrak{B}$ of the space E, forms a semi-ring $\mathfrak{B}^T$. The space $X = E^T$ together with the σ-algebra $\mathfrak{A}$ generated by $\mathfrak{B}^T$ is called a *measurable coordinate space* $(X, \mathfrak{A})$.

We define $\mathfrak{A}(S)$, where $S \subseteq T$, to be the σ-algebra generated by the semi-ring $\mathfrak{B}^S$, that is, by all possible cylinder sets with corresponding parameters $t_1, \ldots, t_n \in S$. If the point $x' = x'(t)$ of the space $X = E^T$ belongs to the set A of $\mathfrak{A}(S)$ and another point $x'' = x''(t)$ is such that the corresponding coordinates of both points coincide, that is, $x'(t) = x''(t)$ for all $t \in S$, then $x'' = x''(t)$ belongs to A, too. Any set A from the σ-algebra $\mathfrak{A} = \mathfrak{A}(T)$ belongs to a σ-algebra $\mathfrak{A}(S)$, where S is a denumerable set which in general depends on the set A.

Let E be a topological space and $\mathfrak{S}$ a basis of its open sets. The coordinate space $X = E^T$ in which the system of all cylinder sets of the form

$$\{x(t_1) \in B_1, \ldots, x(t_n) \in B_n\}$$

with $B_1, \ldots, B_n \in \mathfrak{S}$ is taken as a basis of the open sets will be called a *Tihonov product*.

Mappings of Sets. Let $\varphi = \varphi(x)$ be a function on the set A of the space X with values in the space Y. By the *inverse image* of the set $B \subseteq Y$ under the mapping φ, denoted by $\{\varphi \in B\}$, we mean the set of X which consists of all points $x \in X$ such that $\varphi(x) \in B$. The set of Y which consists of all points $\varphi(x)$ with $x \in A$ is called the *image* of the set A, and is denoted by $\varphi(A)$. The mapping $B \to \{\varphi \in B\}$, $B \subseteq Y$ preserves the set-theoretic operations:

$$\{\varphi \in \cup B\} = \cup \{\varphi \in B\} ,$$
$$\{\varphi \in \cap B\} = \cap \{\varphi \in B\} ,$$
$$\{\varphi \in (B_1 \setminus B_2)\} = \{\varphi \in B_1\} \setminus \{\varphi \in B_2\} .$$

This is not true with the mapping $A \to \varphi(A)$, $A \subseteq X$.

Example. Let X be the real line and $y = \varphi(x)$ the real function described by Fig. 17. The image of each half-line $(-\infty, 1)$ and $(-1, \infty)$ consists of two points: $y = 0$ and $y = 1$, whereas the image of their intersection, that is, of the interval $(-1, 1)$, consists only of the point $y = 0$.

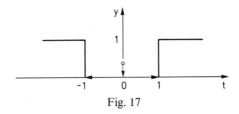

Fig. 17

Let $\varphi = \varphi(x)$ be an arbitrary function on the measurable space $(X, \mathfrak{A})$ with values in an arbitrary space Y. The set B of all sets $B \subseteq Y$ such that the inverse image $\{\varphi \in B\}$ belongs to the σ-algebra $\mathfrak{A}$ of the space $(X, \mathfrak{A})$, is a σ-algebra.

Let X be an arbitrary space and $\varphi = \varphi(x)$ an arbitrary function on X with values in the measurable space $(Y, \mathfrak{B})$. The set $\mathfrak{A}^\varphi$ of all sets A which are inverse images of sets B of $\mathfrak{B}$, that is, $A = \{\varphi \in B\}$, $B \in \mathfrak{B}$, forms a σ-algebra.

Measurable and Continuous Mappings. Let $(X, \mathfrak{A})$ and $(Y, \mathfrak{B})$ be measurable spaces. A function $\varphi = \varphi(x)$ is called $(\mathfrak{A}, \mathfrak{B})$-*measurable* if for any $B \in \mathfrak{B}$ the inverse image $\{\varphi \in B\}$ belongs to the σ-algebra $\mathfrak{A}$. If $\mathfrak{S}$ is any system of sets which generates the σ-algebra $\mathfrak{B}$, then the function φ is measurable if and only if for each $B \in \mathfrak{S}$ the inverse image $\{\varphi \in B\}$ belongs to $\mathfrak{A}$.

Let $(X, \mathfrak{A})$, $(Y, \mathfrak{B})$ and $(Z, \mathfrak{C})$ be measurable spaces, and suppose that the function $\varphi = \varphi(x)$ is $(\mathfrak{A}, \mathfrak{B})$-measurable and the function $\psi = \psi(y)$ is $(\mathfrak{B}, \mathfrak{C})$-measurable. Then the compound function $\psi[\varphi(x)]$ on X is $(\mathfrak{A}, \mathfrak{C})$-measurable.

Let A be an arbitrary set of the space $X = X_1 \times X_2$ and x_2 an arbitrary point of the space X_2. The set A_{x_2} of all points $x_1 \in X_1$ such that the pair (x_1, x_2) belongs to A, is called a *section* of A. In other words, the section A_{x_2} is the inverse image of the set A under the mapping $\varphi(x_1) = (x_1, x_2)$ where x_2 is a fixed point of the space X_2:

$$A_{x_2} = \{(x_1, x_2) \in A\} .$$

Let $(X_1, \mathfrak{A}_1)$ and $(X_2, \mathfrak{A}_2)$ be measurable spaces. If a set A of the space $X = X_1 \times X_2$ belongs to the product of the σ-algebras $\mathfrak{A}_1$ and $\mathfrak{A}_2$, then the sections A_{x_1} and A_{x_2} of this set have the property that $A_{x_2} \in \mathfrak{A}_1$ and $A_{x_1} \in \mathfrak{A}_2$ for any $x_1 \in X_1$ and $x_2 \in X_2$.

Let $\varphi = \varphi(x)$, $x = (x_1, x_2)$, be an arbitrary $(\mathfrak{A}, \mathfrak{B})$-measurable function on a set A of the product $(X, \mathfrak{A})$ of the measurable spaces $(X_1, \mathfrak{A}_1)$ and $(X_2, \mathfrak{A}_2)$ with values in a measurable space $(Y, \mathfrak{B})$. Then for any fixed $x_2 \in X_2$ the function $\varphi_{x_2}(x_1) = \varphi(x_1, x_2)$ is $(\mathfrak{A}_1, \mathfrak{B})$-measurable.

Let $\varphi_1(y)$ and $\varphi_2(y)$ be arbitrary measurable functions on the measurable space $(Y, \mathfrak{B})$ with values in spaces $(X_1, \mathfrak{A}_1)$ and $(X_2, \mathfrak{A}_2)$, respectively. Then the pair $\varphi = (\varphi_1, \varphi_2)$ is a $(\mathfrak{B}, \mathfrak{A})$-measurable function on Y with values in the product $(X, \mathfrak{A})$ of the spaces $(X_1, \mathfrak{A}_1)$ and $(X_2, \mathfrak{A}_2)$.

A function $\varphi = \varphi(x)$ on a topological space X with values in a topological space Y, is called a *Borel function* if the inverse image $\{\varphi \in B\}$ of any open (or any closed) set $B \subseteq Y$ is a Borel set of the space X. The function $\varphi = \varphi(x)$ on X is called *continuous* if the inverse image $\{\varphi \in B\}$ of any open or closed set $B \subseteq Y$ is open or closed, respectively, in X.

Baire Sets. Let $\mathfrak{S}$ be the system of all sets of the topological space X which are inverse images $\{\varphi \in B\}$ of open (or closed) sets B of the real line Y under continuous mappings. The σ-algebra $\mathfrak{A}$ generated by the system of these sets will be called the *Baire σ-algebra* of the space X, and the sets $A \in \mathfrak{A}$ are termed *Baire sets* of this space.

Example. *A Semi-Ring of Baire Sets.* Let F be a closed Baire set in X which is the inverse image of a closed set B on the real line $Y: F = \{\varphi \in B\}$. If we take any continuous function $\psi(y)$ which vanishes on the closed set B and is strictly positive outside of B [for example, $\psi(y)$ can be the distance from the point $y \in Y$ to the set $B \subseteq Y$], then the compound function $\psi[\varphi(x)]$ is continuous on X, and the closed Baire set F under consideration coincides with the inverse image $\{\psi[\varphi] = 0\}$.

The system $\mathfrak{S}$ of all closed Baire sets F which are inverse images of zero under continuous mappings $\varphi = \varphi(x)$ onto the real line, contains with any of its sets F_1 and F_2 their intersection $F_1 \cap F_2$ and their union $F_1 \cup F_2$. If for example $F_1 = \{\varphi_1 = 0\}$ and $F_2 = \{\varphi_2 = 0\}$, then $F_1 \cap F_2 = \{\varphi_1 \cdot \varphi_2 = 0\}$ and $F_1 \cup F_2 = \{|\varphi_1| + |\varphi_2| = 0\}$. The system of all sets A which can be written as differences of the form $F_1 \setminus F_2$ of sets F_1 and F_2 of $\mathfrak{S}$, where $F_2 \subseteq F_1$, is a semi-ring generating the entire σ-algebra of the Baire sets of X.

Metric Spaces. The space X is called a *metric* space if for any two points x' and $x'' \in X$ a "distance" $\varrho(x', x'')$ is defined which has the following properties: 1) $\varrho(x', x'') \geq 0$, and $\varrho(x', x'') = 0$ if and only if $x' = x''$; 2) $\varrho(x', x'') = \varrho(x'', x')$; 3) the so-called *"rectangle-inequality"* holds according to which

$$\varrho(x', x'') \leq \varrho(x', x) + \varrho(x, x'')$$

for any $x, x', x'' \in X$.

By a neighborhood $V_\delta(x)$ of a point x of a metric space X where δ is a positive number, we mean the set of all points x' whose distance from x is smaller than δ. A subset G of X is called open if, given any point $x \in G$, it contains some neighborhood of this point.

A real function $\varphi = \varphi(x)$ on a metric space X is continuous if and only if for every point $x \in X$ and every given number $\varepsilon > 0$ a neighborhood $V_\delta(x)$ of this point can be found such that

$$|\varphi(x) - \varphi(x')| \leq \varepsilon \quad \text{for all} \quad x' \in V_\delta(x).$$

Let F be a closed set and $\varrho(x, F)$ the distance from a point x to F:

$$\varrho(x, F) = \inf_{x' \in F} \varrho(x, x').$$

The function $\varphi = \varphi(x)$ defined by $\varphi(x) = \varrho(x, F)$ is continuous on the space X, and $\varphi(x) = 0$ for $x \in F$ and $\varphi(x) > 0$ for $x \notin F$. Therefore, any closed set F is a Baire set, and the σ-algebras of the Baire and Borel sets coincide. Any closed set F can be written as the intersection of a countable number of open sets, for example $F = \bigcap_{n=1}^{\infty} V_{\frac{1}{n}}(F)$, where $V_\varepsilon(F)$ denotes the set of all points x whose distance $\varrho(x, F)$ from F is smaller than ε. In other words, F is a *set of type G_δ*.

Any open set G is the intersection of a countable number of closed sets, that is, G is a set of type F_σ.

Let A be an arbitrary set of a metric space. A point x is called a *boundary point* of the set A if the distance from x to the set A as well as to its complement $X \backslash A$ is equal to zero:

$$\varrho(x, A) = \varrho(x, X \backslash A) = 0.$$

The set A' of all boundary points x is called the *boundary of the set* A. The boundary of the entire space X is the empty set.

A point x is called a *cluster point* of the set $A \subseteq X$ if every neighborhood $V_\delta(x)$ of x has a non-empty intersection with A. The set of all cluster points of A coincides with the closure $[A]$ of A. The boundary of an arbitrary set A is the difference $[A] \backslash G$ where G denotes the maximal open set G contained in A, that is, the union of all open sets contained in A.

A set $A \subseteq X$ is called *dense* in X if every neighborhood $V_\delta(x)$ of any point $x \in X$ contains a point $x' \in A$. The metric space X is called *separable* if and only if there exists a denumerable set of points $x_1, x_2, \ldots \in X$ which is dense in X.

Let X be a topological space. A sequence of points $x_1, x_2, \ldots$ of this space is called *convergent* to a point x if for every open set V containing x there exists an n such that $x_m \in V$ for $m > n$.

A sequence of points $x_1, x_2, \ldots$ of a metric space X is *convergent* if there exists a point $x \in X$ such that $\varrho(x_n, x) \to 0$ for $n \to \infty$; this point x is called the *limit* $x = \lim x_n$. The sequence $x_1, x_2, \ldots$ will be termed *fundamental* if $\varrho(x_m, x_n) \to 0$ for $m, n \to \infty$. Every convergent sequence is fundamental. The metric space X is called *complete* if every fundamental sequence converges to a point x of space X.

Compact Spaces and their Products. A system of sets $\mathfrak{S}$ will be called *centered* if the intersection of any finite number of sets from $\mathfrak{S}$ is not empty.

A closed set $A \subseteq X$ is called *compact* if every centered system $\mathfrak{S}$ of closed subsets F of A has a non-empty intersection: $\cap F \neq 0$. An arbitrary set A is termed *compact* in X if its closure $F = [A]$ is compact.

If a separable topological space X is compact then a distance $\varrho(x', x'')$ can be defined in such a way that the neighborhoods $V_\delta(x)$ form a basis of this topological space. In this case a set A in X is compact if and only if every sequence of points $x_1, x_2, \ldots$ of A contains a convergent sub-sequence.

If X is an arbitrary compact space, then the system of all open Baire sets forms a basis in X.

Urysohn's Lemma: Given any two disjoint closed sets F_1 and F_2 of a compact space X there exists a continuous real function $\varphi = \varphi(x)$ on X such that $0 \leq \varphi(x) \leq 1$ for all $x \in X$ and

$$\varphi(x) = \begin{cases} 0 & \text{for} \quad x \in F_1 \\ 1 & \text{for} \quad x \in F_2 . \end{cases}$$

The open Baire sets $\{\varphi < 1/2\}$ and $\{\varphi > 1/2\}$ are contained in the given open sets $G_1 = \bar{F}_2$ and $G_2 = \bar{F}_1$.

The topological product of compact spaces is again compact. Let E be an arbitrary compact space, T an arbitrary set, and $X = E^T$ the corresponding *Tihonov product*. The space $X = E^T$ is compact. If in addition the original space E is *separable*, then the Baire σ-algebra $\mathfrak{A}$ of the space $X = E^T$ coincides with the minimal σ-algebra which contains all *cylinder sets*

$$A = \{x(t_1) \in B_1, \ldots, x(t_n) \in B_n\} ,$$

where $B_1, \ldots, B_n$ are sets of a basis of the original space E. In other words, $\mathfrak{A}$ coincides with the σ-algebra $\mathfrak{A}(T)$ generated by the semi-ring $\mathfrak{B}^T$ of all cylinder sets of the form given above, where $\mathfrak{B}$ is the Baire σ-algebra of the space E.

Example. Any closed finite interval $[a, b]$ on the real line $-\infty < x < \infty$ is compact. The entire line $-\infty < x < \infty$ is not compact; it becomes compact if it is completed by the points $x = -\infty$ and $x = +\infty$.

Example. Let E be a closed bounded interval or the entire completed line, T an interval $[t_1, t_2]$, and $X = E^T$ the space of all real functions $x = x(t)$ on the interval $t_1 \leq t \leq t_2$. Each Baire set A belongs to some σ-algebra of sets $\mathfrak{A}(S)$ of the coordinate space $X = E^T$ determined by conditions on the values $x(t)$ where t runs only through a denumerable set $S \subseteq T$. This property is not shared, for example, by the closed set of all functions $x = x(t)$ with $0 \leq x(t) \leq 1$ for $t_1 \leq t \leq t_2$; thus not any Borel set of the Tihonov product $X = E^T$ is also a Baire set. In other words, the σ-algebra of the Borel sets of the space $X = E^T$ is strictly larger than the σ-algebra of the Baire sets which coincides with the σ-algebra $\mathfrak{A}(T)$.

2. Linear Spaces

The space X is called linear if for the elements x of this space operations of addition and of multiplication by real number are defined which satisfy the following conditions: for any $x_1, x_2 \in X$ and arbitrary numbers λ_1, λ_2 the elements $x = \lambda_1 x_1 + \lambda_2 x_2$ again belong to X; there exists an element 0 such that $x + 0 = 0$ and $\lambda \cdot 0 = 0$ for any λ; the equation $0 \cdot x = 0$ holds for any $x \in X$; for any $x \in X$ there exists a so-called inverse element $-x$ which satisfies $x - x = 0$; moreover,

$$x_1 + x_2 = x_2 + x_1, \qquad x_1 + (x_2 + x_3) = (x_1 + x_2) + x_3,$$
$$1 \cdot x = x, \qquad \lambda_1 \cdot (\lambda_2 \cdot x) = (\lambda_1 \cdot \lambda_2) x,$$
$$(\lambda_1 + \lambda_2) x = \lambda_1 x + \lambda_2 x, \qquad \lambda(x_1 + x_2) = \lambda x_1 + \lambda x_2.$$

If instead of the real numbers λ complex numbers are chosen then X is called a *complex linear space*.

The space X is called a *linear topological space* if addition and multiplication by numbers are continuous, that is, the function $\varphi(\lambda_1, \lambda_2, x_1, x_2) = \lambda_1 x_1 + \lambda_2 x_2$ is continuous with respect to all variables considered as a function on the product $E \times E \times X \times X$, where E is the real line or the complex plane.

In order to define the system of all open sets of the linear topological space X it suffices to define a basis $\mathfrak{S}$ of the open sets around the element 0, that is, a system of open sets such that any open set of the space X which contains the element 0, includes a set of $\mathfrak{S}$.

Normed Spaces. The linear space X will be called *normed* if for each of its elements x a norm $\|x\|$ is defined as a function of x with the following properties: 1) $\|x\| \geq 0$; 2) $\|x\| = 0$ if and only if $x = 0$; 3) $\|\lambda x\| = |\lambda| \cdot \|x\|$ for every λ; and finally; 4) $\|x_1 + x_2\| \leq \|x_1\| + \|x_2\|$ for all $x_1, x_2 \in X$. The normed space becomes a *metric* space if the distance in this space is defined by $\varrho(x_1, x_2) = \|x_2 - x_1\|$. A complete normed space will be called a *Banach space*.

The normed space X is termed a *Hilbert space* if a numerical function of two variables x_1 and x_2 is defined to be denoted by (x_1, x_2) and called a *scalar product* which has the following properties:

1) $(x, x) \geq 0$;

2) $(x, x) = 0$ if and only if $x = 0$;

3) $(\lambda_1 x_1 + \lambda_2 x_2, x) = \lambda_1(x_1, x) + \lambda_2(x_2, x)$;

4) $(x, \lambda_1 x_1 + \lambda_2 x_2) = \bar{\lambda}_1(x, x_1) + \bar{\lambda}_2(x, x_2)$

for any λ_1, λ_2 and $x_1, x_2 \in X$. The norm $\|x\|$ of the element of the Hilbert space X is defined as $\|x\| = \sqrt{(x, x)}$.

Denumerably Normed Spaces. Let X be a linear space where a denumerable number of norms

$$\|x\|_1, \|x\|_2, \ldots, \|x\|_n, \ldots$$

is defined. We assume that for any sequence $x_1, x_2, \ldots$ of elements of X which has the property that

$$\|x_n - x\|_p \to 0; \quad \|x_m - x_n\|_q \to 0 \quad \text{for} \quad m, n \to \infty,$$

the relation $\|x_n - x\|_q \to 0$ holds, too. This space X, where the sets of the form

$$\{\|x\|_1 < \varepsilon, \ldots, \|x\|_p < \varepsilon\} \quad (p = 1, 2, \ldots; \varepsilon > 0)$$

are chosen as a basis of the open sets around the zero element, is called a *denumerably normed* space. Any denumerably normed space X is metric. A corresponding distance $\varrho(x_1, x_2)$ can be defined by

$$\varrho(x_1, x_2) = \sum_{p=1}^{\infty} \frac{1}{2^p} \cdot \frac{\|x_1 - x_2\|_p}{1 + \|x_1 - x_2\|_p}.$$

We may assume without any restriction that

$$\|x\|_1 \leq \|x\|_2 \leq \cdots.$$

A denumerably normed space X is called a *denumerably Hilbert space* if each of the norms $\|x\|_p$, $p = 1, 2, \ldots$ is given by a scalar product

$$(x_1, x_2)_p, \quad \|x\|_p = \sqrt{(x, x)_p} \quad (p = 1, 2, \ldots).$$

A denumerably Hilbert space X will be called a *nuclear* space if for any p there exist a q and a nuclear operator A (see p. 69) in the Hilbert space X with the scalar product $(x_1, x_2) = (x_1, x_2)_q$ such that

$$(x_1, x_2)_p = (A x_1, x_2)_q .$$

Example. Let X be the space of all infinitely differentiable functions $x = x(t)$ on the real line $-\infty < t < \infty$ which vanish for $|t| \geq a$. If we introduce the scalar products

$$(x_1, x_2)_p = \int_{-\infty}^{\infty} \sum_{k=0}^{p} x_1^{(k)}(t) \, x_2^{(k)}(t) \, dt \quad (p = 0, 1, \ldots),$$

where $x^{(k)}(t)$ denotes the k-th derivative of $x(t)$, then X is a *nuclear space*.

Linear Functionals. Let U be a linear space. A real- (or complex-) valued function on U, to be denoted by $x = \langle u, x \rangle$, will be called a *linear functional* if

$$\langle \lambda_1 u_1 + \lambda_2 u_2, x \rangle = \lambda_1 \langle u_1, x \rangle + \lambda_2 \langle u_2, x \rangle$$

for all real (complex) λ_1, λ_2 and $u_1, u_2 \in U$. If U is a linear topological space it is usually assumed in addition that the linear functional $x = \langle u, x \rangle$ is continuous.

If U is a complete Hilbert space, then every linear continuous functional $x = \langle u, x \rangle$ which is defined on the entire space U has the form

$$\langle u, x \rangle = (u, x) \quad (u \in U),$$

where x is a fixed element of U and (u, x) the corresponding scalar product.

A linear functional $x = \langle u, x \rangle$ is continuous on an arbitrary normed space U if and only if it is bounded:

$$\|x\| = \sup_{\|u\|=1} |\langle u, x \rangle| < \infty ,$$

where sup is taken for all elements $u \in U$ with $\|u\| = 1$. The number $\|x\|$ is called the *norm of the linear functional* $x = \langle u, x \rangle$.

Given any element u_0 of a normed space U there exists a linear continuous functional $x = \langle u, x \rangle$, $u \in U$ such that $\langle u_0, x \rangle = \|u_0\|$ and $\|x\| = 1$. Any linear continuous functional $x = \langle u, x \rangle$, $u \in U_0$ which is defined only on a linear subspace U_0 of the normed space U can be extended to a linear continuous functional on the entire space U in such a way that

$$\|x\| = \sup_{\substack{\|u\|=1 \\ u \in U_0}} |\langle u, x \rangle| ,$$

where sup is taken only for elements u from the subspace $U_0 \subsetneq U$, $\|u\| = 1$.

5*

In a denumerably normed space U a linear functional $x = \langle u, x \rangle$ is continuous if and only if it is continuous with respect to some norm $\|u\|_p$:

$$\|x\|_p = \sup_{\|u\|_p = 1} |\langle u, x \rangle| < \infty .$$

The Adjoint Space. The set of all linear functionals $x = \langle u, x \rangle$ on a linear space U is a linear space. If x_1 and x_2 are linear functionals, then $x = \lambda_1 x_1 + \lambda_2 x_2$, given by the formula

$$\langle u, x \rangle = \lambda_1 \langle u, x_1 \rangle + \lambda_2 \langle u, x_2 \rangle$$

is a linear functional, too.

Let X be the space of all real linear functionals $x = \langle u, x \rangle$ on a real linear space U. As a basis of the open sets around 0 in X we chose the set of all *cylinder sets* of the form

$$\{\langle u_1, x \rangle < \varepsilon, \ldots, \langle u_n, x \rangle < \varepsilon\} ,$$

where $u_1, \ldots, u_n \in U$ and $\varepsilon > 0$. In this way X becomes a linear topological space. These open cylinder sets are called *weak neighborhoods* of 0, and the topological space X which they define is termed the *(algebraic) adjoint* (dual) *space with the weak topology.*If the original linear space U is normed, then the norm

$$\|x\| = \sup_{\|u\| = 1} |\langle u, x \rangle|$$

can be introduced in the adjoint (dual) space X which consists of all linear *continuous* functionals $x = \langle u, x \rangle$, $u \in U$. In this way X becomes a complete normed space. The sets $\|x\| < \varepsilon$, $\varepsilon > 0$, the so-called *strong neighborhoods* of the 0 element, form a basis of the open sets around 0. The topological space X defined by these neighborhoods is called the *adjoint space with the strong topology.*

Let U be a separable denumerably Hilbert space and X its adjoint space which consists of all linear continuous functionals $x = \langle u, x \rangle$. We endow X with the weak topology. Then any "ball of radius r"

$$S_p(r) = \{\|x\|_p \leqq r\} ,$$

that is, the set of all elements $x \in X$ for which $\|x\|_p = \sup_{\|u\|_p \leqq 1} |\langle u, x \rangle| \leqq r$, is compact. The entire space X can be written as a union of countably many compact sets.

In the adjoint space X endowed with the weak topology of a separable denumerably normed space U the Borel and Baire σ-algebras coincide with the smallest σ-algebra which contains all cylinder sets of the form

$$\{\langle u_1, x \rangle \in B_1, \ldots, \langle u_n, x \rangle \in B_n\} ,$$

where $u_1, ..., u_n$ are arbitrary elements of U, and $B_1, ..., B_n$ arbitrary Borel sets on the real line.

We say that on the linear space U there is given a *linear operator* A if $v = Au$ is a function of $u \in U$ with values in some linear space V such that

$$A(\lambda_1 u_1 + \lambda_2 u_2) = \lambda_1 \cdot Au_1 + \lambda_2 \cdot Au_2$$

for any $u_1, u_2 \in U$ and any numbers λ_1, λ_2. A linear operator A^{-1} defined on the elements of the space V of the form $v = Au$, $u \in U$, is called the *inverse* operator of A if $A^{-1}v = u$ for $v = Au$. Let A_1 and A_2 be any two linear operators on the space U and λ_1, λ_2 any numbers. Then $A = \lambda_1 A_1 + \lambda_2 A_2$, that is

$$Au = \lambda_1 \cdot A_1 u + \lambda_2 \cdot A_2 u \qquad (u \in U)$$

is a linear operator, too.

By the *product of the operators* A and B, where A is a linear operator on U with values in V, and B a linear operator on V, we mean the operator BAu, $u \in U$.

A linear operator A on a linear topological space U which maps U into the linear topological space V is called *continuous*, if the function $v = Au$ is continuous. If U and V are normed spaces, then A is continuous if and only if it is bounded, that is,

$$\|A\| = \sup_{\|u\|=1} \|Au\| < \infty ,$$

where sup is taken for all elements $u \in U$ with $\|u\| = 1$. The number $\|A\|$ is called the *norm* of A.

A linear operator A on a normed space is called *compact* (or *completely continuous*) if the set of the elements Au with $u \in U$, $\|u\| = 1$ is compact in the space V.

Let A be a linear operator in the Hilbert space U, that is, $AU \subseteq U$. The operator A^* defined by $(Au', u'') = (u', A^*u'')$ for all $u', u'' \in U$ is called the *adjoint* to A. The operator A is termed *self-adjoint* if $A^* = A$. A selfadjoint operator A is called a *projection* operator if $A^2 = A$. A self-adjoint operator A is said to be *positive* if $(Au, u) \geq 0$ for all $u \in U$.

An operator A on a Hilbert space U with values in a Hilbert space V will be called *isometric* if $(Au', Au'') = (u', u'')$ for all $u', u'' \in U$. An isometric operator A in a Hilbert space U with the property that $AU = U$ will be called *unitary*.

A family of elements $\{u_\alpha\}$ of a Hilbert space U is said to be *complete* if the linear combinations $\lambda_1 u_1 + \cdots + \lambda_n u_n$ form a dense set in U. Elements u' and u'' are called *orthogonal* if the scalar product (u', u'') is equal to zero. A family of elements $\{u_\alpha\}$ is called *orthonormal* if $(u_\alpha, u_\alpha) = 1$ and $(u_\alpha, u_\beta) = 0$ for $\alpha \neq \beta$.

Let $u_1, u_2, \ldots$ be a complete orthonormal sequence in the Hilbert space U. Any element $u \in U$ can be written as a series

$$u = \sum_n (u, u_n) \, u_n \,.$$

An arbitrary selfadjoint and completely continuous operator A in a complete Hilbert space U admits a complete orthonormal sequence of eigenelements $u_1, u_2, \ldots$ with eigenvalues $\lambda_1, \lambda_2, \ldots$ distinct from 0 with $\lambda_n \to 0$ for $n \to \infty$ such that

$$A u = \sum_n \lambda_n (u, u_n) \cdot u_n \,.$$

A selfadjoint and completely continuous operator A is called a *Hilbert-Schmidt operator* if

$$\sum_n \lambda_n^2 < \infty \,,$$

where $\lambda_1, \lambda_2, \ldots$ is the sequence of all eigenvalues distinct from zero. In this case, for any complete orthonormal sequences $u_1, u_2, \ldots$ and $v_1, v_2, \ldots$ in the space U, the equation

$$\sum_m \sum_n (A u_m, v_n)^2 = \sum_n \lambda_n^2 \,.$$

holds.

A positive completely continuous operator A in the Hilbert space U is called *nuclear* if for some complete orthonormal sequence $u_1, u_2, \ldots$ we have

$$\sum_n (A u_n, u_n) < \infty \,.$$

Let A be a nuclear operator. Then

$$\sum_n (A u_n, u_n) = \sum_n \lambda_n$$

for any complete orthonormal sequence of elements $u_1, u_2, \ldots$

Example. Let $L^2(T)$ be the Hilbert space of all real or complex integrable functions $u = u(t)$ on the interval $T = [a, b]$ with the scalar product

$$(u_1', u_2'') = \int_a^b u_1(t) \cdot \overline{u_2(t)} \, dt \,.$$

Let $B(s, t)$ be a measurable function of the two variables t and s such that $B(s, t) \equiv B(t, s)$ and

$$\int_a^b \int_a^b |B(s, t)|^2 \, ds \, dt < \infty \,.$$

Then the operator B defined as

$$Bu(t) = \int_a^b B(s, t) u(s) ds \quad (t \in T)$$

will be a Hilbert-Schmidt operator. If the function $B(s, t)$ is continuous and *positively definite*, that is, if

$$\Sigma \lambda_k \lambda_j B(t_k, t_j) \geq 0$$

for any numbers $\lambda_1, ..., \lambda_n$ and $t_1, ..., t_n \in T$, then the operator B defined above will be a positive nuclear operator in the space $L^2(T)$.

§ 2. Distributions and Measures

1. Measures in Measurable Spaces

Measure Spaces. Let $(X, \mathfrak{A})$ be an arbitrary measurable space. A non-negative function $\mu = \mu(A)$ on the σ-algebra of sets $\mathfrak{A}$ (which may take the value $+\infty$) is called a *measure* if it is countably additive, that is, for any countable number of disjoint sets $A_1, A_2, ... \in \mathfrak{A}$ and $A = \bigcup_k A_k$ we have

$$\mu(A) = \sum_k \mu(A_k). \tag{2.1}$$

The value $\mu(A)$ is called the *measure of the set* $A \in \mathfrak{A}$.

The measure μ is called *finite* if $\mu(X) < \infty$, and σ-finite if the space X can be represented as a union of countably many sets A_k such that $\mu(A_k) < \infty$, $k = 1, 2, ...$

The triple $(X, \mathfrak{A}, \mu)$ is called a *measure space*.

Distribution. A non-negative finite function $\mu = \mu(A)$ on a semiring of sets $\mathfrak{S}$ in an arbitrary space X is called a *distribution* if for any set $A \in \mathfrak{S}$ which is the union of countably many disjoint sets $A_1, A_2, ... \in \mathfrak{S} : A = \bigcup_k A_k$, the relation (2.1) holds. If a semi-ring of sets $\mathfrak{S}$ under consideration forms a ring, then μ is a distribution if and only if it is finitely additive:

$$\mu(A) = \sum_{k=1}^n \mu(A_k) \quad \text{for} \quad A = \bigcup_{k=1}^n A_k$$

with disjoint sets $A_1, ..., A_n \in \mathfrak{S}$, and continuous:

$$\lim_{n \to \infty} \mu(A_n) = 0$$

for $A_1 \supseteq A_2 \supseteq ...$, and $\bigcap_n A_n = \emptyset$.

A non-negative finite function $\mu = \mu(A)$ on a semi-ring of sets $\mathfrak{S}$ is called a *weak distribution* if for any set $A \in \mathfrak{S}$ represented as the union of finite number of disjoint sets $A_1, \ldots, A_n \in \mathfrak{S}$ the relation (2.1) holds. Every weak distribution $\mu = \mu(A)$ on $\mathfrak{S}$ can be uniquely *extended* to the ring of all sets $A \subseteq X$ which are unions of a finite number of disjoint sets from $\mathfrak{S} : A = \bigcup_{k=1}^{n} A_k$. This extension is given by the formula

$$\mu(A) = \sum_{k=1}^{n} \mu(A_k).$$

A weak distribution $\mu = \mu(A)$ on a ring $\mathfrak{A}$ is a finitely additive function.

Fig. 18

Example. Let X be the real line and $\mathfrak{S}$ the system of all half-intervals $(x', x'']$. We define the function $\mu = \mu(A)$ on $\mathfrak{S}$ by $\mu(A) = x'' - x'$ for $A = (x', x'']$. If $A = (x', x'']$ is "decomposed" into the half-intervals $A_k = (x'_k, x''_k]$, $k = 1, 2, \ldots$ (Fig. 18) we obtain:

$$x''_1 = x'' , \ x''_2 = x'_1, \ldots, x''_{n+1} = x'_n, \ldots,$$

$$(x''_1 - x'_1) + (x''_2 - x'_2) + \cdots = x'' - x' .$$

Thus, the function μ is a distribution.

Extension of Distributions and Measures. Let $\mu = \mu(A)$ be a distribution on the semi-ring of sets $\mathfrak{S}$ in the space X. We assume μ to be bounded:

$$\mu(X) < \infty .$$

We consider the number $\mu^*(A)$ which is called the *exterior measure* of a set $A \subseteq X$ and is defined as

$$\mu^*(A) = \inf \sum_k \mu(A_k),$$

where inf is taken for all countable families of sets $A_1, A_2, \ldots \in \mathfrak{S}$ covering A, that is, $A \subseteq \bigcup_k A_k$. The number $\mu^*(A)$ is finite for every set $A \subseteq X$.

The set A is said to be *measurable* (with respect to μ on $\mathfrak{S}$) if

$$\mu^*(A) = \mu^*(X) - \mu^*(X \backslash A) .$$

The set $\mathfrak{A}$ of all measurable sets is a σ-algebra which contains the semi-ring $\mathfrak{S}$. The function $\mu = \mu(A)$ defined on the σ-algebra $\mathfrak{A}$ by the formula

$$\mu(A) = \mu^*(A) \quad (A \in \mathfrak{A})$$

turns out to be a measure and is called the *extension of the distribution* μ.

In general, the measure μ_1 is called an *extension of the distribution* μ if μ_1 is defined on a σ-algebra $\mathfrak{A}_1$ which contains the semi-ring $\mathfrak{S}$, and $\mu_1(A) = \mu(A)$ for $A \in \mathfrak{S}$. Every extension μ_1 of the measure μ satisfies the inequalities

$$\mu^*(A) \geq \mu_1(A) \geq \mu^*(X) - \mu^*(X \backslash A).$$

The extension of the distribution μ to the σ-algebra $\mathfrak{A}$ of all measurable sets is unique. Given a set $A \subseteq X$ and a number m between the bounds

$$\mu^*(A) > m \geq \mu^*(X) - \mu^*(X \backslash A),$$

there exists an extension μ_1 of the measure μ such that $\mu_1(A) = m$.

If the original distribution μ on the semi-ring $\mathfrak{S}$ is not bounded, then the space X can be represented as the union of countably many disjoint sets $A_1, A_2, \ldots \in \mathfrak{S} : X = \bigcup_k A_k$. In this case a set A is called *measurable* if the intersections $A A_k$ are measurable, that is, the intersection of A with the auxiliary spaces A_k $(k = 1, 2, \ldots)$. The set $\mathfrak{A}$ of all measurable sets is a σ-algebra. The extension of μ is defined by

$$\mu(A) = \sum_k \mu^*(A \cdot A_k) \quad (A \in \mathfrak{A}).$$

Example. *Distributions on the Line.* Let X be the real line and $\mu = \mu(A)$ the distribution on the semi-ring $\mathfrak{S}$ of all half-intervals $A = (x', x'']$ given by the formula

$$\mu(A) = x'' - x' \quad \text{for} \quad A = (x', x''].$$

The extension of this distribution is the so-called *Lebesgue-measure* on the real line. Let $F(x)$ be an arbitrary non-negative monotone increasing and right-continuous function on the real line $-\infty < x < \infty$ such that

$$\lim_{x \to -\infty} F(x) = 0, \qquad \lim_{x \to \infty} F(x) = 1.$$

The formula

$$\mu(A) = F(x'') - F(x'), \qquad A = (x', x'']$$

determines a distribution on the semi-ring $\mathfrak{S}$ of all half-intervals $A = (x', x'']$. The extension of this distribution to the σ-algebra of all measurable sets is a normalized measure μ, $\mu(X) = 1$, which is usually denoted by dF.

A function $F(x)$ of this type is called a *distribution function*. Every normalized Borel measure μ on the real line is derived in this way from the unique distribution function $F(x)$ which is connected with μ by the relation

$$F(x) = \mu(A), \quad A = (-\infty, x].$$

Example. Let $\mu = \mu(A)$ be a normalized Borel measure in the n-dimensional euclidean space X. The relation $F(x_1, \ldots, x_n) = \mu(A)$ for $A = (-\infty, x_1] \times \cdots \times (-\infty, x_n]$ defines a so-called *distribution function* $F = F(x_1, \ldots, x_n)$, $-\infty < x_k < \infty$ $(k = 1, \ldots, n)$. The distribution function F determines uniquely the corresponding distribution $\mu = \mu(A)$ on the semi-ring of sets $A = (x_1', x_1''] \times \cdots \times (x_n', x_n'']$:

$$\mu(A) = \Delta(x_1', x_1'') \ldots \Delta(x_n', x_n'') F,$$

where $\Delta(x', x'')$ is the *difference operator*, acting on a function $\varphi(x)$ of the variable x according to the formula

$$\Delta(x', x'') \varphi = \varphi(x'') - \varphi(x').$$

The distribution function $F(x_1, \ldots, x_n)$ is monotone increasing and continuous from the right with respect to each of the variables $x_1, \ldots, x_n$, and

$$\lim_{x_k \to -\infty} F(x_1, \ldots, x_n) = 0$$

$$\lim_{x_1 \to \infty, \ldots, x_n \to \infty} F(x_1, \ldots, x_n) = 1.$$

However, not any function F with these properties is a distribution function. For example, the function $F(x_1, x_2)$ of the two variables x_1, x_2:

$$F(x_1, x_2) = \begin{cases} 1 & \text{if } x_1, x_2 \geq 0, \ \max(x_1, x_2) \geq 1, \\ 0 & \text{for all other } x_1, x_2, \end{cases}$$

has these properties but is not a distribution function whatever be the measure μ in the plane.

Example. Let $(X, \mathfrak{A}, \mu)$ be an arbitrary space with a finite measure where $\mathfrak{A}$ is the σ-algebra of all μ-measurable sets. Let A be an arbitrary set of the space X which does not belong to $\mathfrak{A}$. The smallest σ-algebra $\mathfrak{A}_1$ containing the σ-algebra $\mathfrak{A}$ and the set A consists of all sets of the form

$$A_1 A \cup A_2 \bar{A} \quad \text{where} \quad A_1, A_2 \in \mathfrak{A}.$$

If the exterior measure $\mu^*(A)$ of A is such that

$$\mu^*(A) = \mu^*(X),$$

then for any measurable sets $A_1, A_2 \in \mathfrak{A}$, which satisfy the condition $A_1 \cdot A = A_2 \cdot A$ the symmetric difference $A_1 \circ A_2$ is contained in the complement $\bar{A}$, and $\mu(A_1 \circ A_2) = 0$. The formula

$$\mu_1(A_1 \, A \cup A_2 \, \bar{A}) = \mu(A_1)$$

defines an extension of the measure μ to the larger σ-algebra $\mathfrak{A}_1$, and

$$\mu_1(A) = \mu^*(A).$$

Complete Measures. The measure $\mu = \mu(A)$ on the σ-algebra $\mathfrak{A}$ is said to be *complete* if any set A' contained in a set $A \in \mathfrak{A}$ of measure zero, that is, $\mu(A) = 0$, belongs to $\mathfrak{A}$. The measure $\mu = \mu(A)$ on the σ-algebra of all measurable sets is complete. Any measure μ can be extended to a complete measure.

2. Measures in Topological Spaces

Baire Measures and their Extension. Let X be a regular topological space, and $\mathfrak{A}$ the σ-algebra of its Baire sets. Any finite measure $\mu = \mu(A)$ on $\mathfrak{A}$ has the so-called *regularity property:* for every Baire set A the equation

$$\mu(A) = \inf_{G \supseteq A} \mu(G)$$

holds where inf is taken for all open Baire sets $G \supseteq A$. Equivalently,

$$\mu(A) = \sup_{F \subseteq A} \mu(F)$$

where sup is taken for all closed Baire sets $F \subseteq A$.

Example. Let X be the real line. Then Baire sets and Borel sets coincide. The measure $\mu(A)$ of any measurable set A is given by

$$\mu(A) = \inf \sum_k \mu(A_k)$$

where inf is taken for all disjoint half-intervals $A_k = (x_k', x_k'']$ whose union contains A. At the same time each half-interval $(x', x'']$ is the intersection of a countable number of open intervals, and it is thus obvious that

$$\mu(A) = \inf \mu(G),$$

where inf is taken for all open sets G, or with respect to unions of open intervals covering A.

An analogous argument applies also in the case of an arbitrary regular space X. In fact any closed Baire set $F \in \mathfrak{A}$, being the inverse image of zero under a continuous mapping $\varphi = \varphi(x)$ into the real line Y, that is

$F = \{\varphi = 0\}$, coincides with the intersection of denumerably many open sets G of the form $G_\delta = \{|\varphi| < \delta\}$, that is, $F = \cap G_\delta$. By virtue of the continuity of the measure μ we have

$$\mu(F) = \inf \mu(G_\delta).$$

For the difference $A = F_1 \backslash F_2$ of such sets F_1 and F_2, where $F_2 \subseteq F_1$, we obtain

$$\mu(A) = \mu(F_1) - \mu(F_2) = \inf \mu(G),$$

where inf is taken for all open sets G of the form $G_1 \backslash F_2$ with $G_1 \supseteq F_1$. The measure of an arbitrary μ-measurable set A equals

$$\mu(A) = \inf \sum_k \mu(A_k)$$

where inf is taken for all sequences of disjoint sets A_k of the form $A_k = F_{1k} \backslash F_{2k}$, whose union covers A; recall that these differences form a semi-ring in $\mathfrak{A}$. Hence $\mu(A)$ obviously coincides with the greatest lower bound $\inf \mu(G)$ taken for all open sets $G \supseteq A$, for example the unions of the corresponding open sets $G_k \supseteq A_k$.

Regular Distributions in Compact Spaces. A weak distribution $\mu = \mu(A)$ on a semi-ring of sets $\mathfrak{S}$ in the topological space X is called *regular* if for any $A \in \mathfrak{S}$

$$\mu(A) = \sup \mu(F)$$

where sup is taken for all closed sets F from $\mathfrak{S}$ with $F \subseteq A$, or

$$\mu(A) = \inf \mu(G),$$

where inf is taken for all open sets G from $\mathfrak{S}$ with $G \supseteq A$. If the semi-ring $\mathfrak{S}$ is a σ-algebra and $\mu = \mu(A)$ a measure on $\mathfrak{S}$, then μ is called a *regular measure*.

Let X be a compact space. Then any weak regular distribution $\mu = \mu(A)$ is a regular distribution. In fact, it may be assumed without restriction that μ is defined on a ring of sets. Consider a sequence of sets $A_1 \supseteq A_2 \supseteq \cdots$ from $\mathfrak{S}$ such that $\lim_{n \to \infty} \mu(A_n) > 0$. The set $A_1, A_2, \ldots$ can be assumed to be closed, and the intersection of any finite number of sets from this sequence is not empty. Hence this centralized system in the compact space X has a non-empty intersection: $\bigcap_n A_n \neq 0$. Thus, if $\bigcap_n A_n = 0$ we have $\lim_{n \to \infty} \mu(A_n) = 0$ so that the function $\mu = \mu(A)$ is continuous and represents a regular distribution. The extension of μ to the σ-algebra of the corresponding measurable sets is a regular measure.

Let $\mu = \mu(A)$ be an arbitrary *Baire measure* in the compact space X, that is, a measure defined on the σ-algebra of the Baire sets in X. Such a measure can be extended to a regular *Borel measure*, that is, to a measure defined on all Borel sets in X. This extension is unique and can be constructed for example in the following way: for any open set $A \subseteq X$

$$\mu(A) = \sup \mu(G),$$

where sup is taken for all open Baire sets $G \subseteq A$, and for an arbitrary Borel set $A \subseteq X$

$$\mu(A) = \inf \mu(G),$$

where inf is taken for all open sets $G \supseteq A$.

A regular weak distribution $\mu = \mu(A)$ on a semi-ring of sets of an arbitrary topological space X is called *tight* if for any $\varepsilon > 0$ there exists a compact set $A \in \mathfrak{S}$ such that $\mu^*(X \setminus A) \leq \varepsilon$. For example, any regular Borel measure in a topological space X which can be represented as a denumerable union of compact sets, is tight. Any measure in an arbitrary separable complete metric space is tight.

The statements made above about distributions in compact spaces remain true if the corresponding distributions are tight in the space X under consideration.

Measures and Mappings. Let $(X, \mathfrak{A}, \mu)$ be a measure space and $\varphi = \varphi(x)$ a function on X with values in the space Y. The relation

$$\mu_\varphi(B) = \mu\{\varphi \in B\}$$

determines a measure $v = \mu_\varphi$ on the σ-algebra $\mathfrak{B} = \mathfrak{B}_\varphi$ of all sets B whose inverse images $\{\varphi \in B\}$ belong to the σ-algebra $\mathfrak{A}$. The measure $v = \mu_\varphi$ is said to be *induced* by the mapping φ.

Let X be an arbitrary space, $\varphi = \varphi(x)$ a function on X with values in Y, and $(Y, \mathfrak{B}, v)$ a measure space. If the set $\varphi(X)$ is measurable, the relation

$$v^\varphi(A) = v\{B \cap \varphi(X)\}, \qquad A = \{\varphi \in B\},$$

defines a measure $\mu = v^\varphi$ on the σ-algebra $\mathfrak{A} = \mathfrak{A}^\varphi$ of all sets of X which are inverse images of set $B \in \mathfrak{B}$. The measure $\mu = v^\varphi$ is said to be *induced* by the mapping φ.

A measure μ on a σ-algebra of sets $\mathfrak{A}$ of a space X is called *perfect* if for any $(\mathfrak{A}, \mathfrak{B})$-measurable mapping $\varphi = \varphi(x)$ of $(X, \mathfrak{A})$ into the real line $(Y, \mathfrak{B})$ with the Borel algebra $\mathfrak{B}$ the measure μ_φ induced on the σ-algebra $\mathfrak{B}_\varphi$ is regular. The measure μ is perfect if and only if for any $(\mathfrak{A}, \mathfrak{B})$-measurable real function $\varphi = \varphi(x)$ and any $A \in \mathfrak{A}$ the image $\varphi(A)$ is a measurable set on the line with respect to the measure $v = \mu_\varphi$ induced by φ.

Every tight measure is perfect.

Let $(X, \mathfrak{A}, \mu)$ be a measurable space with a perfect measure μ. Any mapping $\varphi = \varphi(x)$ of X onto an arbitrary space Y induces in Y a perfect measure $\nu = \mu_\varphi$ on the corresponding σ-algebra $\mathfrak{B}_\varphi$.

3. Joint Distributions

Products of Measures. Let X_1 and X_2 be arbitrary spaces, $\mathfrak{S}_1$ and $\mathfrak{S}_2$ semi-rings of sets in X_1 and X_2, and $\mu_1 = \mu_1(A_1)$ and $\mu_2 = \mu_2(A_2)$ distributions defined for the sets $A_1 \in \mathfrak{S}_1$ and $A_2 \in \mathfrak{S}_2$.

Let $\mathfrak{S}_1 \times \mathfrak{S}_2$ be the semi-ring of all sets A of the space $X = X_1 \times X_2$ which can be represented as $A = A_1 \times A_2$. If we define a non-negative function $\mu = \mu(A)$ on $\mathfrak{S}_1 \times \mathfrak{S}_2$ by setting

$$\mu(A) = \mu_1(A_1) \times \mu_2(A_2) \quad \text{for} \quad A = A_1 \times A_2 ,$$

then μ is a distribution on $\mathfrak{S}_1 \times \mathfrak{S}_2$; $\mu = \mu_1 \times \mu_2$ will be called the *product of the distributions* μ_1 and μ_2.

For fixed A_1 or fixed A_2 any distribution $\mu = \mu(A)$ on the semi-ring $\mathfrak{S}_1 \times \mathfrak{S}_2$ of the rectangular sets $A = A_1 \times A_2$ can be considered as a distribution on $\mathfrak{S}_2$ alone or $\mathfrak{S}_1$ alone, respectively. The distributions

$$\mu_1(A_1) = \mu(A_1 \times X_2) , \quad \mu_2(A_2) = \mu(X_1 \times A_2)$$

are called the *projections* of the distribution μ.

Let X be a topological space which is the product of the topological spaces X_1 and X_2. The distribution μ is regular and tight if each of its projections has the corresponding properties [12a].

Example. Let $l = l(B)$ be the Lebesgue measure on the interval $I = [0, 1]$ and $m = m(A)$ the measure on the Borel sets A of the square $I \times I$ defined by the formula

$$m(A) = l\{(x, x) \in A\} ,$$

where $\{(x, x) \in A\}$ denotes the set of all points $x \in I$ such that $(x, x) \in A$. The measure $m = m(A)$ is "concentrated" on the diagonal D of the square $I \times I$. Let X_1 be a non-measurable set in the interval $[0, 1]$ such that the exterior measure $l^*(X_1)$ and the exterior measure $l^*(X_2)$ of the complementary set $X_2 = I \setminus X_1$ are equal to 1. Let $\mathfrak{S}_1$ and $\mathfrak{S}_2$ be the σ-algebras of all sets $A_1 = B_1 X_1$ and $A_2 = B_2 X_2$ in the spaces X_1 and X_2 where B_1 and B_2 are Borel sets in the interval $I = [0, 1]$. Let $\mathfrak{S}_1 \times \mathfrak{S}_2$ be the semi-ring of all sets in the product $X = X_1 \times X_2$ of the form

$$A = A_1 \times A_2 = (B_1 \times B_2) \cdot (X_1 \times X_2) ,$$

[12a] *Sazonov*, W. W., On perfect measures. Izv. AN SSSR (ser. matem.) **26**, (1962), 391—414 (Russian).

and $\mu = \mu(A)$ the additive function on $\mathfrak{S}_1 \times \mathfrak{S}_2$ defined by the formula

$$\mu(A) = m(B_1 \times B_2) = l(B_1 \cdot B_2).$$

This function is a measure with respect to each of its arguments A_1 and A_2.

Suppose that μ is a distribution and can be extended to a measure. Then it satisfies the relation

$$\mu[A(X_1 \times X_2)] = m(A)$$

for the sets $A \cdot (X_1 \times X_2)$, where A is a Borel set in the square $I \times I$. For $A = D$ (the diagonal of the square $I \times I$) this relation is not satisfied. In fact the intersection $D \cdot (X_1 \times X_2)$ is empty, and if μ is any measure, then $\mu[D \cdot (X_1 \times X_2)] = 0$. On the other hand, $m(D) = 1$. Thus, the function $\mu = \mu(A)$ on the semi-ring of the sets $A = B_1 X_1 \times B_2 X_2$ is not a distribution, although it is a measure with respect to each of its arguments.

Joint Distributions. Let E be some space and $\mathfrak{S}$ a semi-ring of sets in it. Let $X = E^T$ be the set of all functions $x = x(t)$ on a set T with values in E. The system $\mathfrak{S}^T$ of all cylinder sets of X of the form

$$A = \{x(t_1) \in B_1, \ldots, x(t_n) \in B_n\},$$

where $t_1, \ldots, t_n \in T$ and $B_1, \ldots, B_n \in \mathfrak{S}$, is a semi-ring.

Let $\mu = \mu(A)$ be an arbitrary distribution on the semi-ring $\mathfrak{S}^T$. We define the functions $\mu_{t_1, \ldots, t_n}(B_1, \ldots, B_n)$ of the "several variables" $B_1, \ldots, B_n \in \mathfrak{S}$ by setting

$$\mu_{t_1, \ldots, t_n}(B_1, \ldots, B_n) = \mu\{x(t_1) \in B_1, \ldots, x(t_n) \in B_n\}.$$

The functions $\mu_{t_1, \ldots, t_n}(B_1, \ldots, B_n)$ represent a distribution on the semi-ring $\mathfrak{S}$ with respect to each of the arguments $B_1, \ldots, B_n \in \mathfrak{S}$. Moreover,

$$\mu_{t_{i_1}, \ldots, t_{i_n}}(B_{i_1}, \ldots, B_{i_n}) = \mu_{t_1, \ldots, t_n}(B_1, \ldots, B_n)$$

for any simultaneous permutations of $t_1, \ldots, t_n$ and $B_1, \ldots, B_n$, and

$$\mu_{t_1, \ldots, t_n, t_{n+1}}(B_1, \ldots, B_n, E) = \mu_{t_1, \ldots, t_n}(B_1, \ldots, B_n).$$

Any family of functions $\mu_{t_1, \ldots, t_n}(B_1, \ldots, B_n)$ which has these properties will be called a *family of joint distributions.*

Every family of joint distributions $\mu_{t_1, \ldots, t_n}(B_1, \ldots, B_n)$ determines uniquely a weak distribution $\mu = \mu(A)$ on the semi-ring of all cylinder sets. This weak distribution μ is defined by the formula

$$\mu(A) = \mu_{t_1, \ldots, t_n}(B_1, \ldots, B_n)$$

for

$$A = \{x(t_1) \in B_1, \ldots, x(t_n) \in B_n\} \quad (B_1, \ldots, B_n \in \mathfrak{S}).$$

Let E be a compact space, T an arbitrary set, X^T the corresponding Tihonov product, and $\mu_{t_1, \ldots, t_n}(B_1, \ldots, B_n)$ a family of joint regular distributions in the sense of regularity of the distributions $\mu_t(B) = \mu_{t,t_1,\ldots,t_n}(B, E, \ldots, E)$, $t \in T$, on the semi-ring $\mathfrak{S}$ of sets B in E. The weak distribution $\mu = \mu(A)$ determined by it on the semi-ring $\mathfrak{S}^T$ of the cylinder sets is then also regular, and can be uniquely extended to a regular measure on the σ-algebra $\mathfrak{A}$ of all sets A of the space $X = E^T$ which are measurable with respect to the distribution μ. We note that the joint distributions $\mu_{t_1,\ldots,t_n}(B_1, \ldots, B_n)$ defined on the Baire sets of the space E are regular. All statements made here remain true if the original space E is not compact but the joint distributions under consideration are tight in E.

Let E be a separable compact topological space and $\mathfrak{B}$ the σ-algebra of the Baire sets in E. In this case the Baire σ-algebra $\mathfrak{A}$ of the Tihonov product $X = E^T$ is generated by the system of all cylinder sets A of the form $A = \{x(t_1) \in B_1, \ldots, x(t_n) \in B_n\}$, where $B_1, \ldots, B_n$ are Baire sets of the space E, that is $\mathfrak{A} = \mathfrak{A}(T)$.

Every measure $\mu = \mu(A)$ on the σ-algebra $\mathfrak{A}$ can be extended to a regular measure on all Borel sets of the space $X = E^T$. Such an extension is unique and can for example be constructed as follows: for any open set $A \subseteq X$

$$\mu(A) = \sup \mu(G),$$

and for any Borel set $A \subseteq X$

$$\mu(A) = \inf \mu(G),$$

where sup is taken with respect to all open Baire sets $G \subseteq A$ which are unions of a countable number of open cylinder sets, and inf is taken for all open sets [13] $G \supseteq A$.

Joint Distributions in Linear Spaces. Let U be a linear space and X its adjoint space of all linear functionals $x = \langle u, x \rangle$ on U. The system of all cylinder sets $A \subseteq X$ of the form

$$\{\langle u_1, x \rangle \in B_1, \ldots, \langle u_n, x \rangle \in B_n\}$$

where $u_1, \ldots, u_n$ is an arbitrary finite number of elements from U and $B_1, \ldots, B_n$ are arbitrary Borel sets on the line, forms a semi-ring $\mathfrak{S}$. Let $\mu = \mu(A)$ be a distribution on $\mathfrak{S}$. We set

$$\mu_{u_1,\ldots,u_n}(B_1, \ldots, B_n) = \mu(A) \tag{2.2}$$

for $A = \{\langle u_1, x \rangle \in B_1, \ldots, \langle u_n, x \rangle \in B_n\}$.

The functions $\mu_{u_1,\ldots,u_n}(B_1, \ldots, B_n)$ represent a Borel distribution on the line with respect to each of their arguments $B_1, \ldots, B_n$. They do not

---

[13] See E. *Nelson*, Regular probability measures on function space. Ann. Math. **69** (1959), 630—643.

change under any simultaneous permutation of $u_1, \ldots, u_n$ and $B_1, \ldots, B_n$, and they are compatible in the sense that if the cylinder sets

$$A' = \{\langle u_1', x \rangle \in B_1', \ldots, \langle u_m', x \rangle \in B_m'\}$$
$$A = \{\langle u_1, x \rangle \in B_1, \ldots, \langle u_n, x \rangle \in B_n\}$$

coincide then

$$\mu_{u_1', \ldots, u_m'}(B_1', \ldots, B_m') = \mu_{u_1, \ldots, u_n}(B_1, \ldots, B_n).$$

Any family of function $\mu_{u_1, \ldots, u_n}(B_1, \ldots, B_n)$ which has these properties is called a *family of joint distributions*. Joint distributions $\mu_{u_1, \ldots, u_n}(B_1, \ldots, B_n)$ given for all $u_1, \ldots, u_n \in U$ define by the formula (2.2) a weak distribution $\mu = \mu(A)$ on the semi-ring of all cylinder sets.

Let U be a denumerably Hilbert space and X its topological adjoint space of all linear continuous functionals. The weak distribution $\mu = \mu(A)$ given by joint distributions $\mu_{u_1, \ldots, u_n}(B_1, \ldots, B_n)$ on the σ-algebra $\mathfrak{A}$ generated by the semi-ring of all cylinder sets is a genuine distribution if and only if for any $\varepsilon > 0$ there exists a "ball" $S_p(r) = \{\|x\|_p \leq r\}$ such that $\mu(A) \leq \varepsilon$ for $A \subset \overline{S_p(r)}$, that is, for any $A \in \mathfrak{A}$ outside the ball $S_p(r)$. Note that $S_p(r)$ is compact in X in the weak topology.

Each of the functions $\mu_{u_1, \ldots, u_n}(B_1, \ldots, B_n)$ of a joint family of distributions is actually a distribution on the semi-ring of all sets of the form $B_1 \times \cdots \times B_n$ in the n-dimensional space E^n where E stands for the real line, and thus defines a Borel measure in this space. We denote this measure by $\mu_{u_1, \ldots, u_n}$.

Suppose that the space U is not only denumerably normed but also nuclear. Then a sufficient condition in order that a joint family of distributions defines a distribution $\mu = \mu(A)$ on the σ-algebra $\mathfrak{A}$ generated by the semi-ring of all cylinder sets looks like this: for $u_{1k} \to u_1, \ldots, u_{nk} \to u_n$ the Borel distributions $\mu_{u_{1k}, \ldots, u_{nk}}$ corresponding to the functions $\mu_{u_{1k}, \ldots, u_{nk}}(B_1, \ldots, B_n)$, converge weakly[14] to the distribution $\mu_{u_1, \ldots, u_n}$:

$$\mu_{u_{1k}, \ldots, u_{nk}} \Rightarrow \mu_{u_1, \ldots, u_n} \quad \text{for} \quad k \to \infty.$$

§ 3. Measures and Integrals

1. The Integral and its Properties

Let $(X, \mathfrak{A}, \mu)$ be an arbitrary space with a finite complete measure $\mu = \mu(A)$ on the σ-algebra of sets $\mathfrak{A}$. A function $\varphi = \varphi(x)$ on X with values in a space Y is called a *simple* function if it takes only a denumerable

---

[14] *Gelfand, I. M., and N. Y. Vilenkin,* Generalized functions. Vol. IV. Applications of Harmonic Analysis. Academic Press. New York, 1964.

number of different values $y_1, y_2, \ldots$ on corresponding disjoint sets $A_1, A_2, \ldots \in \mathfrak{A}$. The real-valued simple function $\varphi(x)$ on the space X is said to be *integrable* (with respect to the measure μ) if the corresponding series $\Sigma |y_k| \mu(A_k)$ converges.

The integral of a simple integrable function $\varphi(x)$, to be denoted by $\int\limits_X \varphi(x) \mu(dx)$, is defined by the formula

$$\int\limits_X \varphi(x) \mu(dx) = \sum_k y_k \mu(A_k).$$

An arbitrary real function $\varphi(x)$ on X is called *integrable* if it is the limit of a uniformly converging sequence of simple integrable functions $\varphi_1(x), \varphi_2(x), \ldots$:

$$\varphi(x) = \lim_{n \to \infty} \varphi_n(x).$$

The corresponding limit

$$\int\limits_X \varphi(x) \mu(dx) = \lim_{n \to \infty} \int\limits_X \varphi_n(x) \mu(dx)$$

is then called the *integral* of the integrable function $\varphi(x)$.

A function $\varphi(x)$ is said to be *integrable on the set* $A \in \mathfrak{A}$ if the function $\varphi(x) \varphi_A(x)$ is integrable where $\varphi_A(x)$ stands for the indicator of the set A:

$$\varphi_A(x) = \begin{cases} 1 & \text{for} \quad x \in A, \\ 0 & \text{for} \quad x \notin A. \end{cases}$$

The integral $\int\limits_A \varphi(x) \mu(dx)$ of the function $\varphi(x)$ on A is defined as

$$\int\limits_A \varphi(x) \mu(dx) = \int\limits_X \varphi(x) \varphi_A(x) \mu(dx).$$

Any measurable bounded function $\varphi(x)$ is integrable since functions $\varphi_n(x)$ of the form

$$\varphi_n(x) = \frac{k}{n} \quad \text{for} \quad \frac{k-1}{n} < \varphi(x) \leq \frac{k}{n}$$

can be taken to form a sequence of simple integrable functions $\varphi_1(x)$, $\varphi_2(x), \ldots$ which converges uniformly to $\varphi(x)$.

A function $\varphi(x)$ is integrable if and only if it is measurable and its absolute value $|\varphi(x)|$ is integrable. If the functions $\varphi_1(x)$ and $\varphi_2(x)$ are such that $|\varphi_1(x)| \leq |\varphi_2(x)|$, $\varphi_1(x)$ is measurable and $\varphi_2(x)$ is integrable, then the function $\varphi_1(x)$ is integrable, too. If $\varphi_1(x) \leq \varphi_2(x)$, then

$$\int\limits_X \varphi_1(x) \mu(dx) \leq \int\limits_X \varphi_2(x) \mu(dx).$$

We say that a statement is true "*almost everywhere*" or *for almost all* x (with respect to a measure μ) if it is true for all $x \in X$ except, may be, in a $A \subseteq X$ of measure zero: $\mu(A) = 0$. For any function $\varphi(x)$ which is equal to zero almost everywhere the integral $\int\limits_X \varphi(x)\,\mu(dx)$ is equal to zero. If $\int\limits_X |\varphi(x)|\,\mu(dx) = 0$, then $\varphi(x) = 0$ almost everywhere.

For any integrable function $\varphi(x)$ we have

$$\int\limits_A |\varphi(x)|\,\mu(dx) \leqq \text{ess sup} |\varphi| \cdot \mu(A),$$

where ess sup $|\varphi|$, the so-called *essential least upper bound* of the function $|\varphi(x)|$, is defined as the least upper bound of all y for which $\mu\{|\varphi| > y\} > 0$.

For any two integrable functions $\varphi_1(x)$, $\varphi_2(x)$ and any real λ_1 and λ_2 the function $\varphi(x) = \lambda_1 \varphi_1(x) + \lambda_2 \varphi_2(x)$ is integrable, and

$$\int\limits_X \varphi(x)\,\mu(dx) = \lambda_1 \int\limits_X \varphi_1(x)\,\mu(dx) + \lambda_2 \mu_2(dx).$$

Generalized Measures and their Absolute Continuity. Let $v = v(A)$ be a finitely-additive real function on a σ-algebra $\mathfrak{A}$. The expression

$$\text{Var}\, v(A) = \sup \sum_k |v(A_k)|,$$

where sup is taken with respect to all decompositions of the set $A \in \mathfrak{A}$ into disjoint sets $A_1, A_2, \dots \in \mathfrak{A}$, is called the *variation* of the function v on the set A.

If $\text{Var}\, v(A)$ is a *continuous* function on $\mathfrak{A}$, that is, if

$$\lim_{n \to \infty} \text{Var}\, v(A_n) = 0$$

for any sequence $A_1 \supseteqq A_2 \supseteqq \cdots$ of sets from $\mathfrak{A}$ which have an empty intersection, then $v(A)$ is called a *generalized measure*. The variance $\text{Var}\, v(A)$ of a generalized measure $v(A)$ is a measure on $\mathfrak{A}$. The generalized measure $v(A)$ is called *absolutely continuous* with respect to a measure $\mu(A)$ if for any $\varepsilon > 0$ there exists a $\delta > 0$ such that $\text{Var}\, v(A) \leqq \varepsilon$ for $\mu(A) \leqq \delta$, whatever be the set $A \in \mathfrak{A}$. This is equivalent to the fact that $\text{Var}\, v(A) = 0$ for $\mu(A) = 0$, $A \in \mathfrak{A}$.

Given any function $\varphi(x)$ which is integrable with respect to the measure μ the integral

$$I(A) = \int\limits_A \varphi(x)\,\mu(dx) \qquad (A \in \mathfrak{A})$$

is a generalized measure on the σ-algebra $\mathfrak{A}$, and is absolutely continuous with respect to $\mu(A)$. Moreover,

$$\operatorname{Var} I(A) = \int\limits_A |\varphi(x)| \, \mu(dx),$$

$$\operatorname{Var} I(X) = \int\limits_X |\varphi(x)| \, \mu(dx) < \infty.$$

Every generalized measure $v(A)$ on $\mathfrak{A}$ which has a bounded variation and is absolutely continuous with respect to the measure $\mu(A)$, can be written in the form

$$v(A) = \int\limits_A \varphi(x) \, \mu(dx)$$

where $\varphi(x)$ is an integrable function which we call the *density* and denote by $\varphi(x) = \dfrac{v(dx)}{\mu(dx)}$.

Any generalized measure $v(A)$ is absolutely continuous with respect to the measure $\operatorname{Var} v(A)$ and can be represented as $v(A) = \mu_1(A) - \mu_2(A)$ where μ_1 and μ_2 are *mutually singular* or, in other words, *perpendicular measures* on $\mathfrak{A}$. By the singularity of μ_1 and μ_2 we mean that there exist disjoint sets A_1 and A_2 in $\mathfrak{A}$ such that

$$\mu_1(X \setminus A_1) = 0, \qquad \mu_2(X \setminus A_2) = 0.$$

Given any measures v and μ, the measure v can be written as $v(A) = \mu_1(A) + \mu_2(A)$ where μ_1 and μ_2 are mutually singular measures, and μ_1 is absolutely continuous with respect to μ, and μ_2 is perpendicular to μ.

The Space $C(X)$. Let X be a compact space and $\mu = \mu(A)$ a measure on the σ-algebra $\mathfrak{A}$ of all Baire sets of X. Any real continuous function $\varphi(x)$ on X is measurable, bounded and integrable. Let $C(X)$ be the normed space of all real continuous functions $\varphi(x)$ on X with the norm

$$\|\varphi\| = \sup_x |\varphi(x)| .$$

The integral

$$\langle \varphi, I \rangle = \int\limits_X \varphi(x) \, \mu(dx)$$

is a linear continuous functional on the space $C(X)$. This functional is positive in the sense that $\langle \varphi, I \rangle \geq 0$ for $\varphi(x) \geq 0$. Any linear continuous positive functional $\langle \varphi, I \rangle$ on $C(X)$ can be written in the form $\langle \varphi, I \rangle = \int\limits_X \varphi(x) \, \mu(dx)$ where μ is Baire measure. Any linear continuous functional is the difference of two positive linear functionals.

Convergence of Functions and Integrals. Some Inequalities. Let $a(y)$ be a Borel function on the line such that $a(-y) = a(y)$ and $a(y'') \geq a(y') > 0$ for $0 < y' \leq y''$. Then the following inequalities hold for any measurable real function $\varphi(x)$ and any $y > 0$:

$$\mu\{|\varphi| > y\} \leq \frac{\int_X a[\varphi(x)]\,\mu(dx)}{a(y)}.$$

For $a(y) \equiv |y|^\alpha$ ($\alpha > 0$) we obtain

$$\mu\{|\varphi| > y\} \leq \frac{1}{|y|^\alpha} \int_X |\varphi(x)|^\alpha\,\mu(dx),$$

and for $a(y) \equiv e^{\alpha y}$ ($\alpha > 0$):

$$\mu\{|\varphi| > y\} \leq e^{-\alpha y} \int_X e^{\alpha \varphi(x)}\,\mu(dx).$$

Let $(X, \mathfrak{A}, \mu)$ be an arbitrary measure space. A sequence of measurable functions $\varphi_1(x), \varphi_2(x), \dots$ is said to *converge in measure* to a measurable function $\varphi(x)$ if for any $\varepsilon > 0$ we have

$$\lim_{n \to \infty} \mu\{|\varphi_n - \varphi| > \varepsilon\} = 0.$$

Convergence in measure is equivalent to convergence in the metric space of all measurable functions where the distance is defined as

$$\varrho(\varphi', \varphi'') = \int_X \frac{|\varphi'(x) - \varphi''(x)|}{1 + |\varphi'(x) - \varphi''(x)|}\,\mu(dx).$$

Here the equation $\varphi' = \varphi''$ means that $\varphi'(x) = \varphi''(x)$ for almost all x.

This metric space is *complete*, that is, each fundamental sequence in measure $\varphi_1(x), \varphi_2(x), \dots$:

$$\lim_{m,n \to \infty} \mu\{|\varphi_m - \varphi_n| > \varepsilon\} = 0,$$

converges in measure to a measurable function $\varphi(x)$. Every sequence $\varphi_1(x), \varphi_2(x), \dots$ which converges almost everywhere converges in measure. Every sequence $\varphi_1(x), \varphi_2(x), \dots$ which converges in measure contains a subsequence which is convergent almost everywhere. A sequence $\varphi_1(x), \varphi_2(x), \dots$ converges almost everywhere if and only if for every $\varepsilon > 0$:

$$\lim_{n \to \infty} \mu\left(\bigcup_{m > n} \{|\varphi_m - \varphi| > \varepsilon\}\right) = 0.$$

If a sequence $\varphi_1(x)$, $\varphi_2(x)$, ... converges in measure to a function $\varphi(x)$ then any subsequence φ_{n_k}, $k = 1, 2, \ldots$ which satisfies for every $\varepsilon > 0$ the relation

$$\sum_k \mu\{|\varphi_{n_k} - \varphi| > \varepsilon\} < \infty,$$

will converge to $\varphi(x)$ for almost all x.

A sequence of integrable functions $\varphi_1(x)$, $\varphi_2(x)$, ... will be called *convergent in mean* to an integrable function $\varphi(x)$ if

$$\lim_{n \to \infty} \int_X |\varphi_m(x) - \varphi(x)| \, \mu(dx) = 0.$$

This implies

$$\lim_{n \to \infty} \int_X \varphi_n(x) \, \mu(dx) = \int_X \varphi(x) \, \mu(dx).$$

Mean convergence amounts to convergence in the normed space $L^1(X)$ of all integrable functions $\varphi(x)$ with the norm

$$\|\varphi(x)\| = \int_X |\varphi(x)| \, \mu(dx).$$

Again the equation $\varphi' = \varphi''$ means that $\varphi'(x) = \varphi''(x)$ for almost all x. This space is complete, that is, every fundamental sequence $\varphi_1(x)$, $\varphi_2(x), \ldots$ which is fundamental in mean:

$$\lim_{m, n \to \infty} \int_X |\varphi_m(x) - \varphi_n(x)| \, \mu(dx) = 0,$$

converges in mean to an integrable function $\varphi(x)$.

A sequence of functions $\varphi_1(x)$, $\varphi_2(x)$, ... is called uniformly integrable if for any $\varepsilon > 0$ there exists a $\delta > 0$ such that $\mu(A) \leq \delta$, $A \in \mathfrak{A}$ implies

$$\int_A |\varphi_n(x)| \, \mu(dx) \leq \varepsilon$$

for all $n = 1, 2, \ldots$ The sequence $\varphi_1(x)$, $\varphi_2(x)$, ... is uniformly integrable if and only if

$$\int_{A_n} |\varphi_n(x)| \, \mu(dx) \leq \varepsilon, \quad A_n = \{|\varphi_n| > y\}$$

for all $n = 1, 2$, simultaneously for sufficiently large y.

Every sequence $\varphi_1(x)$, $\varphi_2(x)$, ... which converges in mean is uniformly integrable. Likewise, a sequence $\varphi_1(x)$, $\varphi_2(x)$ is uniformly integrable if it satisfies one of the following conditions: $|\varphi_n(x)| \leq \psi(x)$, $n = 1, 2, \ldots$, where $\psi(x)$ is an integrable function; $|\varphi_n(x)| \leq |\varphi_{n+1}(x)|$ and $\int_X |\varphi_n(x)| \, \mu(dx) \leq C$, $n = 1, 2, \ldots$ where the constant C does not depend on n. A sequence of integrable functions $\varphi_1(x)$, $\varphi_2(x)$, ... is mean convergent if and only if it is uniformly integrable and convergent in measure.

If the functions $[\varphi_1(x)]^2$ and $[\varphi_2(x)]^2$ are integrable, then the product $\varphi_1(x)\,\varphi_2(x)$ and the sum $\varphi_1(x) + \varphi_2(x)$ are also integrable, and

$$\int_X |\varphi_1(x)\,\varphi_2(x)|\,\mu(dx) \le \sqrt{\int_X |\varphi_1(x)|^2\,\mu(dx) \cdot \int_X |\varphi_2(x)|^2\,\mu(dx)},$$

$$\sqrt{\int_X |\varphi_1(x) + \varphi_2(x)|^2\,\mu(dx)} \le \sqrt{\int_X |\varphi_1(x)|^2\,\mu(dx)} + \sqrt{\int_X |\varphi_2(x)|^2\,\mu(dx)}.$$

The space $L^2(X)$ of all functions $\varphi(x)$ the squares of which are integrable, is a complete Hilbert space with the scalar product

$$(\varphi_1, \varphi_2) = \int_X \varphi_1(x)\,\varphi_2(x)\,\mu(dx).$$

As before functions $\varphi(x)$ differing only on a set of measure zero are identified.

If the function $\varphi(x), \psi(x)$ are measurable and the functions $|\varphi(x)|^\alpha$ and $|\psi(x)|^\beta$ are integrable where $\alpha, \beta > 0$ and $1/\alpha + 1/\beta = 1$, then the product $\varphi(x)\,\psi(x)$ is also integrable. Moreover the inequality

$$\int_X |\varphi(x)\,\psi(x)|\,\mu(dx) \le \left[\int_X |\varphi(x)|^\alpha\,\mu(dx)\right]^{\frac{1}{\alpha}} \left[\int_X |\psi(x)|^\beta\,\mu(dx)\right]^{\frac{1}{\beta}}$$

holds. For any measurable functions $\varphi_1(x)$ and $\varphi_2(x)$ such that $|\varphi_1|^\alpha$ and $|\varphi_2|^\alpha$, $\alpha \ge 1$, are integrable functions the following inequality is true:

$$\left[\int_X |\varphi_1(x) + \varphi_2(x)|^\alpha\,\mu(dx)\right]^{\frac{1}{\alpha}} \le \left[\int_X |\varphi_1(x)|^\alpha\,\mu(dx)\right]^{\frac{1}{\alpha}} + \left[\int_X |\varphi_2(x)|^\alpha\,\mu(dx)\right]^{\frac{1}{\alpha}}.$$

The space $L^\alpha(X)$ of all measurable functions $\varphi(x)$ with finite norm

$$\|\varphi\| = \left[\int_X |\varphi(x)|^\alpha\,\mu(dx)\right]^{\frac{1}{\alpha}} \qquad (\alpha \ge 1)$$

is a *normed space* if functions differing only on sets of measure zero are identified. The space $L^\beta(X)$ with $1/\alpha + 1/\beta = 1$ is the *adjoint* to the space $L^\alpha(X)$: every linear continuous functional $\langle \varphi, \psi \rangle$ on the elements $\varphi \in L^\alpha(X)$ has the form

$$\langle \varphi, \psi \rangle = \int_X \varphi(x)\,\psi(x)\,\mu(dx),$$

where $\psi(x)$ is a function from the space $L^\beta(X)$. The space $L^\infty(X)$ of all measurable functions $\varphi(x)$ with finite essential least upper bound

$$\|\psi\| = \operatorname{ess\,sup} |\psi(x)| = \lim_{n \to \infty} \left[\int_X |\psi(x)|^n\,\mu(dx)\right]^{\frac{1}{n}}$$

is the adjoint to the space $L^1(X)$. In fact every linear functional $\langle \varphi, \psi \rangle$ on the space $L^1(X)$ of all integrable functions $\varphi(x)$ has the form

$$\langle \varphi, \psi \rangle = \int_X \varphi(x)\,\psi(x)\,\mu(dx)$$

where $\psi(x)$ is a function from $L^\infty(X)$.

Let $L^\alpha(X)$, $0 < \alpha < 1$ be the space of all measurable functions $\varphi(x)$ such that

$$\int_X |\varphi(x)|^\alpha \mu(dx) < \infty .$$

This space is linear. If we identify elements φ' and φ'' for which $\varphi'(x) = \varphi''(x)$ almost everywhere, and if we introduce the distance

$$\varrho(\varphi_1, \varphi_2) = \int_X |\varphi_1(x) - \varphi_2(x)|^\alpha \mu(dx) \quad (\varphi_1, \varphi_2 \in L^\alpha(X)),$$

then $L^\alpha(X)$ becomes a complete linear metric space. Convergence in this space is called *convergence in mean of order* α.

Convergence of Measures. Let $(X, \mathfrak{A})$ be an arbitrary measurable space with a σ-algebra of sets $\mathfrak{A}$. A sequence of measures $\mu_n = \mu_n(A)$ on $\mathfrak{A}$, $n = 1, 2, \ldots$ will be called *convergent in variation* to the measure $\mu = \mu(A)$ if

$$\lim_{n \to \infty} \operatorname{Var}[\mu_n(X) - \mu(X)] = 0$$

where $\operatorname{Var}|\mu_n - \mu)$ denotes the variation of the difference $\mu_n(A) - \mu(A)$ considered as a generalized measure on the σ-algebra $\mathfrak{A}$. The set of all generalized measures $\mu = \mu(A)$ on the σ-algebra $\mathfrak{A}$ is a complete normed space with the norm $\|\mu\| = \operatorname{Var} \mu(X)$. Convergence in variation amounts to convergence in this normed space.

Let $v_n = v_n(A)$, $n = 1, 2, \ldots$, be a sequence of generalized measures which are absolutely continuous with respect to some measure $\mu = \mu(A)$:

$$v_n(A) = \int_A \varphi_n(x)\,\mu(dx) \quad (A \in \mathfrak{A}) .$$

Then convergence in variation of this sequence to the generalized measure $v = v(A)$ is equivalent to mean convergence of the corresponding densities $\varphi_n(x) = \dfrac{v_n(dx)}{\mu(dx)}$; the limit generalized measure v is absolutely continuous with respect to μ:

$$v(A) = \int_A \varphi(x)\,\mu(dx),$$

and for $n \to \infty$

$$\text{Var}[\nu_n(X) - \nu(X)] = \int_X |\varphi_n(x) - \varphi(x)|\, \mu(dx) \to 0.$$

Let X be a topological space, $\mathfrak{A}$ the σ-algebra of all Baire sets in X, and $C(X)$ the space of all real continuous bounded functions $\varphi(x)$ on X with the norm $\|\varphi\| = \sup |\varphi(x)|$. Every real generalized measure $\mu = \mu(A)$, $A \in \mathfrak{A}$ yields a linear continuous functional $\langle \varphi, I \rangle$ on the space $C(X)$:

$$\langle \varphi, I \rangle = \int_X \varphi(x)\, \mu(dx)$$

(see p. 67). The norm of this functional equals

$$\|I\| = \text{Var}\, \mu(X).$$

Convergence in variation of a sequence of Baire measures $\mu_n, n = 1, 2, \ldots$ amounts to the strong convergence of the sequence of the corresponding linear functionals I_n, that is, convergence in the adjoint space with the strong topology. The sequence of Baire measures μ_n, $n = 1, 2, \ldots$ will be called *weakly convergent* to the Baire measure μ, written $\mu_n \Rightarrow \mu$, if the sequence of the corresponding functionals I_n is weakly convergent, that is, the sequence I_n, $n = 1, 2, \ldots$ converges in the adjoint space with the weak topology:

$$\lim_{n \to \infty} \int_X \varphi(x)\, \mu_n(dx) = \int_X \varphi(x)\, \mu(dx)$$

for every continuous bounded function $\varphi(x)$, $\varphi \in C(X)$.

Let X be a separable metric space. The weak convergence of a sequence of measures μ_n, $n = 1, 2, \ldots$ is equivalent to each of the following conditions:

a) $\lim_{n \to \infty} \mu_n(X) = \mu(X)$, $\varliminf_{n \to \infty} \mu_n(G) \geq \mu(G)$ for every open set $G \subseteq X$;

b) $\lim_{n \to \infty} \mu_n(X) = \mu(X)$, $\varlimsup_{n \to \infty} \mu_n(F) \leq \mu(F)$ for every closed set $F \subseteq X$;

c) $\lim_{n \to \infty} \mu_n(A) = \mu(A)$ for every Borel set $A \subseteq X$ such that its boundary

A' has measure zero: $\mu(A') = 0$.

In a complete separable metric space X the set of all Baire measures μ is a complete metric space if the distance is defined by

$$\varrho(\mu', \mu'') = \max(\varrho', \varrho''),$$

where ϱ' and ϱ'' are the greatest lower bounds of the numbers r' and r'', respectively, such that for every closed set $F \subseteq X$ we have

$$\mu'(F) < \mu''(V_{r'}(F)) + r', \quad \mu''(F) < \mu'(V_{r''}(F)) + r'',$$

where $V_\varepsilon(F)$ is the set of all points $x \in X$ whose distance from the closed set F is smaller than $\varepsilon > 0$.

Convergence in this metric space is equivalent to weak convergence. A family of measures μ on the Borel σ-algebra of the space X is *weakly compact*, that is, compact in the metric space of all Borel measures described above, if and only if it is uniformly bounded:

$$\mu(X) \leqq C,$$

and uniformly tight: for every $\varepsilon > 0$ there exists a compact set $A \subseteq X$ such that

$$\mu(X \setminus A) \leqq \varepsilon$$

for all measures of the family under consideration [15].

Example. *Weak Convergence of Distribution Functions.* Any normed Borel set μ on the real line $-\infty < x < \infty$ is uniquely determined by its distribution function $F(x)$ which is connected with μ by the relation

$$F(x) = \mu(A), \qquad A = (-\infty, x].$$

A sequence of measures μ_n, $n = 1, 2, \ldots$ converges weakly to μ if and only if the corresponding sequence of distribution functions F_n, $n = 1, 2, \ldots$ is weakly convergent. The weak convergence $F_n \Rightarrow F$ for $n \to \infty$ is equivalent to each of the following conditions: a) $F_n(x) \to F(x)$ for every x which is a point of continuity of the limit function $F(x)$, including the points $x = \pm \infty$; b) $F_n(x) \to F(x)$ on an everywhere dense set of points x of the real line including $x = \infty$; c) $\varrho(F_n, F) \to 0$ where the distance $\varrho(F', F'')$ between two distribution functions $F'(x)$ and $F''(x)$ is defined as the greatest lower bound of all r such that

$$F''(x - r) - r < F'(x) < F''(x + r) + r$$

for all x. Fig. 19 shows the domain which includes the graphs of all distribution functions at a distance $\varrho(\cdot, F) \leqq r$ from $F(x)$.

Example. Let $X = C[a, b]$ be the space of real continuous functions $x = x(t)$ on the interval $[a, b]$, and $\|x\| = \sup |x(t)|$. A necessary and sufficient condition for the compactness of a family of bounded Baire measures μ in the space $X = C[a, b]$ is the following: for any $\varepsilon > 0$ there exist a number M and a function $\varphi = \varphi(\delta)$ with $\lim_{\delta \to 0} \varphi(\delta) = 0$ such that uni-

---

[15] *Varadarayan, W. S.*, Measures on topological spaces. Matem. sbornik **55** (97), Nr. 1 (1961), 35—100; *Prochorov, J. W.*, Convergence of random processes and limit theorems of probability theory. Teoriya verojatnost. i jejo prim. I, **2** (1956), 177—235 (Russian).

formly with respect to the entire family of measures

$$\mu\{\sup|x(t)|\leqq M\}\geqq\mu(X)-\varepsilon,$$
$$\mu\{\sup_{|\varDelta|\leqq\delta}\omega(\varDelta)\leqq\varphi(\delta)\quad\text{for all}\quad\delta\}\geqq\mu(X)-\varepsilon,$$

where $\varDelta$ is an interval of length $|\varDelta|$ and

$$\omega(\varDelta)=\sup_{t_1,t_2\in\varDelta}|x(t_1)-x(t_2)|.$$

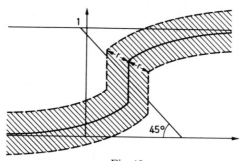

Fig. 19

2. Abstract Measures and Integrals

Let $(X, \mathfrak{A})$ be an arbitrary measurable space with the σ-algebra of sets $\mathfrak{A}$, L a complete normed space, and $\mu = \mu(A)$ a finitely additive function of sets with values in L. The number

$$\operatorname{Var}\mu(A)=\sup\left\|\sum_k\lambda_k\,\mu(A_k)\right\|,$$

where sup is taken with respect to all numbers λ_k, $|\lambda_k|\leqq 1$, and all finite decomposition of the set $A\in\mathfrak{A}$ into disjoint sets $A_k\in\mathfrak{A}$, is called the *variation* of μ on A.

If the variation $\operatorname{Var}\mu(A)$ is a finite and continuous function on the σ-algebra $\mathfrak{A}$, then μ is said to be a *generalized measure* with values in L; by the continuity of the variation $\operatorname{Var}\mu$ we mean that

$$\lim_{n\to\infty}\operatorname{Var}\mu(A)=0$$

for every sequence $A_1\supseteqq A_2\supseteqq\cdots$ of sets from $\mathfrak{A}$ which have an empty intersection.

If the function $\mu=\mu(A)$ on the σ-algebra $\mathfrak{A}$ with values in the normed space L is a generalized measure, then for any linear continuous functional

$v = \langle \cdot, v \rangle$ on L the numerical function

$$v(A) = \langle \mu(A), v \rangle, \qquad A \in \mathfrak{A},$$

is a generalized measure; moreover

$$\operatorname{Var} \mu(A) = \sup_{\|v\| = 1} \operatorname{Var} v(A)$$

where sup is taken with respect to all linear continuous functionals with $\|v\| = 1$.

Example. *Orthogonal Measures.* Let L be a Hilbert space, and $\mu = \mu(A)$ a generalized measure with values in L which has the following property: for any two disjoint sets A_1 and A_2 from $\mathfrak{A}$ the values $\mu(A_1)$ and $\mu(A_2)$ are orthogonal:

$$\big(\mu(A_1), \mu(A_2)\big) = 0.$$

In this case the non-negative function $m = m(A) = \|\mu(A)\|^2$ is a finite measure on the σ-algebra $\mathfrak{A}$. Its variation $\operatorname{Var} \mu(A)$ equals $\sqrt{m(A)}$.

Let $\mu = \mu(A)$ be an arbitrary generalized measure on $(X, \mathfrak{A})$ with values in the normed space L, and $\varphi = \varphi(x)$ a simple real- or complex-valued function on the space X:

$$\varphi(x) = y_k \quad \text{for} \quad x \in A_k \qquad (k = 1, 2, \ldots).$$

We set $B = \bigcup\limits_{k=m}^{n} A_k$ and

$$\operatorname{Var} \int_B \varphi(x) \, \mu(dx) = \sup \left\| \sum_{k, j} \lambda_{kj} \mu(A_{kj}) \right\|,$$

where sup is taken with respect to all numbers λ_{kj}, $|\lambda_{kj}| \leq |y_k|$, and all finite decompositions of the sets A_k, $k = m, m+1, \ldots, n$ into disjoint sets $A_{kj} \in \mathfrak{A}$. The function $\varphi = \varphi(x)$ is said to be *integrable* if

$$\lim_{m, n \to \infty} \operatorname{Var} \int_B \varphi(x) \, \mu(dx) = 0.$$

The integral of this function is defined by the formula

$$\int_X \varphi(x) \, \mu(dx) = \sum_k y_k \mu(A_k).$$

More precisely, the integral $\int_X \varphi(x) \, \mu(dx)$ is the limit of the partial sums $\sum\limits_{k=1}^{n} y_k \mu(A_k)$:

$$\lim_{n \to \infty} \left\| \int_X \varphi(x) \, \mu(dx) - \sum_{k=1}^{n} y_k \mu(A_k) \right\| = 0.$$

An arbitrary function $\varphi(x)$ is called *integrable* if it is the limit of a uniformly convergent sequence of simple integrable functions $\varphi_1(x)$, $\varphi_2(x), \dots$. The integral of such a function $\varphi(x)$ is defined as

$$\int_X \varphi(x)\,\mu(dx) = \lim_{n \to \infty} \int_X \varphi_n(x)\,\mu(dx).$$

The integral of $\varphi(x)$ on the set $A \in \mathfrak{A}$ is defined by the formula

$$\int_A \varphi(x)\,\mu(dx) = \int_X \varphi(x)\,\varphi_A(x)\,\mu(dx),$$

where

$$\varphi_A(x) = \begin{cases} 1 & \text{for } x \in A, \\ 0 & \text{for } x \notin A. \end{cases}$$

Every bounded measurable function is integrable. If the measurable functions $\varphi_1(x)$ and $\varphi_2(x)$ are such that $|\varphi_1(x)| \le \varphi_2(x)|$ and the function $|\varphi_2(x)|$ is integrable, then the function $\varphi_1(x)$ is integrable, too.

For any integrable functions $\varphi_1(x)$, $\varphi_2(x)$ and any numbers λ_1, λ_2 the function $\varphi(x) = \lambda_1 \varphi_1(x) + \lambda_2 \varphi_2(x)$ is also integrable, and

$$\int_X \varphi(x)\,\mu(dx) = \lambda_1 \int_X \varphi_1(x)\,\mu(dx) + \lambda_2 \int_X \varphi_2(x)\,\mu(dx).$$

For any integrable function $\varphi(x)$ the integral

$$I(A) = \int_A \varphi(x)\,\mu(dx)\,\mu \qquad (A \in \mathfrak{A})$$

represents a generalized measure with values in the space L. This generalized measure is *absolutely continuous* with respect to μ, that is, for any $\varepsilon > 0$ there exists a $\delta > 0$ such that $\operatorname{Var}\mu(A) \le \delta$ implies $\operatorname{Var} I(A) \le \varepsilon$ for every $A \in \mathfrak{A}$. Moreover,

$$\operatorname{Var} I(X) = \operatorname{Var} \int_X \varphi(x)\,\mu(dx) < \infty.$$

By the expressions *almost everywhere* or *for almost all x* with respect to the generalized measure μ we will indicate that we are dealing with all $x \in X$ excluding, perhaps, a set $A \in \mathfrak{A}$ such that $\operatorname{Var}\mu(A) = 0$. For every function $\varphi(x)$ which is equal to zero almost everywhere the integral $\int_X \varphi(x)\,\mu(dx)$ equals zero; if $\operatorname{Var} \int_X \varphi(x)\,\mu(dx) = 0$, then $\varphi(x) = 0$ almost everywhere.

The following inequality holds:

$$\operatorname{Var} \int_X \varphi(x)\,\mu(dx) \le \operatorname{ess\,sup}|\varphi| \cdot \operatorname{Var}\mu(X),$$

where ess sup denotes the least upper bound of all y for which $\operatorname{Var}\mu\{|\varphi| > y\} > 0$.

More generally, if the integrable functions $\varphi_1(x)$ and $\varphi_2(x)$ are such that $|\varphi_1(x)| \leq |\varphi_2(x)|$, then

$$\text{Var} \int_X \varphi_1(x)\,\mu(dx) \leq \text{Var} \int_X \varphi_2(x)\,\mu(dx).$$

A sequence of measurable functions $\varphi_1(x), \varphi_2(x), \ldots$ is called *convergent in measure* to the measurable function $\varphi(x)$ if for every $\varepsilon > 0$

$$\lim_{n \to \infty} \text{Var}\,\mu\{|\varphi_n - \varphi| > \varepsilon\} = 0.$$

Every sequence $\varphi_1(x), \varphi_2(x)$ which is convergent almost everywhere converges in measure. If a sequence $\varphi_1(x), \varphi_2(x)$ converges in measure it contains a subsequence which converges almost everywhere.

A sequence of integrable functions $\varphi_1(x), \varphi_2(x), \ldots$ is said to *converge in mean* to the integrable function $\varphi(x)$ if

$$\lim_{n \to \infty} \text{Var} \int_X [\varphi_n(x) - \varphi(x)]\,\mu(dx) = 0.$$

This implies

$$\lim_{n \to \infty} \int_X \varphi_n(x)\,\mu(dx) = \int_X \varphi(x)\,\mu(dx).$$

A sequence of integrable functions $\varphi_1(x), \varphi_2(x), \ldots$ which is convergent in mean is uniformly integrable: for every $\varepsilon > 0$ there exists a $\delta > 0$ that $A \in \mathfrak{A}$ and $\text{Var}\,\mu(A) \leq \delta$ entails the inequality $\text{Var} \int_A \varphi_n(x)\,\mu(dx) \leq \varepsilon$ for all $n = 1, 2, \ldots$.

The sequence $\varphi_1(x), \varphi_2(x), \ldots$ is uniformly integrable if and only if for every $\varepsilon > 0$ there exists a y such that

$$\text{Var} \int_{A_n} \varphi_n(x)\,\mu(dx) \leq \varepsilon, \qquad A_n = \{|\varphi_n| > y\}$$

for all $n = 1, 2, \ldots$. For example a sequence of functions $\varphi_1(x), \varphi_2(x), \ldots$ is uniformly integrable if $|\varphi_n(x)| \leq \psi(x)$, $n = 1, 2, \ldots$, where $\psi(x)$ stands for an integrable function. The sequence $\varphi_1(x), \varphi_2(x), \ldots$ is convergent in the mean if and only if it is uniformly integrable and convergent in measure.

Example. *Spectral Representation of Operators.* Let $E = E(B)$ be an operator-valued function on the σ-algebra of Borel sets B of the real line $-\infty < \lambda < \infty$, and suppose that the values of this function are projection operators $E(B)$ in the Hilbert space U with the following properties:

a) $E\left(\bigcup_n B_n\right) = \sum_n E(B_n)$

for any disjoint sets $B_1, \ldots, B_n$ where $E(B)$ is the identity operator if B is the entire straight line;

b) $E(B' \cdot B'') = E(B') \cdot E(B'')$

for any B' and B''. Then for any fixed $u \in U$ the function $\Phi_u(B) = E(B) u$ will be a generalized orthogonal measure on the real line with values in the Hilbert space U such that $\operatorname{Var} \Phi_u = \|u\|$.

Every bounded measurable function $\varphi = \varphi(\lambda)$ will be integrable with respect to the generalized measure $\Phi_u = \Phi_u(B)$ for any $u \in U$, and the integral

$$A u = \int_{-\infty}^{\infty} \varphi(\lambda) \, \Phi_u(d\lambda) = \int_{-\infty}^{\infty} \varphi(\lambda) \, E(d\lambda) \, u$$

defines a linear bounded operator A on the space U. If A_1 and A_2 are linear operator of this type, then

$$(A_1 u', A_2 u'') = \int_{-\infty}^{\infty} \varphi_1(\lambda) \cdot \overline{\varphi_2(\lambda)} \, F_{u',u''}(d\lambda)$$

where $\varphi_1(\lambda)$ and $\varphi_2(\lambda)$ are the functions on the real line $-\infty < \lambda < \infty$ which define the operators A_1 and A_2, and $F_{u',u''}$ is the generalized (real or complex-valued) Borel measure

$$F_{u',u''}(B) = (\Phi_{u'}(B), \Phi_{u''}(B)) = (E(B) u', u'') .$$

If $\varphi(\lambda)$ is real, then the corresponding operator A will be *selfadjoint*. If $|\varphi(\lambda)| \equiv 1$, the corresponding operator A will be *unitary* (see p. 69). Any bounded selfadjoint operator A can be represented in the form

$$A u = \int_{a}^{b} \lambda \, E(d\lambda) \, u \qquad (u \in U)$$

where $E = E(B)$ is an operator-valued measure of the type described above. Any unitary operator A can be written in the form

$$A u = \int_{-\pi}^{\pi} e^{i\lambda} \, E(d\lambda) \, u \qquad (u \in U).$$

Every operator-valued function $A = A(t)$ on the real line $-\infty < t < \infty$ whose values are unitary operators $A(t)$ in the Hilbert space U and which satisfies the condition

$$A(t_1 + t_2) = A(t_1) \cdot A(t_2)$$

can be written in the form

$$A(t) u = \int_{-\infty}^{\infty} e^{i\lambda t} \, E(d\lambda) \, u \qquad (u \in U).$$

Integration of Abstract Functions. Let $(X, \mathfrak{A}, \mu)$ be an arbitrary space with a finite complete measure μ on the σ-algebra of sets $\mathfrak{A}$, Y a complete normed separable space, and $\mathfrak{B}$ the Borel σ-algebra of Y.

A function $\varphi = \varphi(x)$ on the set A of the space $(X, \mathfrak{A})$ with values in the space $(Y, \mathfrak{B})$ is measurable if and only if one of the following conditions is satisfied:

a) for every continuous functional $z = \langle y, z \rangle$ on Y the numerical function $\langle \varphi(x), z \rangle$, $x \in X$ is measurable;

b) the function $\varphi(x)$ is the limit of a uniformly convergent sequence of simple measurable functions $\varphi_1(x)$, $\varphi_2(x)$, ..., that is,

$$\lim_{n \to \infty} \| \varphi_n(x) - \varphi(x) \| = 0$$

uniformly with respect to $x \in X$.

If the function $\varphi(x)$ is measurable, then the numerical function $\| \varphi(x) \|$ is measurable, too.

Let $y_1, y_2, \ldots$ be a denumerable set of points of Y which is dense in Y. Then a sequence $\varphi_1(x)$, $\varphi_2(x)$, ... of simple measurable functions which converges uniformly to the measurable function $\varphi(x)$ can be constructed in the following way:

$$\varphi_n(x) = y_m \quad \text{for} \quad x \in A_{mn} \quad (m, n = 1, 2, \ldots),$$

where the measurable sets A_{mn} are defined by the formulas

$$A_{1n} = \{ \| \varphi(x) - y_1 \| < 1/n \},$$

$$A_{mn} = \{ \| \varphi(x) - y_m \| < 1/n \} \setminus \bigcup_{k=1}^{m-1} A_{kn} \quad (m = 2, 3, \ldots).$$

The simple function $\varphi(x)$ on the space X with values in the normed space Y given by

$$\varphi(x) = y_k \quad \text{for} \quad x \in A_k \quad (k = 1, 2, \ldots)$$

is called *integrable* if the series

$$\sum_k \| y_k \| \, \mu(A_k)$$

converges.

The *integral* of this function is defined as

$$\int_X \varphi(x) \, \mu(dx) = \sum_k y_k \, \mu(A_k).$$

More precisely, the integral $\int\limits_X \varphi(x)\,\mu(dx)$ is the limit of the partial sums $\sum\limits_{k=1}^{n} y_k\,\mu(A_k)$:

$$\lim \left\| \int\limits_X \varphi(x)\,\mu(dx) - \sum_{k=1}^{n} y_k\,\mu(A_k) \right\| = 0 .$$

An arbitrary function $\varphi(x)$ is called *integrable* if it is a limit of a uniformly convergent sequence of simple integrable functions $\varphi_1(x)$, $\varphi_2(x)$, ...; the integral of this function is defined as the limit

$$\int\limits_X \varphi(x)\,\mu(dx) = \lim_{n\to\infty} \int\limits_X \varphi_n(x)\,\mu(dx) .$$

The integral of $\varphi(x)$ on a set $A \in \mathfrak{A}$ is defined by the formula

$$\int\limits_A \varphi(x)\,\mu(dx) = \int\limits_X \varphi(x)\,\varphi_A(x)\,\mu(dx) ,$$

where

$$\varphi_A(x) = \begin{cases} 1 & \text{for } x \in A , \\ 0 & \text{for } x \notin A . \end{cases}$$

A measurable function $\varphi(x)$ is integrable if and only if the numerical function $\|\varphi(x)\|$ is integrable. Given an integrable function $\varphi(x)$ the integral

$$I(A) = \int\limits_A \varphi(x)\,\mu(dx) \qquad (A \in \mathfrak{A})$$

is a *generalized measure* on the σ-algebra $\mathfrak{A}$ such that

$$\operatorname{Var} I(A) \leq \int\limits_A \|\varphi(x)\|\,\mu(dx) .$$

For any integrable functions $\varphi_1(x), \varphi_2(x)$ and any numbers λ_1, λ_2 the function $\varphi(x) = \lambda_1\,\varphi_1(x) + \lambda_2\,\varphi_2(x)$ is also integrable and

$$\int\limits_X \varphi(x)\,\mu(dx) = \lambda_1 \int\limits_X \varphi_1(x)\,\mu(dx) + \lambda_2 \int\limits_X \varphi_2(x)\,\mu(dx) .$$

Convergence of a sequence of measurable or integrable functions $\varphi_1(x), \varphi_2(x), ...$ to a measurable or integrable function $\varphi(x)$ in the sense of "almost everywhere", "in measure" or "in the mean" is defined by the corresponding convergence of the sequence of numerical functions $\|\varphi_n(x) - \varphi(x)\|$, $n = 1, 2, ...$ to zero. The sequence $\varphi_1(x), \varphi_2(x), ...$ converges in the mean if and only if the functions $\|\varphi_1(x)\|, \|\varphi_2(x)\|, ...$ are uniformly integrable and the sequence $\varphi_1(x), \varphi_2(x), ...$ converges in measure.

These statements remain true in the case where $\mu = \mu(A)$, $A \in \mathfrak{A}$ is a generalized numerical measure of bounded variation; it suffices to replace in an obvious way the generalized measure $\mu(A)$ by the positive measure $\operatorname{Var}\mu(A)$.

Iterated Integration. Let $(X_1, \mathfrak{A}_1)$ and $(X_2, \mathfrak{A}_2)$ be arbitrary measurable spaces, μ_1 a numerical generalized measure on the σ-algebra $\mathfrak{A}_1$, μ_2 a generalized measure on the σ-algebra $\mathfrak{A}_2$ with values in a complete normed space L, and $\varphi(x_1, x_2)$ a measurable function on the product of the measurable spaces $(X_1, \mathfrak{A}_1)$ and $(X_2, \mathfrak{A}_2)$ which takes numerical values or (if the generalized measure μ_2 is numerical) takes values in a complete normed separable space Y.

If $\varphi(x_1, x_2)$ considered as a function of $x_2 \in X_2$ is integrable for almost all $x_1 \in X_1$, then the corresponding integral

$$\varphi_1(x_1) = \int\limits_{X_2} \varphi(x_1, x_2)\, \mu_2(dx_2)$$

represents a measurable function of $x_1 \in X_1$. If $\varphi(x_1, x_2)$ as a function of $x_1 \in X_1$ is integrable for almost all $x_2 \in X_2$, the integral

$$\varphi_2(x_2) = \int\limits_{X_1} \varphi(x_1, x_2)\, \mu_1(dx_1)$$

is a measurable function of $x_2 \in X_2$. In the case of integrable functions $\varphi_1(x_1)$ and $\varphi_2(x_2)$ the equation

$$\int\limits_{X_1} \left[\int\limits_{X_2} \varphi(x_1, x_2)\, \mu_2(dx_2) \right] \mu_1(dx_1) = \int\limits_{X_2} \left[\int\limits_{X_1} \varphi(x_1, x_2)\, \mu_1(dx_1) \right] \mu_2(dx_2)$$

holds.

Suppose that the generalized measures μ_1 and μ_2 are such that their variations $\operatorname{Var}\mu_1(A_1)$, $A_1 \in \mathfrak{A}_1$ and $\operatorname{Var}\mu_2(A_2)$, $A_2 \in \mathfrak{A}_2$ are measures on the σ-algebras $\mathfrak{A}_1$ and $\mathfrak{A}_2$ and let $\mu = \mu_1 \times \mu_2$ be the generalized measure on the product σ-algebra of the σ-algebras $\mathfrak{A}_1$ and $\mathfrak{A}_2$ in the space $X = X_1 \times X_2$ which is given on the semi-ring of sets $A = A_1 \times A_2$ as the product

$$\mu(A) = \mu_1(A_1) \cdot \mu_2(A_2) \qquad (A_1 \in \mathfrak{A}_1, A_2 \in \mathfrak{A}_2).$$

A function $\varphi(x) = \varphi(x_1, x_2)$ of $x = (x_1, x_2)$ is integrable with respect to μ if and only if one of the iterated integrals described above is defined; thus if one of these iterated integrals exists the other one also does, and moreover

$$\int\limits_{X} \varphi(x)\, \mu(dx) = \int\limits_{X_1} \left[\int\limits_{X_2} \varphi(x_1, x_2)\, \mu_2(dx_2) \right] \mu_1(dx_1)$$

$$= \int\limits_{X_2} \left[\int\limits_{X_1} \varphi(x_1, x_2)\, \mu_1(dx_1) \right] \mu_2(dx_2).$$

CHAPTER III

Basic Concepts of Probability Theory

§ 1. Spaces of Elementary Events
Probability Distributions and Characteristic Functions

1. Basic Schemes of Probability Theory

The Space of Elementary Events. The basis of every scheme of probability theory is formed by a so-called space of elementary events $(\Omega, \mathfrak{A}, \mathbb{P})$. This is a measurable space of elements ω which are called *elementary events* or *elementary outcomes*, together with a *probability measure* $\mathbb{P} = \mathbb{P}(A)$ on the σ-algebra $\mathfrak{A}$:

$$\mathbb{P}(\Omega) = 1 .$$

The sets of the space Ω are called *events*, and the measure $\mathbb{P}(A)$ of the set $A \in \mathfrak{A}$ is termed the *probability* of the event A.

Random Variables. Let $(X, \mathfrak{B})$ be a measurable space. An $(\mathfrak{A}, \mathfrak{B})$-measurable function $\xi = \xi(\omega)$ on the space of the elementary events $(\Omega, \mathfrak{A}, \mathbb{P})$ with values in $(X, \mathfrak{B})$ is called a *random variable* in the phase space $(X, \mathfrak{B})$. By the *probability distribution* of this random variable ξ we mean the function $\mathbb{P}_\xi = \mathbb{P}_\xi(B)$ on the σ-algebra $\mathfrak{B}$ of the phase space given by

$$\mathbb{P}_\xi(B) = \mathbb{P}\{\xi \in B\} \quad (B \in \mathfrak{B}) .$$

The probability distribution $\mathbb{P}_\xi$ represents a probability measure in the phase space $(X, \mathfrak{B})$.

Random variables $\xi = \xi(\omega)$ and $\eta = \eta(\omega)$ in the phase space $(X, \mathfrak{B})$ are called *equivalent* if for every set $B \in \mathfrak{B}$ the events $\{\xi \in B\}$ and $\{\eta \in B\}$ coincide with probability one:

$$\mathbb{P}(\{\xi \in B\} \circ \{\eta \in B\}) = 0 .$$

In the case of a separable phase space equivalence amounts to saying that the variables ξ and η are equal with probability one, that is, $\mathbb{P}\{\xi \neq \eta\} = 0$.

The random variable $\xi = \xi(\omega)$ is called *directly given* if each elementary outcome ω is described by the corresponding point x of the phase space, more precisely if $\Omega = X$, $\mathfrak{A} = \mathfrak{B}$ and the function $\xi = \xi(x)$ has the form $\xi(x) = x$, $x \in X$.

Let $\xi_1, \xi_2, \ldots, \xi_n$ be random variables of the space of elementary events $(\Omega, \mathfrak{A}, \mathbb{P})$ in corresponding phase spaces $(X_k, \mathfrak{B}_k)$. The function $\mathbb{P}_{\xi_1, \ldots, \xi_n} = \mathbb{P}_{\xi_1, \ldots, \xi_n}(B_1, \ldots, B_n)$ defined for sets $B_1 \in \mathfrak{B}_1, \ldots, B_n \in \mathfrak{B}_n$ by

$$\mathbb{P}_{\xi_1, \ldots, \xi_n}(B_1, \ldots, B_n) = \mathbb{P}\{\xi_1 \in B_1, \ldots, \xi_n \in B_n\}$$

is called the *joint probability distribution* of these variables. Thus the probability distribution $\mathbb{P}_{\xi_1, \ldots, \xi_n}$ is a distribution on the semi-ring of the sets of the type $B_1 \times \cdots \times B_n$, $B_1 \in \mathfrak{B}_1, \ldots, B_n \in \mathfrak{B}_n$ in the product space $X_1 \times \cdots \times X_n$. The random variables $\xi_1, \ldots, \xi_n$ are called *independent* if for any $B_1, \ldots, B_n$ we have

$$\mathbb{P}_{\xi_1, \ldots, \xi_n}(B_1, \ldots, B_n) = \mathbb{P}_{\xi_1}(B_1) \ldots \mathbb{P}_{\xi_n}(B_n).$$

For any family of probability distributions $\mathbb{P}_t$ in corresponding phase space $(X_t, \mathfrak{B}_t)$ where the parameter t runs through an arbitrary set T, there exists an independent family of random variables $\xi_t = \xi_t(\omega)$ on some space of elementary events $(\Omega, \mathfrak{A}, \mathbb{P})$ with probability distribution $\mathbb{P}_t$. By independence of the family we mean that for any finite set of parameters $t_1, \ldots, t_n \in T$ the variables $\xi_{t_1}, \ldots, \xi_{t_n}$ are independent.

Random Processes. Let $(E, \mathfrak{B})$ be a measurable space and T a set of values of a parameter t. A function $\xi = \xi(t)$ of the parameter $t \in T$ whose values $\xi(t)$ are random variables $\xi(t) = \xi(\omega, t)$ on the space of elementary events $(\Omega, \mathfrak{A}, \mathbb{P})$ in the phase space $(E, \mathfrak{B})$ is called a *random process in the phase space* $(E, \mathfrak{B})$. The joint probability distributions of the random variables $\xi(t_1), \ldots, \xi(t_n)$, $t_1, \ldots, t_n \in T$, that is,

$$\mathbb{P}_{t_1, \ldots, t_n}(B_1, \ldots, B_n) = \mathbb{P}\{\xi(t_1) \in B_1, \ldots, \xi(t_n) \in B_n\} \quad (B_1, \ldots, B_n \in \mathfrak{B}),$$

are called the *finite-dimensional probability distributions* of the random process $\xi = \xi(t)$.

Random processes $\xi = \xi(t)$ and $\eta = \eta(t)$ on set T which take values in the same phase space $(E, \mathfrak{B})$ are called *equivalent* if for any $t \in T$ the corresponding random variables $\xi(t) = \xi(\omega, t)$ and $\eta(t) = \eta(\omega, t)$ are equivalent.

For each fixed $\omega \in \Omega$ the function $\xi(\omega, t)$ of the parameter $t \in T$ with values in the phase space $(E, \mathfrak{B})$ is called a *trajectory* or *realization (sample function)* of the random process $\xi = \xi(t)$. The random process $\xi = \xi(t)$ is called *directly given* if each elementary outcome is described by the corresponding trajectory $x = x(t)$ in the function space $X = E^T$ of all functions on the set T with values in $(E, \mathfrak{B})$. More precisely $\Omega = X$, the σ-algebra $\mathfrak{A}$ is generated by all possible cylinder sets $\{x(t_1) \in B_1, \ldots, x(t_n) \in B_n\}$, where $t_1, \ldots, t_n \in T$ and $B_1, \ldots, B_n \in \mathfrak{B}$, and the values $\xi(t) = \xi(X, t)$ have the form $\xi(x, t) = x(t)$, $x \in X$. Given any random process, a directly given random process can be constructed which has the same finite-dimensional distributions. For each consistent family of finite-dimensional probability distributions $\mathbb{P}_{t_1, \ldots, t_n}(B_1, \ldots, B_n)$ $(t_1, \ldots, t_n \in T, B_1, \ldots, B_n \in \mathfrak{B})$ such that $\mathbb{P}_t = \mathbb{P}_t(B)$, $t \in T$ are tight measures in the topological phase space $(E, \mathfrak{B})$ there exists a directly given random process with the same finite-dimensional probability distributions.

Random Variables in a Linear Phase Space. Let $\xi = \xi(\omega)$ be a random variable in the linear normed space X on the space of elementary events $(\Omega, \mathfrak{A}, \mathbb{P})$. The integral

$$\mathbb{M}\xi = \int_\Omega \xi(\omega)\, \mathbb{P}(d\omega) = \int x\, \mathbb{P}_\xi(dx)$$

is called the *mean value or the mathematical expectation* of the random variable provided that the function $\xi = \xi(\omega)$ is integrable.

Consider a random vector $\xi = (\xi_1, \ldots, \xi_n)$ in the real n-dimensional space $(X, \mathfrak{B})$, where $\mathfrak{B}$ is the Borel σ-algebra. The function $F_\xi(x) = \mathbb{P}\{\xi_1 \leq x_1, \ldots, \xi_n \leq x_n\}$ of the variable $x = (x_1, \ldots, x_n)$, $x \in X$ is called the *distribution function* of the random variable ξ or the *joint distribution function* of the variables $\xi_1, \ldots, \xi_n$. The function

$$\varphi_\xi(u) = \mathbb{M} e^{i\langle u, \xi \rangle} = \int_X e^{i\langle u, x \rangle}\, P_\xi(dx)$$

of the variable $u = (u_1, \ldots, u_n)$ on the n-dimensional real space U, where $\langle u, \xi \rangle = \sum_{k=1}^n u_k \xi_k$, $\langle u, x \rangle = \sum_{k=1}^n u_k x_k$, is called the *characteristic function* of the random variable ξ or the characteristic function of the variables $\xi_1, \ldots, \xi_n$. It is continuous and positively definite in the sense that

$$\sum_{k, j} \lambda_k \bar{\lambda}_j \varphi_\xi(u_k - u_j) \geq 0$$

for any $u_1, u_2, \ldots \in U$ and any numbers $\lambda_1, \lambda_2, \ldots$; moreover $\varphi(0) = 1$. Any function $\varphi = \varphi(u)$ with these properties represents the characteristic function of some random variable ξ.

The distribution $F_\xi = F_\xi(x)$ as well as the characteristic function $\varphi_\xi = \varphi_\xi(u)$ determine uniquely the probability distribution $\mathbb{P}_\xi = \mathbb{P}_\xi(B)$, $B \in \mathfrak{B}$, of ξ.

Generalized Random Processes. Let U be a real or complex linear space of elements u. A function $\xi = \langle u, \xi \rangle$ of the parameter $u \in U$ whose values $\langle u, \xi \rangle$ are real or complex random variables $\langle u, \xi \rangle = \langle u, \xi(\omega) \rangle$ on a space of elementary events $(\Omega, \mathfrak{A}, \mathbb{P})$ is called a *generalized random process* if for any $u_1, u_2 \in U$ and any real or complex numbers $\lambda_1 \lambda_2$

we have

$$\langle \lambda_1 u_1 + \lambda_2 u_2, \xi \rangle = \lambda_1 \langle u_1, \xi \rangle + \lambda_2 \langle u_2, \xi \rangle$$

for almost all $\omega \in \Omega$, in other words, *with probability* 1. The probability distributions of the random variables $\langle u_1, \xi \rangle, \ldots, \langle u_n, \xi \rangle$:

$$\mathbb{P}_{u_1, \ldots, u_n}(B_1, \ldots, B_n) = \mathbb{P}\{\langle u_1, \xi \rangle \in B_1, \ldots, \langle u_n, \xi \rangle \in B_n\},$$

where $u_1, \ldots, u_n \in U$ and $B_1, \ldots, B_n$ are Borel sets of the real line or the complex plane, are called the *finite-dimensional* probability distributions of the generalized process $\xi = \langle u, \xi \rangle$.

The generalized process $\xi = \langle u, \xi \rangle$ is said to be *directly given* if each elementary outcome ω is described by the corresponding linear functional $x = \langle u, x \rangle$ on the space U. More precisely, $\Omega = X$ where X is the space of all linear functionals on U, the σ-algebra $\mathfrak{A}$ is generated by all cylinder sets

$$\{\langle u_1, x \rangle \in B_1, \ldots, \langle u_n, x \rangle \in B_n\}$$

of X, and the values $\langle u, \xi \rangle = \langle u, \xi(x) \rangle$ have the form $\langle u, \xi(x) \rangle = \langle u, x \rangle$, $x \in X$.

Example. Let U be the set of all real or complex functions $u = u(t)$ on the real line $-\infty < t < \infty$ which are infinitely differentiable and vanish outside finite intervals. Let X be the set of all linear functionals on U, which are continuous in the following sense:

$$\lim_{u_n \to u} \langle u_n, x \rangle = \langle u, x \rangle,$$

where by the convergence $u_n \to u$ we mean that all functions $u_n = u_n(t)$ vanish outside a fixed finite interval which is the same for all functions, and $u_n^{(k)}(t) \to u^{(k)}(t)$ uniformly with respect to t for each derivative of order $k = 0, 1, \ldots$. This space X is one of the fundamental spaces in the theory of the so-called *generalized functions*, and the corresponding generalized random process represents one of the fundamental types of generalized processes.

Let $\xi = \langle u, \xi \rangle$ be a real generalized process on U. The function

$$\varphi_\xi(u) = \mathbb{M} e^{i \langle u, \xi \rangle} \qquad (u \in U)$$

is called the *characteristic functional* of the generalized process $\xi = \langle u, \xi \rangle$. This functional determines uniquely the finite-dimensional distributions of the generalized process.

Let U be a denumerably Hilbert space with the scalar products $\langle u', u'' \rangle_1$, $\langle u', u'' \rangle_2, \ldots$, and let X be the adjoint space consisting of all linear continuous functionals $x = \langle u, x \rangle$ on U. Then a function $\varphi = \varphi(u)$, $u \in X$

is the *characteristic functional* of a directly given generalized random process if and only if $\varphi(0) = 1$, the function φ is positively definite in the following sense:

$$\sum_{k,j} \lambda_k \bar{\lambda}_j \, \varphi(u_k - u_j) \geq 0$$

for any $u_1, u_2, \ldots \in U$ and any numbers $\lambda_1, \lambda_2, \ldots$, and finally, the following condition is satisfied: for any $\varepsilon > 0$ there exist an n and a nuclear operator A in the Hilbert space U with the scalar product $\langle u', u'' \rangle_n$ such that $|\varphi(u) - 1| \leq \varepsilon$ for all $u \in U$ with $\langle A u, u \rangle_n \leq 1$. If U is a nuclear space, then this condition is equivalent to the continuity of the function φ.

Example. Let U be an arbitrary linear space and $B(u, v)$ an arbitrary bilinear positive functional on U. There exists always a generalized Gaussian process $\xi = \langle u, \xi \rangle, u \in U$ with the correlation functional $B(u, v)$, $u, v \in U$ (see also § 2.2). If U is a Hilbert space with the scalar product (u, v) and B a linear positive operator on U, then a directly given Gaussian generalized process $\xi = \langle u, \xi \rangle$ on U with the correlation functional $B(u, v) = (B u, v)$ exists if and only if B is a nuclear operator.

Limit Theorems. One of the main tasks of probability theory is the calculation of probabilities of other events which in a certain sense are simpler. Here various schemes of approximate calculations of probabilities play a special rôle. They are usually based on so-called *limit theorems.*

One of several similar general schemes looks like this. We consider a sequence of probability distributions

$$\mathbb{P}_1 = \mathbb{P}_1(B), \quad \mathbb{P}_2 = \mathbb{P}_2(B), \ldots$$

on the topological space $(X, \mathfrak{B})$, and we formulate conditions under which the given sequence converges weakly to some probability distribution $\mathbb{P} = \mathbb{P}(B)$, $B \in \mathfrak{B}$. One of the general results used to derive such theorems is the following.

Let X be a Euclidean space and $\mathfrak{B}$ the σ-algebra of its Borel sets. A sequence $\mathbb{P}_n = \mathbb{P}_n(B)$, $n = 1, 2, \ldots$, of probability distributions on the σ-algebra $\mathfrak{B}$ converges weakly to a distribution $\mathbb{P} = \mathbb{P}(B)$, $B \in \mathfrak{B}$ if and only if the corresponding sequence of characteristic functionals $\varphi_n = \varphi_n(u)$, $u \in U$ converges to the corresponding characteristic functional $\varphi = \varphi(u)$:

$$\lim_{n \to \infty} \varphi_n(u) = \varphi(u) \quad (u \in U).$$

The most important field where this result plays a fundamental rôle is concerned with sums of independent random variables $\xi_{1,n}, \ldots, \xi_{k_n, n}$ with values in a Euclidean space X. The problem is that of limit distribution $\mathbb{P}$ for the normalized sums

$$S_n = \frac{\xi_{1,n} + \cdots + \xi_{k_n, n} - A_n}{B_n},$$

where A_n and B_n are constants, and $n \to \infty$. The decisive fact which guarantees the success of many concrete investigations (see Chapter IV) is that the characteristic function of a sum of independent variables equals the product of characteristic functions of the single terms.

2. Relations Among Various Events and Random Variables

Conditional Probabilities and Conditional Mathematical Expectations. Let $'\Omega, \mathfrak{A}, \mathbb{P})$ be a space of elementary events with the probability distribution $\mathbb{P} = \mathbb{P}(A)$ on the σ-algebra $\mathfrak{A}$, and $\mathfrak{B}$ a σ-algebra of events which is contained in $\mathfrak{A}$. The conditional probability of an event $A \in \mathfrak{A}$ with respect to $\mathfrak{B}$, to be denoted by $\mathbb{P}(A|\mathfrak{B})$, is defined as a non-negative function of the elementary outcomes $\omega, 0 \le \mathbb{P}(A|\mathfrak{A}) \le 1$, which is measurable with respect to $\mathfrak{B}$, and such that

$$\int_B \mathbb{P}(A|\mathfrak{B})\, \mathbb{P}(d\omega) = \mathbb{P}(AB)$$

for any $B \in \mathfrak{B}$. On the space of elementary events Ω the function $\mathbb{P}(A|\mathfrak{B})$ is uniquely determined for almost all ω, and represents the density of the distribution $\mathbb{P}(AB), B \in \mathfrak{B}$ with respect to the probability distribution $\mathbb{P}(B)$ on the σ-algebra $\mathfrak{B} \subseteq \mathfrak{A}$.

If the σ-algebra $\mathfrak{B}$ is generated by a countable number of disjoint events $B_1, B_2, \ldots$ with positive probabilities whose union is the entire space Ω, then the conditional probability $\mathbb{P}(A|\mathfrak{B})$ is the simple function of the elementary outcomes $\omega \in \Omega$ given by

$$\mathbb{P}(A|\mathfrak{B}) = \frac{\mathbb{P}(AB_k)}{\mathbb{P}(B_k)} \quad \text{for} \quad \omega \in B_k \quad (k = 1, 2, \ldots).$$

In any case the conditional probability $\mathbb{P}(A|\mathfrak{B})$ is the limit of a uniformly convergent sequence of simple functions $\mathbb{P}(A|\mathfrak{B}_n), n = 1, 2, \ldots,$ of the type mentioned before:

$$\mathbb{P}(A|\mathfrak{B}_n) = \frac{\mathbb{P}(AB_{kn})}{\mathbb{P}(B_{kn})} \quad \text{for} \quad \omega \in B_{kn} \quad (n, k = 1, 2, \ldots).$$

For the events B_{kn} we can choose, for example, $B_{kn} = \left\{ \dfrac{k-1}{n} \le \mathbb{P}(A|\mathfrak{B}) < \dfrac{k}{n} \right\}$ $(n, k = 1, 2, \ldots)$.

The conditional probability $\mathbb{P}_{\mathfrak{B}} = \mathbb{P}(A|\mathfrak{B})$ regarded as a function from $A \in \mathfrak{A}$ with values in the normed space $L^1(\Omega)$ of all integrable (real or complex) functions $\xi = \xi(\omega)$ on Ω with $\|\xi\| = \mathbb{M}|\xi|$ is a generalized measure on the σ-algebra $\mathfrak{A}$ in Ω; its variation is given by

$$\operatorname{Var} \mathbb{P}(A|\mathfrak{B}) = \mathbb{P}(A) \quad (A \in \mathfrak{A}).$$

Every real or complex random variable $\xi = \xi(\omega)$ whose expectation exists (that is, any integrable function on the space $(\Omega, \mathfrak{A}, \mathbb{P})$ with measure $\mathbb{P}$), is also integrable with respect to the generalized measure $\mathbb{P}_{\mathfrak{B}} = \mathbb{P}(A \mid \mathfrak{B})$. The corresponding integral

$$\mathbb{M}(\xi \mid \mathfrak{B}) = \int_\Omega \xi(\omega) \, \mathbb{P}(d\omega \mid \mathfrak{B})$$

is called the *conditional mathematical expectation* of the random variable ξ.

Suppose we are given a random variable $\eta = \eta(\omega)$ with values in the phase space $(Y, \mathfrak{C})$, or a family of such variables $\eta(t) = \eta(\omega, t)$, $t \in T$, and let $\mathfrak{B}$ be the σ-algebra generated by all possible events $\{\eta \in C\}$ or $\{\eta(t) \in C\}$ $(C \in \mathfrak{C}, t \in T)$. Then conditional probabilities and conditional expectations relative to $\mathfrak{B}$ are denoted by $\mathbb{P}(A \mid \eta)$ and $\mathbb{M}(\xi \mid \eta)$, or $\mathbb{P}(A \mid \eta(t), t \in T)$ and $\mathbb{M}(\xi \mid \eta(t), t \in T)$, respectively.

Conditional probabilities and conditional expectations have the following properties:

Let $\xi = \xi(t)$ be a measurable real- or complex-valued random process on the interval $T = [a, b]$ such that

$$\int_a^b \mathbb{M}|\xi(t)| \, \mathrm{Var}\,\mu(dt) < \infty \,,$$

where μ is a generalized numerical measure on the interval T. Then the trajectories $\xi(\omega, t)$ of this process are integrable functions with probability 1, and

$$\mathbb{M} \left[\int_a^b \xi(\omega, t) \, \mu(dt) \right] = \int_a^b [\mathbb{M}\,\xi(t)] \, \mu(dt) \,.$$

The conditional expectation

$$\mathbb{M} \left[\xi(t) \mid \mathfrak{B} \right] = \int_\Omega \xi(\omega, t) \, \mathbb{P}(d\omega \mid \mathfrak{B}) \qquad (t \in T) \,,$$

considered as a function on the interval $T = [a, b]$ with values in the normed space $L^1(\Omega)$, is defined almost everywhere with respect to the measure μ and represents an integrable function for which

$$\int_a^b \mathbb{M} \left[\xi(t) \mid \mathfrak{B} \right] \mu(dt) = \int_\Omega \left[\int_a^b \xi(\omega, t) \, (dt) \right] \mathbb{P}(d\omega \mid \mathfrak{B})$$

$$= \mathbb{M} \left[\int_a^b \xi(t) \, \mu(dt) \mid \mathfrak{B} \right] \,.$$

Let ξ be a random variable, $\mathbb{M}|\xi| < \infty$, and $\mathfrak{B}$ a σ-algebra of events in Ω. Then

$$\mathbb{M} [\mathbb{M}(\xi \mid \mathfrak{B})] = \mathbb{M}\,\xi \,.$$

Let $\cdots \subseteq \mathfrak{B}_1 \subseteq \mathfrak{B}_0 \subseteq \mathfrak{B}_1 \subseteq \cdots$ be an increasing sequence of σ-algebras contained in $\mathfrak{A}$, and

$$\mathfrak{B}_{-\infty} = \bigcap_n \mathfrak{B}_n = \lim_{n \to -\infty} \mathfrak{B}_n,$$

$$\mathfrak{B}_\infty = \bigcup_n \mathfrak{B}_n = \lim_{n \to \infty} \mathfrak{B}_n.$$

more precisely, $\mathfrak{B}_\infty$ is the minimal σ-algebra contained in $\mathfrak{B}$ which includes every $\mathfrak{B}_n$. For any random variable ξ whose expectation exists we have with probability 1

$$\lim_{n \to -\infty} \mathbb{M}(\xi \mid \mathfrak{B}_n) = \mathbb{M}(\xi \mid \mathfrak{B}_{-\infty}),$$

$$\lim_{n \to \infty} \mathbb{M}(\xi \mid \mathfrak{B}_n) = \mathbb{M}(\xi \mid \mathfrak{B}_\infty).$$

If the random variable ξ is such that $\mathbb{M}|\xi|^\alpha < \infty$, $\alpha \geq 1$, then the sequence $\mathbb{M}(\xi \mid \mathfrak{B}_n)$, $n = 0, \pm 1, \ldots$ converges to the corresponding limits $\mathbb{M}(\xi \mid \mathfrak{B}_{-\infty})$ and $\mathbb{M}(\xi \mid \mathfrak{B}_\infty)$ not only with probability 1 but also in the mean of order α:

$$\lim_{n \to -\infty} \mathbb{M}|\mathbb{M}(\xi \mid \mathfrak{B}_n) - \mathbb{M}(\xi \mid \mathfrak{B}_{-\infty})|^\alpha = 0,$$

$$\lim_{n \to \infty} \mathbb{M}|\mathbb{M}(\xi \mid \mathfrak{B}_n) - \mathbb{M}(\xi \mid \mathfrak{B}_\infty)|^\alpha = 0.$$

If the event A belongs to the σ-algebra $\mathfrak{B}$, we have with probability 1

$$\mathbb{P}(\mathfrak{A} \mid \mathfrak{B}) = \begin{cases} 1 & \text{for } \omega \in A, \\ 0 & \text{for } \omega \notin A. \end{cases}$$

If the random variable $\xi = \xi(\omega)$ is measurable with respect to the σ-algebra $\mathfrak{B}$, then with probability 1

$$\mathbb{M}(\xi \mid \mathfrak{B}) = \xi.$$

Moreover, the equation

$$\mathbb{M}(\xi \eta \mid \mathfrak{B}) = \xi \cdot \mathbb{M}(\eta \mid \mathfrak{B})$$

holds for any random variable $\eta = \eta(\omega)$ such that $\mathbb{M}|\eta| < \infty$ and $\mathbb{M}|\xi \eta| < \infty$.

If the σ-algebras of events $\mathfrak{B}_1$ and $\mathfrak{B}_2$ are such that $\mathfrak{B}_1 \subseteq \mathfrak{B}_2$, then

$$\mathbb{M}[\mathbb{M}(\xi \mid \mathfrak{B}_2) \mid \mathfrak{B}_1] = \mathbb{M}(\xi \mid \mathfrak{B}_1).$$

On the other hand if the σ-algebras $\mathfrak{B}_1$ and $\mathfrak{B}_2$ are *independent*, that is, if for any events $B_1 \in \mathfrak{B}_1$ and $B_2 \in \mathfrak{B}_2$ the equation $\mathbb{P}(B_1 B_2) = \mathbb{P}(B_1)\mathbb{P}(B_2)$ holds, then

$$\mathbb{M}[\mathbb{M}(\xi \mid \mathfrak{B}_1) \mid \mathfrak{B}_2] = \mathbb{M}\xi.$$

In particular, if the random variable ξ does not depend on the events $B \in \mathfrak{B}$, more precisely, if the σ-algebra of all events of the form $\{\xi \in C\}$ where C is a Borel set on the real line or the complex plane, and the σ-algebra $\mathfrak{B}$ are independent, then

$$\mathbb{M}(\xi \mid \mathfrak{B}) = \mathbb{M}\xi .$$

Let $L_{\mathfrak{B}}^2(\Omega)$ be the subspace of the Hilbert space $L^2(\Omega)$ formed by all random variables $\eta = \eta(\omega)$, $\mathbb{M}|\eta|^2 < \infty$ which are measurable with respect to the σ-algebra $\mathfrak{B}$, and suppose that the random variable ξ belong to $L^2(\Omega)$, that is, $\mathbb{M}|\xi|^2 < \infty$. Then the conditional expectation $\mathbb{M}(\xi \mid \mathfrak{B})$ is the projection of ξ onto the subspace $L_{\mathfrak{B}}^2(\Omega)$:

$$\mathbb{M}|\xi - M(\xi \mid \mathfrak{B})|^2 = \min_{\eta \in L_{\mathfrak{B}}^2(\Omega)} \mathbb{M}|\xi - \eta|^2 .$$

Conditional Probability Distributions. Let $\xi = \xi(\omega)$ be a random variable on the space of elementary events Ω with values in the phase space $(X, \mathfrak{A})$, let $\mathfrak{B}$ be a σ-algebra of events and

$$\mathbb{P}_\xi(A \mid \mathfrak{B}) = \mathbb{P}\{\xi \in A \mid \mathfrak{B}\} \qquad (A \in \mathfrak{A})$$

the corresponding conditional probabilities. Then for any disjoint sets $A_1, A_2, \ldots \in \mathfrak{A}$ we have with probability 1

$$\mathbb{P}_\xi \left(\bigcup_k A_k \mid \mathfrak{B} \right) = \sum_k \mathbb{P}_\xi(A_k \mid \mathfrak{B})$$

However the excluded set of elementary outcomes $\omega \in \Omega$ where this relation does not hold depends in general on $A_1, A_2, \ldots$. If the conditional probabilities $P_\xi(A \mid \mathfrak{B})$ $(A \in \mathfrak{B})$ can be chosen in such a way that for almost each fixed $\omega \in \Omega$ the corresponding values $\mathbb{P}_\xi(A \mid \mathfrak{B})$ $(A \in \mathfrak{A})$ satisfy the equation

$$\mathbb{P}_\xi \left(\bigcup_k A_k \mid \mathfrak{B} \right) = \sum_k \mathbb{P}_\xi(A_k \mid \mathfrak{B})$$

for every choice of disjoint sets $A_1, A_2, \ldots \in \mathfrak{A}$, then the probability measures $\mathbb{P}_{\omega, \xi} = \mathbb{P}_\xi(A \mid \mathfrak{B})$, $A \in \mathfrak{A}$ which depend on the elementary outcome $\omega \in \Omega$, are called *conditional probability distributions.*

The conditional distributions $\mathbb{P}_{\omega, \xi} = \mathbb{P}_\xi(A \mid \mathfrak{B})$, $A \in \mathfrak{A}$ always exist if the phase space $(X, \mathfrak{A})$ is separable and the probability distribution $\mathbb{P}_\xi = \mathbb{P}_\xi(A)$, $A \in \mathfrak{A}$ is a perfect measure. In this case, with out restricting the generality, the phase space $(X, \mathfrak{A})$ can be assumed to be simply the real line with the σ-algebra of the Borel sets. It is possible to define for almost all $\omega \in \Omega$ a monotone non-decreasing and tight-continuous function $F_{\omega, \xi} = F_{\omega, \xi}(x)$ on a denumerable dense set of points x in X

in such a way that with probability 1

$$F_{\omega,\xi}(x) = \mathbb{P}\{\xi \leq x \,|\, \mathfrak{B}\} \,.$$

Any such function can be extended so as to become a distribution function on the real line X. The probability distributions $\mathbb{P}_{\omega,\xi}$ together with the corresponding distribution functions $F_{\omega,\xi}$ represent the conditional distributions.

Let $\xi = \xi(\omega)$ be a random variable in an arbitrary phase space $(X, \mathfrak{A})$. if the conditional probability distributions $\mathbb{P}_{\omega,\xi} = \mathbb{P}_{\xi}(A\,|\,\mathfrak{B})$, $A \in \mathfrak{A}$ exist, and if the set $\xi(\Omega)$ formed by all points $x = \xi(\omega)$, $\omega \in \Omega$ belongs to the σ-algebra $\mathfrak{A}$, then the formula

$$\mathbb{P}_{\omega}\{\xi \in A\} = \mathbb{P}_{\omega,\xi}(A) \qquad (A \in \mathfrak{A})$$

for $\omega \in \Omega$ defines probability measure $\mathbb{P}_{\omega}$ on the σ-algebra $\mathfrak{A}^{\xi}$ of all events of the form $\{\xi \in A\}$, $A \in \mathfrak{A}$. These probability distributions $\mathbb{P}_{\omega}$ on $\mathfrak{A}^{\xi}$ have the property that with probability 1 for each fixed $A \in \mathfrak{A}$

$$\mathbb{P}_{\omega}\{\xi \in A\} = \mathbb{P}\{\xi \in A \,|\, \mathfrak{B}\} \,.$$

Partition of Spaces and Decomposition of Measures. Let $(\Omega, \mathfrak{A}, \mathbb{P})$ be a measure space with the probability measure $\mathbb{P} = \mathbb{P}(A)$ on the σ-algebra $\mathfrak{A}$ and let $\mathfrak{B}$ be a σ-algebra $\mathfrak{B} \subseteq \mathfrak{A}$. We assume that there exists a separable σ-algebra $\mathfrak{B}' \subseteq \mathfrak{B}$ with the following property: for each $B \in \mathfrak{B}$ there is a set $B' \in \mathfrak{B}$ such that the measure of the symmetric difference $B' \circ B$ is equal to zero: $\mathbb{P}(B' \circ B) = 0$. We further assume that the conditional probability distributions with respect to $\mathfrak{B}$ on the σ-algebra exist, that is, the conditional distribution with respect to $\mathfrak{B}$ of the identical mapping $\xi(\omega) = \omega$.

Then there exist disjoint sets $B_{\alpha} \in \mathfrak{B}$, where the parameter α runs through some set of real numbers such that

$$\Omega = \bigcup_{\alpha} B_{\alpha} \,,$$

and mutually perpendicular probability distributions $\mathbb{P}_{\alpha} = \mathbb{P}_{\alpha}(A)$, $A \in \mathfrak{A}$, such that

$$\mathbb{P}_{\alpha}(B_{\alpha}) = 1 \,,$$

and such that the following is true: if we define a function $\alpha(\omega)$ on Ω by $\alpha(\omega) = \alpha$ for $\omega \in B_{\alpha}$, then for every $A \in \mathfrak{A}$ the probability $\mathbb{P}_{\alpha(\omega)}(A)$ represents the conditional probability of the event A relative to the σ-algebra $\mathfrak{B}$, that is, $\mathbb{P}_{\alpha(\omega)}(A) = \mathbb{P}(A\,|\,\mathfrak{B})$ and $\mathbb{P}(A) = \mathbb{M}\mathbb{P}_{\alpha(\omega)}(A)$. Moreover, if the σ-algebra $\mathfrak{B}$ separates the points of Ω, then the sets B_{α} are one-point sets:

$$B_{\alpha(\omega)} = \{\omega\} \qquad (\omega \in \Omega) \,,$$

and the corresponding probability distributions $\mathbb{P}_\alpha = \mathbb{P}_\alpha(A)$, $A \in \mathfrak{A}$ are given by

$$\mathbb{P}_{\alpha(\omega)}(A) = \begin{cases} 1 & \text{for} \quad \omega \in A \\ 0 & \text{for} \quad \omega \notin A . \end{cases}$$

Example. We consider a set A of the interval $\Omega = [0, 1]$ which is non-measurable with respect to the Lebesgue measure l and such that the exterior measure $l^*(A)$ as well as the exterior measure $l^*(\overline{A})$ of the complement $\overline{A}$ are equal to 1. Let $\mathfrak{A}$ be the σ-algebra of all sets

$$A_1 A \cup A_2 \overline{A} ,$$

where A_1 and A_2 are arbitrary Borel sets of the interval $\Omega = [0, 1]$. We consider the probability distribution $\mathbb{P} = \mathbb{P}(A)$ on $\mathfrak{A}$ defined by

$$\mathbb{P}(A_1 A \cup A_2 A) = \frac{1}{2} [l(A_1) + l(A_2)] .$$

In this case it is impossible to define a conditional probability distribution on $\mathfrak{A}$ with respect to the σ-algebra $\mathfrak{B}$ of all Borel sets.

In fact, if the conditional distribution would exist, then with probability 1 we would have

$$\mathbb{P}(A|\mathfrak{B}) = \begin{cases} 1 & \text{for} \quad \omega \in A , \\ 0 & \text{for} \quad \omega \notin A , \end{cases}$$

which contradicts the measurability of the conditional probability $\mathbb{P}(\mathscr{A}|\mathfrak{B})$ with respect to the σ-algebra $\mathfrak{B}$.

Densities of Conditional Distributions. Bayes' Formula. Let $\xi = \xi(\omega)$ and $\eta = \eta(\omega)$ be random variables on the same space of elementary events Ω with values in the phase spaces $(X, \mathfrak{A})$ and $(Y, \mathfrak{B})$. We assume that the joint probability distribution $\mathbb{P}_{\xi,\eta}(A, B)$ of the random variables ξ and η is absolutely continuous with respect to the measure $\mathbb{Q}$ on the product of the spaces $X \times Y$ which is the product of the measures $\mathbb{Q}_x$ and $\mathbb{Q}_y$:

$$\mathbb{P}_{\xi,\eta}(A, B) = \int_{A \times B} p(x, y) \, \mathbb{Q}(dx \, dy)$$

for any $A \in \mathfrak{A}$ and $B \in \mathfrak{B}$, where $p(x, y)$ is the corresponding *probability density*.

Then the conditional probability distributions $\mathbb{P}_\xi(A|\eta)$, $A \in \mathfrak{A}$, can be chosen so as to take the same value for all $\omega \in \Omega$ for which the random variable $\eta = \eta(\omega)$ takes a given value $\eta(\omega) = y$. For almost all $y \in Y$ with respect to the distribution $\mathbb{P}_\eta$ in the phase space $(Y, \mathfrak{B})$ the conditional probability distribution $\mathbb{P}_\xi(A|y) = \mathbb{P}_{\omega,\xi}(A)$, where $\omega \in \{\eta = y\}$ and $A \in \mathfrak{A}$, is absolutely continuous with respect to the measure Q_X:

$$Q_X(A) = \int\limits_{A \times Y} Q(dx\,dy),$$

and the corresponding *density of the conditional probability distribution* has the form:

$$p_\xi(x|y) = \frac{\mathbb{P}(dx|y)}{Q_X(dx)} = \frac{p(x, y)}{\int\limits_X p(x, y)\,Q_X(dx)}.$$

All statements remain true also with respect to conditional probability distributions $\mathbb{P}_\eta(B|\xi)$, $B \in \mathfrak{B}$. The densities of the conditional distributions are related with each other by the so-called *Bayes formula*

$$p_\eta(y|x) = p_\xi(x|y) \frac{\int\limits_X p(x, y)\,Q_X(dx)}{\int\limits_Y p(x, y)\,Q_Y(dy)}.$$

Suppose that the random variables ξ and Δ are independent and $\eta = \varphi(\xi, \Delta)$ is a function of ξ and Δ. Suppose next that for fixed $x \in X$ the probability distribution $\mathbb{P}(B|x)$, $B \in \mathfrak{B}$ of the random variable $\varphi(x, \Delta)$ has a density $p(x, y)$ with respect to a measure $Q = Q(B)$ in the phase space $(Y, \mathfrak{B})$:

$$\mathbb{P}(B|x) = \int\limits_B p(x, y)\,Q(dy) \quad (B \in \mathfrak{B}),$$

where $\int\limits_X p(x, y)\,\mathbb{P}_\xi(dx) < \infty$ for almost all y with respect to the measure Q. Then the conditional probability distribution $\mathbb{P}_\xi(A|y)$, $A \in \mathfrak{A}$ of the random variable ξ is absolutely continuous with respect to the original distribution $\mathbb{P}_\xi(A)$, $A \in \mathfrak{A}$:

$$\mathbb{P}_\xi(A|y) = \int\limits_A p_\xi(x|y)\,\mathbb{P}_\xi(dx) \quad (A \in \mathfrak{A})$$

for almost all y, and the corresponding conditional density $p_\xi(x|y)$ is given by the formula

$$p_\xi(x|y) = \frac{p(x, y)}{\int\limits_X p(x, y)\,\mathbb{P}_\xi(dx)}.$$

Entropy and Amount of Information. Let $(X, \mathfrak{A})$ be an arbitrary measurable space, and $\mathbb{P}_1$ and $\mathbb{P}_2$ probability measures on the σ-algebra $\mathfrak{A}$ of X. The variable

$$H = \sup \sum_k \mathbb{P}_1(A_k) \log \frac{\mathbb{P}_1(A_k)}{\mathbb{P}_2(A_k)},$$

where the basis of the logarithms is arbitrary and sup is taken for all partitions of X into a countable number of disjoint sets $A_1, A_2, \ldots \in \mathfrak{A}$, is called the *entropy* of the distribution $\mathbb{P}_1$ with respect to $\mathbb{P}_2$; here we set $\mathbb{P}_1(A) \log \dfrac{\mathbb{P}_1(A)}{\mathbb{P}_2(A)} = 0$ if $\mathbb{P}_1(A) = 0$. If the entropy H is finite, then $\mathbb{P}_1$ is absolutely continuous with respect to $\mathbb{P}_2$, and

$$H = \int\limits_X \left(\log \frac{\mathbb{P}_1(dx)}{\mathbb{P}_2(dx)} \right) \mathbb{P}_1(dx),$$

where $\dfrac{\mathbb{P}_1(dx)}{\mathbb{P}_2(dx)}$ denotes the corresponding density.

The entropy H is always non-negative, and $H = 0$ if and only if $\mathbb{P}_1$ and $\mathbb{P}_2$ coincide on the σ-algebra $\mathfrak{A}$. The entropy $H = H(\mathfrak{A})$ considered as a function of the σ-algebra $\mathfrak{A}$, is monotone non-decreasing in the sense that

$$H(\mathfrak{A}_1) \leqq H(\mathfrak{A}_2) \quad \text{for} \quad \mathfrak{A}_1 \subseteq \mathfrak{A}_2 \, .$$

Let $\xi_1 = \xi_1(\omega)$ and $\xi_2 = \xi_2(\omega)$ be arbitrary random variables in the phase spaces $(X_1, \mathfrak{A}_1)$ and $(X_2, \mathfrak{A}_2)$ with probability distributions $\mathbb{P}_1$ and $\mathbb{P}_2$. Let $X = X_1 \times X_2$ be the product of the spaces X_1 and X_2, $\mathbb{P}_{1,2}$ the probability measure on the σ-algebra $\mathfrak{A} = \mathfrak{A}_1 \times \mathfrak{A}_2$ in X which corresponds to the joint probability distribution of the random variables ξ_1 and ξ_2, and $\mathbb{P} = \mathbb{P}_1 \times \mathbb{P}_2$ the product of the probability measures $\mathbb{P}_1$ and $\mathbb{P}_2$. The number

$$I(\xi_1, \xi_2) = H(\mathfrak{A})$$

which equals the entropy $H(\mathfrak{A})$ of the distribution $\mathbb{P}_{1,2}$ with respect to $\mathbb{P}_1 \times \mathbb{P}_2$ is called the *amount of information* about one variable (ξ_1 or ξ_2) which is included in the other variable (ξ_2 or ξ_1, respectively).

Maximal Correlation-Coefficient. Let $\xi_1 = \xi_1(\omega)$ and $\xi_2 = \xi_2(\omega)$ be arbitrary random variables on the space of elementary events $(\Omega, \mathfrak{A}, \mathbb{P})$, and $L_1^2(\Omega)$ and $L_2^2(\Omega)$ the subspaces of the Hilbert space $L^2(\Omega)$ formed by all real random variables η_1 and η_2 that are functions of ξ_1 and ξ_2, respectively. The number

$$r(\xi_1, \xi_2) = \sup \mathbb{M} \eta_1 \eta_2 \, ,$$

where sup is taken for all random variables $\eta_1 \in L_1^2(\Omega)$ and $\eta_2 \in L_2^2(\Omega)$ such that

$$\mathbb{M} \eta_1 = \mathbb{M} \eta_2 = 0, \quad \mathbb{M} \eta_1^2 = \mathbb{M} \eta_2^2 = 1 \, ,$$

is called the *maximal correlation-coefficient* of the random variables ξ_1 and ξ_2. This coefficient $r(\xi_1, \xi_2)$ is equal to zero if and only if the random variables ξ_1 and ξ_2 are independent.

Besides the maximal correlation-coefficient there are other measures of the independence of the random variables ξ_1 and ξ_2, for example the number

$$\alpha(\mathfrak{A}_{\xi_1}, \mathfrak{A}_{\xi_2}) = \sup \mathbb{M}(\eta_{A_1} \eta_{A_2}) = \sup |\mathbb{P}(A_1 A_2) - \mathbb{P}(A_1) \mathbb{P}(A_2)|,$$

where sup is taken for all variables $\eta_{A_1} \in L_1^2(\Omega)$ and $\eta_{A_2} \in L_2^2(\Omega)$ of the form

$$\eta_A = \begin{cases} 1 - \mathbb{P}(A) & \text{for} \quad \omega \in A, \\ -\mathbb{P}(A) & \text{for} \quad \omega \notin A, \end{cases}$$

and the events A_1 and A_2 belong to the corresponding σ-algebras $\mathfrak{A}_{\xi_1}$ and $\mathfrak{A}_{\xi_2}$ generated by the events $\{\xi_1 \in B_1\}$ and $\{\xi_2 \in B_2\}$, respectively, where $B_1 \in \mathfrak{B}_1$ and $B_2 \in \mathfrak{B}_2$ are arbitrary sets in the corresponding phase spaces $(X_1, \mathfrak{B}_1)$ and $(X_2, \mathfrak{B}_2)$ of ξ_1 and ξ_2.

As further measures of independence may serve the numbers

$$\beta(\mathfrak{A}_{\xi_1} | \mathfrak{A}_{\xi_2}) = \sup_{A_1 \in \mathfrak{A}_{\xi_1}} |\mathbb{P}(A_1 | \mathfrak{A}_{\xi_2}) - \mathbb{P}(A_1)|,$$

which depend on the elementary outcomes $\omega \in \Omega$, and the mathematical expectation

$$\bar{\beta} = \mathbb{M} \beta(\mathfrak{A}_{\xi_1} | \mathfrak{A}_{\xi_2}).$$

Here the variable $2\bar{\beta}$ coincides with the variation of the difference of the probability distributions $\mathbb{P}_{\xi_1, \xi_2}$ and $\mathbb{P}_{\xi_1} \times \mathbb{P}_{\xi_2}$ on the σ-algebra $\mathfrak{B} = \mathfrak{B}_1 \times \mathfrak{B}_2$ in the product $X = X_1 \times X_2$ of the phase spaces X_1 and X_2:

$$\bar{\beta}(\mathfrak{A}_{\xi_1}, \mathfrak{A}_{\xi_2}) = \frac{1}{2} \operatorname{Var}\{\mathbb{P}_{\xi_1, \xi_2} - \mathbb{P}_{\xi_1} \times \mathbb{P}_{\xi_2}\}.$$

Regular Random Processes. Let $\xi = \xi(t)$ be a random process on the real line $-\infty < t < \infty$ in an arbitrary phase space $(E, \mathfrak{B})$. By $\mathfrak{A}(s, t)$ we denote the σ-algebra of events generated by all events of the form $\{\xi(u) \in B\}$ where $s \leq u \leq t$ and $B \in \mathfrak{B}$. The random process $\xi = \xi(t)$ is called *regular* if for every event $A \in \mathfrak{A}(t, \infty)$ we have with probability 1

$$\lim_{s \to -\infty} \mathbb{P}(A | \mathfrak{A}(-\infty, s)) = \mathbb{P}(A).$$

The regularity of the random process $\xi(t)$ amounts to the fact that the σ-algebra $\mathfrak{A}^{-\infty} = \bigcap_s \mathfrak{A}(-\infty, s)$ contains only events of probability 0 or 1.

Also, the regularity of the process $\xi(t)$ is equivalent to the fact that

$$\lim_{s\to-\infty} \sup_{A'\in\mathfrak{A}(-\infty,\,s)} |\mathbb{P}(A\,A') - \mathbb{P}(A)\,\mathbb{P}(A')| = 0$$

for any event $A \in \mathfrak{A}(t, \infty)$.

The random process $\xi = \xi(t)$ is said to be *completely regular* if

$$\alpha(s, t) = \sup_{\substack{A\in\mathfrak{A}(t,\,\infty)\\ A'\in\mathfrak{A}(-\infty,\,s)}} |\mathbb{P}(A\,A') - \mathbb{P}(A)\,\mathbb{P}(A')| \to 0$$

for $t - s \to \infty$ uniformly with respect to all s, t.

3. Random Processes and their Probability Distributions

Separable Random Processes. A random process $\xi = \xi(t)$ on a set T of the real line in the topological phase space $(E, \mathfrak{B})$ is called *separable* if there exists a countable set $S_0 \subseteq T$ and an event A_0 of probability 0 such that for all events of the form

$$A(I\,T) = \{\xi(t) \in F \quad \text{for} \quad t \in I\,T\},$$

where F is a closed set in E and I an interval on the real line, the difference $A(I\,S_0) \backslash A(I\,T)$ is contained in the event A_0:

$$A(I\,S_0) \backslash A(I\,T) \subseteq A_0, \qquad \mathbb{P}(A_0) = 0;$$

we call S_0 a *set of separability*.

Not every random process is separable.

Example. Let $\tau = \tau(\omega)$ be a random variable which is uniformly distributed in the interval $[0, 1]$ and $\xi = \xi(t)$ the random process on the interval $T = [0, 1]$ given by

$$\xi(\omega, t) = \begin{cases} 1 & \text{for} \quad \tau(\omega) = t, \\ 0 & \text{for} \quad \tau(\omega) \neq t. \end{cases}$$

In this case we have for any countable set $S \subseteq T$:

$$\mathbb{P}\{\xi(t) = 0 \quad \text{for} \quad t \in S\} = 1$$

whereas

$$\mathbb{P}\{\xi(t) = 0 \quad \text{for} \quad t \in T\} = 0.$$

Suppose that the phase space $(E, \mathfrak{B})$ is compact with a countable basis. Then for any random process $\xi = \xi(t)$ there exists in this space an equivalent separable random process $\tilde{\xi} = \tilde{\xi}(t)$. The existence of $\tilde{\xi} = \tilde{\xi}(t)$

is true also under conditions which are weaker than the conditions of compactness of the phase space [16].

Directly Given Separable Processes. Consider a compact phase space $(E, \mathfrak{B})$ with a countable basis of open sets and a directly given random process $\xi = \xi(t)$ in $(E, \mathfrak{B})$ in an interval T of the real line for which the corresponding probability distribution $\mathbb{P} = \mathbb{P}_\xi$ in the function space $X = E^T$ is a regular Borel measure. For each set $A \subseteq X$ we define the set $A(S)$, $S \subseteq T$ as the set of all functions $x = x(t)$ which coincide for $t \in S$ with some function $x' = x'(t)$ from A. Then the following is true [17]: for any Borel set $A \subseteq X$ of the type $F_{\sigma\delta}$ there exists a countable set $S \subseteq T$ such that

$$\mathbb{P}\{A(S)\backslash A\} = 0.$$

We introduce the directly separable random process $\xi = \xi(t)$ defined by

$$\xi(x, t) = x(t) \quad (x \in X).$$

In the separable phase space E there exists a countable number of closed sets $F \subseteq E$ such that any closed set E is the intersection of certain sets F. We select such a set F and an interval I with rational endpoints and set

$$A(I\,T) = \{x(t) \in F \quad \text{for} \quad t \in I\,T\}.$$

This is a closed set in the functional space $X = E^T$, and there exists a denumerable set $S \subseteq T$ *such that*

$$\mathbb{P}\{A(I\,S)\backslash A(I\,T)\} = 0.$$

If we set

$$S_0 = \cup S, \quad A_0 = \cup\{A(I\,S)\backslash A(I\,T)\},$$

where the union is taken with respect to all F and I, described above, then the denumerable set S_0 and the set $A_0 \subseteq X$ of probability 0 will satisfy the conditions stipulated in the definition of a separable process.

Measurable and Continuous Random Processes. Let $(\Omega, \mathfrak{A}, \mathbb{P})$ be an arbitrary space of elementary events and T a measurable set on the real line with a σ-algebra of measurable subsets. A random process $\xi = \xi(t)$ on T with values in the phase space $(E, \mathfrak{B})$ is called *measurable* if the function $\xi = \xi(\omega, t)$ of the two variables (ω, t) is measurable when considered as a function on the measurable space $\Omega \times T$ with values in the measurable space $(E, \mathfrak{B})$.

---

[16] *Čentzov, N. N.,* Doob sets and Doob probability distributions. Trudy of the VI Union Conference on Probability Theory and Mathematical Statistics. Vilnius, 1962, 483—493 (Russian).

[17] *Nelson, E.,* Regular probability measures on function space. Ann. Math., (1959), 630—643.

Not every random process is measurable. For example, the directly given real random process $\xi = \xi(t)$ on the interval $T = [a, b]$, that is $\xi(x, t) = x(t)$, $x \in X$, where X is the space of all real functions $x = x(t)$, $t \in T$, is not measurable.

Suppose that the phase space $(E, \mathfrak{B})$ is compact with a countable basis of open sets, that T is a Borel set on the real line with the σ-algebra of all its Borel subsets, and the random process $\xi = \xi(t)$ is stochastically continuous, that is, for every $\varepsilon > 0$ we have

$$\lim_{s \to t} \mathbb{P}\{\varrho[\xi(s), \xi(t)] > \varepsilon\} = 0$$

for all $t \in T$, where $\varrho(\cdot, \cdot)$ denotes the distance between points of the phase space E. Then there exists a separable measurable random process $\tilde{\xi} = \tilde{\xi}(t)$ which is equivalent to the process $\xi = \xi(t)$. In this case any set S_0 which is dense in T is a set of separability of the process $\tilde{\xi} = \tilde{\xi}(t)$.

Let $\xi = \xi(t)$ be a separable random process. Then the event A which consists in the discontinuity of the trajectory of the process $\xi(\omega, t)$, $t \in T$, at a fixed point t_0 has a well-defined probability; in fact it belongs to the σ-algebra of events $\mathfrak{A}$ where the probability measure $\mathbb{P}$ is defined. If this probability is positive, that is, $\mathbb{P}(A) > 0$, then the point t_0 is called a *fixed point of discontinuity*. Let $\mu = \mu(\Delta)$ be a measure on the σ-algebra of the measurable subsets of T. By Δ_0 we denote the set of all fixed points of discontinuity of the random process $\xi = \xi(t)$. If $\mu(\Delta_0) = 0$, then the random process $\xi = \xi(t)$ is measurable. Moreover, with probability 1 its trajectories are continuous functions of the parameter $t \in T$ almost everywhere with respect to the measure μ.

A random process $\xi = \xi(t)$ in a topological phase space E is called *continuous with probability* 1 if for almost all elementary outcomes $\omega \in \Omega$ its trajectories $\xi(\omega, t)$, $t \in T$ are continuous functions on T. In the case of separable processes the continuity on T is equal to the continuity on a countable dense subset $S_0 \subseteq T$.

Suppose that we are given a separable random process $\xi = \xi(t)$ on the interval $T = [a, b]$ in a complete metric space E with the following property: there exist positive constants α, ε and such that

$$\mathbb{M}\varrho[\xi(s), \xi(t)]^\alpha \leq C(t - s)^{1 + \varepsilon}$$

for any $s \leq t$ where $\mathbb{M}$ means expectation and $\varrho(\cdot, \cdot)$ denotes the distance between points of the phase space E. Then the random process $\xi(t)$ is continuous with probability 1.

Example. Let $\tau = \tau(\omega)$ be a random variable which is uniformly distributed on the interval $T = [a, b]$ and $\xi = \xi(t)$ the random process

8*

with the trajectories

$$\xi(\omega, t) = \begin{cases} 0 & \text{for} \quad t < \tau(\omega), \\ 1 & \text{for} \quad t \geq \tau(\omega). \end{cases}$$

For any $s \leq t$

$$\mathbb{M} |\xi(s) - \xi(t)|^\alpha = \mathbb{P} \{s \leq \tau \leq t\} = t - s.$$

At the same time each trajectory $\xi(\omega, t)$, $t \in T$ of this process is discontinuous at the point $\tau = \tau(\omega)$.

Let E be a compact space with a countable basis. Then the set $C(T)$ of all continuous functions $x = x(t)$ on the interval $T = [a, b]$ with values in E is a set of type $F_{\sigma\delta}$ in the functional space $X = E^T$:

$$C(T) = \bigcap_{m=1}^\infty \bigcup_{n=1}^\infty \bigcap_{|t-s| \leq \frac{1}{n}} \left\{ \varrho[x(s), x(t)] \leq \frac{1}{m} \right\}.$$

If the probability distribution $\mathbb{P}$ in X is a regular Borel measure, then there exists a countable set $S \subseteq T$ such that

$$\mathbb{P} \{C(S) \backslash C(T)\} = 0,$$

where $C(S)$ is the set of all functions $x = x(t)$ which are continuous at all points $t \in S$.

Suppose that for some positive constants $\alpha_1, \alpha_2, \varepsilon$ and C the inequality

$$\mathbb{M} \{\varrho[\xi(s), \xi(u)]^{\alpha_1} \cdot \varrho[\xi(u), \xi(t)]^{\alpha_2}\} \leq C(t - s)^{1 + \varepsilon} \quad (s \leq u \leq t),$$

is satisfied. Then with probability 1 the random process $\xi = \xi(t)$ has only discontinuities of the first kind, that is, for almost all elementary outcomes $\omega \in \Omega$ the trajectories $\xi(\omega, t)$, $t \in T$ are functions which have only discontinuity of the first kind, in other words, the one-sided limits

$$\lim_{s \to t - 0} \xi(\omega, s) \quad \text{and} \quad \lim_{s \to t + 0} \xi(\omega, s).$$

exist at any t.

Let the phase space E be compact with a countable basis. Then the set $D(T)$ of all functions $x = x(t)$ on the interval $T = [a, b]$ with values in the phase space E which have only discontinuities of the first kind is a set of type $F_{\sigma\delta}$ in the functional space $X = E^T$:

$$D(T) = \bigcap_{m=1}^\infty \bigcup_{n=1}^\infty \bigcap_{\substack{|t-s| \leq \frac{1}{n} \\ s \leq u \leq t}} \left\{ \min(\varrho[x(s), x(u)], \varrho[x(u), x(t)]) \leq \frac{1}{m} \right\}.$$

If the probability distribution $\mathbb{P}$ in X is a regular Borel measure then there exists a denumerable set $S \subseteq T$ such that

$$\mathbb{P}\{D(S)\backslash D(T)\} = 0,$$

where $D(S)$ is the set of all functions $x = x(t)$ which have only discontinuities of the first kind in S.

First Exit Times. Let E be a topological space, and $X = E^T$ the space of all functions $x = x(t)$ on the finite interval $T = [a, b]$ with values in E.

Let $x = x(t)$ be a function on $[a, b]$ with values in E, $x^{(a,t)}$ the set of all values $x(s)$ on the interval $a \leq s \leq t$, and $[x^{(a,t)}]$ the closure of this set. Given a set $B \subseteq X$, the variable $\tau = \tau_B$ which equals the least upper bound of all t for which $x^{(a,t)}$ is contained in B, is called the *first exit time* from the set $B \subseteq E$; τ is also termed the *first reaching time* of the complementary set $E \backslash B$.

The variable $\bar{\tau}$ defined as the least upper bound of all t for which the set $[x^{(a,t)}]$ is contained in B is called the *first exit time* from inside of B. The variables τ and $\bar{\tau}$ coincide for closed sets B.

If the function $x = x(t)$ is continuous, then the variables τ_B and $\bar{\tau}_B$ coincide for any set B, since $x^{(a,b)} = [x^{(a,b)}]$.

By the symbol $\{[x^{(a,b)}] \subseteq B\}$ we denote the set of all $x = x(t)$ for which $[x^{(a,b)}] \subseteq B$. Let E be compact with a countable basis of open sets. If B is a closed set, then $\{[x^{(a,b)}] \subseteq B\}$ is a closed set in the Tihonov product $X = E^T$; if, however, B is open then $\{[x^{(a,b)}] \subseteq B\}$ is a set of the type F_σ.

Let $\mathbb{P}$ be a regular Borel distribution in the function space $X = E^T$. Then for any Borel set $B \in \mathfrak{B}$ we have

$$\mathbb{P}\{|x^{(a,t)}| \subseteq B\} = \sup \mathbb{P}\{|x^{(a,t)}| \subseteq F\} = \inf \mathbb{P}\{|x^{(a,t)}| \subseteq G\},$$

where sup is taken for all closed sets $F \subseteq B$, and inf for all open sets $G \supseteq B$.

Let $\xi = \xi(t)$ be a random process on the interval $T = [a, b]$ in the topological phase space E. For each elementary outcome $\omega \in \Omega$ we define $\tau_B = \tau_B(\omega)$ as the first exit time from B of the trajectory $\xi(\omega, t)$, and $\bar{\tau}_B = \bar{\tau}_B(\omega)$ as the first exit time from inside of B. Suppose that the phase space E is compact with a countable basis and let $\mathfrak{A}(T)$ be the σ-algebra of events in Ω generated by all events of the form $\{\xi(t) \in B\}$ where $t \in T$ and B is a Borel set in E.

The probability distribution $\mathbb{P}_\xi$ of the random process $\xi = \xi(t)$ can always be extended to a regular Borel measure in the function space $X = E^T$. If on $T = [a, b]$ the set $\xi(\Omega)$ of all trajectories $\xi(\omega, t)$ of this process is measurable, then the probability distribution $\mathbb{P}$ on the σ-algebra

$\mathfrak{A}(T)$ can be extended in such a way that the probabilities of all events $\{\xi \in A\}$ are well-defined, that is to say, the probability of any event which consists in that the trajectory $\xi(\omega, t)$ belongs to a certain Borel set A in the function space $X = E^T$.

In particular, for any Borel set B in the phase space E the first exit time $\bar{\tau} = \bar{\tau}(\omega)$ from inside of B is a measurable function on the space of the elementary events Ω, and

$$\{\bar{\tau}_B > t\} = \{[\xi^{(a,t)}] \subseteq B\} \quad (t \in T).$$

If the random process $\xi = \xi(t)$ is not measurable, then the function $\xi(\omega, \tau(\omega))$ of ω needs not be measurable.

Example. Let τ be an exponentially distributed random variable:

$$\mathbb{P}\{\tau > t\} = e^{-\lambda t} \quad (t \geq 0).$$

We define the random processes $\xi_1 = \xi_1(t)$ and $\xi_2 = \xi_2(t)$ by

$$\xi_1(t) = \begin{cases} 0 & \text{for} \quad 0 \leq t \leq \tau, \\ 1 & \text{for} \quad t > \tau; \end{cases} \qquad \xi_2(t) = \begin{cases} 0 & \text{for} \quad 0 \leq t < \tau, \\ 1 & \text{for} \quad t \geq \tau. \end{cases}$$

The finite-dimensional distributions of these processes coincide. Therefore the corresponding regular Borel probability distributions $\mathbb{P}_1$ and $\mathbb{P}_2$ on the Tihonov product $X = E^{[0, \infty]}$, that is, on the space of all real functions $x = x(t)$ on the half-line $[0, \infty]$ with values in E, also coincide. Let $\xi = \xi(t)$ be the directly given random process: $\xi(x, t) = x(t)$, $x \in X$, and $\tau = \tau(x)$ the first exit time from the point 0. Suppose that the set $\{\xi(x, \tau) = 0\}$ were measurable. Then, obviously

$$\mathbb{P}_1\{\xi(x, \tau) = 0\} = 1, \quad \mathbb{P}_2\{\xi(x, \tau) = 0\} = 0.$$

Since, however, the Borel measure P_1 and P_2 coincide, we should have

$$\mathbb{P}_1\{\xi(x, \tau) = 0\}, \qquad \mathbb{P}_2\{\xi(x, \tau) = 0\}.$$

This contradiction shows that the set $\{\xi(\tau, x) = 0\}$ is actually not measurable.

If the random process $\xi = \xi(t)$ is measurable, more precisely if $\xi(\omega, t)$ is a measurable function on the product $\Omega \times T$ where the interval T is endowed with the σ-algebra of all Borel sets, then for any random variable $\tau = \tau(\omega)$, $\tau \in T$ the function $\xi(\omega, \tau)$ of ω is a random variable, too. This is true, for example, if the random process $\xi = \xi(t)$ is continuous with probability 1.

§ 2. Basic Types of Random Processes

1. Random Processes Considered as Curves in Hilbert Space

The Covariance Function. Let $\xi = \xi(t)$ be a real or complex random process on a set T with finite second moments: $M|\xi(t)|^2 < \infty$. If we do not distinguish between random variables which differ only with probability zero, then the value of the process $\xi(t)$ can be considered as elements of the Hilbert space $L^2(\Omega)$, that is, the space of all random variables η with $M|\eta|^2 < \infty$ endowed with the scalar product

$$(\eta_1, \eta_2) = M \eta_1 \bar{\eta}_2 .$$

Important characteristics of such a random process $\xi(t)$ are its *mathematical expectation*

$$A(t) = M \xi(t) = (\xi(t), 1)$$

and *covariance function*

$$B(s, t) = M \xi(s), \overline{\xi(t)} = (\xi(s), \xi(t)) .$$

Instead of the covariance function we may consider the correlation function $B(s, t) = M \xi(s) \overline{\xi(t)} - A(s) \overline{A(t)}$ which is the covariance function of the process $\xi(t) - A(t)$ with expectation zero.

A function $B(s, t)$ of two variables s and t is the covariance function of some random process $\xi(t)$, $M|\xi(t)|^2 < \infty$, if and only if it satisfies for any $n = 1, 2, \ldots$ the condition to be positive definite:

$$\sum_{k=1}^{n} \sum_{j=1}^{n} B(t_k, t_j) c_k \bar{c}_j \geq 0$$

for all $t_1, t_2, \ldots, t_n \in T$ and all complex numbers $c_1, \ldots, c_n$.

Canonical Representations. We often use canonical decompositions of various kind when studying a random process $\xi = \xi(t)$ considered as a function of the parameter $t \in T$ with values in the Hilbert space $L^2(\Omega)$. By a *canonical representation of the random process $\xi(t)$* we mean a representation in the form

$$\xi(t) = \int_{\Lambda} \varphi(t, \lambda) \, \Phi(d\lambda) \quad (t \in T),$$

where Λ is a measurable space with some σ-algebra of measurable sets, $\Phi = \Phi(\Delta)$ a generalized orthogonal measure on Δ with values in the Hilbert space $L^2(\Omega)$, and $\varphi(t, \lambda)$ a family of functions of the variable $\lambda \in \Lambda$ which depend on the parameter $t \in T$. The orthogonality of the measure $\Phi = \Phi(\Delta)$ means that

$$M \Phi(\Delta_1) \overline{\Phi(\Delta_2)} = 0$$

for any two disjoint measurable sets Δ_1 and Δ_2 of the space Λ.

The equation

$$F(\Delta) = \mathbb{M}|\Phi(\Delta)|^2$$

defines a σ-finite measure $F = F(\Delta)$ on the measurable sets Δ of the space Λ under consideration such that the covariance function $B = B(s, t)$ of the random process $\xi = \xi(t)$ given by the canonical representation above is expressed by the formula

$$B(s, t) = \int_\Lambda (s, \lambda)\, \overline{\varphi(t, \lambda)}\, F(d\lambda).$$

A representation of the covariance function $B = B(s, t)$ of this kind can serve as the starting point for the construction of the corresponding canonical representation of the random process $\xi = \xi(t)$ itself. In fact, let $L^2(\Lambda)$ be the Hilbert space of all measurable real or complex functions $\varphi = \varphi(\lambda)$ on the space Λ with the scalar product

$$(\varphi_1, \varphi_2) = \int_\Lambda \varphi_1(\lambda)\, \overline{\varphi_2(\lambda)}\, F(d\lambda).$$

Let U be an operator which sends the element $\varphi(t, \lambda)$ of the space $L^2(\Lambda)$ into the elements $\xi(t)$ of the space $L^2(\Omega)$, that is,

$$\xi(t) = U\, \varphi(t, \lambda) \qquad (t \in T).$$

This operator U is *isometric*. If we assume, in addition, that the dimension of the space $L^2(\Lambda)$ equals at least the dimension of $L^2(\Lambda)$, then U can be extended to an isometric operator on the entire space $L^2(\Lambda)$. Therefore

$$\Phi(\Delta) = U\, \varphi_\Delta(\lambda), \quad \varphi_\Delta(\lambda) = \begin{cases} 1 & \text{for} \quad \lambda \in \Delta, \\ 0 & \text{for} \quad \lambda \notin \Delta, \end{cases}$$

will be a generalized orthogonal measure on the measurable sets Δ of the space Λ with values in $L^2(\Omega)$ such that

$$\xi(t) = \int_\Lambda \varphi(t, \lambda)\, \Phi(d\lambda).$$

Example. Let $\xi = \xi(t)$ be a random process on the interval $T = [a, b]$ with a continuous covariance function $B = B(t, s)$. In the Hilbert space $L^2[a, b]$ of all functions $\varphi = \varphi(t)$ with the scalar product

$$(\varphi_1\, \varphi_2) = \int_a^b \varphi_1(t)\, \overline{\varphi_2(t)}\, dt$$

the relation

$$B\varphi(t) = \int_a^b B(t, s)\, \varphi(s)\, ds \qquad (t \in T)$$

defines a *positive nuclear operator*. Let $\varphi(t, \lambda)$, $\lambda \in \Lambda$ be a complete orthonormal system of eigenelements $\varphi(t, \lambda)$ with eigenvalues λ where λ runs through a denumerable set Λ. Then

$$B(s, t) = \sum_{\lambda \in \Lambda} \varphi(s, \lambda) \overline{\varphi(t, \lambda)} \lambda = \int_\Lambda \varphi(s, \lambda) \varphi(t, \lambda) F(d\lambda)$$

where F is the following finite measure on the denumerable set Λ: $F(\lambda) = \lambda$ for all $\lambda \in \Lambda$. Correspondingly, the random process $\xi(t)$ itself can be presented as a sum

$$\xi(t) = \sum_{\lambda \in \Lambda} \varphi(t, \lambda) \Phi(\lambda), \quad \Phi(\lambda) = \int_a^b \xi(t) \varphi(t, \lambda) dt,$$

where the $\Phi(\lambda)$ are orthogonal random variables:

$$M \Phi(\lambda_1) \overline{\Phi(\lambda_2)} = 0 \quad \text{for} \quad \lambda_1 \neq \lambda_2, \quad \text{and} \quad M |\Phi(\lambda)|^2 = \lambda .$$

Besides the canonical representations we can also use more general representations

$$\xi(t) = \int_\Lambda \varphi(t, \lambda) \Phi(d\lambda),$$

where the generalized measure Φ need not be orthogonal. Such a representation is closely connected with the corresponding representation of the covariance function:

$$B(s, t) = \int_\Lambda \int_\Lambda \varphi(\lambda, s) \overline{\varphi(\mu, t)} F(d\lambda, d\mu),$$

where $F(d\lambda, d\mu)$ is a measure of bounded variation which takes, in general, complex values such that

$$F(d\lambda, d\mu) = M \Phi(d\lambda) \overline{\Phi(d\mu)} .$$

If the linear space spanned by the functions $\varphi(\lambda, t)$ where the parameter t runs through the set T, is dense in the functional Hilbert space $L^2(\Lambda)$ with the scalar product

$$(\varphi, \psi) = \int_R \int_R \varphi(\lambda) \overline{\psi(\mu)} F(d\lambda, d\mu),$$

then for any measurable set $\Delta \subseteq \Lambda$ the value of the generalized measure $\Phi(\Delta)$ belongs to the close linear space H generated by the values of the process $\xi(t)$, $t \in T$, under consideration. Moreover

$$\Phi(\Delta) = \lim \sum_t c(t) \xi(t)$$

for any sequence of variables $\Sigma\, c(t)\, \xi(t)$ such that the corresponding sequence of functions $\Sigma\, c(t)\, \varphi(\lambda, t)$ converges in $L^2(\Lambda)$ to the function

$$\varphi_\Lambda(\lambda) = \begin{cases} 1 & \text{for} \quad \lambda \in \Lambda, \\ 0 & \text{for} \quad \lambda \notin \Lambda. \end{cases}$$

Linearly Regular Processes. Let $\xi(t)$ be a random process on the real line $-\infty < t < \infty$, $\mathbb{M}\,|\xi(t)|^2 < \infty$ and $\mathbb{M}\,\xi(t) = 0$. By the symbol $H(s, t)$ we denote the closed linear space spanned by the values $\xi(u)$, $s \leq u \leq t$, which we consider as elements of the Hilbert space $L^2(\Omega)$. The random process $\xi = \xi(t)$ is called *linearly regular* if

$$\bigcap_t H(-\infty, t) = 0.$$

The random process $\xi = \xi(t)$ with "discrete time" t, that is, where t runs through the integers only, is linearly regular if and only if it can be written in the following form:

$$\xi(t) = \sum_{s=-\infty}^{t} \varphi(t, s)\, \Phi(s),$$

where $\Phi = \Phi(s)$ is a sequence of uncorrelated random variables with values in the Hilbert space H, $\Phi(t) \in H(-\infty, t)$ for all t, and $\varphi(t, s)$ is a sequence of numbers such that for each t

$$\sum_{s=-\infty}^{t} |\varphi(t, s)|^2\, F(s) < \infty \quad \text{where} \quad F(s) = \mathbb{M}\,|\Phi(s)|^2.$$

The same is true also in the case of a "continuous time" t, that is, if t takes all real values, provided that the space H is separable. In fact, the random process $\xi = \xi(t)$ is linearly regular if and only if it can be represented in the following form:

$$\xi(t) = \sum_{k=1}^{N} \int_{-\infty}^{t} \varphi_k(t, s)\, \Phi_k(ds).$$

Here, the number N may be finite or infinite, $\Phi_k(ds)$ is for each k a generalized orthogonal measure with values in the Hilbert space H such that

$$\mathbb{M}\,|\Phi_k(\Delta)|^2 = F_k(\Delta),$$

and if the sets Δ_1 and Δ_2 are disjoint, then

$$\mathbb{M}\,\Phi_k(\Delta_1)\, \overline{\Phi_k(\Delta_2)} = 0.$$

Moreover, $\Phi_k(\Delta) \in H(-\infty, t)$ for any measurable set Δ included in the interval $[-\infty, t]$. If $k \neq j$ we have

$$\mathbb{M}\,\Phi_k(\Delta_1)\, \overline{\Phi_j(\Delta_2)} = 0$$

for all measurable sets Δ_1 and Δ_2. Finally for each t

$$\sum_{k=1}^{N} \int_{-\infty}^{t} |\varphi(t, s)|^2 F_k(ds) < \infty .$$

Such a representation is unique and is called the *regular canonical representation* of the process $\xi(t)$.

For any finite or countable number N and any family of measures $F_k(dt)$, $k = 1, 2, ..., N$, there exists a linearly-regular random process $\xi(t)$, $t \in T$ with the same number N and measures $F_k(dt)$ appearing in its regular canonical representation[18].

Stationary Random Processes. A random process $\xi(t)$ on the real line $-\infty < t < \infty$ with $M|\xi(t)|^2 < \infty$ is called *stationary in the wide sense* if its expectation $A(t)$ and covariance function $B(s, t)$ do not change under a shift of the parameters, that is, the function $A(t)$ is constant and the function $B(s, t)$ depends only on the difference $t - s$:

$$B(s, t) = B(t - s) .$$

Sometimes the process is also called stationary if only its covariance function is invariant under any shift of the parameter t.

The stationarity of the process $\xi = \xi(t)$ considered as a function with values in the Hilbert space $L^2(\Omega)$ amounts to the fact that the scalar product

$$(\xi(s), \xi(t)) = B(t - s)$$

depends only on the difference $t - s$. This is equivalent to the following: there exists in the closed linear subspace H spanned by the variables $\xi(t)$, $-\infty < t < \infty$, in the Hilbert space $L^2(\Omega)$ a group of unitary operators U_s which satisfy the relation

$$U_s \xi(t) = \xi(t + s) \quad (-\infty < s, t < \infty) .$$

Any process $\xi(t)$, $-\infty < t < \infty$ that is stationary in the wide sense can be represented as a function with values in the Hilbert space H given by an equation

$$\xi(t) = U_t \xi(0) \quad (-\infty < t < \infty),$$

where U_t is a group of unitary operators in H and $U_0 = I$ the identity operator:

$$U_{t_1} \cdot U_{t_2} = U_{t_1 + t_2} .$$

[18] *Cramér, H.*, Stochastic processes as curves in Hilbert space. Teor. Verojat. i jejo prim. IX., **2** (1954), 193–204.

Every stationary process $\xi(t)$ with a continuous covariance function admits a so-called *spectral representation* of the form

$$\xi(t) = \int_{-\infty}^{\infty} e^{i\lambda t} \, \Phi(d\lambda)$$

where Φ is a generalized measure on the real line $-\infty < \lambda < \infty$ with values in the Hilbert space H such that for disjoint measurable sets Δ_1 and Δ_2 we have

$$\left(\Phi(\Delta_1), \Phi(\Delta_2)\right) = \mathbb{M} \, \Phi(\Delta_1) \, \overline{\Phi(\Delta_2)} = 0 \, .$$

The orthogonal measure Φ is defined on the σ-algebra of all sets which are measurable with respect to the non-negative bounded measure $F(\Delta) = \mathbb{M}|\Phi(\Delta)|^2$. The measure $F(\Delta)$ is called the *spectral measure* of the stationary process $\xi(t)$, and is connected with the covariance function $B(t)$ by the relation

$$B(t) = \int_{-\infty}^{\infty} e^{i\lambda t} \, F(d\lambda) \, .$$

A linearly regular stationary process $\xi(t)$ admits a regular representation of the form

$$\xi(t) = \int_{-\infty}^{t} c(t-s) \, \eta(ds) \, ,$$

where $\eta = \eta(\Delta)$ is a generalized orthogonal measure on the real line $-\infty < t < \infty$ with values in the Hilbert space H such that

$$\eta(\Delta) \in H(-\infty, t)$$
$$\mathbb{M}|\eta(\Delta)|^2 = t - s \quad \text{for} \quad \Delta = (s, t) \, .$$

Here as before $H(s, t)$ denotes the closed linear space generated by the values $\xi(u)$, $s \leq u \leq t$.

Generalized Random Processes. Let $\xi = \langle u, \xi \rangle$ be a generalized random process on a linear space U such that $\mathbb{M}|\langle u, \xi \rangle|^2 < \infty$ for all $u \in U$. Such a process $\xi = \langle u, \xi \rangle$ can be considered as a function on U with values in the Hilbert space $L^2(\Omega)$. The functional

$$A(u) = \mathbb{M}\langle u, \xi \rangle \qquad (u \in U)$$

is called the mathematical *expectation* and the functional

$$B(u, v) = \mathbb{M}\{\langle u, \xi \rangle \langle \overline{v, \xi} \rangle\} \qquad u, v \in U)$$

the *covariance functional* of the generalized process $\xi = \langle u, \xi \rangle$.

Let U be the space of all infinitely differentiable functions $u = u(t)$ on the real line $-\infty < t < \infty$ which vanish outside some finite interval. The expectation $A(u)$ and the covariance functional $B(u, v)$ of the generalized process $\xi = \langle u, \xi \rangle$ on this space are usually assumed to be continuous in the sense that

$$A(u_n) \to A(u),$$
$$B(u_n, v_n) \to B(u, v)$$

if for $n \to \infty$ the corresponding sequences of functions $u_n = u_n(t)$ and $v_n = v_n(t)$ converge to the limits $u = u(t)$ and $v = v(t)$, respectively. Here we say that $u_n \to u$ if all functions $u_n(t)$ vanish outside a finite interval, and if the derivatives $u_n^{(p)}(t)$, $p = 1, 2, \ldots$ converge uniformly to the corresponding derivatives $u^{(p)}(t)$ of the limit function $u(t)$.

Let S_t be the *shift transformation* which sends the function $u = u(s)$ into the function $S_t u = u(s + t)$, $-\infty < s < \infty$. The generalized random process $\xi = \langle u, \xi \rangle$ with expectation $A(u)$ and covariance functional $B(u, v)$ is called *stationary in the wide sense* if

$$A(S_t u) = A(u),$$
$$B(S_t u, S_t v) = B(u, v)$$

for any t and $u, v \in U$.

The expectation of such a process is a constant

$$A(u) = a \int_{-\infty}^{\infty} u(t)\, dt,$$

and if we assume the covariance functional to be continuous, it can be written in the form

$$B(u, v) = \int_{-\infty}^{\infty} \tilde{u}(\lambda)\, \overline{\tilde{v}(\lambda)}\, F(d\lambda),$$

where $F = F(\Delta)$ is the so-called spectral measure and $\tilde{u}(\lambda) = \int_{-\infty}^{\infty} e^{i\lambda t} u(t)\, dt$ the Fourier-transform of the function $u \in U$. The generalized stationary process $\xi = \langle u, \xi \rangle$ itself can be represented in the form

$$\langle u, \xi \rangle = \int_{-\infty}^{\infty} \tilde{u}(\lambda)\, \Phi(d\lambda),$$

where $\Phi = \Phi(\Delta)$ is a generalized orthogonal measure on the line $-\infty < \lambda < \infty$ with values in the Hilbert space $L^2(\Omega)$. The generalized measure $\Phi = \Phi(\Delta)$ is defined on the σ-algebra of the sets that are measurable with respect to the σ-finite measure $F = F(\Delta) = \mathbb{M}|\Phi(\Delta)|^2$. The measure $F(\Delta)$ is called the *spectral measure* of the stationary process

$\xi = \langle u, \xi \rangle$. It satisfies the condition

$$\int_{-\infty}^{\infty} (1 + \lambda^2)^{-p} F(d\lambda) < \infty$$

for some finite p. The canonical representation described here is called the *spectral representation* of the generalized stationary process $\xi = \langle u, \xi \rangle$.

2. Gaussian Random Processes

The real random variable ξ is called *Gaussian* if its *characteristic function* $\varphi = \varphi(u)$ has the form

$$\varphi(u) = \exp\left\{ iau - \frac{1}{2}\sigma^2 u^2 \right\}.$$

The parameters a and σ^2 appearing here admit a simple probabilistic interpretation: $a = \mathbb{M}\xi$, $\sigma^2 = \mathbb{D}\xi$. The corresponding probability distribution is also called a *Gaussian* distribution; it is derived from the density

$$p(x) = \frac{1}{\sqrt{2\pi}\,\sigma} \exp\left\{ -\frac{(x-a)^2}{2\sigma^2} \right\}.$$

Random variables $(\xi_1, \ldots, \xi_n)$ are called *Gaussian* if the characteristic function of their joint distribution has the form

$$\varphi(u_1, \ldots, u_n) = \exp\left\{ i \sum_{k=1}^{n} a_k u_k - \frac{1}{2} \sum_{k,j=1}^{n} b_{kj} u_k u_j \right\}.$$

The parameters appearing here are equal to

$$a_k = \mathbb{M}\xi_k, \quad b_{kj} = \mathbb{M}(\xi_k - a_k)(\xi_j - a_j) \quad (k, j = 1, \ldots, n).$$

If the matrix $b = (b_{kj})$ is *non-degenerate*, then the corresponding joint distribution of the variables $\xi_1, \ldots, \xi_n$ is given by a density of the form

$$p(x_1, \ldots, x_n) = \frac{(\det c)^{\frac{1}{2}}}{(2\pi)^{\frac{n}{2}}} \exp\left\{ -\frac{1}{2} \sum_{k,j=1}^{n} c_{kj}(x_k - a_k)(x_j - a_j) \right\}$$

where the matrix $c = (c_{kj})$ with determinant $\det c$ is the inverse of the matrix $b = (b_{kj})$. The joint probability distribution of any variables $\eta_1, \ldots, \eta_m$ which are linear combinations of $\xi_1, \ldots, \xi_n$ is again Gaussian.

A real random process $\xi = \xi(t)$ is called *Gaussian* if the finite-dimensional distributions $\mathbb{P}_{t_1, \ldots, t_n}$ are Gaussian, that is, if the characteristic functions of the joint distributions of the values $\xi_1(t), \ldots, \xi(t_n)$ of this random process have the form

$$\varphi_{t_1,\ldots,t_n}(u_1, \ldots, u_n) = \exp\left\{ i \sum_{k=1}^{n} A(t_k)\, u_k - \frac{1}{2} \sum_{k,j=1}^{n} B(t_k, t_j)\, u_k u_j \right\}.$$

where $A(t) = \mathbb{M}\,\xi(t)$ is the expectation and

$$B(t, s) = \mathbb{M}[\xi(t) - A(t)]\,[\xi(s) - A(s)]$$

the correlation-function.

The probability distribution of a Gaussian process $\xi = \xi(t)$ is completely determined by the following data: the expectation $A(t)$ and correlation function $B(t, s)$, $t, s \in T$. Given any such functions $A(t)$ and $B(t, s)$ there exists a directly given Gaussian random process $\xi = \xi(t)$ such that

$$A(t) = \mathbb{M}\,\xi(t) \quad \text{and} \quad B(t, s) = \mathbb{M}[\xi(t) - A(t)]\,[\xi(s) - A(s)]\,.$$

Generalized Gaussian Processes. The real generalized random process $\xi = \langle u, \xi \rangle$ on the linear space U is called a *Gaussian process* if its characteristic functional $\varphi_\xi = \varphi_\xi(u)$ has the form

$$\varphi_\xi(u) = e^{i\, A(u) - \frac{1}{2} B(u, v)}\,,$$

where $A(u) = \mathbb{M}\langle u, \xi \rangle$ is the *expectation* of the generalized process $\xi = \langle u, \xi \rangle$ and

$$B(u, v) = \mathbb{M}[\langle u, \xi \rangle - A(u)]\,[\langle v, \xi \rangle - A(v)]$$

its *correlation functional*. This is *equivalent* to the fact that all random variables $\langle u, \xi \rangle$, $u \in U$ have a Gaussian probability distribution.

Let U be a denumerably Hilbert space with the scalar products $(u, v)_p$, $p = 1, 2, \ldots$, and let $\xi = \langle u, \xi \rangle$ a generalized directly given Gaussian process on U. The expectation $A(u)$ is a linear continuous functional on U. There exist a natural number p and a nuclear operator B in the Hilbert space U with the scalar product $(u, v) = (u, v)_p$ such that the correlation functional $B(u, v)$ has the form

$$B(u, v) = (Bu, v)_p \quad (u, v \in U)\,.$$

For any such $A(u)$ and $B(u, v)$ there exists a directly given Gaussian generalized process $\xi = \langle u, \xi \rangle$ with expectation $A(u)$ and correlation functional $B(u, v)$.

Example. Let $\xi = \xi(t)$ be a real Gaussian random process on the interval $T = [a, b]$. We suppose that the process $\xi(t)$ is measurable and $\int_a^b \mathbb{M}[\xi(t)]^2\, dt < \infty$. Then almost all trajectories $\xi(\omega, t)$ belong to the space $U = L^2(T)$ of the square integrable functions $u = u(t)$ on the interval

T with the scalar product $(u_1, u_2) = \int_a^b u_1(t)\, u_2(t)\, dt$. The formula

$$\langle u, \xi \rangle = \int_a^b u(t)\, \xi(\omega, t)\, dt \qquad (u \in U)$$

defines a Gaussian generalized random process on this space $U = L^2(T)$. The expectation and the correlation functional of this generalized process $\xi = \langle u, \xi \rangle$ are given by the formulas

$$A(u) = \int_a^b u(t)\, A(t)\, dt\,,$$

$$B(u_1, u_2) = \int_a^b \int_a^b B(s, t)\, u_1(s)\, u_2(t)\, ds\, dt\,,$$

where $A(t)$ and $B(s, t)$ are the expectation and the correlation function of the original process $\xi = \xi(t)$ on the interval $T = [a, b]$. Similarly a generalized process $\xi = \langle u, \xi \rangle$ can be constructed on the nuclear space U of all infinitely differentiable functions $u = u(t)$ that vanish outside the interval (a, b) with the scalar products

$$(u_1, u_2)_p = \int_a^b \sum_{k=0}^p u_1^{(k)}(t)\, u_2^{(k)}(t)\, dt \qquad (p = 0, 1, \ldots)\,.$$

Densities of Arbitrary Gaussian Distributions. Let $\xi(t) = \xi(\omega, t)$ be a family of real functions of $\omega \in \Omega$ on a space Ω which depend on the parameter $t \in T$ where t is an arbitrary set. Let $\mathfrak{A}$ be the minimal σ-algebra of sets in Ω with respect to which all functions $\xi(\omega, t), t \in T$ are measurable. A probability measure $\mathbb{P} = \mathbb{P}(A)$ on the σ-algebra $\mathfrak{A}$ is called *Gaussian* if any family of random variables $\xi(\omega, t_1), \ldots, \xi(\omega, t_n)$ on the space of elementary events $(\Omega, \mathfrak{A}, \mathbb{P})$ is Gaussian.

The Gaussian measure $\mathbb{P} = \mathbb{P}(A)$ is completely determined by the two following data: the expectation

$$A(t) = \int_\Omega \xi(\omega, t)\, \mathbb{P}(d\omega) \qquad (t \in T)$$

and the correlation function

$$B(s, t) = \int_\Omega [\xi(\omega, s) - A(s)]\, [\xi(\omega, t) - A(t)]\, \mathbb{P}(d\omega) \qquad (s, t \in T)\,.$$

Any two arbitrary Gaussian measures $\mathbb{P}$ and $\tilde{\mathbb{P}}$ on the σ-algebra $\mathfrak{A}$ generated by the given family of functions $\xi(\omega, t), t \in T$ on the space Ω are either *mutually absolutely continuous* (in other words, equivalent), or *perpendicular*. A necessary and sufficient condition for the equivalence of $\mathbb{P}$ and $\tilde{\mathbb{P}}$ is that the entropy

$$H = \sup \sum_k \tilde{\mathbb{P}}(A_k) \log \frac{\tilde{\mathbb{P}}(A_k)}{\mathbb{P}(A_k)}$$

is finite, where sup is taken with respect to all partitions of the space Ω into disjoint sets $A_1, A_2, \ldots \in \mathfrak{A}$.

When investigating the problem of the equivalence of Gaussian measures $\mathbb{P}$ and $\tilde{\mathbb{P}}$ on the σ-algebra $\mathfrak{A}$ generated by the given variables $\xi(\omega, t), t \in T$ on the space Ω it can be assumed without restricting the generality that the expectation $A(t)$ is equal to zero, since we can always pass to the variables $\xi(\omega, t) - A(t)$. For $A(t) = 0$ the Gaussian measures $\mathbb{P}$ and $\tilde{\mathbb{P}}$ are equivalent if and only if the pairs $\mathbb{P}$ and $\tilde{\mathbb{P}}_0$, $\tilde{\mathbb{P}}_0$ and $\tilde{\mathbb{P}}$ are equivalent, where $\tilde{\mathbb{P}}_0$ is the Gaussian measure with expectation zero and the same correlation function as $\tilde{\mathbb{P}}$. The corresponding densities are related by the equation:

$$\frac{\tilde{\mathbb{P}}(d\omega)}{\mathbb{P}(d\omega)} = \frac{\tilde{\mathbb{P}}(d\omega)}{\tilde{\mathbb{P}}_0(d\omega)} \cdot \frac{\tilde{\mathbb{P}}_0(d\omega)}{\mathbb{P}(d\omega)}.$$

Suppose that $\mathbb{P} = \tilde{\mathbb{P}}_0$, and let $a(t) = \tilde{A}(t)$ be the expectation of the Gaussian measure $\tilde{\mathbb{P}}$. By H we denote the closed linear space spanned by the given variables $\xi(t)$, $t \in T$ considered as elements of the Hilbert space $L^2(\Omega)$ endowed with the scalar product $(h_1, h_2) = \int_\Omega h_1(\omega) h_2(\omega) \mathbb{P}(d\omega)$ of elements $h_1 = h_1(\omega)$ and $h_2 = h_2(\omega)$. A necessary and sufficient condition for the equivalence of $\mathbb{P}$ and $\tilde{\mathbb{P}}$ is that the function $a(t)$ of $t \in T$ admits an integral representation of the form

$$a(t) = \int_\Omega \xi(\omega, t) \alpha(\omega) \mathbb{P}(d\omega) \qquad (t \in T),$$

where $\alpha = \alpha(\omega)$ is some variable in H. This integral equation for the unknown function $\alpha(\omega)$ on Ω has only one solution in H, which is connected with the density $p(\omega) = \tilde{\mathbb{P}}(d\omega)/\mathbb{P}(d\omega)$ by the following formula:

$$p(\omega) = D e^{\alpha(\omega)},$$

where the normalizing factor D which is determined by the condition $\int_\Omega p(\omega) \mathbb{P}(d\omega) = 1$ equals $D = e^{\frac{1}{2}(\alpha, \alpha)}$.

Suppose that $\mathbb{P} = \mathbb{P}_0$, $\tilde{\mathbb{P}} = \tilde{\mathbb{P}}_0$, and let $b(s, t) = B(s, t) - \tilde{B}(s, t)$ be the difference of the correlation functions of the Gaussian measures $\mathbb{P}$ and $\tilde{\mathbb{P}}$. We denote by $\mathbb{P} \times \mathbb{P}$ the product of the measures on the product space $\Omega \times \Omega$ and by $H \times H$ the closed linear space spanned by the variables $\xi(\omega, s) \cdot \xi(\tilde{\omega}, t)$, $s, t \in T$ in the corresponding Hilbert space $L^2(\Omega \times \Omega)$ with the scalar product

$$(h_1, h_2) = \iint_{\Omega \times \Omega} h_1(\omega, \tilde{\omega}) h_2(\omega, \tilde{\omega}) \mathbb{P}(d\omega) \times \mathbb{P}(d\tilde{\omega})$$

of elements $h_1 = h_1(\omega, \tilde{\omega})$ and $h_2 = h_2(\omega, \tilde{\omega})$. A necessary and sufficient condition for the equivalence of $\mathbb{P}$ and $\tilde{\mathbb{P}}$ is that the function $b(s, t)$ of $s, t \in T$ admits and integral representation of the form

$$b(s, t) = \iint_{\Omega \times \Omega} \xi(\omega, s)\, \xi(\tilde{\omega}, t)\, \beta(\omega, \tilde{\omega})\, \mathbb{P}(d\omega) \times \mathbb{P}(d\tilde{\omega}),$$

where $\beta = \beta(\omega, \tilde{\omega})$ is a variable in the space $H \times H$ and the integral operator in the Hilbert space H given by the kernel $\beta(\omega, \tilde{\omega})$, that is,

$$B h(\omega) = \int_{\Omega} \beta(\omega, \tilde{\omega})\, h(\tilde{\omega})\, \mathbb{P}(d\tilde{\omega}),$$

does not have the eigenvalue 1. The kernel $\beta(\omega, \tilde{\omega}) \in H \times H$ is determined uniquely by this integral representation. If $h_1(\omega), h_2(\omega), \ldots$ is the orthonormal system of all its eigenfunctions belonging to the non-vanishing eigenvalues $1 - \sigma_1^2, 1 - \sigma_2^2, \ldots$, that is,

$$(1 - \sigma_n^2)\, h_n(\omega) = \int_{\Omega} \beta(\omega, \tilde{\omega})\, h_n(\tilde{\omega})\, \mathbb{P}(d\tilde{\omega}) \qquad (n = 1, 2, \ldots),$$

then the density $p(\omega) = \tilde{\mathbb{P}}(d\omega)/\mathbb{P}(d\omega)$ is obtained by the following formula:

$$p(\omega) = \lim_{n \to \infty} \frac{1}{\sigma_1 \ldots \sigma_n} \exp\left\{ -\frac{1}{2} \sum_{m=1}^{n} (\sigma_m^{-2} - 1)\, [h_m(\omega)]^2 \right\}.$$

Example. Suppose that a family of variables $\xi(\Delta) = \xi(\omega, \Delta)$ on a space Ω, where the parameter Δ runs through all Borel sets of an interval T of the real line, is a stochastic Wiener measure with respect to the Gaussian measure $\mathbb{P}$ (see Section 3 of this paragraph). In other words, the expectation and correlation function are given by

$$A(\Delta) = 0, \quad B(\Delta_1, \Delta_2) = l(\Delta_1 \cap \Delta_2),$$

where $l = l(\Delta)$ is the Lebesgue measure on the interval T. Then the Hilbert space H is unitarily isomorphic to the Hilbert space $L^2(T)$ of all real square integrable functions $\varphi = \varphi(t)$ on the interval T where

$$(\varphi_1, \varphi_2) = \int_T \varphi_1(t)\, \varphi_2(t)\, l(dt)$$

is the scalar product of elements $\varphi_1 = \varphi_1(t)$ and $\varphi_2 = \varphi_2(t)$. In fact any variable $h \in H$ can be written as a stochastic integral

$$h = \int_T \varphi(t)\, \xi(dt),$$

where $\varphi = \varphi(t)$ is the function from $L^2(T)$ which corresponds to the variable $h = h(\omega)$. The Hilbert space $H \times H$ is unitarily isomorphic to the Hilbert space $L^2(T \times T)$ of all real square integrable functions $\varphi = \varphi(s, t)$ on the rectangle $T \times T$, the scalar product of elements $\varphi_1 = \varphi_1(s, t)$ and $\varphi_2 = \varphi_2(s, t)$ being

$$(\varphi_1, \varphi_2) = \iint_{T \times T} \varphi_1(s, t) \cdot \varphi_2(s, t) \, l(ds) \times l(dt).$$

In fact any variable $h \in H \times H$ can be represented as a stochastic integral

$$h = \iint_{T \times T} \varphi(s, t) \, \xi(ds) \times \xi(dt),$$

where $\varphi = \varphi(s, t)$ is the function from $L^2(T \times T)$ which corresponds to the variable $h = h(\omega, \omega)$, and where the stochastic measure on sets of the form $\Delta_1 \times \Delta_2$ is defined to be the product of the independent variables $\xi(\omega, \Delta_1)$ and $\xi(\tilde{\omega}, \Delta_2)$.

If $\mathbb{P} = \mathbb{P}_0$ and if $a(\Delta)$ is the expectation of the Gaussian measure $\tilde{\mathbb{P}}$, then $\mathbb{P}$ and $\tilde{\mathbb{P}}$ are equivalent if and only if the function $a(\Delta)$ represents a generalized measure which is absolutely continuous with respect to the Lebesgue measure $l(\Delta)$ and such that the density $\varphi(t) = \dfrac{a(dt)}{l(dt)}$ belongs to the space $L^2(T)$:

$$a(\Delta) = \int_{\Omega} \xi(\omega, \Delta) \, \alpha(\omega) \, \mathbb{P}(d\omega) = \int_{\Delta} \varphi(t) \, l(dt),$$

where

$$\alpha(\omega) = \int_{T} \varphi(t) \, \xi(dt).$$

If the $\mathbb{P} = \mathbb{P}_0$, $\tilde{\mathbb{P}} = \tilde{\mathbb{P}}_0$ and $b(\Delta_1, \Delta_2) = B(\Delta_1, \Delta_2) - \tilde{B}(\Delta_1, \Delta_2)$ is the difference of the correlation functions of the Gaussian measures $\mathbb{P}$ and $\tilde{\mathbb{P}}$, then $\mathbb{P}$ and $\tilde{\mathbb{P}}$ are equivalent if and only if the following is true: the function $b(\Delta_1, \Delta_2)$ is a distribution function and admits an extension to a measure on the Borel sets of the rectangle $T \times T$ which is absolutely continuous with respect to the Lebesgue measure $l(\Delta_1) \times l(\Delta_2)$ and the corresponding density $\varphi(s, t)$ belongs to the space $L^2(T \times T)$:

$$b(\Delta_1, \Delta_2) = \iint_{\Omega \times \Omega} \xi(\omega, \Delta_1) \cdot \xi(\tilde{\omega}, \Delta_2) \, \beta(\omega, \tilde{\omega}) \, \mathbb{P}(d\omega) \times \mathbb{P}(d\omega)$$

$$= \iint_{\Delta_1 \times \Delta_2} \varphi(s, t) \, l(ds) \times l(dt),$$

where

$$\beta(\omega, \tilde{\omega}) = \iint_{T \times T} \varphi(s, t) \, \xi(ds) \times \xi(dt)$$

and the function $\varphi(s, t)$ considered as the kernel of a Fredholm integral operator in the space $L^2(T)$ does not have the eigenvalue 1. The variables

$$h_n(\omega) = \int_{T} \varphi_n(t) \, \xi(dt) \quad (n = 1, 2, \ldots),$$

where $\varphi_1(t)$, $\varphi_2(t)$, ... is the orthonormal system of all eigenfunctions of the kernel $\varphi(s, t)$ belonging to the eigenvalues $1 - \sigma_1^2$, $1 - \sigma_2^2$ unequal to 0, represent the orthonormal system of all eigenfunctions of the kernel $\beta(\omega, \tilde{\omega})$ to the same eigenvalues $1 - \sigma_1^2$, $1 - \sigma_2^2$, ...

The equivalence conditions for arbitrary Gaussian measures $\mathbb{P} = \mathbb{P}_0$ and $\tilde{\mathbb{P}} = \tilde{\mathbb{P}}_0$ as well as the density $p(\omega) = \tilde{\mathbb{P}}(d\omega)/\mathbb{P}(d\omega)$ can also be described in a different way. Let $\mathbb{P} \times \tilde{\mathbb{P}}$ be the product of the measures $\mathbb{P}$ and $\tilde{\mathbb{P}}$ on the product space $\Omega \times \Omega$, and let $H \times \tilde{H}$ be the closed linear space spanned by the variables $\xi(\omega, s) \cdot \xi(\tilde{\omega}, t)$ $(s, t \in T)$ considered as elements of the Hilbert space $L^2(\Omega \times \Omega)$ with the scalar product

$$(h_1, h_2) = \iint\limits_{\Omega \times \Omega} h_1(\omega, \tilde{\omega}) \, h_2(\omega, \tilde{\omega}) \, \mathbb{P}(d\omega) \times \tilde{\mathbb{P}}(d\tilde{\omega})$$

of elements $h_1 = h_1(\omega, \tilde{\omega})$ and $h_2 = h_2(\omega, \tilde{\omega})$. A necessary and sufficient condition for the equivalence of $\mathbb{P}$ and $\tilde{\mathbb{P}}$ is that the difference of the correlation functions admits an integral representation of the form

$$b(s, t) = \iint\limits_{\Omega \times \Omega} \xi(\omega, s) \, \xi(\tilde{\omega}, t) \, \beta(\omega, \tilde{\omega}) \, \mathbb{P}(d\omega) \times \tilde{\mathbb{P}}(d\tilde{\omega}),$$

where $\beta = \beta(\omega, \tilde{\omega})$ is some variable from the space $H \times \tilde{H}$. This integral equation for the unknown function $\beta = \beta(\omega, \tilde{\omega})$ on $\Omega \times \Omega$ has only one solution in $H \times \tilde{H}$ which is connected with the density $p(\omega) = \tilde{\mathbb{P}}(d\omega)/\mathbb{P}(d\omega)$ by the formula

$$p(\omega) = D \exp\left\{ -\frac{1}{2} [\beta(\omega, \omega) - \mathbb{M}\beta] \right\}$$

where the normalizing factor D is determined by the condition $\int\limits_{\Omega} p(\omega) \, \mathbb{P}(d\omega) = 1$. This formula, however, needs some interpretation.

Since the function $\beta(\omega, \tilde{\omega})$ of the two variables $(\omega, \tilde{\omega})$ is determined only almost everywhere with respect to the product measure $\mathbb{P} \times \tilde{\mathbb{P}}$, and therefore its values on the "diagonal" $\tilde{\omega} = \omega$ are not uniquely defined. We note that the variable $\beta(\omega, \tilde{\omega})$ belongs to the subspace which is the closure of all variables of the form

$$h(\omega, \tilde{\omega}) = \sum_{k, j = 1}^{n} c_{kj} \, \xi(\omega, t_k) \, \xi(\tilde{\omega}, t_j)$$

with real coefficients $c_{kj} = c_{jk}$ for which the corresponding variables $h(\omega, \omega) - \mathbb{M}h$ with

$$\mathbb{M}h = \int\limits_{\Omega} h(\omega, \omega) \, \mathbb{P}(d\omega)$$

had already been uniquely defined. The correspondence

$$h(\omega, \tilde{\omega}) \leftrightarrow h(\omega, \omega) - \text{M} h$$

described before remains true when passing to the limit:

$$\lim_{n \to \infty} h_n(\omega, \tilde{\omega}) \leftrightarrow \lim_{n \to \infty} [h_n(\omega, \omega) - \text{M} h_n]$$

where we have in mind mean square convergence with respect to the measures $\mathbb{P} \times \tilde{\mathbb{P}}$ and $\mathbb{P}$, respectively.

Example. Let $\xi(n) = \xi(\omega, n)$, $n = 1, 2, \ldots$, be a sequence of independent Gaussian variables with respect to the probability distribution $\mathbb{P}$ as well as to the distribution $\tilde{\mathbb{P}}$ with vanishing expectations and corresponding correlation functions

$$B(m, n) = \begin{cases} 1 & \text{for} \quad m = n \\ 0 & \text{for} \quad m \neq n; \end{cases} \qquad \tilde{B}(m, n) = \begin{cases} \sigma_n^2 & \text{for} \quad m = n \\ 0 & \text{for} \quad m \neq n. \end{cases}$$

In this case the integral representation described above permits to find at once the coefficients of the expansion of $\beta(\omega, \tilde{\omega})$ relative to the orthogonal system of variables $\xi(\omega, m) \cdot \xi(\tilde{\omega}, n)$, $m, n = 1, 2, \ldots$ in the Hilbert space $H \times \tilde{H}$. In fact,

$$\beta(\omega, \tilde{\omega}) = \sum_{n=1}^{\infty} \frac{1 - \sigma_n^2}{\sigma_n^2} \xi(\omega, n) \, \xi(\tilde{\omega}, n).$$

Obviously, the condition for the equivalence of $\mathbb{P}$ and $\tilde{\mathbb{P}}$ is

$$\sum_{n=1}^{\infty} \left(\frac{1 - \sigma_n^2}{\sigma_n^2} \right)^2 = (\beta, \beta) < \infty.$$

Moreover,

$$\beta(\omega, \omega) - \text{M} \beta = \lim_{n \to \infty} \sum_{m=1}^{n} \frac{1 - \sigma_m^2}{\sigma_m^2} \{ [\xi(\omega, m)]^2 - 1 \}.$$

Gaussian Processes Considered as Curves in Hilbert Space. Gaussian variables ξ_1 and ξ_2 are independent if and only if they are uncorrelated. If $\text{M} \xi_1 = \text{M} \xi_2 = 0$, then their independence is equivalent to the fact that the variables ξ_1 and ξ_2 considered as elements of the Hilbert space $L^2(\Omega)$ are orthogonal:

$$\text{M} \xi_1 \xi_2 = (\xi_1, \xi_2) = 0.$$

Let $\xi_1, \xi_2, \ldots, \xi_n$ be Gaussian random variables with vanishing expectations and correlation matrix $b = (b_{kj})$, $b_{kj} = \text{M} \xi_k \xi_j$, $k, j = 1, 2, \ldots, n$. The conditional expectation $\text{M}(\xi_1 | \xi_2, \ldots, \xi_n)$ is an element of the space H

in the Hilbert space $L^2(\Omega)$ generated by the variables $\xi_2, \ldots, \xi_n$:

$$\mathbb{M}(\xi_1 \mid \xi_2, \ldots, \xi_n) = \sum_{k=2}^{n} c_k \xi_k,$$

where the coefficients $c_2, \ldots, c_n$ can be found from the condition that the difference $\xi_1 - \sum_{k=2}^{n} c_k \xi_k$ be orthogonal to H:

$$\sum_{k=2}^{n} c_k b_{kj} = b_{1j} \qquad (j = 2, \ldots, n).$$

The conditional probability distribution of the random variable ξ_1 with respect to $\xi_2, \ldots, \xi_n$ is again Gaussian. Its expectation and variance are given by

$$a = \mathbb{M}(\xi_1 \mid \xi_2, \ldots, \xi_n) \quad \text{and} \quad \sigma^2 = \mathbb{M}[\xi_1 - \mathbb{M}(\xi_1 \mid \xi_2, \ldots, \xi_n)]^2.$$

Let $\xi = \xi(t)$ be a Gaussian process on an arbitrary set T with vanishing expectation. Let $H(S)$ be the closed linear space generated by the variables $\xi(t), t \in S$, where $S \subseteq T$; thus $H(S)$ is a subspace of the Hilbert space $L^2(\Omega)$. The conditional expectation $\mathbb{M}(\xi(t) \mid \xi(s), s \in S)$ is the orthogonal projection of the element $\xi(t)$ onto the subspace $H(S)$. The conditional distribution of $\xi(t)$ is Gaussian; the corresponding expectation and variance are given by

$$a = \mathbb{M}(\xi(t) \mid \xi(s), s \in S) \quad \text{and} \quad \sigma^2 = \mathbb{M}[\xi(t) - \mathbb{M}(\xi(t) \mid \xi(s), s \in S)]^2.$$

Let S_1 and S_2 be subsets of the set T and $H(S_1)$ and $H(S_2)$ the corresponding subspace of the Hilbert space $L^2(\Omega)$. We set

$$r = \sup \mathbb{M} h_1 h_2$$

where sup is taken for all $h_1 \in H(S_1)$ and $h_2 \in H(S_2)$ such that $\mathbb{M} h_1^2 = \mathbb{M} h_2^2 = 1$. Let $\mathfrak{A}(S)$, $S \subseteq T$ be the σ-algebra generated by all events of the form $\{\xi(s) \in B\}$, $s \in S$, where B is a Borel set on the real line. We denote by $L^2(\Omega, S)$ the subspace in $L^2(\Omega)$ formed by all random variables $\eta = \eta(\omega)$ that are measurable with respect to $\mathfrak{A}(S)$. Then the equation

$$r = \sup \mathbb{M} \eta_1 \eta_2$$

holds where sup is taken for all random variables $\eta_1 \in L^2(\Omega, S_1)$ and $\eta_2 \in L^2(\Omega, S_2)$ such that $\mathbb{M} \eta_1 = \mathbb{M} \eta_2 = 0$, $\mathbb{M} \eta_1^2 = \mathbb{M} \eta_2^2 = 1$.
    Let

$$\alpha = \sup |\mathbb{P}(A_1 A_2) - \mathbb{P}(A_1) \mathbb{P}(A_2)|$$

where sup is taken for all events $A_1 \in \mathfrak{A}(S_1)$ and $A_2 \in \mathfrak{A}(S_2)$. The following relations between α and r are true:

$$\alpha \leq r \leq 2\pi \alpha .$$

Complex Gaussian Processes. By a complex Gaussian process $\xi(t)$, $t \in T$ we usually understand a family of complex random variables

$$\xi(t) = \xi_1(t) + i \xi_2(t)$$

with Gaussian real and imaginary parts $\xi_1(t)$ and $\xi_2(t)$ whose joint distributions are Gaussian for any system of times t, and such that the additional assumption

$$\mathsf{M}\, \xi(s)\, \xi(t) = A(s)\, A(t)$$

is satisfied where $A(t) = \mathsf{M}\, \xi(t)$. This condition is introduced in order to preserve the property of ordinary Gaussian random variables to be uncorrelated if and only if they are independent. It can be rewritten as follows:

$$\mathsf{M}[\xi_1(s) - A_1(s)]\,[\xi_1(t) - A_1(t)]$$
$$= \mathsf{M}[\xi_2(s) - A_2(s)]\,[\xi_2(t) - A_2(t)] = \frac{1}{2}\,\operatorname{Re} B(s, t),$$

$$\mathsf{M}[\xi_1(s) - A_1(s)]\,[\xi_2(t) - A_2(t)] = -\frac{1}{2}\,\operatorname{Im} B(s, t),$$

where

$$A_1(t) = \mathsf{M}\, \xi_1(t),\qquad A_2(t) = \mathsf{M}\, \xi_2(t).$$

3. Martingales and Stochastic Integrals

A real random process $\xi = \xi(t)$ on a set T of the real line is called a *martingale* if $\mathsf{M}\,|\xi(t)| < \infty$ and

$$\mathsf{M}\{\xi(t)\,|\,\mathfrak{A}(-\infty, s)\} = \xi(s)$$

with probability 1 for all $s, t \in T$, $s \leq t$, where the conditional expectation is taken with respect to the σ-algebra $\mathfrak{A}(-\infty, s)$ generated by all events $\{\xi(u) \leq x\}$, $u \leq s$, $u \in T$.

Example. Let $(\Omega, \mathfrak{A}, \mathbb{P})$ be an arbitrary space of elementary events with the probability distribution $\mathbb{P} = \mathbb{P}(A)$, $A \in \mathfrak{A}$, and let $\tilde{\mathbb{P}} = \tilde{\mathbb{P}}(A)$, $A \in \mathfrak{A}$ be an other probability distribution. We consider a monotone sequence of σ-algebras $\mathfrak{A}_1 \subseteq \mathfrak{A}_2 \subseteq \cdots \subseteq \mathfrak{A}$ such that on each σ-algebra the probability measure $\tilde{\mathbb{P}}$ is absolutely continuous with respect to $\mathbb{P}$. Let $p_n(\omega) = \dfrac{\tilde{\mathbb{P}}(d\omega)}{\mathbb{P}(d\omega)}$ be the corresponding densities. The sequence of random variables $\xi = \xi(n)$, $n = 1, 2, \ldots$ defined as

$$\xi(\omega, n) = p_n(\omega) \qquad (n = 1, 2, \ldots)$$

is a martingale.

Example. Let $\xi = \xi(\omega)$ be a real random variable with existing expectation, and $\mathfrak{A}_t$ a family of σ-algebras of events which depend on a real parameter $t \in T$ such that $\mathfrak{A}_s \subseteq \mathfrak{A}_t$ for any $s, t \in T$, $s \leq t$. Then the random process $\xi = \xi(t)$ defined on the set T by

$$\xi(t) = \mathbb{M}\{\xi \mid \mathfrak{A}_t\}$$

is a martingale.

The Convergence Theorem. If the random process $\xi = \xi(t)$ is a martingale, the expectation $\mathbb{M}|\xi(t)|$ represents a monotone non-decreasing function of $t \in T$. Let $\xi = \xi(t)$ be a separable martingale and $b = \sup\limits_{t \in T} t$. If

$$\sup\limits_{t \in T} \mathbb{M}|\xi(t)| = M < \infty ,$$

then the limit

$$\xi = \lim\limits_{t \to b} \xi(t)$$

exists with probability 1. The limit random variable $\xi = \xi(b)$ has the property that the following conditions are equivalent[19]:

  a) $\mathbb{M}|\xi(b)| = M$,
  b) $\lim\limits_{t \to b} \mathbb{M}|\xi(t) - \xi(b)| = 0$,
  c) the random variables $\xi(t)$, $t \in T$ are uniformly integrable. If one of them is satisfied, the random process $\xi = \xi(t)$ on the extended set $T \cup b$ is a martingale and can be represented in the form

$$\xi(t) = \mathbb{M}(\xi \mid \mathfrak{A}(-\infty, t)) \qquad (t \in T \cup b) .$$

If for any $\alpha > 1$

$$\sup\limits_{t \in T} \mathbb{M}|\xi(t)|^\alpha < \infty ,$$

then

$$\mathbb{M}|\xi(b)|^\alpha < \infty \quad \text{and} \quad \lim\limits_{t \to b} \mathbb{M}|\xi(t) - \xi(b)|^\alpha = 0 .$$

---

[19] *Krickeberg, K.*, Convergence of martingales with a directed index set. Trans. Amer. Math. Soc. **83** (1956), 2.

Submartingales. A real random process $\xi = \xi(t)$ on a set T of the real line is called a *submartingale* (or semimartingale) if $\mathbb{M}|\xi(t)| < \infty$ and

$$\mathbb{M}(\xi(t)|\mathfrak{A}(-\infty, s)) \geq \xi(s)$$

for any $s, t \in T$, $s \leq t$.

If $\xi = \xi(t)$ is a martingale, then the process $\eta(t) = |\xi(t)|$ is a submartingale. For any real continuous and convex function $\varphi = \varphi(x)$ of the real variable x the random process $\eta(t) = \varphi[\xi(t)]$ is a submartingale on the set T. For example, the function

$$\varphi(x) = \begin{cases} \log_c x & \text{for} \quad x > 0, \\ 0 & \text{for} \quad x \leq 0 \end{cases} \quad (c > 1)$$

has this property.

Let $\xi = \xi(t)$ be a separable submartingale on the set T and suppose that $\sup_{t \in T} \mathbb{M}|\xi(t)| < \infty$. Then the limit $\xi = \lim_{t \to b} \xi(t)$, $b = \sup_{t \in T} t$, exists with probability 1.

Martingales and Stochastic Measures. Let $\xi = \xi(t)$ be a martingale on the real line $-\infty < t < \infty$, and $\mathbb{M}|\xi(t)|^2 < \infty$. For $\Delta = (s, t]$ we set

$$\eta(\Delta) = \xi(t) - \xi(s).$$

For any Δ the expectation $\mathbb{M}\eta(\Delta)$ is equal to zero, and for any two disjoint half-intervals Δ_1, Δ_2 we have

$$\mathbb{M}[\eta(\Delta_1)\eta(\Delta_2)] = 0.$$

Moreover, if $\Delta_1 = (s_1, t_1]$, $\Delta_2 = (s_2, t_2]$ and $t_2 \leq s_2$, the equation

$$\mathbb{M}[\eta_1 \eta(\Delta_2)] = 0$$

holds for any random variable $\eta_2 = \eta_2(\omega)$ which is measurable with respect to the σ-algebra $\mathfrak{A}(s_1, t_1)$.

The function $m = m(\Delta)$ defined by $m(\Delta) = \mathbb{M}[\eta(\Delta)]^2$ is a distribution on the semi-ring of all half-intervals $\Delta = (s, t]$, and can be extended to a Borel measure. The corresponding stochastic function $\eta = \eta(\Delta)$ on the half-intervals $\Delta = (s, t]$ can be extended to a stochastic measure on the σ-algebra of all sets on the real line which are measurable with respect to m. The relations given above for half-intervals Δ_1 and Δ_2 remain true for arbitrary measurable sets Δ_1, Δ_2 such that $\Delta_1 \subseteq (s_1, t_1]$ and $\Delta_2 \subseteq (s_2, t_2]$.

Example. *Gaussian Stochastic Measures.* Let $m = \mathrm{m}(\Delta)$ be an arbitrary finite Borel measure on the real line $-\infty < t < \infty$. The function $B(\Delta_1, \Delta_2) = m(\Delta_1 \cap \Delta_2)$ of the parameters Δ_1, Δ_2 which are measurable sets with respect to m, satisfies the condition to be positive definite:

$$\sum_{k,j=1}^{n} \lambda_k \lambda_j B(\Delta_k, \Delta_j) = \int_{-\infty}^{\infty} [\Sigma \lambda_k \varphi_{\Delta_k}(t)]^2 m(dt) \geq 0,$$

where

$$\varphi_\Delta(t) = \begin{cases} 1 & \text{for} \quad t \in \Delta. \\ 0 & \text{for} \quad t \notin \Delta. \end{cases}$$

There exists a Gaussian random function $\eta = \eta(\Delta)$ with expectation zero, that is, $A(\Delta) = M\eta(\Delta) = 0$, and with the correlation function $B(\Delta_1, \Delta_2) = M\eta(\Delta_1)\eta(\Delta_2)$. This function $\eta = \eta(\Delta)$ represents a stochastic measure on the σ-algebra of all measurable sets Δ of the real line $-\infty < t < \infty$ such that for any two disjoint sets Δ_1 and Δ_2 the corresponding values $\eta(\Delta_1)$ and $\eta(\Delta_2)$ are independent. For every real square integrable function $\varphi = \varphi(t)$ the random process $\xi = \xi(t)$ given by

$$\xi(t) = \int\limits_{-\infty}^{t} \varphi(s)\,\eta(ds) \quad (-\infty < t < \infty)$$

is a martingale.

If $m = m(\Delta)$ is the Lebesgue measure on the line, the corresponding stochastic function $\eta = \eta(\Delta)$ is called the *stochastic Wiener measure*. The corresponding random process $\xi = \xi(t)$ of the form

$$\xi(t) = \int\limits_{a}^{t} \eta(ds) \quad (a \leq t < \infty)$$

is called the *Wiener process* or the *Brownian motion process*. Any martingale $\xi = \xi(t)$ on the half-line $a \leq t < \infty$ which has continuous trajectories with probability 1 and satisfies the condition

$$M\{[\xi(t) - \xi(s)]^2 \mid \mathfrak{A}(-\infty, s)\} = t - s,$$

for any $a \leq s \leq t < \infty$ is a Brownian motion process.

Stochastic Integrals. Let $\eta = \eta(\Delta)$ be a stochastic measure on the measurable subsets Δ of a set T of the real line such that

$$M\eta(\Delta) = 0, \quad M[\eta(\Delta)]^2 = m(\Delta) < \infty,$$

and such that for any Δ_1 and Δ_2, $\Delta_1 \subseteq (s_1, t_1]$ and $\Delta_2 = (s_2, t_2]$, $t_1 \leq s_2$, we have

$$M\{\eta(\Delta_2) \mid \mathfrak{A}(\Delta_1)\} = 0,$$

where $\mathfrak{A}(\Delta_2)$ denotes the σ-algebra of events generated by all events of the form $\{\eta(\Delta) \leq y\}$, $\Delta \subseteq \Delta_2 \cap T$.

Let $\varphi = \varphi(t)$ be a random function on T which has the following property: for each $t \in T$ the value $\varphi(t) = \varphi(\omega, t)$ is measurable with respect to the corresponding σ-algebra $\mathfrak{A}(-\infty, t)$. In addition we assume that

$$\int\limits_{T} M|\varphi(t)|^2\, m(dt) < \infty,$$

where $m = m(\Delta)$ is the measure on T given by $m(\Delta) = M[\eta(\Delta)]^2$.

By the *stochastic integral* of a "simple" random function $\varphi = \varphi(t)$ of the type described before whose values $\varphi(t) = \varphi(t, \omega)$ are constant random variables on the intervals $\Delta_k = (t_k, t_{k-1}]$, $k = 1, \ldots, n$, that is,

$$\varphi(t, \omega) = \varphi_k(\omega) \quad \text{for} \quad t \in \Delta_k$$

we mean the expression

$$\int_T \varphi(t)\,\eta(dt) = \sum_k \varphi_k(\omega)\,\eta(\Delta_k).$$

The stochastic integrals defined in this way have the following properties:

$$\mathbb{M} \int_T \varphi(t)\,\eta(dt) = 0,$$

$$\mathbb{M}\left[\int_T \varphi_1(t)\,\eta(dt) \int_T \varphi_2(t)\,\eta(dt)\right] = \int_T \mathbb{M}[\varphi_1(t)\,\varphi_2(t)]\,m(dt).$$

In particular

$$\mathbb{M}\left[\int_T \varphi_1(t)\,\eta(dt) - \int_T \varphi_2(t)\,\eta(dt)\right]^2 = \int_T \mathbb{M}[\varphi_1(t) - \varphi_2(t)]^2\,m(dt).$$

Any random function $\varphi(t)$ of the type described above is the limit of a sequence of "simple" random functions $\varphi_n(t)$, $n = 1, 2, \ldots$:

$$\lim_{n \to \infty} \int_T \mathbb{M}[\varphi_n(t) - \varphi(t)]^2\,m(dt) = 0.$$

The corresponding sequence of stochastic integrals $\int_T \varphi_n(t)\,\eta(dt), n = 1, 2, \ldots$ converges in the mean square to a limit

$$\int_T \varphi(t)\,\eta(dt) = \lim_{n \to \infty} \int_T \varphi_n(t)\,\eta(dt)$$

which we call the *stochastic integral* of the random function $\varphi = \varphi(t)$.

Let $T = [a, b]$ and $\xi(t) = \xi(a) + \int_a^t \varphi(\omega, s)\,ds + \int_a^t \psi(\omega, s)\eta(ds)$. For each $t \in T$ the values $\xi(t)$ are random variables which are defined only with probability 1. However, they can always be defined in such a way that the random function $\xi = \xi(t)$ on T is a separable and measurable random process.

The integral representation of the random process $\xi = \xi(t)$ can also be written in the differential form

$$d\xi(t) = \varphi(t)\,dt + \psi(t)\,\eta(dt).$$

This expression is called a *stochastic differential*.

A Formula for Changing Variables. Let $\eta = \eta(\Delta)$ be the stochastic Wiener measure and $\xi = \xi(t)$ a random process the stochastic differential of which has the form

$$d\xi(t) = \varphi(t)\, dt + \psi(t)\, \eta(dt).$$

Suppose that the real function $f(t, x)$ of the two variables t and x has a continuous first derivative with respect to t and a continuous second derivative with respect to x. Then the random process $\tilde{\xi} = \tilde{\xi}(t)$ defined by $\tilde{\xi}(t) = f[t, \xi(t)]$ has the stochastic differential[20]

$$d\tilde{\xi}(t) = \tilde{\varphi}(t)\, dt + \tilde{\psi}(t)\, \eta(dt),$$

where

$$\tilde{\varphi}(t) = \frac{\partial}{\partial t} f[t, \xi(t)] + \frac{\partial}{\partial x} f[t, \xi(t)]\, \varphi(t)$$

$$+ \frac{1}{2} \frac{\partial^2}{\partial x^2} f[t, \xi(t)]\, [\psi(t)]^2,$$

$$\tilde{\psi}(t) = \frac{\partial}{\partial x} f[t, \xi(t)]\, \psi(t).$$

4. Markov Random Processes

A random process $\xi = \xi(t)$ on a set T of the real line in the phase space $(E, \mathfrak{B})$ is called a *Markov* process if the conditional probabilities $\mathbb{P}(A \mid \mathfrak{A}(-\infty, s))$ of events $A \in \mathfrak{A}(t, \infty)$ with respect to the σ-algebra $\mathfrak{A}(-\infty, s)$ satisfy for $s \leq t$ the equation

$$\mathbb{P}(A \mid \mathfrak{A}(-\infty, s)) = P(A \mid \xi(s))$$

with probability 1 where $\mathfrak{A}(u, v)$ denotes the σ-algebra generated by all events $\{\xi(t) \in B\}$, $t \in [u, v] \cap T$, $B \in \mathfrak{B}$. If the parameter t is interpreted as the time, then this Markov property of the random process $\xi = \xi(t)$ means, roughly spoken, that, given a fixed state $x = \xi(t)$, the behavior of the process after the moment t does not depend on its behavior until the time t. More precisely, for any events $A_1 \in \mathfrak{A}(-\infty, t_1)$ and $A_2 \in \mathfrak{A}(t_2, \infty)$ and any $t \in T$, $t_1 \leq t \leq t_2$, we have

$$\mathbb{P}(A_1 A_2 \mid \xi(t)) = \mathbb{P}(A_1 \mid \xi(t))\, \mathbb{P}(A_2 \mid \xi(t))$$

with probability 1.

The validity of the Markov property depends in an essential way on the choice of the phase space of the process under consideration. This is illustrated by the following example. Suppose the real random process $\xi = \xi(t)$ on the interval $T = [a, b]$ is described by a differential

---

[20] K. Ito: On a formula concerning stochastic differentials Nagoya Math. J. 3, 55—65 (1951).

equation of the first order

$$\xi' = f(t, \xi).$$

If we fix the value $\xi(t_0) = x$, then for any elementary outcome ω the trajectory $\xi(\omega, t)$, $t \geq t_0$ of this process is uniquely determined by the differential equation $\xi'(\omega, t) = f[t, \xi(\omega, t)]$ and the "initial condition" $\xi(\omega, t_0) = x$. Thus the process $\xi = \xi(t)$ is Markovian. If, however, the process $\xi = \xi(t)$ is described by a differential equation of n-th order:

$$\xi^{(n)} = f[t, \xi^{(1)}, ..., \xi^{(n-1)}],$$

then it will be no longer a Markov process; the Markov property is satisfied if we consider the n-dimensional random process $\{\xi(t), \xi^{(1)}(t), ..., \xi^{(n-1)}(t)\}$ whose components are the original random process $\xi(t)$ and its derivatives $\xi^{(k)}(t)$ up to the order $n-1$, inclusively.

Another example. Let $\xi = \xi(t)$ be a random process on the real line $-\infty < t < \infty$ in an arbitrary phase space $(E, \mathfrak{B})$, X the space of all functions $x = x(s)$ with values in E, each of them being defined on some interval $-\infty < s \leq t$, and $\mathfrak{A}$ the σ-algebra generated by all cylinder sets

$$\{x(t_1) \in B_1, ..., x(t_n) \in B_n\},$$

where $B_1, ..., B_n \in \mathfrak{B}$. By $\xi(\omega, s)$, $-\infty < s \leq t$ we denote the trajectory of the original random process ξ on the half-line $-\infty < s \leq t$; this is a random variable with values in the new phase space $(X, \mathfrak{A})$. If we define an "extended" random process in the phase space $(X, \mathfrak{A})$ by taking as its value at the time t the corresponding trajectory $\xi(\omega, s)$, $-\infty < s \leq t$, then this process will have the Markov property.

Conditional Distributions and Transition Functions. A function $P(s, x, t, B)$ of the variables $s, t \in T$, $s \leq t$, and $x \in E$, $B \in \mathfrak{B}$ is called a *transition function* of the Markov process $\xi = \xi(t)$ on the set T in the phase space $(E, \mathfrak{B})$ if this function is a probability distribution on the σ-algebra $\mathfrak{B}$ for fixed $s, t \in T$ and $x \in E$, and a measurable function of $x \in E$ for fixed $s, t \in T$ and $B \in \mathfrak{B}$ such that with probability 1

$$P(s, \xi(s), t, B) = \mathbb{P}\{\xi(t) \in B | \xi(s)\}$$

and

$$P(s, x, s, B) = \begin{cases} 1 & \text{for} \quad x \in B, \\ 0 & \text{for} \quad x \notin B. \end{cases}$$

Roughly spoken, $P(s, x, t, B)$ is the probability that within the period of length $t - s$ the process passes from the state $x = \xi(s)$ into one of the states belonging to B.

A transition function $P(s, x, t, B)$ always exists if the phase space $(E, \mathfrak{B})$ is separable and the probability distributions $\mathbb{P}_t(B) = \mathbb{P}\{\xi(t) \in B\}$,

$B \in \mathfrak{B}$ are perfect measures. For any $s, t \in T$ and $B \in \mathfrak{B}$ and almost all $x \in E$ with respect to the corresponding distributions $\mathbb{P}_t$ this function satisfies the relation

$$P(s, x, t, B) = \int_E P(s, x, u, dy) P(u, y, t, B) \qquad (s \leqq u \leqq t),$$

which is known as the *Chapman-Kolmogorov equation*.

The finite-dimensional probability distributions of a random process $\xi = \xi(t)$ with transition function $P(s, x, t, B)$ are expressed by the following formula:

$$\mathbb{P}_{t_1, \ldots, t_n}(B_1, \ldots, B_n) = \int_{B_1} \int_{B_2} \cdots \int_{B_{n-1}} P(t_{n-1}, x_{n-1}, t_n, B_n)$$
$$P(t_{n-2} x_{n-2}, t_{n-1}, dx_{n-1}) \ldots P(t_1, x_1, t_2, dx_2) \mathbb{P}_{t_1}(dx_1).$$

Suppose that the random process $\xi = \xi(t)$ on the set T in the phase space $(E, \mathfrak{B})$ has a transition function $P(s, x, t, B)$ which satisfies the Chapman-Kolmogorov equation for all $x \in E$. We assume that the set $\xi(\Omega)$ in the functional space $X = E^T$ which consists of all trajectories $\xi(\omega, t)$ considered as functions on T with values in E, $\omega \in \Omega$ belongs to to the σ-algebra generated by the semi-ring of all cylinder sets $\mathfrak{B}^T$. Then there exists a family of probability distributions $\mathbb{P}_{s,x} = \mathbb{P}_{s,x}(A)$ such that $\mathbb{P}_{s,x}$ is defined on the corresponding σ-algebra of events $\mathfrak{A}(s, \infty)$ in the space of elementary events Ω and

$$\mathbb{P}_{s,x}\{\xi(t) \in B\} = P(s, x, t, B)$$

for any $s, t \in T$, $s \leqq t$, and $x \in E$, $B \in \mathfrak{B}$. Furthermore we have with probability 1 with respect to $\mathbb{P}_{s,x}$

$$\mathbb{P}_{s,x}\{\xi(t) \in B \mid \mathfrak{A}(s, u)\} = P(u, \xi(u), t, B)$$

for any $u \in T$, $s \leqq u \leqq t$.

Let T be an arbitrary set on the real line, $(E, \mathfrak{B})$ an arbitrary measurable space, and $P(s, x, t, B)$ a function of the variables $s, t \in T$, $s \leqq t$ and $x \in E$, $B \in \mathfrak{B}$, with the following properties: for fixed $s, t \in T$ and $x \in E$ it is a probability distribution on the σ-algebra $\mathfrak{B}$ in E; for fixed $s, t \in T$ and $B \in \mathfrak{B}$ it is measurable with respect to x and satisfies the Chapman-Kolmogorov equation for all $x \in E$. Then there exists a directly given Markov process $\xi = \xi(t)$ on the set T in the phase space $(E, \mathfrak{B})$ with this transition function $P(s, x, t, B)$.

Conditional Transition Functions. Let $\xi_1 = \xi_1(t)$ and $\xi_2 = \xi_2(t)$ be random processes on a set T of the real line in corresponding phase spaces $(E_1, \mathfrak{B}_1)$ and $(E_2, \mathfrak{B}_2)$ such that the "two-dimensional" random process $\xi = \{\xi_1, \xi_2\}$ in the phase space $E = E_1 \times E_2$ as well as the process

$\xi_1 = \xi_1(t)$ is Markovian. Suppose that the transition function of the "two-dimensional" Markov process $\xi = \xi(t)$ satisfies for any $s, t \in T$ and $B_1 \in \mathfrak{B}_1, x_2 \in E_2$ the equation

$$P\{s, (x_1, x_2), t, B_1 \times E_2\} = P(s, x_1, t, B_1),$$

where $P(s, x_1, t, B_1)$ is the transition function of the Markov process $\xi_1 = \xi_1(t)$. We assume that the phase spaces $(E_1, \mathfrak{B}_1)$ and $(E_2, \mathfrak{B}_2)$ are separable and the probability distributions of the values $\xi_1(t)$ and $\xi_2(t) \, t \in T$ are perfect measures. Then the so-called *conditional transition function* $P(s, x_2, t, B_2, \omega)$ of the random process $\xi_2 = \xi_2(t)$ exists, that is, with probability 1 we have

$$P(s, \xi_2(s), t, B_2, \omega) = \mathbb{P}\{\xi_2(t) \in B_2 | \xi_2(s); \, \xi_1(u), u \leq s\}.$$

For each fixed elementary outcome $\omega \in \Omega$ the conditional transition function meets all requirements of a transition function, that is, it represents a probability distribution on the σ-algebra $\mathfrak{B}_2$ which is measurable with respect to $x_2 \in E_2$ and satisfies the Chapman-Kolmogorov equation:

$$P(s, x_2, t, B_2, \omega) = \int_{E_2} P(s, x_2, u, dy, \omega) \, P(u, y, t, B_2, \omega) \qquad (s \leq u \leq t).$$

The random process $\xi_2 = \xi_2(t)$ with the conditional transition function $P(s, x_2, t, B_2, \omega)$ is called a *conditional Markov process*.

Coefficient of Ergodicity. Let $\xi = \xi(t)$ be a random Markov process in the phase space $(E, \mathfrak{B})$ with the transition function $P(s, x, t, B)$. The equation

$$\beta(s, t) = \sup_{A \in \mathfrak{A}(t, \infty)} |\mathbb{P}(A | \mathfrak{A}(-\infty, s) - \mathbb{P}(A)| = \sup_{B \in \mathfrak{B}} |P(s, \xi(s), t, B) - P_t(B)|$$

holds with probability 1.

The function

$$k(s, t) = 1 - \sup_{x_1, x_2, B} |P(s, x_1, t, B) - P(s, x_2, t, B)|$$

is called the *coefficient of ergodicity* of the random Markov process $\xi = \xi(t)$. The inequality

$$\beta(s, t) \leq 1 - k(s, t)$$

holds with probability 1.

The Chapman-Kolmogorov equation being satisfied by the transition function $P(s, x, t, B)$, it yields the following relation:

$$1 - k(s, t) \leq \prod_{i=1}^{n} [1 - k(s_i, t_i)],$$

where $s \leq s_1 \leq t_1 \leq \cdots \leq s_n \leq t_n = t$. If $k(s, t) \geq k > 0$ for $t - s \geq \delta$, then the estimate $1 - k(s, t) \leq C e^{-Dt}$ holds, where C and D are positive constants.

Markov Times and the Strong Markov Property. Let $\xi = \xi(t)$ be a random Markov process on the set T in the phase space $(E, \mathfrak{B})$, and $\mathfrak{A}^*(s, t)$ the σ-algebra of events generated by all events of the form $\{\xi(u) \in B\}$, $u \in [s, t] \cap T$, $B \in \mathfrak{B}$ and completed by adding all sets of probability zero. A random variable $\tau = \tau(\omega)$ with values in T is called a *Markov time* or a *variable which does not depend on the future* if $\{\tau > t\} \in \mathfrak{A}^*(-\infty, t)$ for any t. As an example of a Markov time may serve the time where the trajectory $\xi(\omega, t)$ of the random process $\xi = \xi(t)$ first hits a certain set in the phase space E, etc.

Let $\tau = \tau(\omega)$ be a Markov time and $\mathfrak{A}^*(s, \tau)$ the σ-algebra of all events $A \in \mathfrak{A}^*(-\infty, \infty)$ such that the intersection $A \cdot \{\tau \leq t\}$ belongs to the σ-algebra $\mathfrak{A}^*(-\infty, t)$. Next, let $\eta = \eta(\omega)$ be a random variable with values in T which is measurable with respect to $\mathfrak{A}^*(-\infty, \tau)$ and such that $\eta(\omega) \geq \tau(\omega)$. Finally suppose that T is a Borel set and that the Markov process $\xi = \xi(\omega, t)$ is measurable with respect to the intersection of the σ-algebra $\mathfrak{A}^*(-\infty, \infty)$ with the σ-algebra of all Borel subsets of T. Then the process $\xi = \xi(t)$ is called a *strong Markov process* if for any τ, η and $B \in \mathfrak{B}$

$$\mathbb{P}\{\xi(\eta) \in B \mid \mathfrak{A}^*(-\infty, \tau)\} = P\{\tau, \xi(\tau), \eta, B\} .$$

Consider a Markov process $\xi = \xi(t)$ in the metric phase space $(E, \mathfrak{B})$. We assume that its transition function $P(s, x, t, B)$ has the following property: for $s \to s_0$ and $x \to x_0$ the corresponding probability distributions $P(s, x, t, B)$, $B \in \mathfrak{B}$ converge weakly to the distribution $P(s_0, x_0, t, B)$, that is,

$$\int_B P(s, x, t, dy) \varphi(y) \to \int_E P(s_0, x_0, t, dy) \varphi(y)$$

for any bounded continuous function $\varphi = \varphi(x)$, $x \in E$. If with probability 1 the random process $\xi = \xi(t)$ is right-continuous, then it is a strong Markov process.

Let C be a compact set of the metric phase space $(E, \mathfrak{B})$ and $\tau_C = \tau_C(\omega)$ the first exit time from C of the trajectory $\xi(\omega, t)$ of the separable process $\xi = \xi(t)$ in the interval $T = [a, b]$. We assume that the transition function $P(s, x, t, B)$ satisfies the condition of "uniform stochastic continuity": for every $\varepsilon > 0$,

$$P\{s, x, t, E \backslash V_\varepsilon(x)\} \leq \delta_\varepsilon(t - s) ,$$

where $x \in E$, $V_\varepsilon(x)$ is the ε-neighborhood of the point x and $\delta(h) \to 0$ for $h \to 0$. Then the trajectories $\xi(\omega, t)$ on the interval $(a, \tau_C(\omega))$ can have with probability 1 only discontinuities of the first kind. Moreover there exists a random process $\tilde{\xi} = \tilde{\xi}(t)$ which is equivalent to the original process $\xi = \xi(t)$, and has right-continuous trajectories up to the first exit time $\tau_C = \tau_C(\omega)$ from the compact set C. If for every ε the given relation is satisfied with a function $\delta_\varepsilon = \delta_\varepsilon(h)$ such that $\delta_\varepsilon(h) = o(h)$ for $h \to 0$, then the trajectories $\xi(\omega, t)$ are continuous functions with probability 1 on the interval $(a, \tau_C(\omega))$.

Terminating Markov Processes. Let Ω be a space of elementary events, T a set of the real line, $(E, \mathfrak{B})$ a phase space, $\tau = \tau(\omega)$ a function on Ω with values in T, and $\xi = \xi(\omega, t)$ a function of the two variables (ω, t), $\omega \in \Omega$ and $t \in T \cap (-\infty, \tau(\omega))$ with values in the phase space $(E, \mathfrak{B})$. Let $\mathfrak{A}_s^t$ denote the σ-algebra of events in the "subspace" $\Omega_t = \{\tau > t\}$ generated by all events of the form $\{\xi(u) \in B, \tau > t\}$, $\xi(u) = \xi(\omega, u)$, where $u \in T \cap (s, t)$ and $B \in \mathfrak{B}$. Let $\mathfrak{A}(s, t)$ be a σ-algebra of events of the basic space Ω which contains all $\mathfrak{A}_s^u, u \leq t$. Suppose that for each $s \in T$ and $x \in E$ a probability distribution $\mathbb{P}_{s,x} = \mathbb{P}_{s,x}(A)$ is defined on the σ-algebra $\mathfrak{A}(s, \infty)$ such that for any $s, t \in T$, $s \leq t$, and $B \in \mathfrak{B}$

$$P(s, x, t, B) = \mathbb{P}_{s,x}\{\xi(t) \in B\}$$

is a measurable function of $x \in E$,

$$P(s, x, s, B) = \begin{cases} 1 & \text{for} \quad x \in B, \\ 0 & \text{for} \quad x \notin B, \end{cases}$$

and for almost all ω with respect to $\mathbb{P}_{s,x}$ we have

$$\mathbb{P}_{s,x}\{\xi(t) \in B \mid \mathfrak{A}_s^u\} = P(u, \xi(u), t, B)$$

for all $u \in T$, $s \leq u \leq t$. The corresponding random function $\xi = \xi(t)$ whose values $\xi(t) = \xi(\omega, t)$ are random variables defined for elementary outcomes $\omega \in \Omega$ with $\tau(\omega) > t$, is called a *terminated Markov process*. The random variable $\tau = \tau(\omega)$ is termed the *life time* of the process $\xi = \xi(t)$; it can be interpreted as the exit time from the phase space E under consideration.

For example if $\xi = \xi(t)$ is an interminated Markov process and $\tau = \tau(\omega)$ a certain Markov time (the exit time from a certain set of the phase space, say), then the random process with trajectories $\xi(\omega, t)$, $t < \tau(\omega)$, will be a stopped Markov process with life time τ.

5. Homogeneous and Stationary Random Processes

Shift Transformations and Invariant Distributions. Let T be a certain group (or semigroup) on the real line, that is, the operation $t_1 + t_2$ is defined for any $t_1, t_2 \in T$, and the point $t = t_1 + t_2$ belongs again to T. Let $(E, \mathfrak{B})$ be a measurable space and $X = E^T$ the space of all functions

$x = x(t)$ on the set T with values in E. We consider the following transformation S_u, $u \in T$ in the function space X: if $x = x(t) \in X$, then

$$S_u x(t) = x(t + u).$$

Let $S_u^{-1} A$ be the inverse image of the set $A \subseteq X$ under the mapping S_u. We consider $S_u^{-1} = S_u^{-1} A$ as a transformation of sets in the function space X. The *shift transformation* S_u^{-1} preserves the set-theoretic operations:

$$S_u^{-1} \left(\bigcup_k A_k \right) = \bigcup_k (S_u^{-1} A_k),$$

$$S_u^{-1} \left(\bigcap_k A_k \right) = \bigcap_k (S_u^{-1} A_k),$$

$$S_u^{-1}(A_1 \backslash A_2) = S_u^{-1} A_1 \backslash S_u^{-1} A_2.$$

Moreover each cylinder set A of the form

$$A = \{ x(t_1) \in B_1, \ldots, x(t_n) \in B_n \}$$

is transformed into the cylinder set

$$S_u^{-1} A = \{ x(t_1 + u) \in B_1, \ldots, x(t_n + u) \in B_n \}.$$

If $\mathfrak{A}(s, t)$ is the σ-algebra generated by all cylinder sets $\{ x(u) \in B \}$, where $u \in T \cap [s, t]$ and $B \in \mathfrak{B}$, then the set of all sets $S_u^{-1} A$, $A \in \mathfrak{A}(s, t)$ coincides with the σ-algebra $\mathfrak{A}(s + u, t + u)$. If on the σ-algebras $\mathfrak{A}(s, t)$ and $\mathfrak{A}(s + u, t + u)$ there are given probability distributions $\mathbb{P}_s$ and $\mathbb{P}_{s+u}$, respectively, such that the equation

$$\mathbb{P}_{s+u}(S_u^{-1} A) = \mathbb{P}_s(A)$$

holds for every cylinder set $A \in \mathfrak{A}(s, t)$, then it holds for every set $A \in \mathfrak{A}(s, t)$.

Let $\xi = \xi(t)$ be a random process on the set T with values in the phase space $(E, \mathfrak{B})$. We consider the mapping ξ of the corresponding space of elementary events into the functional space X: $x = \xi(\omega, t)$. The mapping ξ sends each elementary outcome $\omega \in \Omega$ to the trajectory $\xi(\omega, t)$ on T. Let $\xi^{-1} A$ be the inverse image of a set $A \subseteq X$ under the mapping ξ, and let $\mathfrak{A}_\xi(s, t)$ denote the σ-algebra of events generated by all events $\{ \xi(u) \in B \}$, where $u \in T \cap [s, t]$ and $B \in \mathfrak{B}$. The set of all events of the form $\xi^{-1} A$, $A \in \mathfrak{A}(s, t)$ coincides with the σ-algebra $\mathfrak{A}_\xi(s, t)$.

Let $\xi^{-1} A$ with $A \in \mathfrak{A}(-\infty, \infty)$ be some event of the σ-algebra $\mathfrak{A}_\xi(-\infty, \infty)$. We set

$$S_u^{-1}(\xi^{-1} A) = \xi^{-1}(S_u^{-1} A).$$

Given the event $\xi^{-1} A$ the corresponding event $\xi^{-1}(S_u^{-1} A)$ is, in general, not uniquely defined since events $\xi^{-1} A_1$ and $\xi^{-1} A_2$ may coincide although A_1 and A_2 are different.

Suppose that probability distributions $\mathbb{P}_s$ and $\mathbb{P}_{s+u}$ are given on the σ-algebras $\mathfrak{A}_\xi(s, t)$ and $\mathfrak{A}_\xi(s + u, t + u)$, respectively, such that for any event $\{\xi(t_1) \in B_1, \ldots, \xi(t_n) \in B_n\}$, where $t_1, \ldots, t_n \in T \cap [s, t]$ and $B_1, \ldots, B_n \in \mathfrak{B}$, the equation

$$\mathbb{P}_{s+u}\{\xi(t_1 + u) \in B_1, \ldots, \xi(t_n + u) \in B_n\} = \mathbb{P}_s\{\xi(t_1) \in B_1, \ldots, \xi(t_n) \in B_n\}$$

is satisfied. Then for any sets $A_1, A_2 \in \mathfrak{A}(s, t)$ such that $\xi^{-1} A_1 = \xi^{-1} A_2$, the corresponding events $\xi^{-1}(S_u^{-1} A_1)$ and $\xi^{-1}(S_u^{-1} A_2)$ differ from each other only by an event of probability zero:

$$\mathbb{P}_{s+u}\{\xi^{-1}(S_u^{-1} A_1) \circ \xi^{-1}(S_u^{-1} A_2)\} = 0.$$

If we do not distinguish between such events, then the *shift transformation* S_u^{-1} on the σ-algebra $\mathfrak{A}_\xi(s, t)$ will be *uniquely defined*. Moreover, for any event $A \in \mathfrak{A}_\xi(s, t)$ the corresponding event $S_u^{-1} A$ belongs to the σ-algebra $\mathfrak{A}_\xi(s + u, t + u)$ and every event of $\mathfrak{A}_\xi(s + u, t + u)$ can be represented as $S_u^{-1} A$, $A \in \mathfrak{A}_\xi(s, t)$, that is,

$$S_u^{-1} \mathfrak{A}_\xi(s, t) = \mathfrak{A}_\xi(s + u, t + u).$$

If we do not distinguish between random variables $\eta = \eta(\omega)$ which coincide with probability 1, then the *shift transformation* U_u can be defined for each random variable $\eta = \eta(\omega)$ which is measurable with respect to the σ-algebra $\mathfrak{A}_\xi(s, t)$. In fact, for a simple random variable η such that $\eta(\omega) = y_k$ for $\omega \in A_k$ $(k = 1, 2, \ldots)$ the shift transformation can be defined as

$$U_u \eta(\omega) = y_k \quad \text{for} \quad \omega \in S_u^{-1} A_k \quad (k = 1, 2, \ldots).$$

If η is arbitrary, we can set

$$U_u \eta(\omega) = \lim_{n \to \infty} U_u \eta_n(\omega),$$

where $\eta_n(\omega)$, $n = 1, 2, \ldots$, is a sequence of simple random variables which converges uniformly to $\eta(\omega)$. The shift transformation U_u fulfils for any Borel function $\varphi = \varphi(x_1, \ldots, x_n)$ on the space $(E^n, \mathfrak{B}^n)$ the equation

$$U_u \varphi[\xi(t_1), \ldots, \xi(t_n)] = \varphi[\xi(t_1 + u), \ldots, \xi(t_n + u)].$$

Homogeneous Markov Processes. In order to have something definite in mind, suppose that T is the set of all non-negative numbers or all integers $t \geq 0$. A Markov process $\xi = \xi(t)$ on the set T in the phase space $(E, \mathfrak{B})$ is called *homogeneous* if its transition function $P(s, x, t, B)$ satisfies for any $u, s, t \in T$ with $s \leq t$ and all $x \in E$, $B \in \mathfrak{B}$ the *stationary condition*

$$P(s + u, x, t + u, B) = P(s, x, t, B).$$

If the Markov process $\xi = \xi(t)$ is homogeneous, the transition function actually depends only on $t - s$, x and B, and therefore may be written in the form $P(t - s, x, B)$. The corresponding conditional distributions $\mathbb{P}_{s,x} = \mathbb{P}_{s,x}(A)$, $A \in \mathfrak{A}_\xi(s, \infty)$ of the homogeneous Markov process $\xi = \xi(t)$ fulfil the equation

$$\mathbb{P}_{s+u,x}\{\xi(t_1 + u) \in B_1, \ldots, \xi(t_n + u) \in B_n\} = \mathbb{P}_{s,x}\{\xi(t_1) \in B_1, \ldots, \xi(t_n) \in B_n\}$$

for any $t_1, \ldots, t_n \in T \cap [s, \infty)$ and $B_1, \ldots, B_n \in \mathfrak{B}$.

The corresponding shift transformations S_u can be defined on each of the σ-algebras $\mathfrak{A}_\xi(s, \infty)$. They have the property that $S_{u_1} S_{u_2} = S_{u_1 + u_2}$ for all $u_1, u_2 \in T$ and

$$\mathbb{P}_{s+u,x}(S_u^{-1} A) = \mathbb{P}_{s,x}(A) \qquad (A \in \mathfrak{A}_\xi(s, \infty)).$$

Thus all distributions $\mathbb{P}_{s,x}(A)$ are determined, for example, by the distribution

$$\mathbb{P}_x(A) = \mathbb{P}_{0,x}(A) \qquad (A \in \mathfrak{A}_\xi(0, \infty)).$$

Stationary Random Processes. Again to have something definite in mind, let T now be the set of all real numbers or all integers t. A random process $\xi = \xi(t)$ on T in the phase space $(E, \mathfrak{B})$ is called *stationary in the strict sense* if its finite-dimensional distributions satisfy the stationary condition

$$\mathbb{P}_{t_1 + u, \ldots, t_n + u}(B_1, \ldots, B_n) = \mathbb{P}_{t_1, \ldots, t_n}(B_1, \ldots, B_n)$$

for all $u, t_1, \ldots, t_n \in T$ and $B_1, \ldots, B_n \in \mathfrak{B}$.

Given a stationary process $\xi = \xi(t)$ the shift transformation S_u is defined for each $u \in T$ on the entire σ-algebra of events $\mathfrak{A}_\xi(-\infty, \infty)$, and the corresponding probability distribution $\mathbb{P} = \mathbb{P}(A), A \in \mathfrak{A}_\xi(-\infty, \infty)$ is invariant with respect to the transformations S_u, that is,

$$\mathbb{P}(S_u^{-1} A) = \mathbb{P}(A)$$

for all $u \in T$, $A \in \mathfrak{A}_\xi(-\infty, \infty)$. For any $u_1, u_2 \in T$ we have

$$S_{u_1} S_{u_2} = S_{u_1 + u_2}.$$

Let $L^2(\Omega)$ be the Hilbert space of all random variables $\eta = \eta(\omega)$ which are measurable with respect to $\mathfrak{A}_\xi(-\infty, \infty)$, endowed with the scalar product $(\eta_1, \eta_2) = \mathbb{M}(\eta_1 \cdot \bar{\eta}_2)$. The shift transformation U_u, $u \in T$, considered as a transformation in $L^2(\Omega)$, is a unitary operator and for any $u_1, u_2 \in T$ we have

$$U_{u_1} U_{u_2} = U_{u_1 + u_2}.$$

Example. *The Stationary Markov Process.* Let $\xi = \xi(t)$ be a homogeneous Markov process on the real line T in the phase space $(E, \mathfrak{B})$, and suppose that its transition function $P(t, x, B)$ admits in the phase space $(E, \mathfrak{B})$ a so-called *invariant* or *stationary probability distribution* $\mathbb{P}^0 = \mathbb{P}^0(B)$, $B \in \mathfrak{B}$, that is,

$$\mathbb{P}^0(B) = \int_E \mathbb{P}^0(dx)\, P(t, x, B)$$

for all $B \in \mathfrak{B}$ and $t \in T$. This probability distribution $\mathbb{P}^0$ has the property that the homogeneous Markov process $\xi(t)$ with transition function $P(t, x, B)$ and distributions

$$\mathbb{P}_t(B) = P\{\xi(t) \in B\} = \mathbb{P}^0(B) \qquad (B \in \mathfrak{B})$$

is stationary in the strict sense.

CHAPTER IV

Limit Theorems in Probability Theory

§ 1. Distributions and their Characteristic Functions

1. One-to-one Correspondance
between Distributions and Characteristic Functions

The problem of summation of random variables which need not necessarily take real values represents up to the present time one of the main subjects of investigation in probability theory. Moreover, the case of dependent random variables is often reduced by this or that technique to the case of independent ones. Here the basic tools are characteristic functions as defined earlier (see Chapter III, § 1.1). Let $\mathbb{P}_\xi$ be the distribution of a random variable or a finite-dimensional random vector $\xi \in R^s$. The characteristic function $\varphi_\xi = \varphi_\xi(t)$ is obtained by the formula

$$\varphi_\xi(t) = \varphi(t; \mathbb{P}_\xi) = \mathbb{M} e^{i(t, \xi)} = \int_{R^s} e^{i(t, x)} \mathbb{P}_\xi(dx).$$

The *multiplicativity*

$$\varphi_{\xi_1 + \xi_2} = \varphi_{\xi_1} \varphi_{\xi_2}$$

for independent ξ_1 and ξ_2 is connected with the fact that for fixed t the function $e^{i(t, x)}$ represents a *character* of the additive group of the real number or the vectors of a finite-dimensional euclidean space, respectively:

$$e^{i(t, \xi_1 + \xi_2)} = e^{i(t, \xi_1)} e^{i(t, \xi_2)}.$$

This remark is the starting point for the construction of the concept of characteristic functions of random variables with values in more general groups. As the domain of the characteristic function may serve in the commutative case the set of all characters or in the non-commutative case the set of all unitary irreducible representations of the corresponding group. We can just as well take as the domain the set of all elementary positive definite functions normalized by the condition to take the value one on the unit element of the group which we then write multi-plicatively [21]. In this chapter we mainly deal with the commutative case.

The fact that characteristic functions and distributions *determine each other uniquely* is based on the existence of sufficiently many characters. By this we mean in the present context that, vaguely speaking, any continuous and bounded function of x can be uniformly approximated on any given compact set by finite linear combinations of characters.

For example, consider the question of the uniqueness of the correspondance on the real line, that is, for real-valued random variables. Let $\mathbb{P}_{\xi_1}$ and $\mathbb{P}_{\xi_2}$ be two distributions on the line such that

$$\varphi_{\xi_1} \equiv \varphi_{\xi_2},$$

and let f be any continuous bounded function. The characteristic functions being equal we have the equality

$$\int_{-\infty}^{\infty} \left(\sum_j c_j e^{it_j x} \right) \mathbb{P}_{\xi_1}(dx) = \int_{-\infty}^{\infty} \left(\sum_j c_j e^{it_j x} \right) \mathbb{P}_{\xi_2}(dx)$$

for all trigonometric polynomials. Taking into account that (a) every distribution on the line is "almost entirely" concentrated on some compact set and that (b) every continuous bounded function can be approximated uniformly on any compact set by trigonometric polynomials we conclude that

$$\int_{-\infty}^{\infty} f(x) \mathbb{P}_{\xi_1}(dx) = \int_{-\infty}^{\infty} f(x) \mathbb{P}_{\xi_2}(dx)$$

for any bounded continuous function f, and this implies that the distributions coincide [22].

On the other hand distributions need not coincide if the corresponding characteristic functions are equal only on some interval of the real line. One way of constructing examples which illustrate this phenomenon starts from Pólya's theorem according to which any continuous real-valued even function $g(t)$ such that $g(0) = 1$, $g(t) \to 0$ for $t \to \infty$, g is convex on $[0, \infty)$, represents a characteristic function.

A simple and convenient sufficient condition for the uniqueness in this framework is that the characteristic function be analytic in some neighborhood of 0. In terms of the corresponding distribution this

[21] *Grenander, U.,* Probabilities on Algebraic Structures. London: John Wiley 1963.

[22] *Prohorov, Yu. V.,* The method of characteristic functionals. Proc. 4th Berkeley Symp., Vol. **2**, (1961), 403–419.

requirement is equivalent to the so-called condition of *Cramér*: the integral

$$\int_{-\infty}^{\infty} e^{hx} \, \mathbb{P}_{\xi}(dx)$$

is finite for all sufficiently small h. *Cramér's* condition can also be formulated in terms of the derivatives of the characteristic functions at the point zero or in terms of the moments: there exists an $H > 0$ such that

$$\mathbb{M} \xi_1^{2k} \leqq (2k)! \, H^{2k} \quad (k = 0, 1, 2, \ldots);$$

further results are given in § 3 of this chapter.

On the other hand we can also formulate conditions for non-uniqueness. For example if the characteristic function $\varphi(t)$ has the property that

$$\varphi(t) = \int_{-\infty}^{\infty} e^{itx} p(x) \, dx, \quad p(x) \in L_2(R^1)$$

and

$$\int_{-\infty}^{\infty} \frac{|\log p(x)|}{1 + x^2} \, dx < \infty,$$

then for every a there is another characteristic function $\varphi_a(t)$ such that

$$\varphi(t) = \varphi_a(t) \quad \text{for} \quad |t| \leqq a.$$

Similar statements are true in the more general case of distributions with non-vanishing absolutely continuous components.

Under special assumptions on the random variables we can use side by side with characteristic functions their analogues: in the case of an integer-valued random variable ξ the *generating function*

$$\sum_n z^n \, \mathbb{P}\{\xi = n\},$$

and if ξ is positive the *Laplace transform* of the corresponding distribution

$$\int_0^{\infty} e^{-sx} \, \mathbb{P}_{\xi}(dx).$$

Moreover the two-sided Laplace transform can be used for the investigation of distributions whose distribution functions tend exponentially to zero or one for arguments tending to $-\infty$ or $+\infty$, respectively. Generating functions as well as the Laplace transform have the multiplicative property, that is, products correspond to the convolution of the distributions, and they determine uniquely the corresponding distributions.

2. Inversion Formulas

An essential supplement to the uniqueness theorems on characteristic functions consists in the computation of $\mathbb{P}_\xi(A)$ for various classes of sets A in terms of characteristic functions. If ξ is a random variable with values in the finite-dimensional space R^s and with an *absolutely integrable* characteristic function

$$\int_{R^s} |\varphi_\xi(t)|\, dt < \infty ,$$

then the distribution of ξ has a continuous density, and the *inversion formula for Fourier integrals* implies

$$p_\xi(x) = (2\pi)^{-s} \int_{R^s} e^{-i(t,x)}\, \varphi_\xi(t)\, dt .$$

Integrating with respect to x for $x \in A$ we obtain, at least in the case of a bounded set A,

$$\mathbb{P}_\xi(A) = (2\pi)^{-s} \int_{R^s} \left(\int_A e^{-i(t,x)}\, dx \right) \varphi_\xi(t)\, dt .$$

A similar formula for arbitrary distributions can be obtained with the help of the so-called "smoothing" technique which represents a very convenient and often used device. We start with the following assertion: let $H(x)$ be a function represented in the form

$$H(x) = (2\pi)^{-s} \int_{R^s} e^{i(t,x)} h(t)\, dt$$

with absolutely integrable $h(t)$. Then

$$\mathbb{M}\, H(\xi) = (2\pi)^{-s} \int_{R^s} \varphi_\xi(t)\, h(t)\, dt .$$

Since

$$\mathbb{P}_\xi(A) = \mathbb{M}\, I_A(\xi)$$

where I_A is the indicator function of A, that is, $I_A(x) = 1$ if $x \in A$ and $I_A(x) = 0$ if $x \notin A$, in order to obtain an "inversion formula" it suffices to be able to approximate $I_A(x)$ by functions $H(x)$ of the type described before. This can be achieved, for example, by setting

$$H_\sigma(x) = \int_{R^s} I_A(y)\, (2\pi)^{-\frac{s}{2}}\, \sigma^{-s} \exp\left\{ -\frac{(x-y,\, x-y)}{2\sigma^2} \right\} dy$$

$$= (2\pi)^{-s} \int_{R^s} e^{i(t,x)} \left(\int_A e^{-i(t,v)}\, dv \right) e^{-\frac{\sigma^2(t,t)}{2}}\, dt .$$

We always have

$$0 \leq H_\sigma(x) \leq 1 \,,$$

and if $\sigma \to 0$, then $H_\sigma(x) \to 1$ if x is an interior point of A, and $H_\sigma(x) \to 0$ if x is an interior point of the complement of A. Therefore if A is a set of continuity of the distribution $\mathbb{P}_\xi$, that is, $\mathbb{P}_\xi$ (boundary A) = 0, we obtain

$$\mathbb{P}_\xi(A) = \lim_{\sigma \to 0} (2\pi)^{-s} \int_{R^s} \left(\int_A e^{-i(t,v)} \, dv \right) e^{-\frac{\sigma^2(t,t)}{2}} \varphi_\xi(t) \, dt \,.$$

In particular, consider the balls

$$A = S_{a,r} = \{x : |x - a| \leq r\} \,.$$

Since

$$\int_{S_{a,r}} e^{-i(t,v)} \, dv = e^{-i(t,a)} \left(\frac{2\pi r}{|t|} \right)^{\frac{s}{2}} J_{\frac{s}{2}}(r|t|) \,,$$

where $J_{s/2}(z)$ is the Bessel function of order $s/2$, we have

$$\mathbb{P}_\xi(S_{a,r}) = \lim_{\sigma \to 0} (2\pi)^{-s} \int_{R^s} \left(\frac{2\pi r}{|t|} \right)^{\frac{s}{2}} J_{\frac{s}{2}}(r|t|) e^{-\frac{\sigma^2(t,t)}{2}} e^{-i(t,a)} \varphi_\xi(t) \, dt \,.$$

Apart from inversion formulas we can obtain in this way also convenient inequalities. We state one example. Let $\sum a_{j,k} t_j t_k$ be a nonnegative quadratic form. If the inequality

$$\sum_{j,k} a_{j,k} t_j t_k \leq 1$$

implies the inequality

$$1 - \operatorname{Re} \varphi_\xi(t) \leq \varepsilon \,,$$

then

$$\mathbb{P}\{|\xi| \geq r\} \leq \frac{\sqrt{e}}{\sqrt{e} - 1} \left(\varepsilon + \frac{\sum_k a_{k,k}}{r^2} \right) \,.$$

Continuity of the Correspondance Between Distributions and Characteristic Functions. The following continuity property of the correspondance between distributions in a euclidean space and their characteristic functions holds: the pointwise convergence of characteristic functions is equivalent to the weak convergence of the corresponding distributions, and the equi-continuity of a family of characteristic functions at the point zero is equivalent to the weak compactness of the corresponding family of distributions. If not the characteristic functions themselves but only their absolute values are equi-continuous at the point zero, then the corresponding family of distributions is "shift-compact", that is, the family of the distributions of the random vectors $\xi_n - A_n$ is weakly compact for a suitable choice of the constant A_n.

Sometimes it is desirable to consider stronger types of convergence than weak convergence. Then the problem arises to formulate equivalent conditions in terms of characteristic functions. This problem usually turns out to be hard (see the following paragraph).

3. Properties of Distributions in Terms of Characteristic Functions

Absolute Continuity and Singularity. If the characteristic function is absolutely integrable, then, as mentioned before, the distribution has a continuous density which is bounded on the entire space. If

$$\int\limits_{R^s} |\varphi_\xi(t)|^2 \, dt < \infty \,,$$

then the distribution of ξ is absolutely continuous. In R^1 the following rather deep statement is true which represents in some sense the converse to the statement given before[23]: if the function $\varphi(t)$ on R^1 is sufficiently regularly decreasing for $|t| \to \infty$ and

$$\int\limits_{-\infty}^{\infty} \varphi^2(t) \, dt = \infty,$$

which is at any rate true for functions equivalent to

$$\frac{1}{\sqrt{|t|}} \,, \quad \frac{1}{\sqrt{|t| \log |t|}} \,, \quad \frac{1}{\sqrt{|t| \cdot \log |t| \log \cdot \log |t|}} \,, \cdots$$

for $|t| \to \infty$ etc., there exists a singular distribution $\mathbb{P}$ such that

$$\varphi(t; \mathbb{P}) = 0(\varphi(t)) \quad \text{for} \quad |t| \to \infty \,.$$

This result can be used to construct examples of singular distributions which after a certain number of convolutions with themselves become absolutely continuous. In R^1 such examples may seem "pathological". However in R^s for $s \geq 2$ there exist simple and natural examples of distributions with similar properties.

---

[23] *Ivašev-Musatov, O. S.*, On coefficients of Fourier-Stieltjes of singular functions. Dokl. Akad. Nauk SSSR **82**, 1 (1952), 9—11 (Russian).

Example. If $\mathbb{P}$ is the uniform distribution on the unit circle in R^2, then $\mathbb{P}$ is singular relative to the Lebesgue measure, but the convolution $\mathbb{P} * \mathbb{P}$ has the density

$$p(x, y) = \frac{1}{\pi^2 r \sqrt{4 - r^2}} \qquad (r^2 = x^2 + y^2).$$

The existence of the density is connected with the fact that the characteristic function

$$\varphi(t_1, t_2) = J_0^2(\sqrt{t_1^2 + t_2^2})$$

of the distribution $\mathbb{P} * \mathbb{P}$ fulfils for $t \to \infty$ the relation

$$\varphi(t_1, t_2; \ \mathbb{P} * \mathbb{P}) = 0\left(\frac{1}{\sqrt{t_1^2 + t_2^2}}\right).$$

This example can be generalized in the sense that the characteristic function of the uniform distribution on the surface of a sufficiently smooth convex body with non-vanishing curvature is of the order of magnitude $0(|t|^{-s/2})$ where $|t| = \sqrt{t_1^2 + t_2^2 + \cdots + t_s^2}$. Characteristic functions of many other singular distributions in R^s decrease like $|t|^{-\alpha}$, $\alpha > 0$; this is true, for example, for the characteristic function of the joint distribution of the powers $(\xi, \xi^2, \ldots, \xi^s)$ of a given continuous distribution of a random variable ξ [24].

Let us return to the case of the space R^1 and add some remarks on absolute continuity and singularity.

If the distribution $\mathbb{P}$ has an absolutely continuous component, then

$$\overline{\lim_{|t| \to \infty}} |\varphi(t, \mathbb{P})| < 1. \tag{C}$$

In the case of a discrete distribution we always have $\overline{\lim_{|t| \to \infty}} |\varphi(t, \mathbb{P})| = 1$. On the other hand let us consider a characteristic function of the form

$$\varphi(t) = \prod_{j=1}^{\infty} \left(1 - \frac{1}{\lambda_j} + \frac{1}{\lambda_j} e^{it 2^{-j}}\right),$$

where $2 < \lambda_n \to \infty$ and $\prod_{j=1}^{\infty} \left(1 - \frac{1}{\lambda_j}\right) = 0$. The corresponding distribution admits no point of positive mass. At the same time the equality $\overline{\lim_{|t| \to \infty}} |\varphi(t, \mathbb{P})| = 1$ is still true. Thus

$$\overline{\lim_{|t| \to \infty}} |\varphi(t, \mathbb{P})^n| = 1$$

---

[24] See footnotes in the paper of *Sadikova, S. M.*, Some inequalities for characteristic functions. Teoriya veroyatn. i primen. XI, 3 (1966), 500—506 (Russian).

for every n, and the corresponding distribution contains no absolutely continuous component for any n.

Under additional restrictions the inequality (C) can be sharpened. If the distribution $\mathbb{P}$ is concentrated on a finite interval $[-L, L]$ and has a bounded density

$$p(x) \leqq A < \infty ,$$

then

$$\sup_{|t| \geqq \pi/2L} |\varphi(t, \mathbb{P})| \leqq 1 - C A^{-2} L^{-2}$$

where C is an absolute constant; for example we may take $C = 1/128$.

In the case of symmetric and unimodal distributions $\mathbb{P}$ we can establish inequalities of the following type. We assume without restricting the generality that the maximum of the density is equal to $1/2$. Then

1) $\varphi(t) \leqq \dfrac{\sin t}{t}$, $\qquad 0 < t < \dfrac{\pi}{2}$;

2) $\varphi(t) \leqq \dfrac{1}{t}$, $\qquad \dfrac{\pi}{2} \leqq t$;

3) $\varphi(t) > -\sin \dfrac{\gamma}{\gamma}$ $\quad 0 < t < \gamma$,

where γ is the smallest positive root of the equation $\gamma = \operatorname{tg}\gamma$ ($\gamma = 4.49 \ldots$);

4) $\varphi(t) \geqq \dfrac{\sin t}{t}$, $\qquad \gamma \leqq t < \dfrac{3\pi}{2}$

5) $\varphi(t) \geqq -\dfrac{1}{t}$, $\qquad \dfrac{3\pi}{2} \leqq t$.

All estimates are sharp; equality may hold in 1), 2), 4), 5). Moreover in the inequalities 1) and 4) the equality between $\varphi(t)$ and the corresponding expression on the right side can hold even for a single value of t only in the case of the uniform distribution on $[-1, 1]$. This implies that $|\varphi(t)| \leqq \sin t/t$ for $|t| \leqq \pi/2$.

The following lemma by *H. Cramér* belongs into the present context: if a characteristic function $\varphi(t)$ fulfils for $|t| \geqq a$ the inequality $|\varphi(t)|^2 \leqq b^2$, then for $|t| < a$ we have

$$|\varphi(t)|^2 \leqq 1 - \dfrac{1 - b^2}{8a^2} t^2 .$$

This lemma allows to exploit an estimate of a characteristic function outside of some neighborhood of zero in order to describe its behavior within this neighborhood.

Sharper inequalities of a different type concerning the behavior of characteristic functions near zero are based on the use of *moments*. For example, let $\xi_1, \xi_2, \ldots, \xi_n$ be independent random variables,

$$\mathsf{M}\xi_i = 0, \qquad \mathsf{M}\xi_i^2 = \sigma_i^2, \qquad \mathsf{M}|\xi_i|^3 = \beta_i$$

and

$$s_n = \xi_1 + \cdots + \xi_n, \qquad \sigma^2 = \sum_{i=1}^{n} \sigma_i^2, \qquad \varepsilon = \frac{1}{\sigma^3} \sum_{i=1}^{n} \beta_i.$$

Then for every t

$$\varphi_{\frac{s_n}{\sigma}}(t) \leqq \exp\left\{ -\frac{t^2}{2}(1 - K\varepsilon|t|) \right\},$$

where

$$K = 4 \sup_{x>0} \frac{\cos x - 1 + \dfrac{x^2}{2}}{x^3} = 0.396648 \ldots$$

Lattice Distributions. We recall that the set L of points of the s-dimensional space R^s is called a lattice if there exist linearly independent vectors $l_1, l_2, \ldots, l_s$ and a vector l_0 such that L consists of all points of the form

$$l_0 + k_1 l_1 + \cdots + k_s l_s, \tag{1.1}$$

where k_j $(1 \leqq j \leqq s)$ runs through the set of all integers from $-\infty$ to ∞. To any lattice L we attach its step, that is, the volume $h(L)$ of the parallelepiped spanned by the vectors $l_1, \ldots, l_s$. The lattice generated by the vectors $l_1, l_2, \ldots, l_s$ can also be generated by other vectors, for example $l_1 + l_2, l_2, \ldots, l_s$. Of course, the step of the lattice does not depend on the choice of the representation. A distribution $\mathbb{P}$ in R^s is called a *lattice distribution* if there is some lattice L such that $\mathbb{P}(L) = 1$. The number $h(L)$ is then termed the *step of the distribution*. The lattice L is called *fundamental* if

$$\mathbb{P}(L') < 1$$

for every sublattice $L' \subset L$. In this case if L'' is any lattice such that $\mathbb{P}(L'') = 1$, the ratio $h(L)/h(L'')$ is an integer, and $h(L)$ is called the *maximal step of the distribution*. The number $h(L)$ is equal to $s!$ times the greatest common divisor of the volumes of all s-dimensional simplices whose vertices are possible values of the distribution $\mathbb{P}$.

Suppose that the lattice (1.1) satisfies the equation $\mathbb{P}(L) = 1$. Consider an s-tupel $\tilde{l}_1, \ldots, \tilde{l}_s$ and a reciprocal s-tupel $l_1, \ldots, l_s$, that is, with scalar products

$$(l_i, \tilde{l}_j) = \delta_{i,j} = \begin{cases} 1 & \text{for} \quad i=j, \\ 0 & \text{for} \quad i \neq j \end{cases}$$

where $\delta_{i,j}$ is *Kronecker's* symbol. Then the characteristic function $\varphi(t) = \varphi(t, \mathbb{P})$ fulfils the equation

$$|\varphi(2\pi \tilde{l}_j)| = 1 \quad (j = 1, \dots, s). \tag{1.2}$$

If the lattice L is fundamental, then the absolute value of φ is smaller than 1 in every point of the closed parallelepiped $\tilde{D}$ spanned by the vectors $2\pi \tilde{l}_1, \dots, 2\pi \tilde{l}_s$ except in its vertices. Conversely, if the equation (1.2) holds for some s-tupel, then there exists a vector l_0 such that the distribution $\mathbb{P}$ is concentrated on the lattice determined by l_0 and the reciprocal s-tupel. This lattice is fundamental if $|\varphi(t)| < 1$ for every $t \in \tilde{D}$ except the vertices.

Let us fix our attention for the moment at the one-dimensional case and consider without restricting the generality a distribution concentrated on the lattice of all integers. According to what we said before, if the maximal step of the distribution equals $h = 1$, then $|\varphi(t)| < 1$, $0 < t < 2\pi$. However inside of this interval $|\varphi(t)|$ can be arbitrarily close to one. This statement is obviously true in examples where the distribution is almost entirely "concentrated" on some sublattice L' of the lattice of all integers, say, $\mathbb{P}$ assigns the masses $\dfrac{1-\varepsilon}{2}, \varepsilon, \dfrac{1-\varepsilon}{2}$ to the points $-1, 0, 1$ respectively, where ε is small. Apart from this trivial case there may be others. In fact let $\mathbb{P}$ assign probabilities p_0, p_1, p_2 to the points with coordinates 0, k_1 *and* k_2, respectively, where $0 < k_1 < k_2$ and k_1 and k_2 are mutually prime, and let l_1/l_2 be the last convergent fraction for k_1/k_2. Then $k_1 l_2 - k_2 l_1 = \pm 1$, and a simple computation shows that

$$\left| \varphi \left(2\pi \frac{l_2}{k_2}, \mathbb{P} \right) \right|^2 \geq 1 - p_1(1-p_1) \left(\frac{2\pi}{k_2} \right)^2.$$

For example, if $p_0 = p_1 = p_2 = 1/3$, $k_1 = 3$, $k_2 = 10$, then

$$\left| \varphi \left(2\pi \frac{3}{10} \right) \right|^2 \geq 0.91.$$

The existence of points of this type can reduce significantly the accuracy in local theorems (see below).

The values of a characteristic function in points commensurable with 2π are connected with the probability to fall into some sublattice of the lattice of all integers. In fact if

$$L_{l_0,h} = \{l : l = l_0 + kh, \; -\infty < k < \infty\},$$

then

$$\varphi\left(2\pi \frac{r}{h}\right) = \sum_{l_0=0}^{h-1} \mathbb{P}(L_{l_0,h}) \, e^{\left(2\pi i \frac{r}{h} l_0\right)} = \sum_{j=0}^{h-1} \mathbb{P}(L_{l_j,h}) \, e^{\frac{2\pi i j}{h}},$$

$$r l_j \equiv j (\mathrm{mod}\, h).$$

§ 2. Estimates of the Nearness of Distributions in Terms of the Nearness of their Characteristic Functions

1. Uniform Distances

At the present time several methods are being used to measure the "distance" between distribution functions. As will be seen below these methods have various degrees of generality. The space of all distributions given on the σ-algebra of all Borel sets of a complete separable metric space can be metrized in such a way that convergence in the sense of this metric is equivalent to weak convergence. We will not continue now in this direction. It is possible to define a "distance" by the formula

$$\varrho_{\mathfrak{A}}(\mathbb{P}, \mathbb{Q}) = \sup_{A \in \mathfrak{A}} |\mathbb{P}(A) - \mathbb{Q}(A)|,$$

where the least upper bound is taken for some subclass $\mathfrak{A}$ of the class of all measurable sets. In the case of distributions in the euclidean space R^s the most natural cases are the following:
a) $\mathfrak{A}$ coincides with the class $\mathfrak{C}$ of all convex sets;
b) $\mathfrak{A}$ coincides with the class $\mathfrak{B}$ of all Borel sets.
Let us consider $\varrho_{\mathfrak{C}}(\mathbb{P}, \mathbb{Q})$ first in R^1. There we have

$$\sup_x |F(x) - G(x)| \le \varrho_{\mathfrak{C}}(\mathbb{P}, \mathbb{Q}) \le 2 \sup_x |F(x) - G(x)|,$$

where F and G are the distribution functions of the measures $\mathbb{P}$ and $\mathbb{Q}$, respectively. The convergence

$$\sup_x |F_n(x) - G(x)| \to 0 \quad (n \to \infty)$$

is equivalent with the convergence

$$\sup_t |\varphi_n(t) - \psi(t)| \to 0 \quad (n \to \infty)$$

for the corresponding characteristic functions. However, there exist examples where

$$\lim_{n \to \infty} \sup_t |\varphi_n(t) - \psi_n(t)| = 0$$

and still

$$\lim_{n \to \infty} \sup_x |F_n(x) - G_n(x)| > 0 .$$

For example, if we take two real numbers a and b $(0 < a < b)$ and consider the distribution functions

$$F(x) = \left(\frac{1}{2} \log \frac{x^2 + b^2}{x^2 + a^2} \right) \bigg/ \left(\log \frac{a}{b} \right) \qquad (x \leq 0)$$

and

$$G(x) = 1 - F(-x),$$

then we have

$$F(0) - G(0) = 1 .$$

On the other hand the difference of the characteristic functions can be estimated by

$$|\varphi(t) - \psi(t)| = \left| i\pi \frac{t}{|t|} [e^{-a|t|} - e^{-b|t|}] \right| \left(\log \frac{b}{a} \right)^{-1} < \pi \left(\log \frac{b}{a} \right)^{-1}$$

where logarithms are taken with respect to the basis e.

The basis of the proof of many limit theorems is the following inequality by Esseen where $G(x)$ need not be a distribution function but only a function of bounded variation: for any $T > 0$

$$\sup_x |F(x) - G(x)| \leq \frac{2}{\pi} \int_0^T \left| \frac{\varphi(u) - \psi(u)}{u} \right| du + \frac{24}{\pi} \cdot \frac{\sup |G'|}{T} .$$

We can list several inequalities similar in meaning to the preceeding one. For example, it can be proved that there exists an absolute constant C such that for any $A, T, \varepsilon > 0$, any non-decreasing function $F(x)$ and any function $G(x)$ of bounded variation satisfying the conditions

1) $F(-\infty) = G(-\infty)$,
2) $G'(x)$ exist for all x and $|G'(x)| \leq A$,
3) $|\varphi(t) - \psi(t)| < \varepsilon$ for $|t| < T$,

it follows that for any $L > 2/T$

$$|F(x) - G(x)| < C \left(\varepsilon \log(LT) + \frac{A}{T} + \gamma(L) \right)$$

where

$$\gamma(L) = \operatorname*{Var}_{-\infty < x < \infty} G(x) - \sup_x \operatorname*{Var}_{x \leq y \leq x+L} G(y) .$$

Finally if F and G vary only by jumps situated at integers, then

$$|F(x) - G(x)| \leqq \frac{1}{4} \int\limits_{-\pi}^{\pi} \left| \frac{\varphi(t) - \psi(t)}{t} \right| dt .$$

There is no adequate expression in terms of characteristic functions for the convergence "in variation", that is, for the convergence in the sense of the distance $\sup\limits_{\mathfrak{B}} |\mathbb{P}(A) - \mathbb{Q}(A)|$. Limit theorems on the convergence in variation have to be proved by indirect methods.

We remark that if $\mathbb{P}$ and $\mathbb{Q}$ are absolutely continuous relative to some measure, Lebesgue measure, say:

$$\mathbb{P}(A) = \int\limits_{A} p(x)\, dx , \qquad \mathbb{Q}(A) = \int\limits_{A} q(x)\, dx ,$$

then

$$\sup\limits_{\mathfrak{B}} |\mathbb{P}(A) - \mathbb{Q}(A)| = \frac{1}{2} \int\limits_{-\infty}^{+\infty} |p(x) - q(x)|\, dx .$$

Convergence of densities $p_n(x)$ to a density $p(x)$ is usually obtained by representing $p_n(x)$ in the form

$$p_n(x) = \lambda_n q_n(x) + \mu_n r_n(x) \qquad (\lambda_n + \mu_n = 1,\, \lambda_n \geqq 0,\, \mu_n \geqq 0)$$

where q_n and r_n are some densities and $q_n(x)$ converges to $q(x)$ uniformly on the entire line, and $\mu_n \to 0$ for $n \to \infty$.

2. The Multi-Dimensional Case

Let us now turn to the case of several dimensions. Here relatively little is known. We first formulate the analogue of the classical theorem by *Pólya* according to which weak convergence of a sequence of distribution functions to a continuous distribution function is automatically uniform. Let $\mathbb{P}$ be a probability measure in R^s such that every convex subset of R^s has a boundary of $\mathbb{P}$-probability zero. Then the condition $\mathbb{P}_n \Rightarrow \mathbb{P}$ holds if and only if

$$\sup\limits_{C \in \mathfrak{C}} |\mathbb{P}_n(C) - \mathbb{P}(C)| \to 0 \qquad (n \to \infty)$$

where $\mathfrak{C}$ is the class of all convex measurable sets. In particular this is true if the measure $\mathbb{P}$ is absolutely continuous with respect to Lebesgue measure.

An estimate of the nearness of distributions on spheres in terms of the nearness of their characteristic functions in view of treating special cases of the convergence to the normal law is due to *Esseen*[25].

"Uniform" distances and limit theorems connected with it cease to be useful if it is necessary to estimate small probabilities with high accuracy. The most important case of "large deviations" has been explored rather completely (see § 10 of this chapter). To this end "uniform" theorems are being employed as essentially auxiliary means[26].

§ 3. Moments and Semi-Invariants

1. Formal Relations

Moments. Let ξ be a real-valued random variable and $\mathbb{P}_\xi$ its probability distribution; thus $\mathbb{P}_\xi$ is a Borel probability measure on the real line. Let $F = F_\xi$ be the distribution function and $\varphi = \varphi_\xi$ the characteristic function which corresponds to this measure, that is, the distribution function and the characteristic function of the random variable ξ:
$F_\xi(x) = \mathbb{P}\{\xi \leq x\}$, $\varphi_\xi(t) = \mathbb{M}\, e^{it\xi}$.

The expectation $\mathbb{M}\, \xi^k$ if it exists is called the *moment of order k* of the random variable ξ; the number $\mathbb{M}|\xi|^k$ is called the *absolute moment of order k* and the number $\mu_k = \mathbb{M}(\xi - \mathbb{M}\,\xi)^k$ is called the *central moment of order k*. The central moment of second order

$$\mu_2 = \mathbb{D}\xi = \mathbb{M}(\xi - \mathbb{M}\,\xi)^2 = \mathbb{M}\,\xi^2 - (\mathbb{M}\,\xi)^2$$

is called the *variance* (or dispersion) of the random variable ξ.

If $\mathbb{M}|\xi|^k < \infty$, then the characteristic function $\varphi_\xi(t)$ has continuous derivatives up to the order k, and

$$\mathbb{M}\,\xi^k = (-i)^k \left. \frac{d}{dt^k}\, \varphi_\xi(t) \right|_{t=0} .$$

Conversely the existence of the derivative $\left. \dfrac{d^{2k}}{dt^{2k}}\, \varphi_\xi(t) \right|_{t=0}$ implies the existence of the absolute moment of order $2k$, that is, $\mathbb{M}|\xi|^{2k} < \infty$.

Semi-Invariants. If $\mathbb{M}|\xi|^k < \infty$, then in some neighborhood of the point $t = 0$ the function $\log \varphi_\xi(t)$ where log stands for the principle value

[25] *Esseen*, K. G., Fourier analysis of distribution functions. Acta Math., **77** (1945), 1—125.
[26] *Feller*, W., An introduction to probability theory and its applications. Vol. 2, Wiley, N. Y., 1966.

11*

of the logarithm is a continuously differentiable function up to the order k. The number

$$\varkappa_k = (-i)^k \frac{d^k}{dt^k} \log \varphi_\xi(t) \bigg|_{t=0}$$

is called the *semi-invariant of order* k; here and in what follows logarithms are taken to the basis e. We remark that

$$\varkappa_1 = \mathbb{M}\xi = \alpha_1, \quad \varkappa_2 = \mathbb{D}\xi = \mu_2, \quad \varkappa_3 = \mathbb{M}(\xi - \varkappa_1)^3 = \mu_3.$$

Let $\xi_1, ..., \xi_n$ be real random variables. Their joint distribution function $F = F_{\xi_1, ..., \xi_n}$ is defined by

$$F_{\xi_1, ..., \xi_n}(x_1, ..., x_n) = \mathbb{P}\{\xi_1 < x_1, ..., \xi_n < x_n\}.$$

The characteristic function $\varphi = \varphi_{\xi_1, ..., \xi_n}$ of the of the *joint distribution* of the random variables $\xi_1, ..., \xi_n$ is obtained by the formula

$$\varphi_{\xi_1, ..., \xi_n}(t_1, ..., t_n) = \mathbb{M} \exp\{i(t_1\xi_1 + \cdots + t_n\xi_n)\}.$$

If $\mathbb{M}|\xi_j|^k < \infty$ for every $j = 1, ..., n$, then the *mixed moments* $\alpha_{k_1, ..., k_n} = \mathbb{M}\xi_1^{k_1} \ldots \xi_n^{k_n}$ exist for all $k_j \geq 0$ such that $k_1 + \cdots + k_n \leq k$. In this case the characteristic function $\varphi = \varphi_{\xi_1, ..., \xi_n}$ has continuous partial derivatives up to the order k, and

$$\alpha_{k_1, ..., k_n} = (-i)^{k_1 + \cdots + k_n} \frac{\partial^{k_1 + \cdots + k_n}}{\partial t_1^{k_1} \ldots \partial t_n^{k_n}} \varphi \bigg|_{t_1 = \cdots = t_n = 0}.$$

In some neighborhood of the point $t_1 = \cdots = t_n = 0$ the function $\log \varphi$ has continuous derivatives of the same order; the numbers

$$\varkappa_{k_1, ..., k_n} = (-i)^{k_1 + \cdots + k_n} \frac{\partial^{k_1 + \cdots + k_n}}{\partial t_1^{k_1} \ldots \partial t_n^{k_n}} \log \varphi \bigg|_{t_1 = \cdots = t_n = 0}$$

are called *semi-invariants*.

Relations between Moments and Semi-Invariants. Moments and semi-invariants may be considered the most important characteristics of the probability distribution of random variables $\xi_1, ..., \xi_n$. They are connected by simple relations. In fact let

$$\eta_1 = \xi_1, ..., \eta_{k_1} = \xi_1,$$
$$\eta_{k_1+1} = \xi_2, ..., \eta_{k_1+k_2} = \xi_2,$$
$$\cdots\cdots\cdots\cdots\cdots\cdots\cdots$$
$$\eta_{m-k_n+1} = \xi_n, ..., \eta_m = \xi_n,$$

where $m = k_1 + \cdots + k_n$, and let $I_p = (i_1, \ldots, i_p)$ be a set of natural numbers. The moments

$$\alpha(I_p) = \mathbb{M} \eta_{i_1} \ldots \eta_{i_p}$$

and the semi-invariants

$$\varkappa(I_p) = \frac{\partial^p}{\partial t_{i_1} \ldots \partial t_{i_p}} \log \varphi(0)$$

depend only I_p and are connected with the moments $\alpha_{k_1, \ldots, k_n}$ and the semi-invariants $\varkappa_{k_1, \ldots, k_n}$ defined above by the formulas [27]

$$\alpha_{k_1, \ldots, k_n} = \sum \prod_{p=1}^{q} \alpha(I_p)$$

$$\varkappa_{k_1, \ldots, k_n} = \sum (-1)^{q-1} (q-1)! \prod_{p=1}^{q} \varkappa(I_p)$$

where the sum is taken for all partitions of the set of natural numbers $1, \ldots, m$ into non-overlapping sets I_p.

In particular in the case of one dimension the relation

$$\alpha_m = \sum_{r=0}^{m} \sum \left(\frac{\varkappa_{l_1}}{l_1} \right)^{j_1} \cdots \left(\frac{\varkappa_{l_r}}{l_r!} \right)^{j_r} \frac{m!}{j_1! \ldots j_r!},$$

holds, where the inner sum is extended over all non-negative j and l for which

$$l_1 j_1 + \cdots + l_r j_r = m.$$

Therefore we obtain, for example,

$$\mu_2 = \varkappa_2,$$
$$\mu_3 = \varkappa_3,$$
$$\mu_4 = \varkappa_4 + 3\varkappa_2^2,$$
$$\mu_5 = \varkappa_5 + 10\varkappa_3\varkappa_2,$$
$$\mu_6 = \varkappa_6 + 15\varkappa_2\varkappa_4 + 10\varkappa_3^2 + 15\varkappa_2^3,$$
$$\mu_7 = \varkappa_7 + 21\varkappa_5\varkappa_2 + 35\varkappa_4\varkappa_3 + 105\varkappa_3\varkappa_2^2$$

etc.

The expression of the semi-invariants in terms of the moments yields the formulas

$$\varkappa_m = m! \sum_{r=0}^{m} \sum \frac{(-1)^{j-1}(j-1)!}{j_1! \ldots j_r!} \left(\frac{\alpha_{l_1}}{l_1!} \right)^{j_1} \cdots \left(\frac{\alpha_{l_r}}{l_r!} \right)^{j_r},$$

---

[27] *Leonov, V. P.,* and *A. N. Shiryaev,* On computation techniques of semi-invariants. Teoriya veroyatn. i primen. IV, 3 (1959), 342—355 (Russian).

where the summation goes over all non-negative numbers j and l which satisfy the conditions

$$l_1 j_1 + \cdots + l_r j_r = m , \qquad j_1 + \cdots + j_r = j .$$

Assuming $\alpha_1 = 0$ we thus obtain

$$\varkappa_2 = \alpha_2 ,$$
$$\varkappa_3 = \alpha_3 ,$$
$$\varkappa_4 = \alpha_4 - 3\alpha_2^2 ,$$
$$\varkappa_5 = \alpha_5 - 10\alpha_3\alpha_2 ,$$
$$\varkappa_6 = \alpha_6 - 15\alpha_4\alpha_2 - 10\alpha_3^2 + 30\alpha_2^3 ,$$
$$\varkappa_7 = \alpha_7 - 21\alpha_5\alpha_2 - 35\alpha_4\alpha_3 + 210\alpha_3\alpha_2^2$$

etc.

2. The Moment Problem

In order that a probability distribution $\mathbb{P}$ be uniquely determined by its moments, the following condition by *Carleman* is sufficient:

$$\sum_1^\infty (\alpha_{2n})^{-\frac{1}{2n}} = \infty .$$

In the case of the distribution of a random vector ξ in m dimensions we set

$$\alpha_{p_1 \ldots p_m} = \int_{R^m} x_1^{p_1} \ldots x_m^{p_m} \, \mathbb{P}_\xi(dx_1 \ldots dx_m) ,$$

$$A_n = \alpha_{n0\ldots0} + \alpha_{0n0\ldots0} + \cdots + \alpha_{0\ldots0n} .$$

Then the condition

$$\sum_0^\infty (A_{2n})^{-\frac{1}{2n}} = \infty$$

is sufficient in order that the m-dimensional distribution be uniquely determined by its moments.

On the other hand some conditions are known under which a distribution is certainly not determined by its moments. For example this will be the case if the distribution function $F(x)$ satisfies the condition

$$\int_{-\infty}^\infty \frac{\log F'(x)}{1 + x^2} \, dx > -\infty$$

where F' is the derivative of the absolutely continuous part of F.

A Classical Example. Let $\alpha > 0, 0 < \varrho < 1$; then the densities

$$p(x) = k \exp\{-\alpha |x|^{\varrho}\} \{1 + \varepsilon \cos(\alpha |x|^{\varrho})\}$$

have the same moments for all ε in the interval $|\varepsilon| < 1$.

Another Example. Let ξ be a normally distributed random variable such that $\mathbb{M}\xi = 0$ and $\mathbb{D}\xi = 1$; then the distribution of ξ^k for $k \geq 3$ is not uniquely determined by its moments. Likewise the distribution of e^{ξ}, the so called *logarithmic normal distribution*, is not uniquely determined by its moments.

3. Inequalities

We now pass to inequalities which connect moments, or moments and semi-invariants. Semi-invariants can be estimated in terms of the absolute central moments $\beta_r = \mathbb{M}|\xi - \mathbb{M}\xi|^r$ by the inequality

$$|\varkappa_r| \leq r^r \beta_r.$$

However in most applications this inequality appears to be rather coarse. For example in the case of the uniform distribution on the interval $\left[-\dfrac{1}{2h}, \dfrac{1}{2h}\right]$ we have

$$\varkappa_{2j+1} = 0, \quad \varkappa_{2j} = B_{2j}\frac{h^{2j}}{2j},$$

where B_{2j} are the Bernoulli numbers ($B_2 = 1/6$, $B_4 = -1/30$, $B_6 = 1/42$, $B_8 = -1/30$ etc.). Hence, for example,

$$|\varkappa_4| = \frac{4}{3}\beta_4$$

whereas the preceding inequality yields only

$$|\varkappa_4| \leq 256\beta_4.$$

Similarly in the case of the discrete distribution which assigns to the points $1, 2, \ldots, n$ the same probability $1/n$ we have for $j \geq 1$

$$\varkappa_{2j+1} = 0, \quad \varkappa_{2j} = B_{2j}\frac{n^{2j}-1}{2j}.$$

The moments of an arbitrary random variable ξ are connected by inequalities which amount to statements about the convexity of the function $\gamma(r) = \log \mathbb{M}|\xi|^r$ in the domain where this function is defined.

The largest amount of information on relations between moments can be obtained if we assume that ξ is the sum of independent random variables subject, may be, to some additional restrictions.

Example. Suppose that the random variables $\xi_1, \ldots, \xi_n$ take the values ± 1 with probability $1/2$ each. Then for arbitrary $b_i > 0$ and $s \geq 2$

$$\mathbb{M} |\Sigma b_j \xi_j|^s \leq C(s, n) (\Sigma b_j^2)^{\frac{s}{2}},$$

where

$$C(s, n) = 2^{-n} n^{-\frac{s}{2}} \sum_{k=0}^{n} C_n^k |n - 2k|^s \leq \frac{2^{\frac{s}{2}}}{\sqrt{\pi}} \Gamma\left(\frac{s+1}{2}\right).$$

Equality holds here if and only if either $s = 2$ or all b_i coincide. Making use of conditional distributions the following statement can be derived from this inequality. If all ξ_i are symmetric, $|\xi_i| \leq 1$ and $\Sigma b_j^2 = 1$, then for every integer s

$$\mathbb{M} |\Sigma b_j \xi_j|^{2s} \leq 1 \cdot 3 \cdot \cdots \cdot (2k - 1).$$

Another type of inequalities on the moments of the sum $s_n = \xi_1 + \cdots + \xi_n$ of symmetric terms ξ_j can be obtained by keeping fixed a certain number of moments of the non-decreasing function

$$G(x) = F_1(x) + \cdots + F_n(x), \qquad F_j(x) = \mathbb{P}\{\xi_j < x\}.$$

In fact let ξ_j be symmetrically distributed with moments up to the order $2k$. Then for fixed

$$x_{2j} = \int_{-\infty}^{\infty} u^{2j} dG(u) \qquad (1 \leq j \leq k)$$

we have

$$\sup_{\xi_j, n} \mathbb{M} s_n^{2k} = \mathbb{M} \tau^{2k},$$

where τ is an infinitely divisible random variable (see the following paragraph) with the characteristic function

$$\varphi_\tau(t) = \exp\left\{ \int_{-\infty}^{\infty} (e^{itu} - 1) dG(u) \right\}.$$

By taking the sequence $k = 2, 3, \ldots$, we obtain the inequalities

$$\mathbb{M} s_n^4 \leq x_4 + 3 x_2^2,$$
$$\mathbb{M} s_n^6 \leq x_6 + 15 x_4 x_2 + 15 x_2^3 \quad \text{etc.}$$

As another example we can mention the inequality

$$\text{M}|s_n|^r \leq C(r, n) \sum_{j=1}^{n} \text{M}|\xi_j|^2 ,$$

where we have

$$C(r, n) \leq 2$$

if we assume that the ξ_j are independent and $\text{M}\xi_j = 0$.

4. Convergence of Moments

The use of moments in proving limit theorems is based on the following fact. Let F_n be a sequence of distribution functions with finite moments, and suppose that for every integer $k \geq 1$ the convergence

$$\alpha_k(F_n) = \int_{-\infty}^{\infty} x^k \, dF_n \to \alpha_k \neq \pm\infty \qquad (n \to \infty)$$

takes place. Then there exists a subsequence F_{n_j} which converges weakly to some distribution function F which has the moments α_k. If these moments determine F uniquely, then the entire sequence F_n converges weakly to F.

Example. One consequence of this fact looks like this. Let

$$E_{n,1}, \ldots, E_{n,n}$$

be a sequence of sequences of random events, and suppose that for $n \to \infty$ and every $r = 1, 2, 3, \ldots$ we have

$$S_{n,r} = \sum_{i_1 < \cdots < i_r} \mathbb{P}\{E_{n,i_1} \cdots E_{n,i_r}\} \to \frac{a^r}{r!} .$$

Then the probability $P_n(m)$ that exactly m events of the n-th sequence occur has the limit

$$\lim_{n \to \infty} P_n(m) = e^{-a} \frac{a^m}{m!} .$$

This statement plays a rôle, for example, in the investigation of the deviation of an empirical distribution from the theoretical one.

We mention two more typical examples where the method of moments appears useful. First consider a sequence of sums s_n of independent identically distributed random variables with expectation zero, finite variance and $s_0 = 0$. Let v_n be the number of changes of sign in the sequence $s_0 \, s_1, \ldots, s_n$. Then under rather broad assumptions we can establish by the method of moments that for $x \geq 0$

$$\lim_{n \to \infty} \mathbb{P}\left\{ v_n \leq x \frac{\beta_1}{2\sigma} \sqrt{n} \right\} = \sqrt{\frac{2}{\pi}} \int_0^x e^{-z\frac{2}{2}} dz$$

where

$$\beta_1 = \mathbb{M}|\xi_j|, \qquad \sigma^2 = \mathbb{M}\xi_j^2.$$

We remark in passing that it is possible to construct an example of two distributions which have the same moments but different absolute first moments. This implies that the asymptotic behavior of v_n is not determined by the moments of the distribution in contrast to s_n.

Secondly the method of moments appears to be a basic tool in the investigation of sums of the type

$$\sum_{m=0}^{n-1} f(T^m x), \tag{3.1}$$

where T is a measure preserving metrically transitive transformation of a measure space [28].
For example, let g be a natural number, $0 < \alpha < 1$ and $T\alpha$ the fractional part of $g\alpha$. Then for any sufficiently smooth real periodic function f with period 1 such that $\int_0^1 f(x)\,dx = 0$ we have

$$\lim_{n \to \infty} \text{mes}\left\{ \alpha : 0 < \alpha < 1, \sum_{m=0}^{n-1} f(g^m \alpha) < z \sqrt{n} \right\} = \frac{1}{\sqrt{2\pi}\sigma} \int_{-\infty}^z e^{-\frac{u^2}{2\sigma^2}}\,du.$$

The following theorem contains a more general result.

Let T be an ergodic endomorphism of a commutative compact group G, μ an invariant measure on G, $f(x) \in L_2(G)$ and suppose that the coefficients c_k of the expansion of f in terms of the characters $\chi_k(x)$ of the group satisfy the condition

$$\sum_{j=0}^{\infty} \sum_{k \neq 0} |c_k|\,|c_{A(k)}| < \infty,$$

where $A(k)$ is the transformation of the indices defined by the relation

$$\chi_{A(k)}(x) = \chi_k(Tx).$$

Then the sum (3.1) is asymptotically normal.

[28] Leonov, V. P., Some applications of the high semi-invariants in the theory of stationary random processes. Nauka, Moscow 1964 (Russian).

§ 4. Infinitely Divisible Distributions and their Connection with Limit Theorems

1. Definition and Connection with Limit Theorems

A distribution on R^1 with distribution function $F(x)$ and characteristic function $\varphi(t)$ is called *infinitely divisible* if for any n it can be represented as a convolution of n identical distributions or, what amounts to the same, if

$$\varphi(t) = (\varphi_n(t))^n$$

where φ_n is a characteristic function. A random variable ξ defined over the probability space $(\Omega, \mathfrak{A}, \mathbb{P})$ is called *infinitely divisible* if for any n it can be represented as a sum of n identically distributed independent random variables. Obviously every infinitely divisible random variable has an infinitely divisible distribution. The converse case need not be true. In fact, if we choose the discrete probability space which consists of all non-negative integers with the Poisson probabilities

$$P(m) = \frac{\lambda^m}{m!} e^{-\lambda},$$

then the random variable $\lambda(m) = m$ will not be infinitely divisible in spite of the fact that the Poisson distribution is.

In the following we will mainly deal with infinitely divisible distributions. It follows easily from the definition that $\varphi(t) \neq 0$, and that

$$n[\varphi_n(t) - 1] \rightarrow \log \varphi(t)$$

for $n \rightarrow \infty$ uniformly in each finite interval.

The following analytical fact is the basis of the so-called canonical representation of infinitely divisible laws and of conditions for the convergence of sequence of infinitely divisible laws. Consider the space Y the points of which are the continuous functions on the entire line; the topology in Y is generated by the uniform convergence on each finite interval. The class Ψ of all functions of the form

$$\psi(t) = i\gamma t + \lambda[\varphi(t) - 1],$$

where γ is a constant and φ a characteristic function, is not a closed subset of Y. Its closure Ψ^* consists of all functions which can be written as

$$\psi^*(t) = i\gamma t + \int_{-\infty}^{\infty} L(u, t) \frac{1 + u^2}{u^2} dG(u)$$

where

$$L(u, t) = e^{iut} - 1 - \frac{itu}{1 + u^2},$$

γ is a constant and $G(u)$ a non-decreasing function of bounded variation such that $G(-\infty)=0$. For $u=0$ the integrand takes the value $-t^2/2$. The correspondance between ψ^* and (γ, G) is one-to-one and bi-continuous. By the latter statement we mean that the uniform convergence

$$\psi_n^*(t) \to \psi^*(t)$$

on each finite interval is equivalent to the following two requirements:
a) $\gamma_n \to \gamma$,
b) $G_n(u)$ converges weakly to $G(u)$.

The connection between infinitely divisible laws and limit theorems for sums of independent random variables has been thoroughly investigated [29]. Here we quote only some statements which illustrate this connection in a more conspicuous way. Let

$$\xi_{n,1}, \xi_{n,2}, \ldots, \xi_{nk_n} \qquad (n = 1, 2, \ldots)$$

be a *sequence of families* of random variables. These variables are assumed to be independent within each family and *infinitely small* in the following sense: for each $\varepsilon > 0$ we have

$$\lim_{n \to \infty} \sup_{1 \le k \le k_n} \mathbb{P}\{|\xi_{n,k}| > \varepsilon\} = 0.$$

Let

$$s_n = \sum_{k=1}^{k_n} \xi_{n,k}.$$

Then in order that a distribution function F can be the limit of the distribution functions of random variables $s_n - A_n$ for some choice of of the A_n, it is *necessary and sufficient that F be infinitely divisible.*

The canonical representation of the logarithm of the characteristic function of an infinitely divisible law which, as said before has the form

$$\log \varphi(t) = i\gamma t + \int\limits_{-\infty}^{\infty} L(u, t) \frac{1+u^2}{u^2} \, dG(u),$$

is often used in a somewhat different form. If we set

$$dM(u) = \frac{1+u^2}{u^2} \, dG(u), \qquad dN(u) = \frac{1+u^2}{u^2} \, dG(u)$$

$$M(-\infty) = N(\infty) = 0,$$

[29] Gnedenko, B. V., and A. N. Kolmogorov, Limit Distributions for Sums of Independent Random Variables. Cambridge: Addison-Wesley 1954.

for $u < 0$ and $u > 0$, respectively, we obtain two non-decreasing functions $M(u)$ and $N(u)$ on the intervals $(-\infty, 0)$ and $(0, \infty)$, respectively such that for any $\varepsilon > 0$ we have

$$\int_{-\varepsilon}^{-0} u^2 \, dM(u) + \int_{+0}^{\varepsilon} u^2 \, dN(u) < \infty .$$

Let $\sigma^2 = G(+0) - G(-0)$. Then

$$\log \varphi(t) = i\gamma t - \frac{1}{2} \sigma^2 t^2 + \int_{-\infty}^{-0} L(u, t) \, dM(u) + \int_{+0}^{\infty} L(u, t) \, dN(u) .$$

In contrast to G the functions M and N have an immediate probabilistic interpretation which is given in the theory of processes with independent increments. The rôle of these functions in limit theorems becomes clear for example from the following fact. Using the previous notations we assume that for some choice of the constants A_n the distribution functions of the differences $s_n - A_n$ converge weakly to a limit distribution function. Then in order that this be a distribution function with given M and N it is necessary and sufficient that the relations

$$\lim_{n \to \infty} \mathbb{P}\{\min_k \xi_{n,k} < u\} = \begin{cases} 1 - e^{-M(u)} & \text{for} \quad u < 0, \\ 1 & \text{for} \quad u > 0 \end{cases}$$

and

$$\lim_{n \to \infty} \mathbb{P}\{\max_k \xi_{n,k}\} = \begin{cases} 0 & \text{for} \quad u < 0, \\ e^{N(u)} & \text{for} \quad u > 0 \end{cases}$$

are fulfilled.

It is easy to see that $M \equiv 0$ and $N \equiv 0$ for the normal law. Therefore, if the limit law of $s_n - A_n$ exists, it will be normal if and only if

$$\lim_{n \to \infty} \mathbb{P}\{\max_k |\xi_{n,k}| > u\} = 0 \quad \text{for every} \quad u > 0$$

or, what amounts to the same, if

$$\lim_{n \to \infty} \sum_k \mathbb{P}\{|\xi_{n,k}| > u\} = 0 .$$

2. Properties of Infinitely Divisible Laws

Since the class of infinitely divisible laws has been described in terms of characteristic functions, properties of these laws should be described with the help of properties of the function G which appears in the canonical representation, or, equivalently, in terms of M, N and σ.

Example. The infinitely divisible distribution function F is discrete if and only if G is discrete and $\int_{-\infty}^{\infty} u^{-2} dG(u) < \infty$; F is continuous if and only if $\int_{-\infty}^{\infty} u^{-2} dG(u) = \infty$. For the absolute continuity of F only sufficient conditions in terms of M and N are known.

The moment of order $2k$ of the infinitely divisible distribution function F, where k is a positive integer, exists if and only if the moment of the same order of the function G exists. It is known that a bounded random variable cannot have an infinitely divisible distribution unless it is constant almost surely. However conditions for boundedness from above or from below are known. If ξ is a random variable with infinitely divisible distribution, then for the existence of a constant A such that $\mathbb{P}\{\xi > A\} = 0$ the conditions

$$N(u) \equiv 0, \ \sigma^2 = 0 \text{ and } \lim_{\varepsilon \to 0} \int_{-1}^{-\varepsilon} M(u)\, du < \infty \text{ are necessary and sufficient }[30].$$

§ 5. Sequences of Independent Random Variables
(General Properties)

An essential part of probabilistic intuition is derived from the example of independent random variables and its most important particular case, sequences of independent identically distributed variables. Such sequences have a number of properties which on one hand can be comparatively easily established if we impose restrictions like finiteness of the moments of any order, or existence of densities of the variables under consideration etc. but which, on the other hand, by their very nature seem to be connected only with the fact that the terms of the sequence are independent and identically distributed. The proof of such properties in the general case is often not at all easy. We consider some typical examples and start with the simplest ones.

Example. *Decrease of Concentration of Distributions* (weak form). Let $\xi_1, \xi_2, ..., \xi_n, ...$ be a sequence of independent identically distributed variables with a non-degenerate distribution function $F(x)$, and let

$$s_0 = 0, \quad s_n = \xi_1 + \cdots + \xi_n \quad (n = 1, 2, ...).$$

We can show that for any fixed a and b the probability of the inequality $a \leq s_n \leq b$ converges to zero when $n \to \infty$. Moreover if

$$Q_\xi(l) = \sup_x \mathbb{P}\{x \leq \xi \leq x + l\}$$

---

[30] See the survey by *Fisz, M.*, Infinitely divisible distributions: recent, results and applications. Ann. Math. Stat. **33**, 1 (1962), 68—84.

is the so-called *concentration function* of ξ we obtain

$$\lim_{n \to \infty} Q_{s_n}(l) = 0$$

for any $l > 0$. The simplest way to prove this is to use the method of "smoothing". Suppose that η is a random variable which does not depend on the sequence $\{\xi_n\}$ and has a distribution whose characteristic function is absolutely integrable over the entire line. For the distribution of η we can choose for example the "triangular" distribution with the density

$$p(x) = \begin{cases} 1 - |x| & \text{for} \quad |x| \leq 1, \\ 0 & \text{for} \quad |x| > 1 \end{cases}$$

and the characteristic function

$$\varphi_n(t) = \left(\frac{\sin(t/2)}{t/2} \right)^2.$$

The sum $s_n + \eta$ has a density given by the inversion formula

$$p_{s_n + \eta}(x) = \frac{1}{2\pi} \int_{-\infty}^{\infty} e^{-itx} [\varphi_{\xi_1}(t)]^n \, \varphi_\eta(t) \, dt.$$

Since $|\varphi_{\xi_1}(t)| \leq 1$ for all t and equality can hold only in a countable set of points we obtain

$$\lambda_n = \sup_x p_{s_n + \eta}(x) \to 0$$

for $n \to \infty$. Hence

$$\mathbb{P}\{x \leq s_n \leq x + l\} \leq \mathbb{P}\{x - 1 \leq s_n + \eta \leq x + l + 1\} \leq (l + 2)\lambda_n,$$

that is

$$Q_{s_n}(l) \leq (l + 2)\lambda_n \to 0 \quad (n \to \infty).$$

Example. *Passing Beyond Two-Sided Bounds.* We can prove that with probability one

$$\overline{\lim_{n \to \infty}} \, |s_n| = \infty.$$

This statement follows from the following somewhat stronger statement[31]: for any sequence $\{\xi_n\}$ and any $a < 0 < b$ there exist two numbers C and q with $C > 0$ and $0 < q < 1$ such that

$$P_N(a, b) = \mathbb{P}\left\{ \bigcap_{n=1}^{N} (a \leq s_n \leq b) \right\} \leq C q^N.$$

This, in turn, can be derived from the preceding example.

---

[31] *Wald, A.*, Sequential analysis. London: Wiley 1947.

Example. *Upper and Lower Functions.* The function $g(n)$ is called an *upper* function for the sequence of sums s_n if $\mathbb{P}\{s_n \leq g(n)$ from some n_0 on$\} = 1$, and a *lower* function if $\mathbb{P}\{s_n \geq g(n)$ for infinitely many $n\} = 1$. Under the assumption of non-degenerate independent and identically distributed terms each function is either an upper or a lower function. The following examples require some additional assumptions on the random variables under consideration.

Example. Suppose that $-\infty \leq \mathbb{M}\xi_j \leq 0$. Then with probability one

$$\varliminf_{n \to \infty} s_n = -\infty . \tag{5.1}$$

For $\mathbb{M}\xi_j < 0$ this statement follows from the strong law of large numbers if $\mathbb{M}\xi_j$ is finite, and for $\mathbb{M}\xi_j = -\infty$ it follows from some generalization of this law. Therefore consider the case $\mathbb{M}\xi_j = 0$. Then the strong law of large numbers does not suffice to establish the limit relation (5.1). We can, however, exploit the following result by *Chung* and *Fuchs*. If the possible values of ξ_j are not divisible by one and the same number, and if $\mathbb{M}\xi_j = 0$, then for any x and ε we have

$$\mathbb{P}\{|s_n - x| < \varepsilon \quad \text{for infinitely many } n\} = 1 ; \tag{5.2}$$

if, on the other hand, the possible values ξ_j are divisible by a certain number, and if x_0 is the largest in absolute value with this property, then (5.2) holds for all numbers divisible by x_0.

This result implies the following. If $\mathbb{M}\xi_j$ exists, then

$$\mathbb{P}\{s_n > 0 \text{ for infinitely many } n\} = \mathbb{P}\{s_n < 0 \text{ for infinitely many } n\} = 1$$

if and only if $\mathbb{M}\xi_j = 0$.

Example. *Upper Functions for Sums of Symmetrically Distributed Terms.* For any sequence of symmetrically distributed random variables ξ_j

$$\mathbb{P}\left\{ \varlimsup_{n \to \infty} \frac{s_n}{\sqrt{2n \log \log n}} = \sigma^2 \right\} = 1 \tag{5.3}$$

where

$$\sigma^2 = \int_{-\infty}^{\infty} x^2 \, dF(x) \leq \infty .$$

If $\sigma^2 < \infty$ the assertion (5.3) follows from the law of the iterated logarithm; for $\sigma^2 = \infty$ the proof of (5.3) requires some simple additional arguments.

Example. *A Better Estimate of the Decrease of Concentration.* By developing the method of *P. Lévy*, *A. N. Kolmogorov* obtained the first absolute estimate, that is, an estimate that contains merely absolute constants, for the concentration of a sum when the concentrations of the terms are given. This result was then strengthened by B. A. *Rogozin*, who succeeded in finding a formulation which includes as particular cases all former theorems on the decrease of concentration and the increase of the spread of sums of independent random variables. These results of *Rogozin* are based on a lemma which relies on deep combinatorial facts.

Let D_n be the maximal probability in the symmetric Bernoulli scheme with n trials:

$$D_n = C_n^{\left[\frac{n}{2}\right]} \frac{1}{2^n} < \frac{1}{\sqrt{n+1}}$$

and let $\xi_1, \xi_2, \ldots$ be independent random variables which need not be identically distributed, such that

$$\mathbb{P}\{\xi_i = x_i\} = \mathbb{P}\{\xi_i = -x_i\} = \frac{1}{2} \quad \left(x_i \geq \frac{l}{2}\right).$$

Lemma. *The sums of the random variables* $\xi_1, \xi_2, \ldots$ *described before satisfy the inequality*

$$Q_{s_n}(l-0) \leq D_n.$$

By a simple application of this lemma we obtain the corollary: Let $p = \sup_x \mathbb{P}\{\xi_i = x\}$, then

$$\sup P\{s_n = x\} \leq \frac{C_1}{\sqrt{n(1-p)}}; \tag{5.4}$$

in the case of symmetric ξ_i we can choose $C_1 = 1$. It should be mentioned that for identically distributed integral-valued ξ_i with the characteristic function $\varphi(t)$ the inequality given above is equivalent to the following one:

$$\int_0^\pi |\varphi(t)|^n \, dt \leq \frac{C_2}{\sqrt{n(1-p)}}. \tag{5.5}$$

Hence by proving (5.5) analytically[32] we also can prove (5.4).

The most general result on estimates of concentration functions is contained in the following statement by B. A. *Rogozin* where the ξ_i are merely assumed to be independent but need not be identically distributed. Let

$$S = \sum_{k=1}^n \left(1 - Q_k(l_k) \, l_k^2\right) \quad \text{and} \quad Q_k = Q_{\xi_k}.$$

---

[32] On an analytic proof see *Esseen*, K. G., On the Kolmogorov-Rogozin inequality for the concentration function. Zeitschr. für Wahrscheinlichkeitstheorie und verwandte Gebiete **5** (1966), 210—216.

Then there exists an absolute constant C such that for $L > 1/2 \max\limits_{k} l_k$ we have

$$Q_{s_n}(L) \leqq \frac{CL}{\sqrt{S}}.$$

Example. *An Approximation of the Distributions of Sums with Infinitely Divisible Distributions.* As before, let ξ_i be a sequence of independent identically distributed random variables and $F^{n*}(x)$ the distribution function of the sums s_n. Let $\mathfrak{G}$ stand for the class of all infinitely divisible laws, and let

$$\varrho(F, G) = \sup |F(x) - G(x)|,$$
$$S(\mathfrak{G}, \varepsilon) = \{F : \varrho(F, \mathfrak{G}) < \varepsilon\}.$$

Many interesting papers[33] deal with the location of the set of "powers" in the sense of the convolution F^{n*} of the distribution functions F. The following result has been obtained comparatively recently: there exists an absolute constant C such that for any F

$$F^{n*} \in S\left(\mathfrak{G}, \frac{C}{\sqrt[3]{n}}\right).$$

Example. *Decrease of Concentration in the Summation of Random Vectors.* Let ξ be a random vector with values in R^k. The function

$$Q_l^{\xi}(v) = \sup_{A \subset C_{l,v}} \mathbb{P}\{\xi \in A\} \qquad (1 \leqq l \leqq k)$$

is called the concentration function of l-th order corresponding to the random vector ξ; here, $C_{l,v}$ denotes the class of all closed convex sets whose intersection with all possible l-dimensional hyperplanes is of l-dimensional area not larger than v. Let ξ_i be independent identically distributed random vectors in R^k and $\zeta_n = \sum\limits_{1}^{n} \xi_i$. We assume that for some $n = n_0$ the distribution of the random vector ξ_{n_0} has a component of the following kind: it is the translate of a measure that is absolutely continuous with respect to the Lebesgue measure of an l-dimensional subspace, and is then considered as a measure in R^k. Under this assumption for $m \leqq l$ the inequalities

$$Q_m^{\zeta_n}(v) \leqq C n^{-\frac{1}{2}(l-m+1)}$$

---

[33] See footnotes in the monograph by *B. V. Gnedenko* and *A. N. Kolmogorov* quoted above.

hold where C is a constant which, generally speaking, depends on v and the distribution law of the single terms.

The discrete case can be described separately. We suppose that the ξ_i are independent random vectors with identical discrete non-degenerate distributions in R^k, and $\zeta_n = \sum_1^n \xi_i$. Then the inequalities

$$Q_m^{\zeta_n}(v) \leq C n^{-\frac{1}{2}(k-m+1)}$$

are fulfilled for all m with $1 \leq m \leq k$.

§ 6. Sequences of Independent Random Variables Convergence to the Normal Law

1. Conditions for Convergence

This paragraph deals with sequences of independent identically distributed random variables or vectors unless anything is said to the contrary.

First consider the one-dimensional case. Let ξ_n be a sequence of random variables and $F(x) = \mathbb{P}\{\xi_n < x\}$. In order that for some constants A_n and $B_n > 0$ the distribution of the normalized sum

$$\eta_n = \frac{S_n - A_n}{B_n} = \frac{\xi_1 + \cdots + \xi_n - A_n}{B_n}$$

converges to a normal distribution it is necessary and sufficient that

$$\lim_{X \to \infty} \frac{X^2 \int\limits_{|x|>X} dF(x)}{\int\limits_{|x|<X} x^2 \, dF(x)} = 0 \, .$$

The normalizing constants B_n can either increase like $\sqrt{n}$, or differ from $\sqrt{n}$ by a slowly varying factor. It is known that $B_n \sim \sqrt{n}$ if and only if the terms have finite variance σ^2. If we assume in addition that the ξ_n have a finite third moment, then for

$$F_n(x) = \mathbb{P}\left\{\frac{S_n - \mathbb{M} s_n}{\sigma \sqrt{n}} < x\right\}$$

we can prove the inequality

$$|F_n(x) - \Phi(x)| < C \frac{\beta_3}{\sigma^3 \sqrt{n}}, \qquad \Phi(x) = \frac{1}{\sqrt{2\pi}} \int\limits_{-\infty}^{x} e^{-\frac{1}{2}z^2} \, dz,$$

12*

where $\beta_3 = \mathbb{M}|\xi_n - \mathbb{M}\xi_n|^3$ and C is an absolute constant. The following estimates have been successively proposed for C: 7.59; 2.9 *(Esseen)*; 2.05 *(Wallace)*; 0.9051 *(Zolotariev)*. It is also known that $C > \dfrac{1}{\sqrt{2\pi}}$.

Fairly recently *I. A. Ibragimov* gave necessary and sufficient conditions in order that $|F_n(x) - \Phi(x)| = 0(n^{-\frac{1}{2}})$:

First, we should have

$$\int_{-\infty}^{\infty} x^2 \, dF(x) < \infty$$

and secondly, for $z \to \infty$

$$\int_{|x|>z} x^2 \, dF(x) = 0(z^{-1}), \qquad \int_{|x|\leq z} x^3 \, dF(x) = 0(1).$$

2. Sharpenings

If the ξ_n have an absolute moment of order greater than three and under certain assumptions on the smoothness of $F(x)$ we can give sharper estimates on the difference [34] $F_n(x) - \Phi(x)$. We start from the expansion of the characteristic function which has the same form in spaces of any finite number s of dimensions as in Banach spaces:

$$\varphi_\xi(t) = \sum_{k=0}^{r} \frac{i^k}{k!} \mathbb{M}(t, \xi)^k + o(|t|^{r+1})$$

which holds under the assumption that

$$\mathbb{M}|\xi|^r < \infty \; ;$$

here ξ denotes any of the variables ξ_j, and (t, ξ) is the scalar product of the vectors t and ξ. From this expansion we deduce for $\mathbb{M}(t, \xi) \equiv 0$ with the help of standard methods the relation

$$\left[\varphi_\xi\left(\frac{t}{\sqrt{n}}\right) \right]^n = e^{-\frac{1}{2}\mathbb{M}(t,\xi)^2} \left(1 + \sum_{k=1}^{r-2} P_k \cdot n^{-\frac{k}{2}} \right) + o\left(n^{-\frac{r-2}{2}} \right),$$

where the P_k are polynomials in $\mathbb{M}(t, \xi)^j$, $1 \leq j \leq r$.

---

[34] See the monograph by *V. B. Gnedenko* and *A. N. Kolmogorov* quoted before or the textbook: *I. A. Ibragimov, Yu. V. Linnik*, Independent and stationarily connected variables. (Russian.) Moscow, Nauka 1965.

The formal inversion of the latter equation yields

$$\mathbb{P}\left\{\frac{\xi_1 + \cdots + \xi_n}{n} \in A\right\} = \Phi(A) + \sum_{k=1}^{r-2} \Phi_k(A)\, n^{-\frac{k}{2}} + o\left(n^{-\frac{r-2}{2}}\right).$$

In a finite-dimensional space, Φ is the normal distribution with the same first and second moments as the distribution of ξ, and Φ_k is the linear combination of generalized measures with the Fourier transform

$$(it_1)^{m_1} \ldots (it_s)^m \; e^{-\frac{1}{2} \mathbb{M}(t,\xi)^2}.$$

The corresponding coefficients are determined from the moments up to the r-th order inclusively.

The afore-mentioned formal inversion is valid in the one-dimensional case if, for instance, we assume that the variables ξ_j have an absolutely integrable characteristic function. For A we can choose any Borel set. If we know only that

$$\varlimsup_{|t| \to \infty} |\varphi_\xi(t)| < 1,$$

we obtain the following decomposition of the distribution function[35]

$$F_n(x) = \Phi(x) + \Phi'(x) \sum_{k=1}^{r-2} Q_k(x)\, n^{-\frac{k}{2}} + o\left(n^{-\frac{r-2}{2}}\right),$$

where Q_k is a polynomial of degree $3k - 1$ with coefficients depending on

$$\frac{\alpha_3}{\sigma^3}, \ldots, \frac{\alpha_{k+2}}{\sigma^{k+2}} \qquad (\alpha_p = \mathbb{M}\,\xi^p).$$

The construction of transformations which "improve the convergence" to the normal law represents one of the most useful applications of the latter result. Here is the point. Suppose that the sequence η_n is asymptotically normal with parameters $(0, 1)$. We want to select simple (and easily invertible) functions $f_n(\cdot)$ such that the random variables $\zeta_n = \xi_n + f_n(\xi_n)$ are "more normal" than the η_n.

This is not a very precise formulation. We can illuminate the problem with the help of the following example. The variables $\chi_n^2, \sqrt{2\chi_n^2}, (\chi_n^2/n)^{1/3}$ are asymptotically normal[36] for $n \to \infty$. The uniform deviation of the distribution functions under consideration from their normal approximations is less than 0.01 for χ_n^2 if $n \geq 354$ and for $\sqrt{2\chi_n^2}$ if $n \geq 23$; for $(\chi_n^2/n)^{1/3}$ it is at most 0.007 as soon as $n \geq 3$.

---

[35] See the monographs by B. V. Gnedenko and A. N. Kolmogorov and by W. Feller quoted above.

[36] The random variable χ_n^2 is the sum of the squares of n independent identically normally distributed random variables with parameters (0.1).

A method for the construction of such transformations looks as follows [37]. Let $\xi_1, \xi_2, \ldots, \xi_n, \ldots$ be independent random variables with the same probability distribution, let $\varkappa_j$ be the j-th semi-invariant of the random variable ξ_1, and let η_n be the normalized sum:

$$\eta_n = \frac{1}{\sqrt{n\varkappa_2}} \sum_{i=1}^{n} (\xi_j - \varkappa_1).$$

Let further U_r be the set of all functions $u(x, v)$ defined in the domain $|x| < \infty$, $0 \leq v \leq V$ where V is a positive constant and suppose that

1) $\dfrac{\partial^{r-2}}{\partial v^{r-2}}$ exists and is continuous in x on the line given by the equation $v = 0$;

2) there exists the positive partial derivative u/x in the domain

$$|x| < C v^{-\frac{(r-2)}{(r-1)}} \quad (C > 0, r \geq 3).$$

In this case, if $|\varkappa_r| < \infty$ and $u(x, v) \in U_r$, the distribution function $G_n(z)$ of the random variable

$$\zeta_n = u(\eta_n, n^{-\frac{1}{2}})$$

satisfies the condition

$$G_n(z) = \Phi(z) + 0\left(n^{-\frac{r-2}{2}}\right)$$

if and only if the asymptotic formula

$$u(x, v) = x + \sum_{m=1}^{r-3} P_{3m-1}(x)\, v^m + 0(v^{r-2})$$

holds for $v \to 0$. Here, the $P_i(x)$ are polynomials which can be determined as follows. First we write down the expansion

$$F_n(x) - \Phi(x) = \varphi(x) \sum_{m=1}^{r-3} Q_k(x)\, n^{-\frac{m}{2}} + 0\left(n^{-\frac{r-2}{2}}\right)$$

where

$$\Phi(x) = \int_{-\infty}^{x} \varphi(t)\, dt, \qquad \varphi(x) = \frac{1}{\sqrt{2\pi}}\, e^{-\frac{1}{2}x^2},$$

[37] Bolshev, L. N., On transformations of random variables. Teor. veroyatn. i primen. IV, (1959), 136—149; Asymptotic Pearson transformations, Teor. veroyatn. i primen. VIII, (1963), 129—155 (Russian).

and the expansion of the right-hand side of the equation

$$y(x) = \Phi^{-1}[\Phi + (F_n - \Phi)]$$

by powers of $F_n - \Phi$ at the point Φ. If we substitute for $F_n - \Phi$ its expansion and rearrange the terms we obtain

$$y(x) = x + \sum_{m=1}^{r-3} P_{3m-1}(x) n^{-\frac{m}{2}} + R_r(x),$$

where $P_i(x)$ are the polynomials sought for and $R_r(x) = 0 \left(n^{-\frac{r-2}{2}}\right)$

For $m = 1$ and $m = 2$ we have

$$P_2(x) \frac{\varkappa_3}{6\varkappa_2^{\frac{3}{2}}}(x^2 - 1),$$

$$P_5(x) \frac{\varkappa_3^2}{36\varkappa_2^3}(4x^3 - 7x) - \frac{\varkappa_4}{24\varkappa_2^2}(x^3 - 3x).$$

The papers of *L. N. Bolshev* referred to above contain many examples of applications of this device.

A general drawback of the asymptotic expansions and approximate formulas given above is that the estimate of the corresponding errors which occurs during the proof is very large. At the same time the application of these formulas to many examples which arise in a natural way shows their extraordinary accuracy [38]. Thus the problem of finding a sufficiently broad class of distributions for which the guaranteed accuracy of the normal approximation and its sharpenings corresponds to the one actually observed, still remains open.

3. The Binomial Distribution

Having discussed continuous distributions we now consider the most important case of a discrete distribution, the binomial distribution. Let n be the total number of Bernoulli trials with the probability of success p, and let $q = 1 - p$, $\sigma = \sqrt{npq}$,

$$z_k = \frac{k - np}{\sigma}.$$

By $P_{\lambda, \mu}$ we denote the probability that the number of successes satisfies the inequality $\lambda \leq m \leq \mu$. Moreover, for some function $R(z)$ let

$$R_{\lambda, \mu} = R\left(z_\mu + \frac{1}{2\sigma}\right) - R\left(z_\lambda - \frac{1}{2\sigma}\right).$$

---

[38] See, for example, the explanatory part of the compendium by *L. N. Bolshev*, *N. V. Smirnov*, Tables of mathematical statistics. Moscow, Nauka, 1965 (Russian).

The strongest among the uniform normal approximations to the binomial distribution is apparently the one proposed by Y. *Uspensky:*

$$P_{\lambda,\mu} = \Phi_{\lambda,\mu} + \Psi_{\lambda,\mu} + \omega$$

where

$$\Psi(z) = \frac{q-p}{6\sigma\sqrt{2\pi}}(1-z^2)e^{-z^2/2}$$

and, if $\sigma \geq 5$,

$$|\omega| < (0,13 + 0,18\,|p-q|)\,\sigma^{-2} + e^{-3\sigma/2}.$$

However, the relative accuracy of such an approximation for probabilities of the type $1 - P_{\lambda,\mu}$ turns out to be insufficient as soon as these are small. In order to improve the situation *S. N. Bernstein* followed by *W. Feller* have proposed other formulas. *S. N. Bernstein* suggests to determine the solution α_x and β_x of the quadratic equations

$$x - \frac{3}{2} - np = \sigma\,\alpha_x + \frac{q-p}{6}\,\alpha_x^2,$$

$$x + \frac{1}{2} - np = \sigma\,\beta_x + \frac{q-p}{6}\,\beta_x^2.$$

Then the inequalities

$$\Phi(\beta_\mu) - \Phi(\beta_\lambda) \leq P_{\lambda,\mu-1} \leq \Phi(\alpha_\mu) - \Phi(\alpha_\lambda)$$

hold for $\sigma^2 \geq 62.5$,

$$\alpha_\lambda \geq 0,$$
$$\beta_\mu \leq \sqrt{2}\sigma^{1/3}.$$

Feller's inequality has a broader domain of application. Let

$$\sigma^2 \geq 9,\ \lambda \geq (n+1)\,p,\ \mu + \frac{1}{2} \leq (n+1)\,p + \frac{2}{3}\,\sigma^2.$$

Then

$$P_{\lambda,\mu} \leq e^{\frac{5(1-pq)}{36\sigma^2}}\,[\Phi(\eta_{\mu+1}) - \Phi(\eta_\lambda)]$$

where

$$\eta_k = \frac{k-(n+1)\,p}{\sigma} + \frac{a}{\sigma}\left(\frac{k-(n+1)\,p}{\sigma}\right)^2 + \frac{2a}{\sigma} - \frac{1}{2\sigma^2}.$$

The preceding inequality is replaced by the opposite one if we set

$$\eta_k = \frac{k-(n+1)p}{\sigma} + \frac{a}{\sigma}\left(\frac{k-(n+1)p}{\sigma}\right)^2 + \frac{2a}{\sigma} + \frac{M}{6\sigma} + \frac{1}{7\sigma},$$

where

$$a = \frac{p-q}{6}, \qquad M = \frac{[k+\frac{1}{2}-(n+1)p]^3}{\sigma^4}.$$

4. The Multi-Dimensional Case

We now make some remarks on the multidimensional case. The natural normalization of a sequence of sums of identically distributed vectors is realized by subtracting the mathematical expectations and dividing by $\sqrt{n}$. For non-identically distributed terms it is natural to consider a normalization by linear transformations. One of the results obtained in this way has the following form: Let ξ_n be a sequence of independent uniformly bounded random vectors:

$$|\xi_n| \leqq C < \infty,$$

and let $\zeta_n = \sum_1^n \xi_k$; then the condition

$$\lim_{n\to\infty} \mathbb{D}(t, \zeta_n) = \infty \quad \text{for all} \quad t \neq 0 \quad (t \in R^m)$$

is necessary and sufficient for the existence of a sequence A_n of linear transformations and a sequence a_n of vectors such that the distributions of the random vectors $\eta_n = A_n \zeta_n + a_n$ converge weakly to a non-degenerate normal distribution $\mathbb{N}$. This condition is also necessary and sufficient for the existence of a sequence of non-degenerate normal distributions $\mathbb{N}_n$ in R^m such that

$$\lim_{n\to\infty} \sup_{A\in\mathfrak{C}} |\mathbb{P}_{\zeta_n}(A) - \mathbb{N}_n(A)| \to 0$$

where $\mathfrak{C}$ denotes the class of all convex sets.

Sharpenings of the normal approximation in the multidimensional case for smooth distributions look much the same as in the one-dimensional case. If we do not assume some smoothness property, the order of the difference

$$\mathbb{P}_{\eta_n}(A) - \mathbb{N}(A)$$

where $\mathbb{P}_{\eta_n}(A)$ is the distribution of the normalized sum and $\mathbb{N}$ some m-dimensional normal distribution, depends [39] on the "form" and "loca-location" of the set A.

---

[39] *Bergström, H.*, On the central limit theorem in the case of not equally distributed random variables. Skand. Aktuarietidskr., 1—2 (1949), 37—62. *Rao, R.*, On the central limit theorem in R_k. Bull. Amer. Math. Soc. **67**, 4 (1961), 359—361.

§ 7. Sequences of Independent Random Variables Convergence to Stable Laws

1. Definition and Some Properties of Stable Laws

It was mentioned in § 5 that the n-fold convolution $F^{n*} = F * F * \cdots * F$ of any fixed distribution function $F(x)$, that is, the law of the sum s_n of independent identically distributed variables $\xi_1, \ldots, \xi_n$ such that $\mathbb{P}\{\xi_j < x\} = F(x)$, approaches to the set of all infinitely divisible laws; in other words, there exists a sequence $G_n(x)$ of infinitely divisible laws such that

$$\sup_x |F^{n*}(x) - G_n(x)| \to 0 \qquad (n \to \infty).$$

Given F, it is rather complicated to construct such distributions G_n. However the most important rôle is played by the case where all G_n are obtained from one and the same distribution G by a linear substitution of the argument

$$G_n(x) = G(x B_n + A_n)$$

where $B_n > 0$ and A_n are some constants. In this case the distribution of "the normalized sum"

$$\frac{s_n - A_n}{B_n} = \frac{1}{B_n}(\xi_1 + \cdots + \xi_n - A_n)$$

converges to $G(x)$. Necessary and sufficient conditions are known on the original function F in order that such a distribution G exists, and the class of all distributions G which may arise in a similar way has been described. This class coincides with the class of all *stable distributions*.

A distribution is called *stable* if for arbitrary $a_1 > 0$, $b_1, a_2 > 0$, b_2 there exist numbers $a > 0$ and b such that for all x we have

$$F(a_1 x + b_1) * F(a_2 x + b_2) = F(a x + b).$$

It was shown by *A. Ya. Hinčin* and *P. Lévy* that the natural logarithms of the characteristic functions of stable distributions, and only these admit a presentation

$$\log \varphi(t) = i \gamma t - c |t|^\alpha \left\{ 1 + i \beta \frac{t}{|t|} \omega(t, \alpha) \right\},$$

where α, β, γ, c are constants, $0 < \alpha \leq 2$, $-1 \leq \beta \leq 1$, $c \geq 0$, γ is arbitrary, and $\omega(t, \alpha) = \operatorname{tg} \frac{\pi}{2} \alpha$ if $\alpha \neq 1$ and $\omega(t, \alpha) = \frac{2}{\pi} \log |t|$ if $\alpha = 1$. Since the characteristic functions of stable laws are absolutely integrable the corresponding distributions have continuous densities; stronger statements are given below. However, the explicit form of the densities of stable laws is known only in some special cases like the normal law, the Cauchy law and some others.

The densities of stable laws are *unimodal* and differ from zero either on the entire axis, or on a half-line, say, for $x \geq A$ or $x \leq A$. The asymptotic behavior of the densities at the endpoints of the domain of positivity is known. Before deriving asymptotic formulas we set $\gamma = 0$, $c = 1$ without restriction of generality. We can show that under these conditions the density of a stable law satisfies the relations:

$$p(x; \alpha, \beta) = p(-x; \alpha, -\beta) \quad \text{for all} \quad x, \alpha \text{ and } \beta;$$

$$p(x; \alpha, \beta) = x^{-1-\alpha} p(-x^{-\alpha}; \alpha^{-1}, \tilde{\beta}) \quad \text{for} \quad \alpha > 1, x > 0$$

where

$$\tilde{\beta} = (\alpha - 1)(\beta - 1) - \beta.$$

Next we indicate some results which refer to the asymptotic behavior of stable densities. Details and proofs can be found in the monograph by *I. A. Ibragimov* and *Yu. V. Linnik* [40]. It is expedient to separate the case of the extreme distributions, that is, distributions with $\beta = \pm 1$, from the case $|\beta| < 1$.

A. If $-1 < \beta \leq 1$, then for $\alpha < 1$ and $x \to \infty$

$$p(x; \alpha, \beta) \sim \frac{1}{\pi} \Gamma(\alpha + 1) \sin\left[\frac{\pi}{2} \alpha(\beta + 1)\right] \cdot x^{-(1+\alpha)};$$

for $\alpha > 1$ and $x \to \infty$

$$p(x; \alpha, \beta) \sim \frac{1}{\pi} \Gamma(\alpha + 1) \sin\left[\frac{\pi}{2}(\alpha + (2 - \alpha)\beta)\right] \cdot x^{-(1+\alpha)};$$

for $\alpha = 1$ and $x \to \infty$

$$p(x; 1, \beta) \sim \frac{1}{\pi}(1 + \beta) x^{-2}.$$

B. If $\beta = -1$ and $\alpha < 1$, then $p(x; \alpha, -1) = 0$ for $x > 0$ and, moreover, for $x \uparrow 0$ we have

$$p(x; \alpha, -1) \sim \frac{\alpha^{\gamma/2\alpha}}{\sqrt{2\pi(1-\alpha)}} |x|^{-1-\gamma/2} \exp\{-(1-\alpha)\alpha^{\gamma} x^{-\gamma}\}$$

---

[40] See footnote on p. 180.

where $\gamma = \alpha/(1 - \alpha)$; for $\alpha = 1$ and $x \to \infty$ the relation

$$p(x; 1, -1) \sim \frac{1}{2\sqrt{e}} \exp\left\{\frac{\pi}{4} x - \frac{2}{\pi e} e^{-\frac{\pi}{2}x}\right\}$$

holds.

We remark that in the case of the extreme law with $\alpha = 1/2$ and $\beta = 1$ the explicit form of the density is known:

$$p\left(x; \frac{1}{2}, 1\right) = \frac{1}{\sqrt{2\pi}} x^{-\frac{3}{2}} e^{-\frac{1}{2x}} \qquad (x > 0).$$

2. Conditions for Convergence. Sharpenings

The following theorem gives conditions in order that the distributions of the normalized sums of random variables converge to stable distributions which are different from the normal distribution, that is, to distributions with $0 < \alpha < 2$. *Necessary and sufficient for this kind of convergence is that*

$$F(-x) \sim c_1 \frac{h_1(x)}{|x|^\alpha}, \qquad 1 - F(x) \sim c_2 \frac{h_2(x)}{x^\alpha} \qquad (c_1 \geq 0, c_2 \geq 0, c_1 + c_2 > 0)$$

for $x \to \infty$, where h_i are slowly varying functions. Here, the B_n differ from $n^{1/\alpha}$ only by a slowly varying factor. We can choose $B_n = n^{1/\alpha}$ if and only if

$$F(-x) \sim \frac{c_1}{|x|^\alpha}, \qquad 1 - F(x) \sim \frac{c_2}{x^\alpha}.$$

One of the applications of stable laws is connected with the *theory of renewal*. Assume that the time intervals during which a "system" returns successively to the original state are independent identically distributed random variables. Then the time until the *n*-the return is the sum n of these variables, and under the conditions described above its distribution will be asymptotically stable. Let v_t be the number of returns to the original state within the time t. The obvious relation

$$\mathbb{P}\{v_t \geq n\} = \mathbb{P}\{s_n \leq t\}$$

allows to obtain the asymptotic distribution of v_t for $t \to \infty$.

Example. Consider the example of the symmetric random walk given in chapter I, § 5.4. In this example the distribution of the time s_n until the *n*-th return to the original state, normalized by $A_n = 0$, $B_n = n^2$ converges to the stable law with density $p(x; 1/2, 1)$. An explicit expression of this density had been given at the end of the preceding section. Accordingly, it is easy to see that

$$\mathbb{P}\{v_t \geqq z\sqrt{t}\} \to \int_0^{z^{-2}} p\left(x; \frac{1}{2}, 1\right) dx = \sqrt{\frac{2}{\pi}} \int_0^{z} e^{-\frac{x^2}{2}} dx.$$

One of the interesting problems is that of sharpening the limit theorems on convergence to stable laws with $0 < \alpha < 2$; it is similar to the sharpening in the case of convergence to the normal law. One of the basic results has been established by H. Cramér and can be described in the following way. Let $F(x)$ be a distribution function which satisfies the conditions:

a) for $x \to \infty$

$$F(-\infty) = \frac{c_1}{x^\alpha} + \frac{d_1}{x^{\alpha_1}} + r_1(x), \qquad r_1(x) = 0(x^{-\gamma}),$$

$$1 - F(x) = \frac{c_2}{x^\alpha} + \frac{d_2}{x^{\alpha_1}} + r_2(x), \qquad r_2(x) = 0(x^{-\gamma})$$

$$(\alpha < \alpha_1 < \gamma; \ c_1 \geqq 0, \ c_2 \geqq 0, c_1 + c_2 > 0);$$

b) in the case $0 < \gamma \leqq 1$ the functions $r_1(x) \pm r_2(x)$ are assumed to be monotone for sufficiently large $x > 0$.

Let $\beta = (c_1 - c_2)/(c_1 + c_2)$, $g_\alpha(t)$ the characteristic function of the distribution with density $p(x; \alpha, \beta)$, and $G_{\alpha,\beta}(x)$ the corresponding distribution function. We further denote

$$k = k_1 \alpha + k_2(\alpha_1 - \alpha) + k_3(2 - \alpha) + k_4,$$

where the k_i are non-negative integers, one of them being different from zero; thus we have $k > 0$. Let $P_{k_1,k_2,k_3,k_4}(t)$ be a polynomial of degree $k_1 + \cdots + k_4 - 1$ in t with in general complex coefficients.

Theorem. *If α, β and γ are not integers and if F satisfies the conditions* a) *and* b), *then we can choose normalizing constants A_n and $B_n = b_n^{1/\alpha}$ and polynomials P_{k_1,k_2,k_3,k_4} such that for $n \to \infty$ we have uniformly with respect to x*

$$F_n(x) = G_{\alpha,\beta}(x) + \sum_{0 < k < \lambda} G_{\alpha,\beta}(x; P_{k_1,k_2,k_3,k_4}) n^{-\frac{k}{\alpha}} + 0\left(n^{-\frac{\lambda}{\alpha}}\right),$$

where

$$G_{\alpha,\beta}(x; P_{k_1,k_2,k_3,k_4}) = -\frac{1}{\pi} \mathrm{Im} \left[\int_0^\infty t^{k+\alpha-1} P_{k_1,k_2,k_3,k_4}(t^\alpha) g_\alpha(t) e^{-itx} dt \right]$$

$$\lambda = \min(1, \gamma - \alpha).$$

The summation is extended over all k defined by the formula above which satisfy the inequality $0 < k < \lambda$.

In the case of integers α and α_1 an analogous result holds whose formulation, however, is more complicated.

§ 8. Local Theorems for Lattice-Distributions

1. Asymptotic Uniform Distributions

Let $\xi_1, \xi_2, ..., \xi_n$ be independent random variables taking only integral values

$$p_{nk} = \mathbb{P}\{\xi_n = k\}, \quad s_n = \xi_1 + \cdots + \xi_n, \quad P_n(m) = \mathbb{P}\{s_n = m\},$$
$$A_n = \mathbb{M} s_n, \quad B_n^2 = \mathbb{D} s_n.$$

We say that the sequence ξ_n satisfies the *local theorem* if

$$P_n(m) = \frac{1}{\sqrt{2\pi} B_n} e^{-\frac{(m - A_n)^2}{2 B_n^2}} + o\left(\frac{1}{B_n}\right)$$

for $n \to \infty$ uniformly with respect to m.

It is easy to see that, if the local theorem can be applied to the ξ_n, "*global*" *convergence* follows: the distribution functions $F_n(x)$ of the normalized sums $(s_n - A_n)/B_n$ converge to the normal distribution function $\Phi(x)$. Since conditions for "global" convergence, that is, conditions for the validity of the *central limit theorem*, are well known the question arises naturally what has to be added to the conditions for the central limit theorem in order that the local theorem holds.

We introduce a definition needed. The sequence s_n is called *asymptotically uniformly distributed* if for any fixed h the relation

$$\lim_{n \to \infty} \mathbb{P}\{s_n \equiv j(\mathrm{mod}\, h)\} = \frac{1}{h} \quad (j = 0, 1, ..., h - 1)$$

holds. It is not hard to see that, like the applicability of the local theorem, the property of the sums of being asymptotically uniformly distributed can depend on the structure of some initial terms. This is true in the example where $\xi_2, \xi_3, ...$ are identically distributed:

$$\mathbb{P}\{\xi_2 = \pm 1\} = \frac{1}{2}, \quad \text{and} \quad \mathbb{P}\{\xi_1 = 1\} = 1 - \mathbb{P}\{\xi_1 = 0\} = p \leq \frac{1}{2}.$$

We exclude such a situation from our considerations and *confine ourselves to the case where such a dependance does not exist*, that is, the given sequence as well as any sequence obtained from it by changing or deleting a finite number of initial terms is also asymptotically uniformly distributed or satisfies the local theorem, respectively. Under this restriction we can assert that the condition

$$\sum_{n=0}^{\infty} \min_{0 \leq a \leq h-1} \mathbb{P}\{\xi_n \notin L_{a,h}\} = \infty,$$

where $L_{a,h}$ are the following sublattices of a lattice of all integers: $L_{a,h} = \{m: m = a + kh\}$, is necessary and sufficient in order that there is an asymptotically uniform distribution.

It is known that, if the local theorem is true, the sums s_n are asymptotically uniformly distributed. It is also known that under sufficiently general conditions the local theorem follows from global convergence and an asymptotically uniform distribution of the sums s_n, for example, if the terms are uniformly bounded or are such that

$$\int_{|x - \mathbb{M}\xi_n| > z} (x - \mathbb{M}\xi_n)^2 \, \mathbb{P}_{\xi_n}(dz) \to 0 \qquad (z \to \infty)$$

uniformly with respect to n.

A similar result is true in the multi-dimensional case. In general, however, global convergence and an asymptotically uniform distribution of the sums s_n do not imply the local theorem.

2. Integral-Valued Identically Distributed Terms

We now confine ourselves to the case of identically distributed integral-valued terms. If finite second moments exist, there is a necessary and sufficient condition for the local theorem which has the same form in the case of any finite number of dimensions. It consists in the fact that the maximal step of the distribution is equal to one. However, even in simple examples the accuracy in the local theorem may be small for small or moderate values of n.

Example. Consider terms which take the values 0, 3, 9 with probability 1/3 each. In this case behavior of the probabilities $P_n(m)$ is almost as "correct" as in the case of the Bernoulli scheme which is illustrated in all textbooks by convincing diagrams. If, however, we take 0, 3, 10 as the possible values, preserving the probabilities, then the situation will change completely. In fact if n is of the order of some tens, the probabilities $P_n(m)$ behave extremely irregular. The explanation consists in the fact that within the interval $0 < t < 2\pi$ the absolute value of the characteristic function of the terms comes extremely close to one:

$$\left| \varphi \left(2\pi \cdot \frac{3}{10} \right) \right|^2 \geq 0.91$$

(see § 1 of this chapter).

Sufficient analytic conditions for the applicability of the local theorem are known; these conditions contain the requirement that a certain integral of the absolute value of the characteristic functions of the sums s_n should be "small"[41]. We can also present necessary conditions of an analogous kind. They are based on the following inequality.

Let

$$\sup_m \left| P_n(m) - \frac{1}{\sqrt{2\pi B_n}} e^{-\frac{(m-A_n)^2}{2B_n^2}} \right| = \frac{\lambda_n}{B_n}.$$

Then

$$B_n \int_{\frac{2\pi}{2k_n+1} \leq |t| \leq \pi} \prod_{j=1}^{n} |\varphi(t; \xi_j)|^2 \, dt \leq C\left(\frac{C_1}{B_n} + C_2 \lambda_n \right),$$

where C, C_1 and C_2 are absolute constants and k_n is equal to the integral part of $B_n \sqrt{\frac{C_1}{B_n} + C_2 \lambda_n}$; we can set $C = 2 + \frac{1}{8\sqrt{\pi}}$, $C_1 = \frac{2(1+\sqrt{2\pi})}{\pi}$, $C_2 = 2$.

The latter inequality can be exploited in order to estimate the number of terms needed to achieve a given accuracy in the local theorem.

§ 9. Local Theorems for Densities

Consider again a sequence of independent identically distributed variables $\xi_1, \ldots, \xi_n$, and set

$$s_n = \xi_1 + \cdots + \xi_n.$$

We assume that for $n = n_0$ the distribution of the sum s_n has a density. Sometimes it will be expedient to understand by a density the *derivative of the absolutely continuous part* of the distribution under the assumption that it be different from zero; in this case we speak of a "density". The sums s_n have a density for $n \geq n_0$, too, and the question naturally arises how this density behaves for $n \to \infty$.

We consider two types of convergence: *uniform convergence and convergence in mean.* As before let

$$\mathbb{M} s_n = A_n, \qquad \mathbb{D} s_n = B_n^2, \qquad \eta_n = (s_n - A_n)/B_n$$

and

$$p_n(x) = p_{\eta_n}(x), \qquad \varphi(x) = \Phi'(x) = \frac{1}{\sqrt{2\pi}} e^{-\frac{1}{2}x^2}.$$

[41] *Petrov, V. V.*, A local theorem for densities of sums of independent random variables. Theory of Prob. and its Applications, Vol. **1** (1956), 316—322.

If in addition to the existence of an r-th moment $M|\xi_j|^r$ we impose the condition:

a) *there exists a number n_0 such that the density $p_{n_0}(x)$ is bounded,* then we obtain for $n \to \infty$ the convergence

$$p_n(x) \to \varphi(x)$$

uniformly with respect to x and for $r \geq 3$ the asymptotic expansion

$$p_n(x) = \varphi(x) + \frac{d}{dx} \left[\varphi(x) \sum_{k=1}^{r-2} Q_k(x) n^{-\frac{k}{2}} \right] + o \left(n^{-\frac{r-2}{2}} \right)$$

where the estimate of the remainder is again uniform with respect to x. We remark that the condition a) turns out to be necessary, too, for the uniform convergence of $p_n(x)$ to $\varphi(x)$.

If to the condition that a moment of order r $(r \geq 3)$ exists, we add the condition

b) *for some n_0 there exists the "density" $p_{n_0}(x)$,* then the densities converge in mean:

$$\int_{-\infty}^{\infty} |p_n(x) - \varphi(x)| \, dx \to 0 \qquad (n \to \infty).$$

Condition b) is also necessary for this kind of convergence.

We remark that, if $\mathbb{P}$ and $\mathbb{Q}$ are two distributions on the line and if $\mathbb{Q}$ is absolutely continuous with respect to the Lebesgue measure, then

$$\sup_A |\mathbb{P}(A) - \mathbb{Q}(A)| = \alpha + \frac{1}{2} \int_{-\infty}^{\infty} |\beta h_2(x) - q(x)| \, dx \,,$$

where h_2 and q are the densities of the measures $\mathbb{H}_2$ and $\mathbb{Q}$ respectively, and $\mathbb{H}_2$ is the absolutely continuous component in the decomposition

$$\mathbb{P}(A) = \alpha \mathbb{H}_1(A) + \beta \mathbb{H}_2(A)$$

$(\alpha \geq 0, \beta \geq 0, \alpha + \beta = 1, \mathbb{H}_1(R') = \mathbb{H}_2(R') = 1)$, that is, in the decomposition of $\mathbb{P}$ into a singular and an absolutely continuous part.

It follows that in the case where a second moment exists the condition b) is necessary and sufficient for the convergence "in variation":

$$\sup_A \left| \mathbb{P}\{\eta_n \in A\} - \int_A \varphi(x) \, dx \right| \to 0 \qquad (n \to \infty).$$

Assuming that moments of higher order exist we can obtain estimates for

$$\sup_A \left| \mathbb{P}\{\eta_n \in A\} - \int_A \left[\varphi(x) + \frac{d}{dx} \varphi(x) \sum_{k=1}^{r-3} Q_k(x) n^{-\frac{k}{2}} \right] dx \right|.$$

Passing to the case of non-identically distributed terms we have to remark at once that we cannot expect any necessary and sufficient conditions for the applicability of the local theorem to densities of sums of independent random variables. The meaning of this can be explained by the example of the independent random variables $\{\xi_n\}$ where ξ_1 is uniformly distributed on $(-1, 1)$ and ξ_n for $n \geq 2$ takes the values $\pm 1/\sqrt{n}$ with probability $1/2$. Here the normalized sums η_n have densities which converge to the density of the normal law, but all terms starting from the second one are discrete.

Many sufficient conditions are known in order that the local theorem be true for densities[42].

Here we only mention a class of distributions for which the convergence "in variation" follows from the weak convergence of the distributions of the sums to the normal distribution. This is always the case if all terms are uniformly or "almost uniformly" distributed. The latter assumption is defined by requiring that the ξ_n have densities for all n and that the maxima A_n of these densities are connected with the corresponding variances σ_n^2 by the relations

$$A_n \sigma_n^2 \leq C$$

where C is a constant which does not depend on n. We remark that always $A_n \sigma_n^2 \geq 1/12$. Other types of convergence of densities have been considered, too, for example, convergence in the sense of the "distance"

$$\varrho(\mathbb{P}, \mathbb{Q}) = \left(\int\limits_{-\infty}^{\infty} x^a |p(x) - q(x)|^\beta \, dx \right)^{\frac{1}{\beta}}$$

etc. The results concerning the case of identically distributed terms admit an immediate extension to the multi-dimensional case as well as to the case of convergence to stable limit distributions[43].

§ 10. Probabilities of Large Deviations
Inequalities and Asymptotic Formulas

The subjects mentioned in the title are extensively discussed in the literature, at least for sums of independent identically distributed random variables[44]. The essence of the matter can be illustrated in the following way. Let η_n be the normalized sum $s_n = \xi_1 + \cdots + \xi_n$ of in-

---

[42] See the book by *I. A. Ibragimov* and *Yu. V. Linnik* (footnote on p. 180).
[43] See *I. A. Ibragimov* and *Yu. V. Linnik* (footnote on p. 180).
[44] See *I. A. Ibragimov* and *Yu. V. Linnik* (footnote on p. 180).

dependent random variables $\xi_1, \ldots, \xi_n$:

$$\eta_n = \frac{s_n - \mathbb{M} s_n}{\sqrt{\mathbb{D} s_n}},$$

and suppose that the η_n satisfy the central limit theorem:

$$F_n(x) = \mathbb{P}\{\eta_n < x\} \to \Phi(x) = \frac{1}{\sqrt{2\pi}} \int_{-\infty}^{x} e^{-\frac{1}{2}z^2} dz.$$

For large $|x|$, that is, for small $F_n(x)$ $(x < 0)$ or $1 - F_n(x)$ $(x > 0)$ absolute estimates of the nearness of F_n to Φ turn out to be useless, and estimates are needed for the relative accuracy of the approximation, that is, for the ratios

$$\frac{F_n(x)}{\Phi(x)} \quad \text{for} \quad x < 0 \quad \text{and} \quad \frac{1 - F_n(x)}{1 - \Phi(x)} \quad \text{for} \quad x > 0.$$

To be specific we confine ourselves to the case $x > 0$. The following theorem gives a typical result on identically distributed variables: *if* $\mathbb{M}\xi_i = 0$ *and*

$$\mathbb{M} e^{h|\xi_i|} < \infty \quad \text{for} \quad |h| \leq h_0 \quad (h_0 > 0),$$

then for $x > 1$, $x = 0(\sqrt{n})$ *we have*

$$\frac{1 - F_n(x)}{1 - \Phi(x)} = \exp\left(-\frac{x^3}{\sqrt{n}}\right) \lambda\left(\frac{x}{\sqrt{n}}\right)\left[1 + 0\left(\frac{x}{\sqrt{n}}\right)\right]$$

where $\lambda(z) = \sum_{n=0}^{\infty} c_n z^n$ *is a power series which converges in a sufficiently small neighborhood of zero, and the c_n are determined by the ratios* $\mathbb{M}\xi_j^k / \sigma^k$, $k = 2, 3, \ldots, n + 2$. *Details of the construction of the series* $\lambda(z)$ *will be given below.*

Theorems of this type are usually formulated with remainder terms of the form 0 or o, and therefore are not suited for the computation of the corresponding probabilities within guaranteed limits of accuracy. The only exception seems to be the result of *W. Feller*[45]. Let ξ_n be a sequence of independent random variables subject to the conditions

$$|\xi_k| < \lambda_n \sqrt{\mathbb{D} s_n} = \lambda_n B_n, \qquad \mathbb{M}\xi_k = 0.$$

We set $\sigma_k^2 = \mathbb{D}\xi_k$, $\alpha_{k,\nu} = \mathbb{M}\xi_k^\nu$ and denote by $\varkappa_{k,\nu}$ the ν-th semi-invariant of the random variable ξ_k and $K_{n,\nu} = \sum_{k=1}^{n} \varkappa_{k,\nu}$. We define h as the solution

[45] *Feller, W.*, Generalization of a probability limit theorem of Cramér. Trans. Amer. Math. Soc. **54**, 2 (1943), 361—372.

of the equation

$$x = \frac{1}{B_n} \sum_{v=2}^{\infty} K_{n,v} \frac{h^{v-1}}{(v-1)!}$$

and introduce the power series $Q_n(x) = \sum_{v=1}^{\infty} q_{n,v} x^v$ by setting

$$\frac{x^2}{2} + \frac{x^2}{2} Q_n(x) = \sum_{v=0}^{\infty} K_{n,v} \frac{v-1}{v!} h^v .$$

Then we can show that

$$q_{n,1} = \frac{1}{3 B_n^3} \sum_{k=1}^{n} \alpha_{k,3} ,$$

$$q_{n,2} = \frac{1}{12 B_n^4} \sum_{k=1}^{n} \alpha_{k,4} - \frac{1}{4 B_n^4} \sum_{k=1}^{n} \alpha_{k,2}^2 - \frac{1}{4 B_n^6} \left(\sum_{k=1}^{n} \alpha_{k,3} \right)^2 \quad \text{etc.}$$

If $0 < \lambda_n x < 1/4(3 - \sqrt{5})$, then

$$1 - F_n(x B_n) = e^{-\frac{1}{2} x^2 Q_n(x)} \left[\{1 - \Phi(x)\} + \theta \lambda_n e^{-\frac{1}{2} x^2} \right] .$$

If, however, $0 < \lambda_n x < 1/12$, then $|\theta| < 9$ and $|q_{n,v}| < 1/7 (12 \lambda_n)^v$. Making use of the fact that for $x > 0$

$$1 - \Phi(x) = \frac{1}{\sqrt{2\pi} x} e^{-\frac{x^2}{2}} \left(1 - \frac{\vartheta}{x^2} \right) \quad (0 < \vartheta < 1),$$

we can also write

$$1 - F_n(x B_n) = (2\pi)^{-\frac{1}{2}} x^{-1} e^{-\frac{1}{2} x^2 (1 + Q_n(x))} \left(1 - \frac{\vartheta}{x^2} + \sqrt{2\pi} \theta \lambda_n x \right).$$

It is interesting to compare these results with the so-called "exponential boundaries"[46]. For the sake of simplicity we assume that $M e^{h \xi_k}$ exists for all real h. Čebyshev's inequality yields

$$1 - F_n(x B_n) \leq e^{-h x B_n} M e^{h s_n} .$$

Determining h so as to minimize the right side of the last inequality we obtain

$$x B_n = \frac{d}{dh} \log M e^{h s_n} = \sum_{v=2}^{\infty} K_{n,v} \frac{h^{-1}}{(v-1)}$$

$$1 - F_n(x B_n) \leq e^{-\frac{x^2}{2} [1 + Q_n(x)]}$$

[46] Bernštein, S. N., Theory of Probability. 4 ed. Moscow, Gostehizdat, 1946, Chapt. IV (Russian).

This shows to what extent the theorems given above are sharper than Čebyshev's inequality. Recall that under additional conditions, for example, if the terms are uniformly bounded or their moments are subject to restrictions on their growth like

$$|\mathbf{M}\,\zeta_k^\nu| \leq \frac{\sigma_k^2}{2}\,H^{\nu-2}\nu!$$

where H is a constant not depending on k, the method based on Čebyshev's exponential inequality yields inequalities of the type

$$1 - F_n(x\,B_n) < e^{-\frac{x^2}{4}}\left(0 < x < \frac{B_n}{H}\right),$$

$$1 - F_n(x\,B_n) < e^{-\frac{x\,B_n}{4H}}\left(x > \frac{B_n}{H}\right).$$

The local variant of the theorem which had been given at the beginning of this paragraph can be formulated for terms with continuous distributions as well as for lattice distributed terms. If, for example, we add to the conditions of this theorem the requirement that the terms have a bounded density on the entire line, then we obtain for $x \geq 1$, $x = o(\sqrt{n})$ and $n \to \infty$

$$p_n(x) = \varphi(x) \exp\left[\frac{x^2}{\sqrt{n}}\,\lambda\left(\frac{x}{\sqrt{n}}\right)\right]\left[1 + 0\left(\frac{x}{\sqrt{n}}\right)\right]$$

where $p_n(x)$ is the density of the normalized sum.

Local theorems on large deviations admit an extension in the same form to the multi-dimensional case which permits to obtain estimates for the probabilities of hitting domains "far" from the origin; here the expectations of the terms are assumed to be equal to zero[47].

Recently a "unilateral treatment" of problems of large deviation was proposed. The behavior of sums of independent random variables for $x \to \infty$ or $x \to -\infty$, respectively, is connected with the behavior of the terms for $x \to \infty$, $(x \to -\infty)$ under minimal restrictions on the behavior on the negative or positive half-line[48].

---

[47] *Richter, W.*, Multi-dimensional local theorems for large deviations. Probability theory and its Appl. Vol. III, (1958), 100—106. *Rogozin, B. A.* and *A. A. Borovkov*, Teoriya veroyatn. i primen. X (1965), 61—69 (Russian).

[48] *Zolotariev, V. M.*, Unilateral treatment and sharpening of inequalities of Čebyshev type. Litov. mat. sbornik V **2** (1965), 233—250 (Russian).

§ 11. Concluding Remarks

In the course of this chapter our main attention was directed to schemes of summation of independent random variables or vectors. The composition of random elements with values in various groups and corresponding limit theorems are considered in the book by *U. Grenander* (see footnote on p. 151) [49].

1. We investigate the scheme of multiplication of complex-valued random variables, unequal to zero. Although this group is isomorph ($\zeta \leftrightarrow (\log|\zeta|, \arg\zeta)$) to the direct sum of two well investigated groups (the additive group of real numbers and the group of rotation), a non-trivial theory of the multiplication of "almost unit vector" complex variables

$$\zeta_{n,1}, \zeta_{n,2}, \ldots, \zeta_{n,k_n}$$

and the corresponding infinitely divisible laws can be constructed.

2. *Marginal Distributions.* A certain type of limit theorems can be illustrated as follows. We choose a uniform distribution on the $(n-1)$-dimensional sphere

$$x_1^2 + x_2^2 + \cdots + x_n^2 = 1 .$$

We consider the joint distribution of a fixed number of coordinates, say, $x_1, x_2, \ldots, x_j$. Then the variables

$$\sqrt{n}\, x_1, \ldots, \sqrt{n}\, x_j$$

are asymptotically independent for $n \to \infty$ and normally distributed with parameters $(0, 1)$.

Similarly for the uniform distribution in the simplex

$$x_1 + x_2 + \cdots + x_n = 1 , \qquad x_1 \geqq 0, \ldots, x_n \geqq 0$$

the variables $n x_1, \ldots, n x_j$ are asymptotically independent for $n \to \infty$ and have an exponential probability distribution.

3. *Zeros of Random Polynomials.* Starting with *Hardy* and *Littlewood* many mathematicians have busied themselves with the distribution of zeros of random polynomials. A typical result looks like this: for polynomials of degree n with independent identically distributed real coefficients we have for $n \to \infty$

$$\mathbb{P}\{\varepsilon_n \log n < N_n < \alpha(\log n)^2\} \to 1 ,$$

---

[49] See also the later review of *V. V. Sazonov* and *V. N. Tutubalin*, Probability distribution on topological groups. Teoriya veroyatn. i primen. XI, **1** (1966), 13—55 (Russian).

where N_n is the number of real roots, α a constant and ε_n an arbitrary sequence such that $\varepsilon_n \to 0$ and $\varepsilon_n \log n \to \infty$. Here all logarithms are natural.

4. *Random Matrices and Random Determinants.* Let

$$\xi_1 = \begin{Bmatrix} \xi_1^{(1)} \\ \vdots \\ \xi_1^{(l)} \end{Bmatrix}, \dots, \xi_l = \begin{Bmatrix} \xi_l^{(1)} \\ \vdots \\ \xi_l^{(l)} \end{Bmatrix}$$

be independent and identically distributed l-dimensional random column vectors, and A the matrix consisting of the components $\xi_j^{(i)}$, $\varDelta$ its determinant which equals, as is well known, the orientated volume of the l-dimensional parallelepiped constructed from these vectors.

The distribution of $\varDelta$ is known only in two cases: if the ξ_j are uniformly distributed on the l-dimensional unit sphere of the l-dimensional space and if the ξ_j are normally distributed with vanishing mean vector and non-degenerate correlation matrix. In the latter case the ration $\varDelta^2/\det \Sigma$, where Σ denotes the correlation matrix, is distributed like the product $\chi_1^2 \dots \chi_l^2$, where the χ_j^2 are independent and have χ^2-distributions with $1, 2, \dots, l$ degrees of freedom, respectively. From this we can derive that for $l \to \infty$ the variable $\log(\varDelta^2/\det \Sigma)$ is asymptotically normal with parameters $(\log(l-1)!, \sqrt{2\log l})$. No other asymptotic formulas are known up to the present time.

We illustrate the passage to the limit from discrete schemes to continuous ones only by a very simple example. We start with the symmetric Bernoulli scheme, that is, in other words, with the sequence

$$\xi_1, \xi_2, \dots, \xi_n, \dots$$

of independent random variables taking the values ± 1 with probability $1/2$ each. Consider a fixed section

$$\xi_1, \xi_2, \dots, \xi_N$$

of the sequence $\{\xi_n\}$ and the corresponding "increasing sums"

$$s_0 = 0, \ s_1 = \xi_1, \dots, s_N = \xi_1 + \dots + \xi_N.$$

By making use of combinatorial methods we can write down the exact formulas for the probabilities of various events connected with these sums [50]. For example the probability that $a \leq s_N \leq b$ is given by the formula

$$P_N(a, b) = \frac{1}{2^N} \sum_{j=a}^{b} C_N^j.$$

[50] *Feller, W.*, Introduction to Probability Theory and its Applications. New York: Wiley 1960.

The probability that the sums s_k ($0 \leq k \leq N$) do not attain the values a and $-b$, where a and b are positive integers, is equal to

$$P_{a,b,N} = \frac{2}{a+b} \sum_{h=1}^{a+b-1} \frac{\sin \dfrac{\pi h}{a+b}}{1 - \cos \dfrac{\pi h}{a+b}} \sin \frac{\pi a h}{a+b} \left(\cos \frac{\pi h}{a+b} \right)^N .$$

In the case of an even $N = 2N'$ the probability that the relations

$$s_{j-1} \geq 0, \qquad s_j \geq 0$$

are fulfilled for at most $2k$ of the indices j is equal to [51]

$$P_{2k, 2N'} = \sum_{j \leq k} \frac{1}{2^N} C_{2j}^j C_{2N'-2j}^{N'-j} .$$

Formulas of this kind are not suited for computation if N is large, but an application of *Stirling's formula* and other methods of asymptotic analysis yields sufficiently simple approximate expressions for these probabilities. In fact for $a \sim \dfrac{\alpha}{2} \sqrt{N}$, $b \sim \dfrac{\beta}{2} \sqrt{N}$, $2k \sim 2N'\gamma$ we have the following asymptotic formulas:

$$P_N(a, b) \sim \frac{1}{\sqrt{2\pi}} \int_\alpha^\beta e^{-z^2/2} \, dz ,$$

$$P_{a,b,N} \sim \frac{2}{\pi} \sum_{j=0}^\infty \frac{(-1)^j}{j+\frac{1}{2}} \cos \left(\left(j + \frac{1}{2} \right) \pi \frac{a-b}{a+b} \right)$$

$$\cdot \exp \left\{ -2 \left(j + \frac{1}{2} \right)^2 \frac{\pi^2}{(a+b)^2} \right\},$$

$$P_{2k, 2N'} \sim \frac{2}{\pi} \arcsin \sqrt{\gamma} .$$

Isolated asymptotic formulas of this type can be derived for more general variables than the ones considered above. However in order to obtain a more or less complete description of the class of all such asymptotic relations it is convenient to depart from a more general point of view and to consider the passage from the discrete process constructed in terms of the "increasing sums" to a continuous random process. This

---

[51] The number of these indices for $N \to \infty$ merely inessentially differs from the number of non-negative sums among $s_0, s_1, \dots, s_N$.

passage can be realized in various essentially equivalent forms[52]. Here we describe one of them, probably the most "geometric" one.

The behavior of the sums $s_0, s_1, \ldots, s_N$ can be represented with the help of a "random broken line" $s_N(t)$ obtained by connecting the points $\left(\dfrac{k}{N}, \dfrac{s_k}{\sqrt{\mathbb{D}s_N}}\right)$ successively by straight lines. The random broken line $s_N(t)$, $0 \leq t \leq 1$, generates a distribution $\mathbb{P}_N$ in the space $C\,[0, 1]$ of all continuous functions on the interval $[0, 1]$ endowed with the distance

$$\varrho(x, y) = \sup_{0 \leq t \leq 1} |x(t) - y(t)| .$$

The sequence $\mathbb{P}_N$ turns out to be fundamental in the sense of the metric which generates the concept of weak convergence of distributions in $C\,[0, 1]$, and therefore has a weak limit $\mathbb{W}$, in fact, the distribution which corresponds to the so-called Wiener process or the one-dimensional Brownian motion. Hence, on account of the properties of weak convergence we conclude that

$$\mathbb{P}_N(A) \to \mathbb{W}(A)$$

for any $A \subset C[0, 1]$ such that $\mathbb{W}(\dot{A}) = 0$ where $\dot{A}$ is the boundary of the set A. In addition we can assert that given any $\mathbb{W}$-almost everywhere continuous functional its distribution computed in terms of $\mathbb{P}_N$ converges to its distribution computed in terms of $\mathbb{W}$. In this way we obtain a broad class of asymptotic relations. The relations presented above are obtained if we choose sets A_1 and A_2 of the form

$$A_1 = \{x \in C[0, 1] : \alpha \leq x(1) \leq \beta\},$$
$$A_2 = \{x \in C[0, 1] : \alpha < \inf_t x(t) \leq \sup_t x(t) < \beta\}$$

and the functional

$$f(x) = \int_0^1 \frac{1 + \operatorname{sign} x(t)}{2} \, dt$$

and take into account that

$$\mathbb{W}(A_1) = \frac{1}{\sqrt{2\pi}} e^{-\frac{z^2}{2}} dz ,$$

$$\mathbb{W}(A_2) = \frac{2}{\pi} \sum_{j=0}^{\infty} \frac{(-1)^j}{j + \frac{1}{2}} \cos\left[\left(j + \frac{1}{2}\right)\pi \frac{a - b}{a + b}\right]$$
$$\cdot \exp\left\{-2\left(j + \frac{1}{2}\right)^2 \frac{\pi^2}{(a + b)^2}\right\},$$

$$\mathbb{W}\{x : f(x) < \gamma\} = \frac{2}{\pi} \arcsin \sqrt{\gamma} .$$

[52] *Prohorov, Yu. V.*, Convergence of random processes and limit theorems in probability theory. Theory of Probability and its Appl. Vol. **1** (1956), 157—214.

The next step consists in the construction of asymptotic formulas for the distributions of functionals of sums s_n which are not defined for the limit process. Such functionals are, for example, the number if changes of sign in the sequence $s_0, s_1, \ldots, s_N$, the number of maxima and minima etc.[53]

It is remarkable that all relations obtained in this way hold under extremely broad assumptions on the random variables ξ_j ("invariance principle").

The transition from discrete to continuous processes is a powerful tool in order to obtain asymptotic formulas, in any case the main terms.

[53] *Skorohod, A. V.*, Studies in the Theory of Random Processes. Cambridge: Addison-Wesley 1954.

CHAPTER V

Markov Processes

§ 1. Markov Processes
with a Finite or Denumerable Number of States (Markov Chains)

1. Markov Property and Transition Probabilities

The Markov Property. The characteristic property of Markov processes can be recognized already in a simple example like the well known game "Fair and softly goes far". In this game the chip of the player has to pass through a finite set of points $1, \ldots, m$. At any time the transition from one point to another is determined by throwing a die. Specifically, if at a given step the chip is at the point i then under the rules of the game it passes at the next step to a point depending on the number of spots on the die. From the arbitrary point i the chip moves to one of the points j with a probability p_{ij} independently of the way it went until the point i was reached.

The definition of the so-called *Markov processes* is based on this property. Consider a system which can be in any of some states of phase $E_1, E_2, \ldots$; it will often be convenient to denote the states of phase simply by the numbers $1, 2, \ldots$. Suppose that the state of the system changes in dependence on a parameter t, and that the transition from one state into another one also depends on chance. We usually call the parameter t the *time* and assume that t runs either through integers or through real numbers. Let $\xi(t)$ be the state of the system at time t, and suppose that the following law is being observed: if at a given time s the system is in state i then at a later time t it is in state j with probability p_{ij} independently of the behavior of the system until the time s.

The process $\xi(t)$ which describes the behavior of the system is termed a *Markov chain*. The probabilities

$$p_{ij}(s, t) = \mathbb{P}\{\xi(t) = j \mid \xi(s) = i\} \qquad (i, j = 1, 2, \ldots)$$

are called the *transition probabilities* of the Markov chain $\xi(t)$.

Usually we consider the behavior of the Markov chain $\xi(t)$ starting from some instant $t = t_0$. If

$$p_i^0 = \mathbb{P}\{\xi(t_0) = i\} \qquad (i = 1, 2, \ldots)$$

is the *initial probability distribution*, then

$$\mathbb{P}\{\xi(t_0) = i, \xi(t_1) = i_1, \ldots, \xi(t_n) = i_n\} = p_i^0\, p_{ii_1}(t_0, t_1) \ldots p_{i_{n-1}i_n}(t_{n-1}, t_n)\,(t_{n-1}, t_n)$$

for any $i, i_1, \ldots, i_n$ and $t_0 \leq t_1 \leq \cdots \leq t_n$.

Markov Times. Let τ be a random time which does not depend on the future; by this we mean that for arbitrary t the event $\{\tau > t\}$ is determined by the behavior of the system until the instant t. Then τ is called a *Markov time*.

Let A be an arbitrary event the realization of which depends entirely on the behavior of the system after the time τ. Then under the condition that the behavior of the system until the time τ is known, the probability of this event coincides with its conditional probability under the condition that only the state of the system at the time τ is known:

$$\mathbb{P}\{A \mid \xi(s), s \leq \tau\} = \mathbb{P}\{A \mid \xi(\tau)\}\,.$$

In particular, we have for any $i_1, \ldots, i_n$ and $t_1 \leq \cdots \leq t_n$

$$\mathbb{P}\{\xi(t_1 + \tau) = i_1, \ldots, \xi(t_n + \tau) = i_n \mid \xi(s), \ s \leq \tau\}$$
$$= p_{\xi(\tau), i_1}(\tau, t_1 + \tau) \ldots p_{i_{n-1}, i_n}(t_{n-1} + \tau, t_n + \tau)\,.$$

Suppose that we are given a sequence $\tau_0 \leq \tau_1 \leq \cdots \leq \tau_n \leq \cdots$ of times such that at each of the moments τ_n the corresponding state $i_n = \xi(\tau_n)$ is known. For example, τ_0 may be the moment when the system is in state i for the first time, τ_1 the moment of first return into this state, τ_2 the moment of second return etc. Then arbitrary events $A_1, A_2, \ldots, A_n, \ldots$ with the property that every event is entirely determined by the behavior of the system in the corresponding time interval from τ_{n-1} to τ_n, are mutually independent.

Homogeneity of the Process. The Markov chain $\xi(t)$ is called *homogeneous* if the transition probabilities $p_{ij}(s, t)$ depend only on the difference $t - s$:

$$p_{ij}(s, t) = p_{ij}(t - s) \qquad (i, j = 1, 2, \ldots)\,.$$

Example. *Random Walk.* Consider the random walk of a particle on the integers of the real line where the particle moves at every step by 1 with probability p and by -1 with probability $q = 1 - p$. Let $\xi(n)$ be the position of the particle after n steps. The sequence $\xi(0), \xi(1), \xi(2), \ldots$ forms a Markov chain; in fact if the particle is located at some point i, then its future behavior does not depend on anything that happened before it reached the point i, and after n more steps the particle enters the various states j with probability $p_{ij}(n)$. It is clear that for $|i-j| < n$ a transition from i to j is impossible, and $p_{ij}(n) = 0$. It is also clear that after n steps the particle can enter only states j for which the difference $|i-j|$ has the same parity as n, that is, for which the number

$$m = \frac{n + |i-j|}{2}$$

is an integer. For $j \geq i$ the particle can enter the state j if and only if among the n steps exactly $m = \dfrac{n + |i-j|}{2}$ steps are taken in positive direction. The probability that this will happen equals

$$p_{ij}(n) = C_n^m p^m q^{n-m} \qquad (j \leq i).$$

Example. *Radioactive Disintegration.* It is known that radium Ra is converted into radon Rn in the course of time t. During this process an α-particle is emitted which is the nucleus of a Helium atom He. If we assume that during a period of time t each atom Ra is converted into radon Rn with probability $p(t)$ independently of what happened before, then the total number $v(t)$ of α-particles emitted during this period is distributed according to a Poisson law:

$$\mathbb{P}\{v(t) = k\} = \frac{a^k}{k!} e^{-a} \qquad (k = 0, 1, 2, \ldots)$$

where $a = np(t)$ and n is the initial number of atoms Ra. The number of atoms Ra remaining equals $\xi(t) = n - v(t)$.

If the quantity of the radiation is known at a certain moment s, say $\xi(s) = i$, then independently of the character of the disintegration process until the moment s, k α-particles will be emitted with probability $\dfrac{a^k}{k!} e^{-a}$, $a = ip(t-s)$, within a period of length $t-s$. Thus $\xi(t)$ is a Markov process with transition probabilities

$$p_{ij}(s, t) = \frac{a^{i-j}}{(i-j)!} e^{-a}, \qquad a = ip(t-s), \qquad j \leq i.$$

It is clear that for $j > i$ a transition from i to j is impossible and $p_{ij}(s, t) = 0$.

The Waiting Time for a Change of State. Let $\xi(t)$ be a homogeneous Markov chain. If its state is fixed at some Markov time $\tau : \xi(\tau) = x$, then the further behavior of the process $\xi(t)$, $t \geq \tau$ does not depend on its behavior until the time τ, and the course of the process $\xi(t)$ after τ follows the same laws as if this were the initial moment $\tau = 0$.

Consider the case of continuous t and suppose that at some instant of time t_0, say, $t_0 = 0$, the state of the process $\xi(t_0) = x$ is known. A change of this state takes place at a random moment. By τ we denote the time elapsed until $\xi(t)$ enters a new state, and we call τ *the waiting time* for a change of state. What is the probability distribution of the random variable τ?

On account of the equations

$$\mathbb{P}\{\tau > s + t \mid \xi(0) = x\} = \mathbb{P}\{\tau > s + t \mid \xi(0) = x, \tau > s\}\, \mathbb{P}\{\tau > s \mid \xi(0) = x\}$$
$$= \mathbb{P}\{\tau > s + t \mid \xi(s) = x\}\, \mathbb{P}\{\tau > s \mid \xi(0) = x\}$$

the probability

$$F(t) = \mathbb{P}\{\tau > t \mid \xi(0) = x\} \qquad (t > 0)$$

considered as a function of t satisfies the functional equation

$$F(s + t) = F(s)\, F(t)$$

for any $s, t > 0$. Hence the probability $F(t)$ has to be an exponential function:

$$F(t) = e^{-\lambda t} \qquad (t > 0),$$

where λ is a non-negative constant; the value $\lambda = \infty$ is not excluded.

Thus the waiting time τ has an *exponential probability distribution* with parameter λ. The constant λ is called the *transition density* from the state x under consideration.

If $\lambda = 0$, the process $\xi(t)$ remains in the state x forever; such a state is called *absorbing*. For $\lambda = \infty$ the process $\xi(t)$ instantaneously leaves the state x; therefore the state is called *instantaneous*. For $0 < \lambda < \infty$ the probability that the state x of the process $\xi(t)$ changes within a short interval of time Δt is equal to

$$\lambda\, \Delta t + o(\Delta t),$$

where $o(\Delta t)$ is small of a higher order than Δt.

If the system is observed only at discrete moments $t = 0, 1, 2, \ldots,$ then it is natural to consider instead of the waiting time for a change of the state of $\xi(t)$ the "number of steps" until the process enters a new state, different from x. We have again

$$F(t) = \mathbb{P}\{\tau > t \mid \xi(0) = x\} = e^{-\lambda t} \qquad (t = 0, 1, 2, \ldots)$$

where $e^{-\lambda}$ is the probability of a "transition" in a single step from the state x into this very same state.

Example. *Process of Radioactive Disintegration.* The probabilistic model of radioactive disintegration described above, that is, the conversion of radium Ra into radon Rn, is such that the transition Ra $\rightarrow$ Rn represents a homogeneous Markov process with two states for each atom: Ra or Rn, and with the only possible transition Ra $\rightarrow$ Rn. If in the beginning at time $t = 0$ the number of atoms Ra is equal to n_0, then the number $v(t)$ of α-particles emitted within the time t has a Poisson distribution with parameter $a = n_0 p(t)$:

$$\mathbb{P}\{v(t) = k\} = \frac{a^k}{k!} e^{-a} \quad (k = 0, 1, 2, \ldots).$$

Here $p(t)$ is the probability that the state Ra changes within a period of time t. This probability should have the form

$$p(t) = 1 - e^{-\lambda t}$$

where λ is the corresponding transition density of Ra $\rightarrow$ Rn for any single atom, that is, a constant such that the probability of the transition Ra $\rightarrow$ Rn within a time interval Δt is equal to $\lambda \Delta t + o(\Delta t)$.

Consider an amount of radium during a period of time t. If the number of α-particles is equal to $v(t)$, then the number of the remaining atoms Ra will be $\xi(t) = n_0 - v(t)$. The average amount of radium within a period of time t equals

$$n(t) = \mathrm{M}\,\xi(t) = n_0 - n_0 p(t) = n_0 e^{-\lambda t}.$$

The exponential character of the function $n(t)$ entails in particular that the time T such that

$$n(T) = \frac{n_0}{2}$$

is an absolute constant. This is the time during which half of the original material disintegrates; it is called the *radioactive period*. It is connected with the transition density of Ra $\rightarrow$ Rn by the equation $T\lambda = \log 2$.

Kolmogorov Equations. The transition probabilities $p_{ij}(s, t)$ of a Markov chain satisfy the following relation:

$$p_{ij}(s, t) = \sum_k p_{ik}(s, u) \cdot p_{kj}(u, t) \quad (i, j = 1, 2, \ldots)$$

where $s \leq u \leq t$.

Let $\xi(t)$ be a homogeneous Markov chain. If we consider it only at discrete instants $t = nh$ $(n = 0, 1, \ldots; h > 0)$, then the probabilities $p_{ij}(nh)$ of a "transition in n steps" are uniquely determined by the probabilities $p_{ij} = p_{ij}(h)$ of a "transition in one step":

$$p_{ij}(nh) = \sum_k p_{ik} \cdot p_{kj}[(n-1)h] = \sum_k p_{ik}[(n-1)h] \cdot p_{kj} \quad (i, j = 1, 2, \ldots)$$

for all $n = 1, 2, \ldots$.

Suppose that the time t changes continuously and let

$$p_{ij}(0) = \lim_{h \to 0} p_{ij}(h) = \begin{cases} 1 & \text{for } j = i \\ 0 & \text{for } j \neq i. \end{cases}$$

If the transition probabilities $p_{ij}(t)$ of a homogeneous Markov chain have this continuity property, then they are continuously differentiable for $t > 0$. Also the limits

$$\lim_{h \to 0} \frac{p_{ij}(h) - p_{ij}(0)}{h} = \lambda_{ij} \quad (i, j = 1, 2, \dots)$$

exist and λ_{ij} for $i \neq j$ is necessarily finite:

$$0 \leq \lambda_{ij} < \infty \quad \text{and} \quad \lambda_{ii} = -\lambda_i,$$

where λ_i is the density of a transition from the state i. The coefficient λ_{ij} is called the *transition density* from i to j.

If we assume that for $t = 0$ the system is in state i, if τ_i is the moment when the process $\xi(t)$ leaves the state i for the first time and τ_{ij} is the moment when it reaches the states j for the first time, that is,

$$\tau_i = \sup_{\xi(t) = i} t, \qquad \tau_{ij} = \inf_{\xi(t) = j} t,$$

then the probability that $\xi(t)$ when leaving the state i moves just to the state j is equal to

$$\mathbb{P}\{\tau_{ij} = \tau_i \,|\, \xi(0) = i\} = \frac{\lambda_{ij}}{\lambda_i} \quad (j \neq i).$$

The transition densities λ_{ij} always satisfy the inequalities

$$\sum_{j \neq 1} \lambda_{ij} \leq \lambda_i \quad (i = 1, 2, \dots).$$

If the equations

$$\sum_{j \neq i} \lambda_{ij} = \lambda_i$$

are satisfied, then the transition probabilities $p_{ij}(t)$ satisfy the system of the so-called *backward Kolmogorov differential equations*:

$$p'_{ij}(t) = \sum_k \lambda_{ik} p_{kj}(t) \quad (i, j = 1, 2, \dots).$$

Under some restrictions (for example boundedness of the densities λ_{ij}) the system of so-called *forward differential equations* holds:

$$p'_{ij}(t) = \sum_k \lambda_{kj} p_{ik}(t) \quad (i, j = 1, 2, \dots).$$

Example. *Poisson Process.* The uniform flow of independent events (see p. 37) obviously has the property that the number $\xi(t)$ of events occuring within the time t represents a Markov process. The corresponding transition densities λ_{ij} are given by

$$\lambda_{ij} = \begin{cases} \lambda & \text{for} \quad j=i+1, \\ 0 & \text{for} \quad j \neq i+1 \end{cases} \quad (i=0,1,2,\ldots),$$

that is, only direct transitions from state i to the following state $j=i+1$ ($i=0,1,2,\ldots$) can take place.

Obviously, $p_{ij}(t)=p_{0,j-i}(t)$. We set

$$p_j(t)=p_{0j}(t) \quad (j=0,1,\ldots).$$

In this case the Kolmogorov differential equations for the functions $p_j(t)$ have the form:

$$\begin{aligned} p_0'(t) &= -\lambda p_0(t), \\ p_k'(t) &= \lambda p_{k-1}(t) - \lambda p_k(t) \end{aligned} \quad (k=1,2,\ldots).$$

Introducing the new functions $f_k(t)=e^{\lambda t}p_k(t)$ we obtain

$$f_0'(t)=\lambda f_0(t)+e^{\lambda t}p_0'(t)=\lambda f_0(t)-\lambda e^{\lambda t}p_0(t)=0,$$

$$f_k'(t)=\lambda f_k(t)+e^{\lambda t}p_k'(t)=\lambda f_k(t)+\lambda e^{\lambda t}p_{k-1}(t)-\lambda e^{\lambda t}(t)=\lambda f_{k-1}(t)$$

where $f_0(0)=1$ and $f_1(0)=f_2(0)=\cdots=0$.

The system of differential equations of the form

$$f_0'(t)=0, \quad f_k'=\lambda f_{k-1}(t) \quad (k=1,2,\ldots)$$

with the initial conditions stated above has the following solution:

$$f_0(t)=1, \quad f_1(t)=\lambda t, \ldots, f_n(t)=\frac{(\lambda t)^n}{n!}, \ldots.$$

Returning to the original functions $p_k(t)=e^{-\lambda t}f_k(t)$ we obtain

$$p_k(t)=\frac{(\lambda t)^k}{k!}e^{-\lambda t} \quad (k=0,1,\ldots).$$

Example. Suppose that demands are being made on a certain service system which follow a Poisson process with parameter λ_1, and the satisfaction of each single demand requires a random time τ that obeys the exponential distribution law with parameter λ_2, that is, $\mathbb{P}\{\tau>t\}=e^{-\lambda_2 t}$. Consider two states of the service system: E_1 is the vacant, E_2 the occupied system.

The Poisson flow of demands has the property that the appearance of the next demand after an arbitrary fixed moment $t=t_1$ does not depend on the way the demands had come in up to this moment. Therefore, if at a moment t_1 the system is in state E_1 then its further behavior does not depend on the preceding one, and, in particular, it will reach the state E_2 in the time interval Δt following t_1 with probability $\lambda_1 \Delta t + o(\Delta t)$, that is, with the same probability with which the next demand comes up in this time interval.

We suppose that at the time t_2 the system is in state E_2. Let τ be the random time of transition from state E_2 into state E_1; thus τ is the moment where the service ends. According to the exponential law for the distribution of the service time the equation

$$\mathbb{P}\{\tau > t \,|\, \tau > t_2\} = e^{-\lambda_2(t - t_2)} \qquad (t > t_2).$$

holds. It is obvious that during the time interval from t_2 to t the system passes to state E_1 with probability $1 - \exp\{-\lambda_2(t - t_2)\}$ independently of its behavior until time t_2. Thus the evolution of the system is described by a Markov process with two states E_1 and E_2 and corresponding transition densities λ_1 and λ_2.

Let $p_{ij}(t)$ be the corresponding transition probabilities. In the case considered here $p_{12}(t) = 1 - p_{11}(t)$, $p_{21}(t) = 1 - p_{22}(t)$, and the system of the Kolmogorov differential equations is split into the following two single equations:

$$p'_{11}(t) + (\lambda_1 + \lambda_2)\, p_{11}(t) = \lambda_2 ,$$

$$p'_{22}(t) + (\lambda_1 + \lambda_2)\, p_{22}(t) = \lambda_1 ,$$

the solution of which is given by the formulas

$$p_{11}(t) = \left(1 - \frac{\lambda_2}{\lambda_1 + \lambda_2}\right) e^{-(\lambda_1 + \lambda_2)t} + \frac{\lambda_2}{\lambda_1 + \lambda_2} ,$$

$$p_{22}(t) = \left(1 - \frac{\lambda_1}{\lambda_1 + \lambda_2}\right) e^{-(\lambda_1 + \lambda_2)t} + \frac{\lambda_1}{\lambda_1 + \lambda_2} .$$

Stability of the Process. In the case of a continuous time t a homogeneous Markov chain $\xi(t)$ can have so-called instantaneous states for which the corresponding transition densities are equal to $\lambda_i = \infty$. When reaching such a state i the system leaves it instantaneously:

$$\mathbb{P}\{\tau_i = 0 \,|\, \xi(0) = i\} = 1$$

where τ_i is the moment of leaving the state i for the first time. During an arbitrarily small time interval Δt after the moment $t = 0$ the system then leaves this state and again returns to it infinitely often.

If, generally, Δ_i denotes the time the system spends in the state i during a time interval Δt, then we have

$$\mathbb{P}\left\{\lim_{\Delta t \to 0} \frac{\Delta_i}{\Delta t} = 1 \mid \xi(0) = i\right\} = 1 .$$

The state i is called *stable* if $\lambda_i < \infty$. Once the system is in a stable state i it remains there with probability 1 during a positive period of time:

$$P\{\tau_i > 0 \mid \xi(0) = i\} = 1 .$$

The Markov chain is called *stable* if with probability 1 the system passes during an arbitrary finite period only a finite number of times from one state to another.

Suppose that the Markov chain $\xi(t)$ has no instantaneous states, that is, all transition densities λ_i are finite, and let τ_0 be the moment of leaving the state i for the first time, τ_1 the moment of leaving the next state $i_1 = \xi(\tau_0)$ for the first time, etc.; τ_n the moment of leaving the state $i_n = \xi(\tau_{n-1})$ for the first time. In order that the chain be stable the following condition is necessary and sufficient:

$$\sum_{n=1}^{\infty} \frac{1}{\lambda_{\xi(\tau_n)}} = \infty$$

with probability 1. Each chain with a finite number of states is stable.

Example. *Pure Birth Process.* Suppose that some particles reproduce themselves in such a way that if their number equals i at time t, then during the subsequent interval of time Δt one more particle will appear with probability $\lambda_i \Delta t + o(\Delta t)$, but the probability that a large number of particles is added is of order $o(\Delta t)$. This process is a Markov chain with states $i = 1, 2, \ldots$ and transition densities

$$\lambda_{ij} = \begin{cases} \lambda_i & \text{for } j = i+1 \\ -\lambda_i & \text{for } j = i , \\ 0 & \text{for } j \neq i, \, i+1 . \end{cases}$$

The condition of stability results from the fact that the time τ needed by the system for infinitely many transitions is infinite with probability 1. This condition is equivalent to $\mathbb{M} e^{-\tau} = 0$. If τ_n denotes the moment of leaving the state n then

$$\tau = \tau_1 + (\tau_2 - \tau_1) + (\tau_3 - \tau_2) + \cdots = \lim_{n \to \infty} \tau_n$$

where $\tau_1, \tau_2 - \tau_1, \tau_3 - \tau_2, \ldots$ are mutually independent random variables and $\tau_k - \tau_{k-1}$ is exponentially distributed with parameter λ_k. Hence

$$\mathsf{M} e^{-\tau} = \prod_{k=1}^{\infty} \mathsf{M} e^{-(\tau_k - \tau_{k-1})} = \prod_{k=1}^{\infty} \left(1 - \frac{1}{1 + \lambda_k} \right).$$

Thus it is obvious that the chain is stable if and only if

$$\prod_{k=1}^{\infty} \left(1 - \frac{1}{1 + \lambda_k} \right) = 0,$$

which is equivalent to the condition

$$\sum_{k=1}^{\infty} \frac{1}{\lambda_k} = \mathsf{M}\tau = \infty.$$

Minimal Transition Probabilities. In the case of a stable chain the transition probabilities $p_{ij}(t)$ are the *only* solutions of the Kolmogorov differential equations. This is not true in the case of an arbitrary chain, but there exists always a minimal solution $\bar{p}_{ij}(t)$, $i, j = 1, 2, \ldots$ such that for any other solution $p_{ij}(t)$ of these equations which satisfies the same initial conditions the inequalities

$$\bar{p}_{ij}(t) \le p_{ij}(t)$$

hold for all t. The components of the minimal solution $\bar{p}_{ij}(t)$ are the transition probabilities from i to j within the time t if the system makes only finitely many transitions from one state to another.

The minimal solution $\bar{p}_{ij}(t)$ describes the behavior of the chain until the moment $\tau = \lim_{n \to \infty} \tau_n$ where τ_n denotes the moment of the n-th transition.

Example. *Pure Birth Process.* Suppose that the transition densities satisfy the inequality

$$\sum_{i=1}^{\infty} \frac{1}{\lambda_i} < \infty$$

and that there exists exactly one particle to start with. We introduce one more state which serves to describe the fact that there exist infinitely many particles. The process reaches this state after a time t with a positive probability $p_{1,\infty}(t)$ although the corresponding transition densities are all equal to zero, and the forward differential equation for $p_{1,\infty}$ has the form

$$p'_{1,\infty}(t) = 0, \qquad p_{1,\infty}(0) = 0.$$

It is obvious that $p_{1,\infty}(t)$ is actually not a solution of this equation, since $p_{1,\infty}(t) > 0$. The minimal solution of the entire forward system can be successively determined from the equations

$$\bar{p}'_{1,1}(t) = -\bar{p}_{1,1}(t)\,\lambda_1\,,$$

$$\cdots\cdots\cdots\cdots\cdots\cdots\cdots\cdots$$

$$\bar{p}'_{1,n}(t) = -\bar{p}_{1,n}(t)\,\lambda_n + \bar{p}_{1,n-1}(t)\,\lambda_{n-1}\,,$$

$$\cdots\cdots\cdots\cdots\cdots\cdots\cdots\cdots\cdots\cdots$$

2. Classification of States of a Homogeneous Markov Chain

Recurrent and Non-Recurrent States. The original state i is called *non-recurrent* (transient) if after the elapsing of a finite period of time τ the system will with probability 1 return to this state never more.

In general, let T_i be the time spent in state i during the infinite interval of time $0 \le t \le \infty$. The state i is non-recurrent if and only if the random variable T_i has a finite expectation:

$$\mathbb{M}\,T_i = \sum_{t=0}^{\infty} p_{ii}(t) < \infty \qquad \text{for discrete } t$$

$$\mathbb{M}\,T_i = \int_{0}^{\infty} p_{ii}(t)\,dt < \infty \qquad \text{for continuous } t\,.$$

Consider a Markov chain $\xi(t)$ only at the discrete instants of time $t = nh$ $(n = 0, 1, \ldots; h > 0)$. Let

$$q_{ii}(nh) = \mathbb{P}\{\xi(h) \neq i, \ldots, \xi((h-1)h) \neq i, \quad \xi(nh) = i \,|\, \xi(0) = i\}\,,$$

that is, $q_{ij}(nh)$ is the probability that the first return to the original state i takes place in exactly n steps, and let

$$q_{ii} = \sum_{n=0}^{\infty} q_{ii}(nh)\,,$$

that is, q_{ii} is the probability of ever returning to the original state i. The generating functions $\varphi(z) = \sum_{n=0}^{\infty} p_{ii}(nh)\,z^n$ and $\psi(z) = \sum_{n=0}^{\infty} q_{ii}(nh)\,z^n$ are connected by the relation

$$\varphi(z) = \frac{1}{1 - \psi(z)}\,.$$

In the case of a Markov chain $\xi(t)$ with discrete time t which corresponds to the value $h = 1$, the state i is non-recurrent if and only if the probability q_{ii} of ever returning to this state is strictly smaller than 1.

In the case of a Markov chain $\xi(t)$ with continuous time t the state i is non-recurrent if and only if the probability of ever returning to it at discrete moments $t = nh$ $(n = 1, 2, ...)$ is smaller than 1: $q_{ii} < 1$ for any $h > 0$.

A state i which is not non-recurrent is called *recurrent*.

Null States and Positive States. The state i is called a *null* state if the average fraction of time the system spends in the state i during the infinite time interval $0 \leq t \leq \infty$ is equal to zero, more precisely, if

$$\lim_{T \to \infty} \frac{1}{T} \sum_{t=0}^{T} p_{ii}(t) = 0 \qquad \text{for discrete } t$$

$$\lim_{T \to \infty} \frac{1}{T} \int_{0}^{T} p_{ii}(t) \, dt = 0 \qquad \text{for continuous } t.$$

Average Return Time. Consider the Markov chain $\xi(t)$ at the discrete moments $t = nh$ $(n = 0, 1, ...; h > 0)$. Let

$$Q_i = \begin{cases} \sum_{n=1}^{\infty} n q_{ii}(nh) & \text{if } q_{ii} = 1 \\ \infty & \text{if } q_{ii} < 1. \end{cases}$$

In the case of a Markov chain with discrete time, corresponding to the value $h = 1$, the number Q_i represents the average return time to the original state i. The state i is null if and only if $Q_i = \infty$. In the case of a Markov chain with continuous time Q_i does not depend on the value of $h > 0$ selected; the average return time to the original state i at the discrete moments $t = nh$ equals hQ_i. Therefore the state i is null if and only if $Q_i = \infty$.

If j is a null state, then for any original state i we have

$$\lim_{t \to \infty} p_{ij}(t) = 0.$$

A state i which is not null is called *positive*. If the state i is positive, then

$$\lim_{T \to \infty} \frac{1}{T} \sum_{t=0}^{T} p_{ij}(t) = \frac{1}{Q_i} \qquad \text{for discrete } t$$

$$\lim_{T \to \infty} \frac{1}{T} \int_{0}^{T} p_{ii}(t) \, dt = \frac{1}{Q_i} \qquad \text{for continuous } t.$$

Periodic States. A state i in a chain with discrete time is called *periodic* if a return to it is possible only in a number of steps n which is divisible by a certain integer d:

$$p_{ii}(n) = 0 \quad \text{for} \quad n \neq kd, \qquad k = 1, 2, \dots .$$

The largest number d which has this property is called the *period of the state i*.

In the case of a continuous time t all probabilities $p_{ii}(t)$ are strictly positive for $t > 0$, hence there cannot be any periodic states.

Closed Sets of States. A set of states A is called *closed* if given the condition that $\xi(t)$ is in A for $t = t_0$, $\xi(t)$ remains in this set of states for all $t > t_0$.

We say that the state j can be *reached* from the state i if the probability to pass at some time from i to j is positive. The state j can be reached from i if and only if $p_{ij}(t) > 0$ for some $t > 0$. In the case of a continuous time we either have $p_{ij}(t) \equiv 0$ or $p_{ij}(t) > 0$ for all $t > 0$. The set of all states j which can be reached from a fixed state i is closed.

Two states i and j are said to *communicate* if each of them can be reached from the other one. Communicating states are of the same type: they are both either recurrent or non-recurrent, positive or null states, aperiodic or periodic with one and the same period d.

A closed set of states is called *minimal* or a *closed class* if it does not contain any other closed sets. Two closed classes either have no state in common or are identical. Each closed class consists of a set of mutually communicating states, where states outside the closed class cannot be reached from the states of the class. A closed class is called recurrent or non-recurrent, positive or null, aperiodic or periodic with period d according to the type of its states. The set of all recurrent states can be decomposed into closed classes.

Subclasses of a Periodic Chain. Given a chain with discrete time each periodic closed class A of period d can be decomposed into d not overlapping subclasses $B_1, B_2, \ldots, B_d$ of the following sort: from any state i in B_k the system passes necessarily at the next step into one of the states j in the subclass B_{k+1}. In this way the system evolves cyclically $B_1 \to B_2 \to \cdots \to B_d \to B_1 \to \cdots$.

If the system is one of the states i of a subclass B at the initial time $t = t_0$ then it hits the states of this subclass again after any number of steps nd divisible by d. Considering the system at the instants of time $t = t_0 + nd$ $(n = 0, 1, \ldots)$ only, we obtain a new Markov chain with a set of states B and transition probabilities $p_{ij} = p_{ij}(d)$, $i, j \in B$ which, however, is aperiodic.

Decomposition into Closed Classes of States. A state i is called *inessential* if there exists a state j which can be reached from i, whereas i cannot be reached from j: $p_{ji}(t) \equiv 0$ for all $t > 0$. Any non-recurrent state from which some recurrent state can be reached is inessential; the set E_0 of all these inessential states has the property that the states not in E_0 form a closed set E. In this set E we can separate the closed classes $A_1, A_2, \ldots$ of recurrent states and the remaining set A_0 of non-recurrent states. The set A_0 is closed but not necessarily a closed class. The original set E_0, that is, the set of inessential states, does not contain any closed set.

Let q_{ij} be the probability of a transition from i to j at some time. If j is recurrent, q_{ij} coincides with the probability q_{iA} that at some time a transition takes place from i to the closed class A of recurrent states which contains j. In particular, we have $q_{ij} = 1$ for states i in the same closed class A as j, and $q_{ij} = 0$ for states i belonging to other closed classes.

Let q_{iA} be the probability that the system which is in state i at the initial moment reaches the set of states A at some time. Given any fixed inessential state i of the set E_0 singled out above, the probabilities q_{iA} where A runs through the closed sets A_0, A_1 described before add up to 1. For any $A = A_0, A_1, \ldots$ the probabilities q_{iA} where i runs through the entire set E_0 are the only bounded solution of the following system of linear equations:

$$q_{iA} - \sum_{k \in E_0} p_{ik} q_{kA} = \sum_{j \in A} p_{ij}$$

where $p_{ij} = p_{ij}(h)$, and $h = 1$ if the time takes only integral values and $h > 0$ for a continuous time t.

Example. *Random Walk.* Consider a random motion of a particle through the integers on the real line where the particle takes one step of length 1 to the right with probability p and to the left with probability $1 - p$. All states have the period $d = 2$. If at each step the particle moves to the right with a large probability $p > 1/2$, then in the course of time it will move towards $+\infty$. We have

$$p_{ii}(2n) = \frac{(2n)!}{n!\,n!}\,[p(1-p)]^n \sim \frac{[4p(1-p)]^n}{\sqrt{\pi n}},$$

and since $4p(1-p) < 1$ for $p \neq 1/2$ we then obtain

$$\sum_n p_{ii}(2n) < \infty,$$

hence all states are non-recurrent.

If the random walk is symmetric, that is, $p = 1/2$ we have $p_{ii}(2n) \sim 1/\sqrt{\pi n}$ and the series $\sum_n p_{ii}(2n)$ converges, hence all states are recurrent.

For any p all states are null since $\lim_{n \to \infty} p_{ii}(2n) = 0$.

Random Walk with an Absorbing Barrier. Suppose that there exists a so-called *absorbing* barrier at the point $i = 0$: if the particle reaches the point $i = 0$ it will always remain there. Of course a transition from an arbitrary state $i > 0$ to an arbitrary state $j > 0$ is always possible with positive probability. The probabilities q_{ij} of passing from i to j satisfy the equations

$$q_{ij} = p\,q_{i+1,j} + (1-p)\,q_{i-1,j}\,.$$

This relation represents a finite difference equation for the probability q_{ij} as a function of $i = 1, 2, \ldots$. In order to determine q_{ij} as a solution of this equation we have to impose additional "boundary conditions". They can be obtained from the following considerations. For $i \neq j$ the probabilities will not change if we put another absorbing barrier at the point j. In this case we have obviously $q_{0j} = 0$ and $q_{jj} = 1$. The function q_{ij} of $i = 1, 2, \ldots, j-1$ which corresponds to these "boundary conditions" has the form

$$q_{ij} = A_i + B_j \left(\frac{1-p}{p}\right)^i \qquad (0 < i < j)$$

for $p \neq 1/2$ where

$$A_i = \frac{1}{1 - \left(\dfrac{1-p}{p}\right)^i}\,, \qquad B_j = -\,\frac{1}{1 - \left(\dfrac{1-p}{p}\right)^j}\,;$$

if, however, $p = 1/2$, then

$$q_{ij} = \frac{i}{j} \qquad (0 < i < j)\,.$$

It is clear that analogous formulas also hold if the absorbing barrier is established at some point k and $k < i < j$. It suffices to replace on the right side of the formulas above i by $i - k$ and j by $j - k$. If $k \to -\infty$, then the influence of the absorbing barrier vanishes, and the asymptotic formulas yield an expression for the probabilities q_{ij} of the transition from a point i to a point $j > i$ for the ordinary random walk without any absorbing barrier. These expressions have the form

$$q_{ij} = \begin{cases} \left(\dfrac{p}{1-p}\right)^{j-i} & \text{for } p < \dfrac{1}{2}, \\[2mm] 1 & \text{for } p \geq \dfrac{1}{2} \end{cases} \qquad (i \leq j)\,.$$

Replacing here p by $1 - p$ we obtain expressions for the probabilities q_{ij} with $i > j$:

$$q_{ij} = \begin{cases} \left(\dfrac{1-p}{p}\right)^{i-j} & \text{for } p > \dfrac{1}{2}, \\[2mm] 1 & \text{for } p \leq \dfrac{1}{2} \end{cases} \qquad (i \geq j)\,.$$

All these formulas have been derived under the assumption that there is an absorbing barrier at the point j, and of course for $i = j$ they yield the value $q_{ij} = 1$. The true probability of a return to the original state $i = j$ can be found from the probabilities q_{ij} with $i \neq j$ already known as follows:

$$q_{ii} = p\, q_{i+1,i} + (1-p)\, q_{i-1,i} .$$

This yields the following expression for the return probability:

$$q_{ii} = \begin{cases} 2p & \text{for } p < \dfrac{1}{2} \\[2mm] 2(1-p) & \text{for } p > \dfrac{1}{2}, \\[2mm] 1 & \text{for } p = \dfrac{1}{2}. \end{cases}$$

3. Ergodic Properties of Homogeneous Markov Chains

Final Probabilities. Suppose that the states of a homogeneous Markov chain $\xi(t)$ form a single closed positive aperiodic class. Then given any state j there exists the limit

$$\lim_{t \to \infty} p_{ij}(t) = P_j \qquad (j = 1, 2, \ldots)$$

and is the same for all initial states $i = 1, 2, \ldots$. The asymptotic values $P_1, P_2, \ldots$ represent a probability distribution: P_j is the final probability of being in state j; moreover

$$P_j = \frac{1}{Q_j} \qquad (j = 1, 2, \ldots)$$

where Q_j is the mean return time to the state j at the discrete moments $t = 0, 1, 2, \ldots$.

Let T_A be the time spent in the set of states A within an interval of time T. We have

$$\lim_{T \to \infty} \frac{T_A}{T} = \sum_{i \in A} P_i$$

with probability 1 for any set A.

Stationary Distribution. The initial probability distribution $p_i^0 = i = 1, 2, \ldots$ is called stationary if the probabilities $p_j(t)$ that the system is in the states $j = 1, 2, \ldots$, respectively, remain unchanged in the course of time t:

$$p_j(t) = \sum_i p_i^0 \cdot p_{ij}(t) \equiv p_j^0 \qquad (j = 1, 2, \ldots).$$

In the case of a stationary initial distribution the probabilities of more complicated events remain unchanged, too:

$$\mathbb{P}\{\xi(t_1 + t) = i_1, \ldots, \xi(t_n + t) = i_n\} = \mathbb{P}\{\xi(t_1) = i_1, \ldots, \xi(t_n) = i_n\}$$

for every $t > 0$.

Stationarity of the Final Distribution. On the positive states the final probabilities P_j, $j = 1, 2, \ldots$ determine a stationary distribution, and in the case of a closed class they are the only solution of the system of equations

$$P_j = \sum_i P_i \, p_{ij}(h) \qquad (j = 1, 2, \ldots).$$

Here $h = 1$ for an integral-valued time, and $h > 0$ arbitrary for a continuous time t.

In the case of a continuous time t the stationary probabilities P_j can also be determined from the system of linear equations

$$\sum_i P_i \lambda_{ij} = 0 \qquad (j = 1, 2, \ldots),$$

where λ_{ij} are the corresponding transition densities.

Assume that the *coefficient of ergodicity*

$$k(h) = 1 - \frac{1}{2} \sup_{i,\,k} \sum_{j=1}^{\infty} |p_{ij}(h) - p_{kj}(h)|$$

is positive for $h > 0$. Then the convergence to a stationary distribution will be exponentially fast:

$$|p_{ij}(t) - P_j| \leq C e^{-Dt}$$

where C and D are positive constants.

Example. *Pile of Books.* A pile of m books is lying on a table. If we number them, we can describe their order downward by a permutation of m numbers $(i_1, \ldots, i_m)$, where i_1 is the number of the book on top, i_2 the number of the next book, $\ldots$, and i_m the number of the last (lowest) book. Suppose that the i-th book is selected for reading with a certain probability p_i $(i = 1, \ldots, m)$, and is afterwards returned by simply putting it on top of the pile. How does the order of the books change?

We take an arbitrary state $(i_1, \ldots, i_m)$. At the next step this state either remains unchanged with probability p_{i_1}, that is, if the book with the number i_1 lying on top is chosen, or it changes into one of $m - 1$

states of the form $(i_k, i_1, ...)$ with probability p_{i_k}, that is, if the book with the number i_k is chosen. So we have a Markov chain the states of which are described by the permutations $(i_1, ..., i_m)$.

We denote by $p_{(i_1, ..., i_m)(j_1, ..., j_m)}$ the transition probability from state $(i_1, ..., i_m)$ to state $(j_1, ..., j_m)$:

$$p_{(i_1, ..., i_m), (j_1, ..., j_m)} = \begin{cases} p_{i_k} & \text{for } (j_1, ..., j_m) = (i_k, i_1, ...) \\ 0 & \text{for the remaining } (j_1, ..., j_m) \end{cases}$$

where the permutation $(i_k, i_1, ...)$ is obtained from $(i_1, ..., i_m)$ by chosing i_k and putting it in the first place. The final probabilities $p^*_{(j_1, ..., j_m)}$ are the solutions of the following system of linear equations:

$$p^*_{(j_1, ..., j_m)} = p_{j_1} \sum_{k=1}^{m} p^*_{(j_2, ..., j_{k-1}, j_1, j_k, ...)} .$$

After a sufficient large number of steps a stationary probability distribution will practically have established itself, that is, the pile of books will have the order $(i_1, ..., i_m)$ with constant probabilities $p^*_{(i_1, ..., i_m)}$; for $m = 2$ this distribution takes place immediately, at the first step. What is the final probability that any of the books in the pile appears on top?

The probability that the book with the number i lies on top is

$$p^*_i = \sum_{i_2, ..., i_m} p^*_{(i, i_2, ..., i_m)}$$

where the summation is extended over all states in which i stands at the first place. From the equations for the final probabilities we obtain

$$p^*_i = \sum_{i_2, ..., i_m} p_i \sum_{k=1}^{m} p^*_{(i_2, ..., i_{k-1}, i, i_k, ...)} = p_i \sum_{(i_1, ..., i_m)} p^*_{(i_1, ..., i_m)} = p_i$$

that is, after a sufficiently large number of steps the i-th book occurs at the top with the same probability p_i with which it had been taken from the pile.

Example. *A Multi-Channel Service System.* Consider a system which at the same time can satisfy m demands. We suppose that there are m lines, and the next demand is received on one of these lines if at least one of them is free; in the opposite case the demand is rejected and leaves the sphere of service. Suppose that the flow of demands obeys the Poisson law with parameter λ_0, and the serving time on each channel is exponentially distributed with parameter λ where the demands are served independently of each other.

Consider the states $E_0, E_1, ..., E_m$ where E_k means that exactly k channels are busy. In particular, E_0 says that the system is free, and E_m

that the system is completely occupied. The transition of the system from state to state within a period of time t is a Markov process for which the transition densities have the form

$$\lambda_{0j} = \begin{cases} -\lambda_0 & \text{for } j = 0 \\ \lambda_0 & \text{for } j = 1 \, ; \end{cases}$$

$$\lambda_{ij} = \begin{cases} i\lambda & \text{for } j = i-1 \\ -(\lambda_0 + i\lambda) & \text{for } j = i, \\ \lambda_0 & \text{for } j = i+1 \end{cases} \quad (1 \le i < m);$$

$$\lambda_{mj} = \begin{cases} m\lambda & \text{for } j = m-1, \\ -m\lambda & \text{for } j = m. \end{cases}$$

For $t \to \infty$ the transition probabilities $p_{ij}(t)$ converge exponentially fast to their final values $P_j, j = 0, \dots, m$. The final probabilities P_j can be obtained from the following system:

$$-\lambda_0 P_0 + \lambda P_1 = 0,$$

$$\lambda_0 P_{k-1} - (\lambda_0 + k\lambda) P_k + (k+1)\lambda P_{k+1} = 0 \quad (1 \le k < m),$$

$$\lambda_0 P_{m-1} - m\lambda P_m = 0,$$

with the solution

$$P_k = -\frac{\dfrac{1}{k!}\left(\dfrac{\lambda_0}{\lambda}\right)^k}{\displaystyle\sum_{i=1}^{m}\frac{1}{i!}\left(\frac{\lambda_0}{\lambda}\right)^i} \quad (k = 0, 1, \dots, m).$$

These expressions for the final probabilities are called *Erlang's formulas*.

Unbounded Stationary Distributions. Suppose that the states of a Markov chain form a single closed class of recurrent null states. In this case there exists an unbounded stationary distribution $P_j, j = 1, 2, \dots$ which is up to a factor the only solution of the system of equations

$$P_j = \sum_i P_i p_{ij}(h) \quad (j = 1, 2, \dots)$$

where $h > 0$ can be arbitrary. All P_i are positive, and $\displaystyle\sum_{i=1}^{\infty} P_i = \infty$.

If the variable T_A denotes the time the system spends in the set of states A within an interval of time T, the limit

$$\lim_{T \to \infty} \frac{T_A}{T_B} = \frac{\displaystyle\sum_{i \in A} P_i}{\displaystyle\sum_{j \in B} P_j}$$

exists for any initial probability distribution and any bounded sets A and B with probability 1.

Example. Consider a random walk where a particle moves from a point i to the neighboring point $j = i + 1$ with probability p_i and returns to the origin $j = 1$ with probability $1 - p_i$. This Markov chain has the transition probability

$$p_{ij} = \begin{cases} p_i & \text{for} \quad j = i+1 \\ 1 - p_i & \text{for} \quad j = 1, \\ 0 & \text{for} \quad j \neq 1, i+1. \end{cases}$$

The probability of a first return to the state 1 at the $(n+1)$-step is

$$q_{11}(n+1) = \begin{cases} 1 - p_1 & \text{for} \quad n = 0, \\ p_1 p_2 \cdots p_{n-1}(1 - p_n) & \text{for} \quad n = 1, 2, \ldots, \end{cases}$$

hence the probability of a return equals

$$q_{11} = \sum_{n=0}^{\infty} q_{11}(n+1) = 1 - \lim_{n \to \infty} (p_1 p_2 \cdots p_n) .$$

It is obvious that the state 1 is recurrent if and only if

$$\lim_{n \to \infty} (p_1 p_2 \cdots p_n) = 0 .$$

All remaining states $i = 2, 3, \ldots$ are recurrent or non-recurrent according to as the state 1 is.

The expectation Q_1 of the time of return to the state 1 is equal to

$$Q_1 = \sum_{n=0}^{\infty} (n+1) q_{11}(n+1) = 1 + \sum_{n=1}^{\infty} p_1 p_2 \cdots p_n ,$$

hence the state 1 is positive if and only if

$$\sum_{n=1}^{\infty} p_1 p_2 \cdots p_n < \infty .$$

All remaining states are positive or null according to as 1 is.

In the case of recurrent states the stationary probability distribution $P_j, j = 1, 2, \ldots$ which then exists and is a solution of the system of equations $P_j = \Sigma P_i p_{ij}$, equals

$$P_1 ,$$
$$P_2 = P_1 p_1 ,$$
$$\cdots \cdots \cdots \cdots$$
$$P_n = P_{n-1} p_{n-1} = P_1 p_1 \cdots p_{n-1} ,$$
$$\cdots \cdots \cdots \cdots \cdots \cdots \cdots \cdots$$

In the case of positive states

$$\sum_{n=1}^{\infty} P_n = P_1 \left(1 + \sum_{n=1}^{\infty} p_1 p_2 \cdots p_n \right) < \infty ,$$

and there exists a stationary probability distribution given by

$$P_1 = \frac{1}{1 + \sum_{n=1}^{\infty} p_1 p_2 \cdots p_n} .$$

Example. *Symmetric Random Walk.* Consider a random walk of a particle on the integers where at each step the particle takes one step to the right or left side with the same probability. All states $i = 0, \pm 1, \ldots$ are null recurrent. The corresponding unbounded stationary distribution is "uniform": $P_j = 1$ for all j. For any intervals $A = (a_1, a_2)$ and $B = (b_1, b_2)$ we have with probability 1

$$\lim_{T \to \infty} \frac{T_A}{T_B} = \frac{a_2 - a_1}{b_2 - b_1}$$

where T_A is the time the particle spends in the set of states A within a time of the interval T.

4. General Markov Jump Processes

Let $\xi(t)$ be a random process in an arbitrary measurable space $(E, \mathfrak{B})$ and suppose that the behavior of $\xi(t)$ displays the following probabilistic regularities. If at a given instant of time t the process is in state x, then during a subsequent short interval of time Δt it remains unchanged with probability $1 - \lambda(t, x) \Delta t + o(\Delta t)$, and it passes to some state of a set B in the phase space $E, x \notin B$ with probability $\lambda(t, x, B) \Delta t + o(\Delta t)$; the transition happens independently of the path of the process until the instant of time t under consideration.

We assume that the transition densities $\lambda(t, x, B)$ into a set $B, B \in \mathfrak{B}$ which does not contain x define a bounded measure for fixed t and x:

$$\lambda(t, x, E \setminus x) = \lambda(t, x) \leq C ,$$

and that as a function of t the transition densities $\lambda(t, x, B)$ are uniformly continuous with respect to x and B. Then in any bounded interval of time the process $\xi(t)$ changes its state with probability 1 only a finite number of times. Starting from the initial state $x_0 = \xi(t_0)$ the process remains there during some positive interval of time, and then jumps to another state x_1 at some random moment τ_1. It also stays at x_1 during a positive interval of time, then passes to a state x_2 at the random moment τ_2, etc. This process is Markovian with a transition function $P(s, x, t, B)$ satisfying

$$P(t, x, t + \Delta t, B) = \lambda(t, x, B) \Delta t + o(\Delta t)$$

for $x \notin B$.

Suppose that this relation is fulfilled uniformly with respect to t, x, B, and let $\varphi = \varphi(x)$ be an arbitrary measurable bounded function on the phase space $(E, \mathfrak{B})$. We set

$$\varphi(s, x) = \int_E \varphi(y) P(s, x, t, dy) \qquad (s \leq t).$$

The function $\varphi(s, x)$ satisfies the integro-differential equation

$$\frac{\partial}{\partial s} \varphi(s, x) = - \int_E \varphi(s, y) \lambda(s, x, dy) \qquad (s < t)$$

with the "final" condition

$$\varphi(t, x) = \varphi(x).$$

If we choose for φ a function of the form

$$\varphi(x) = P(t, x, B) = \begin{cases} 1 & \text{for} \quad x \in B, \\ 0 & \text{for} \quad x \notin B, \end{cases}$$

then we obtain the so-called *backward integro-differential equation* for the transition function $\varphi(s, x) = P(s, x, t, B)$. This equation can be solved by the method of successive approximation:

$$\varphi_0(s, x) = \varphi(x),$$

$$\dotfill$$

$$\varphi_{n+1}(s, x) = \varphi(x) + \int_s^t \int_E \varphi_n(u, y) \lambda(u, x, dy) du \qquad (n = 0, 1, 2, \ldots),$$

where

$$\sup_x |\varphi_n(s, x) - \varphi(s, x)| \to 0 \qquad (n \to \infty)$$

uniformly with respect to s on the interval $t_0 \leq s \leq t$.

Let $Q = Q(A)$ be a generalized bounded measure on the phase space $(E, \mathfrak{B})$. We set

$$Q(t, B) = \int_E Q(dx) P(s, x, t, B) \qquad (t \geq s).$$

The function $Q(t, B)$ of t and $B \in \mathfrak{B}$ satisfies the integro-differential equation

$$\frac{\partial}{\partial t} Q(t, B) = \int_E \lambda(t, x, B) Q(t, dx) \qquad (t > s)$$

with the initial condition

$$Q(s, B) = Q(B).$$

If we choose the function $Q(B) = P(s, x, s, B)$, $B \in \mathfrak{B}$, then we obtain the so-called *forward integro-differential equation* for the transition function $Q(t, B) = P(s, x, t, B)$. This equation can be solved by the method of successive approximation:

$$Q_0(t, B) = Q(B),$$

$$\cdots\cdots\cdots\cdots$$

$$Q_{n+1}(t, B) = Q(B) + \int_s^t \int_E \lambda(u, x, B) Q_n(u, dx) du \qquad (n = 0, 1, \ldots),$$

where

$$\mathrm{Var}[Q_n(t, B) - Q(t, B)] \to 0 \qquad (n \to \infty)$$

uniformly with respect to t on each interval $s \leqq t \leqq t_1$.

§ 2. Branching Processes

1. General Description of a Branching Process

A branching process is a probabilistic model which describes processes of reproduction and transformation of active particles. Examples of such processes are given by various physical and chemical chain reactions.

Example. Consider the following simplified picture of a chain reaction, that is, the formation of neutrons during the disintegration of uranium nuclei. In this reaction the so-called "slow" neutrons whose energy is comparatively small play the decisive rôle. These neutrons induce the disintegration of uranium nuclei with an atomic weight 235. The "fast" neutrons causing the disintegration of uranium nuclei with an atomic weight 238 are also of some importance. The "fast" neutrons by passing through a certain layer of material slow down in their movement and become "slow" neutrons. Each "slow" neutron when "caught" by a nucleus of uranium 235 causes its disintegration which results in v_1 "slow" and v_2 "fast" neutrons; v_1 and v_2 are random numbers. Besides, a "slow" neutron can be absorbed by admixtures, in other words, it can vanish. A "fast" neutron when caught by the nucleus of uranium 238 induces the generation of a random number of "slow" neutrons as well as of "fast" neutrons. On the other hand, it can vanish and thus leave the sphere of the reaction under consideration; for example, it may leave the container which holds the uranium.

Since the disintegration of any nucleus happens practically independently of the state of other nuclei, the reproduction of the particles (neutrons) described above takes place in such a way that the destiny of the descendants of any particle practically does not depend on the history previous to its birth, and the transformation of other particles is subject to the same probabilistic laws.

Let us call "slow" neutrons particles of type T_1, and "fast" neutrons particles of type T_2. A particle of type T_1 is transformed with probability $P_1(k_1, k_2)$ into k_1 particles of the same type T_1 and k_2 particles of the other type T_2. Particles of type T_2 are transformed with probability $P_2(k_1, k_2)$ into k_1 particles of the other type T_1 and k_2 particles of the same type T_2.

Example. A chain reaction of the same type takes place if hydrochloric acid HCl is produced from a mixture of hydrogen H_2 and chlorine Cl_2 under the influence of light (photochemical reaction). A chlorine molecule Cl_2 disintegrates under the action of a photon into single atoms: $Cl_2 \rightarrow Cl + Cl$, and the atomic chlorine releases a chain reaction with up to 10^5 transformations which schematically looks as follows:

$$Cl + H_2 \rightarrow H + HCl$$
$$H + Cl_2 \rightarrow Cl + HCl.$$

Here we have three types of particles: chlorine Cl is a particle of type T_1, hydrogen H a particle of type T_2, and hydrochloric acid HCl a particle of type T_3. A particle of type T_1 is transformed into a particle of type T_2 and a particle of type T_3; a particle of type T_2 is transformed into a particle of type T_1 and a particle of type T_3, and a particle of type T_3 remains unchanged. Thus the process of successive transformations is completely deterministic. If, however, we consider its evolution in time then it turns out that the speed with which hydrochloric acid is produced is random.

General Scheme of a Branching Process. Generally speaking there exist particles of various types $T_1, T_2, ..., T_n$ which in the course of time t undergo transformations. The state of the process at the instant of time t is described by a vector $\xi(t) = \{\xi_1(t), ..., \xi_n(t)\}$ with integral components each of which gives the number of particles of the corresponding type existing at time t. The transformation of any particle does not depend on the previous evolution of the process. In the case of a discrete time t

a single particle is transformed in one step (during one unit of time) with probability p_k, where $k = (k_1, ..., k_n)$ and $\Sigma p_k = 1$, into k_1 particles of type $T_1, ...,$ and into k_n particles of type T_n.

In the case of a continuous time each particle existing at time t remains unchanged with probability $1 - \lambda \cdot \Delta t + o(\Delta t)$, and is transformed during a subsequent infinitely small interval of time Δt with probability $\lambda_k \cdot \Delta t + o(\Delta t)$ into k_1 particles of type $T_1, ...,$ and into k_n particles of type T_n where

$$\sum_k \lambda_k = \lambda .$$

It is understood that in the case of a discrete time the probabilities p_k and in the case of a continuous time the densities λ_k depend on the type of the particle under consideration.

The branching random process $\xi(t) = \{\xi_1(t), ..., \xi_n(t)\}$ described before is a homogeneous Markov chain whose states are represented by vectors $i = \{i_1, i_2, ..., i_n\}$ with integral components. The corresponding transition probabilities p_{ij} in the case of a discrete time and the transition densities λ_{ij} in the case of continuous time are expressed in terms of initial characteristics of the branching process $\xi(t)$; in the case of a discrete time the characteristics are the parameters p_k, and in the case of a continuous time the parameters λ_k.

2. Branching Processes with One Type of Particles

Transition Probabilities and Generating Functions. Let $\xi = \xi(t)$ be a branching process with one type of particles. Within a period of time t a particle is transformed with probability $p_k(t)$ into k particles independently of the behavior of other particles. If at a certain initial moment t_0, say $t_0 = 0$, there exist exactly i particles, then after the time t the total number of particles will be

$$\xi(t) = \xi_1(t) + \cdots + \xi_i(t)$$

where $\xi_1(t), ..., \xi_i(t)$ are independent identically distributed random variables which give the number of particles generated by the respective initial particles. Moreover,

$$\mathbb{P}\{\xi_j(t) = k\} = p_k(t) \quad (k = 0, 1, 2, ...; j = 1, 2, ..., i) .$$

Let $p_{ij}(t)$ be the transition probabilities of the random branching process $\xi(t)$; thus $p_{ij}(t)$ is the probability that i particles are transformed into j particles within time t. It will be convenient to consider the correspond-

15*

ing generating functions

$$x(t, z) = \sum_{k=0}^{\infty} p_k(t) z^k ,$$

$$x_i(t, z) = \sum_{j=0}^{\infty} p_{ij}(t) z^j$$

instead. Since $p_k(t) = p_{1k}(t)$ the following equations hold:

$$x_i(t, z) = [x(t, z)]^i ,$$

$$p_{ik}(t) = \sum_{k_1 + \cdots + k_i = k} p_{k_1}(t) \cdots p_{k_i}(t) .$$

The connection between the transition probabilities $p_k(t)$ for various t can be expressed in terms of the generating functions by the following general relation:

$$x(s + t, z) = x[t, x(s, z)] .$$

In the case of a discrete time this relation permits to find the generating functions $x(t, z)$ and the transition probabilities $p_k(t)$ from the given probabilities p_k or the corresponding generating function

$$x(z) = \sum_{k=0}^{\infty} p_k z^k$$

by recursion; there p_k is the probability that a single particle is transformed into k particles in one step, that is, during one unit of time. In fact,

$$x(0, z) = z , \quad x(1, z) = x(z), \ldots, \quad x(n, z) = x[x(n-1, z)] .$$

In the case of a discrete time if the *backward system of differential equations* holds for the transition probabilities $p_{ij}(t)$, the corresponding differential equation for the generating function $x(t, z)$ has the form

$$\frac{d}{dt} x(t, z) = \varphi[x(t, z)]$$

where

$$\varphi(z) = \sum_{k=0}^{\infty} \lambda_k z^k$$

and where λ_k is the transition density from the state 1 to the state k, $\lambda_1 = -\lambda$; the variable z may be taken as parameter with $0 \le z \le 1$. The initial condition for the generating function $x(t, z)$ is

$$x(0, z) = z .$$

The solution of this equation can be written in the following implicit form:

$$t = \int_z^x \frac{dz}{\varphi(z)}.$$

Example. Let $\lambda_0 = \lambda$, $\lambda_1 = -\lambda$ and $\lambda_k = 0$ be the transition densities for $k = 2, 3, \ldots$. In this case

$$\varphi(z) = \lambda(1-z),$$

$$t = \int_z^x \frac{dz}{\varphi(z)} = -\frac{1}{\lambda}[\log(1-x) - \log(1-z)].$$

We can easily find the function $x = x(t, z)$ from this relation. In fact,

$$\log(1-x) = -\lambda t + \log(1-z),$$

hence

$$x(t, z) = 1 - e^{-\lambda t}(1-z).$$

The probabilities $p_k(t)$ which are determined by the expansion $x(t, z) = \sum_{k=0}^{\infty} p_k(t) z^k$ are in this case equal to

$$p_0(t) = 1 - e^{-\lambda t}, \quad p_1(t) = e^{-\lambda t} \quad \text{and} \quad p_k(t) = 0 \quad \text{for} \quad k = 2, 3, \ldots$$

Example. Let $\lambda_0 = 0$, $\lambda_1 = -1$ and $\lambda_k = \dfrac{1}{(k-1)k}$ for $k = 2, 3, \ldots$. Then

$$\varphi(z) = \sum_{k=1}^{\infty} \lambda_k z^k = \sum_{k=2}^{\infty} \frac{1}{k-1} z^k - \sum_{k=1}^{\infty} \frac{1}{k} z^k$$
$$= -z \log(1-z) + \log(1-z) = (1-z) \log(1-z),$$

$$t = \int_z^x \frac{dz}{\varphi(z)} = \int_z^x \frac{dz}{(1-z)\log(1-z)}$$

$$= -\int_{\log(1-z)}^{\log(1-x)} \frac{dz}{z} = -\log\log(1-x) + \log\log(1-z).$$

Again we can easily find the function $x = x(t, z)$ from this relation. In fact

$$\frac{\log(1-x)}{\log(1-z)} = e^{-t},$$

hence

$$x(t, z) = 1 - (1 - z) e^{-t}.$$

The corresponding probabilities $p_k(t)$ can be obtained by successive differentiation:

$$p_k(t) = \frac{1}{k!} \frac{d^k}{dz^k} x(t, 0) \quad (k = 0, 1, \ldots).$$

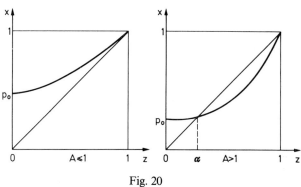

Fig. 20

Some Properties of Generating Functions. Let $x(z)$ be the generating function of a branching process $\xi(t)$ with discrete time:

$$x(z) = \sum_{k=0}^{\infty} p_k z^k.$$

The function $x(z)$ is analytic for $0 < z < 1$, monotone non-decreasing and convex from below (Fig. 20). We set

$$A = x'(1).$$

If $A \leq 1$, the equation

$$x(z) = z$$

has a unique root in the interval $0 \leq z \leq 1$, namely $z = 1$; if $A > 1$ there exists one more root α of this equation such that $0 \leq \alpha < 1$.

The smallest root α of the equation $x(z) = z$ in the interval $0 \leq z \leq 1$ can be obtained by the method of successive approximation:

$$\alpha = \lim_{n \to \infty} x(n, z)$$

where $x(1, z) = x(z), \ldots, x(n, z) = x[x(n-1), z)]$ and z is an arbitrary point of the interval $0 \leq z \leq 1$.

Let $\varphi(z)$ be the generating function of a branching process $\xi(t)$ with continuous time:

$$\varphi(z) = \sum_{k=0}^{\infty} \lambda_k z^k$$

where the transition densities λ_k satisfy the condition $\sum_k \lambda_k = 0$. The function $\varphi(z)$ is analytic and convex for $0 \le z < 1$ (Fig. 21). We set $a = \varphi'(1)$. If $a \le 0$ the equation

$$\varphi(z) = 0$$

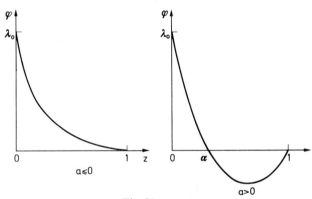

Fig. 21

has a unique root in the interval $0 \le z \le 1$, namely, $z = 1$; if $a > 0$ there exists one more root α of this equation such that $0 \le \alpha < 1$.

Consider the integral curves of the differential equations

$$\frac{dx}{dt} = \varphi(x), \qquad \frac{dt}{dx} = \frac{1}{\varphi(x)};$$

their solution $x = x(t)$, $x(0) = z$ is the generating function $x(t) = x(t, z)$. Let α be a root of the equation $\varphi(z) = 0$ and let $x(t) \equiv \alpha$ be the corresponding integral curve of the differential equations under consideration. We choose an integral curve running through a fixed point $t = 0$, $x = z_0$ ($0 \le z_0 < \alpha < 1$):

$$t = \int_{z_0}^{x} \frac{dz}{\varphi(z)}.$$

Since the derivative $\varphi'(\alpha)$ is finite and since the function $\varphi(z)$ for $x \sim \alpha$ has the form $\varphi(z) \sim \varphi'(\alpha)(z - \alpha)$, it follows that for $x \to \alpha$ the value of t increases unboundedly along the integral curve $t = \int_{z_0}^{x} \dfrac{dz}{\varphi(z)}$; this curve does not intersect the integral curve $x(t) \equiv \alpha$ anywhere

The function $\varphi(z)$ is positive in the interval $0 \leq z < \alpha$, hence x is monotone increasing for $t \to \infty$ along the integral curve $t = \int_{z_0}^{x} \dfrac{dz}{\varphi(z)}$ and remains bounded by the value $x = \alpha$, that is, $x = x(t)$ is a bounded monotone function.

Integral curves which for $t = 0$ pass through a point z of the interval $\alpha < z < 1$ behave in a complete analogous way. The only difference consists in the fact that $x = x(t)$ is monotone decreasing (Fig. 22).

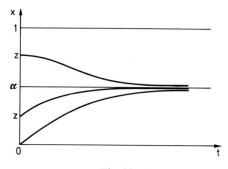

Fig. 22

Consider the behavior of the integral curves near the line $x(t) \equiv 1$. Suppose that for some z_0 where $0 \leq z_0 < 1$ we have

$$\int_{z_0}^{1} \frac{dz}{\varphi(z)} = -\infty;$$

this is always true if $a = \varphi'(1) < \infty$. In this case the integral curve of the form

$$t = t_0 + \int_{z_0}^{x} \frac{dz}{\varphi(z)} \qquad (0 \leq z < 1)$$

which runs through the point (t_0, z_0) has the property that the value t decreases unboundedly for $z \to 1$:

$$t = t_0 + \int_{z_0}^{x} \frac{dz}{\varphi(z)} \to -\infty.$$

Therefore given any $t_0 > 0$, there exists an $x = z$, $0 \leq z < 1$, such that the equation

$$t(z) = t_0 + \int_{z_0}^{z} \frac{dz}{\varphi(z)} = 0$$

holds.

All integral curves intersect the axis $t = 0$ in some point $(0, z)$ where $0 \leq z < 1$, hence $x(t) \equiv 1$ is the only integral curve which passes through the point $t = 0$, $x = 1$.

Suppose that

$$\int_{z_0}^{1} \frac{dz}{\varphi(z)} > -\infty.$$

Then for sufficiently large $t_0 > 0$ the integral curve $t = t_0 + \int_{z_0}^{x} \frac{dz}{\varphi(z)}$

intersects the integral curve $x(t) \equiv 1$ which is its tangent at a certain point $t = \tau$, $x = 1$ where

$$\tau = t_0 + \int_{z_0}^{1} \frac{dz}{\varphi(z)}$$

(Fig. 23). In this case an entire family of integral curves $x(t)$ passes through the point $(0, 1)$, each curve being determined by its value $\tau \geq 0$. Among

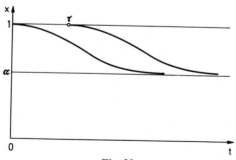

Fig. 23

them we have the integral curve $x_0(t)$ which corresponds to the value $\tau = 0$ and has the property that it lies below all other integral curves $x_\tau(t)$: $x_0(t) \leq x_\tau(t)$ $(0 \leq t < \infty)$. This results from the fact that within the domain $0 \leq x < 1, 0 \leq t < \infty$ the solution of the corresponding differential equation is unique and integral curves do not intersect each other in this domain. The integral curve $x_0(t)$ is the limit curve of the integral curves $x(t, z)$ lying below it and passing through the points $(0, z), 0 \leq z < 1$, respectively:

$$x_0(t) = \lim_{z \to 1} x(t, z).$$

Probability of Degeneration. Suppose that at the initial instant $t_0 = 0$ we are given i particles. Then the probability that all particles vanish during the time t equals $[x(t, 0)]^i$. If τ is the moment when the branching random process $\xi(t)$ degenerates, that is, when the state $j = 0$ is reached, then

$$[x(t, 0)]^i = \mathbb{P}\{\tau < t\},$$

hence

$$\lim_{t \to \infty} [x(t, 0)]^i = \mathbb{P}\{\tau < \infty\}$$

is the probability that after a finite period of time no particle is left over. The limit

$$P_0 = \lim_{t \to \infty} x(t, 0)$$

coincides with the smallest root α of the equation

$$x(z) = z \qquad (0 \leq z \leq 1) \quad \text{for discrete } t,$$

and of the equation

$$\varphi(z) = 0 \qquad (0 \leq z \leq 1) \quad \text{for continuous } t.$$

We have $P_0 < 1$, if $A > 1$ or $a > 0$, and $P_0 = 1$ if $A \leq 1$ or $a \leq 0$.

For $t \to \infty$ the difference $1 - x(t, 0)$ behaves asymptotically in such a way that for discrete t

$$1 - x(t, 0) \sim \begin{cases} k A^t & \text{for} \quad A < 1, \\ \dfrac{2}{Bt} & \text{for} \quad A = 1 \end{cases}$$

where k is some constant and $B = x''(1)$, and for continuous t

$$1 - x(t, 0) \sim \begin{cases} k e^{at} & \text{for} \quad a < 0, \\ \dfrac{2}{bt} & \text{for} \quad a = 0, \end{cases}$$

where k is a constant and $b = \varphi''(1)$.

Average Number of Particles. If i particles exist at the initial moment $t_0 = 0$, then by the time t the average amount of particles $M\xi(t)$ is equal to

$$M\xi(t) = i A^t \quad \text{for discrete } t,$$
$$M\xi(t) = i e^{at} \quad \text{for continuous } t.$$

Example. Suppose that the generating function $x(z)$ of the branching process $\xi(t)$ with discrete time t is fractionally linear. It depends on two parameters, and in the case $A > 1$ it may be represented in the form

$$x(z) = 1 - A\frac{\alpha - 1}{\alpha - A} \cdot \frac{1 - z}{1 - \dfrac{A - 1}{\alpha - A}z}$$

where $\alpha < 1$ is the smallest non-negative root of the equation $x(z) = z$.

We set $x(1, z) = x(z), \ldots, x(n, z) = x[x(a - 1, z)]$. The parameter remains to be the root of the equation $x(n, z) = z$ for any of the functions $x(n, z)$; moreover $x'(n, 1) = A^n$ so that

$$x(n, z) = 1 - A^n\frac{\alpha - 1}{\alpha - A^n} \cdot \frac{1 - z}{1 - \dfrac{A^n - 1}{\alpha - A^n}z}.$$

Expanding $x(n, z)$ into powers of z we obtain:

$$p_0(n) = 1 - A^n\frac{\alpha - 1}{\alpha - A^n},$$

$$p_k(n) = A^n\left(\frac{\alpha - 1}{\alpha - A^n}\right)^2\left(\frac{1 - A^n}{\alpha - A^n}\right)^{k-1} \quad (k = 1, 2, \ldots).$$

If $A = 1$, and thus $\alpha = 1$, the generating function $x(z)$ depends on a single parameter which we can conveniently choose as $B = x''(1)$. Then the function $x(z)$ may be written in the form

$$x(z) = 1 - \frac{\dfrac{2}{2 + B}(1 - z)}{1 - \dfrac{B}{2 + B}z}.$$

We have $x''(n, 1) = nB$, hence

$$x(n, z) = 1 - \frac{\dfrac{2}{2 + nB}(1 - z)}{1 - \dfrac{nB}{2 + nB}z}.$$

If we expand $x(n, z)$ into powers of z we obtain

$$p_0(n) = 1 - \frac{2}{2 + nB},$$

$$p_k(n) = \left(\frac{2}{2 + nB}\right)^2 \left(\frac{nB}{2 + nB}\right)^{k-1} \qquad (k = 1, 2, \ldots).$$

It can be seen that

$$p_0(n) \to \begin{cases} \alpha, & \text{if } A > 1, \\ 1, & \text{if } A = 1, \end{cases}$$

for $n \to \infty$

Example. Assume that the generating function $\varphi(z)$ of the branching process $\xi(t)$ with continuous time t has the form

$$\varphi(z) = p - (p + q) z + q z^2.$$

The corresponding transition densities are $\lambda = p + q$, $\lambda_0 = p$ and $\lambda_2 = q$. The differential equation for the generating functions $x(t, z)$ looks like this:

$$\frac{dx}{(1 - x)(p - qx)} = dt, \qquad x(0, z) = z.$$

For $p \neq q$ its solution is

$$x(t, z) = \frac{p(1 - z) + (qz - p) e^{(p-q)z}}{q(1 - z) + (qz - p) e^{(p-q)z}}.$$

Expanding the function $x(t, z)$ into powers of z we obtain:

$$p_0(t) = \frac{p}{q} + \frac{1 - e^{(p-q)t}}{1 - \frac{p}{q} e^{(p-q)t}},$$

$$p_k(t) = \left(1 - \frac{p}{q}\right)^2 \frac{[1 - e^{(p-q)t}]^{k-1}}{\left[1 - \frac{p}{q} e^{(p-q)t}\right]^{k+1}} e^{(p-q)t} \qquad (k = 1, 2, \ldots).$$

For $p = q$ the generating function $x(t, z)$ is the solution of the equation

$$\frac{dx}{p(1 - x)^2} = dt, \qquad x(0, z) = z$$

and has the form

$$x(t, z) = 1 - \frac{1 - z}{1 - pt(1 - z)}.$$

Expanding $x(t, z)$ into powers z we obtain:

$$p_0(t) = 1 - \frac{1}{1 + pt}$$

$$p_k(t) = \frac{(pt)^{k-1}}{(1 + pt)^{k+1}} \qquad (k = 1, 2, \ldots).$$

The smallest root of the equation $\varphi(z) = 0$ in the interval $0 \leq z \leq 1$ is given by $\alpha = \min\left(1, \dfrac{p}{q}\right)$; the parameter $a = \varphi'(1)$ is equal to $q - p$. It can be seen immediately from the formulas for the probabilities $p_k(t)$ that $p_0(t) \rightarrow \alpha$ if $t \rightarrow \infty$.

Phenomenon of Explosion. Assume that $\xi(t)$ is a random branching process with continuous time, and generated by exactly one particle. If the particles multiply sufficiently fast, then, generally spoken, an infinite number of particles will arise with positive probability during some finite time τ; this phenomenon is usually called an *explosion*. The probability that an explosion takes place until time t equals

$$p_\infty(t) = 1 - \mathbb{P}\{\xi(t) < \infty\} = 1 - \lim_{z \to 1} x(t, z).$$

If

$$\int_{z_0}^{1} \frac{dz}{\varphi(z)} = -\infty$$

for some z_0, this probability is equal to zero, hence under this condition an explosion is impossible. If however,

$$\int_{z_0}^{1} \frac{dz}{\varphi(z)} > -\infty,$$

the probability of an explosion is positive and equals the difference $1 - x_0(t)$ where $x_0(t)$ is the minimal solution of the differential equation $x' = \varphi(x)^{-1}$ with the initial condition $x(0) = 1$.

Limit Distributions. For $t \rightarrow \infty$ there exists a limit probability distribution of the normalized random variables

$$\eta(t) = \xi(t) \frac{1 - x(t, 0)}{M(t)}.$$

These limit distributions differ sharply in the various cases $a < 0$, $a = 0$ and $a > 0$. The limit distribution is discrete for $a < 0$ and continuous for

$a>0$. If $a<0$ or $a>0$, the limit distributions depend in a somewhat complicated way on other characteristics of the branching process $\xi(t)$; if, however, $a=0$, the limit distribution is exponential: for $t\to\infty$ we have

$$F_{\eta(t)}(y)\Rightarrow F(y)=\begin{cases}0, & \text{if } y<0,\\ 1-e^{-y} & \text{if } y>0.\end{cases}$$

The limit distribution is also approximately exponential for a small parameter a. More precisely, suppose that

$$b=\varphi''(1)<\infty, \qquad c=\varphi'''(1)<\infty.$$

Then for $t\to\infty$ and $a\to0$ the weak convergence

$$F_{\eta(t)}(y)\Rightarrow F(y)$$

holds uniformly with respect to $b\geq b_0>0$ and $c\leq c_0<\infty$ [54].

§ 3. Random Processes with Independent Increments

1. Sequences of Sums of an Increasing Number of Independent Random Variables

The random process $\xi=\xi(t)$ on a set T of the real line is termed a *process with independent increments* if the increments $\xi_k=\xi(t_{k+1})-\xi(t_k)$, $k=0,1,2,\dots$ are independent random variables for any $t_0\leq t_1\leq t_2\leq\cdots$ of T. A random process $\xi=\xi(t)$ with independent increments and "discrete time" t, say, $t=0,1,\dots$, is a sequence of sums of an increasing number of independent variables $\xi_k=\xi(k+1)-\xi(k)$:

$$\xi(t)-\xi(0)=\xi_0+\xi_1+\cdots+\xi_{t-1}.$$

Zero-One Law. Suppose that $\xi_1,\xi_2,\dots$ is a sequence of independent random variables. We denote by $\mathfrak{A}(n,\infty)$ the σ-algebra generated by the variables $\xi_n,\xi_{n+1},\dots$ and set

$$\mathfrak{A}^\infty=\bigcap_n\mathfrak{A}(n,\infty).$$

Then the following *zero-one law* holds: the probability of any event A of the σ-algebra $\mathfrak{A}^\infty$ is equal to 0 or 1:

$$\mathbb{P}(A)=0 \quad\text{or}\quad 1.$$

---

[54] Sevastianov, B. A., Transient phenomena in branching stochastic processes. Teoriya veroyatn. i primen. IV (1959), 121—135 (Russian).

This law can also be formulated in a different way: any random variable which is measurable with respect to $\mathfrak{A}^\infty$ is equal to a constant with probability 1.

Example. Consider a sequence of sums

$$\eta_n = \sum_{k=1}^{n} \xi_k \quad (n = 1, 2, \ldots).$$

The existence of the $\lim_{n \to \infty} \eta_n$ is an event of $\mathfrak{A}^\infty$; hence the series $\sum_{k=1}^{\infty} \xi_k$ either converges with probability 1 or with probability 0.

Kolmogorov's Inequality. Let $\xi_1, \xi_2, \ldots$ be independent random variables with finite expectations $a_k = M \xi_k$ and variances $\sigma_k^2 = D \xi_k$. Then the following *inequality* due to *Kolmogorov* holds:

$$\mathbb{P} \left\{ \max_{1 \leq m \leq n} \left| \sum_{k=1}^{m} (\xi_k - a_k) \right| > \varepsilon \right\} \leq \frac{1}{\varepsilon^2} \sum_{k=1}^{n} \sigma_k^2.$$

There is an analogous inequality for arbitrary independent variables $\xi_1, \xi_2, \ldots$:

$$\mathbb{P} \left\{ \max_{1 \leq m \leq n} \left| \sum_{k=1}^{m} \xi_k \right| > \delta + \varepsilon \right\} \leq \frac{1}{1-p} \mathbb{P} \left\{ \left| \sum_{k=1}^{n} \xi_k \right| > \varepsilon \right\},$$

provided that the non-negative numbers δ and $p, p < 1$ are chosen in such a way that we have for all $m, 1 \leq m \leq n$:

$$\mathbb{P} \left\{ \left| \sum_{k=1}^{m} \xi_k \right| > \delta \right\} \leq p.$$

Convergence of Series of Independent Terms. Let $\xi_1, \xi_2, \ldots$ be a sequence of independent random variables. Suppose that the series $\sum_{k=1}^{\infty} a_k$ and $\sum_{k=1}^{\infty} \sigma_k^2$ converge where $a_k = M \xi_k$ and $\sigma_k^2 = D \xi_k$. Then the sequence of the partial sums converges for $n \to \infty$ to a random variable η with probability 1.

Define the variables $\tilde{\xi}_k, k = 1, 2, \ldots$ by setting

$$\tilde{\xi}_k = \begin{cases} \xi_k & \text{for } |\xi_k| \leq C, \\ x_k & \text{for } |\xi_k| > C \end{cases}$$

where C is an arbitrary constant and the series $\sum_{k=1}^{\infty} x_k$ converges. Then the limit $\lim_{n \to \infty} \eta_n$ exists with probability 1 if and only if each of the following three series converge:

$$\sum_{k=1}^{\infty} \mathbb{P}\{\xi_k \neq \tilde{\xi}_k\}, \quad \sum_{n=1}^{\infty} \tilde{a}_k \quad \text{and} \quad \sum_{k=1}^{\infty} \tilde{\sigma}_k^2$$

where

$$\tilde{a}_k = \mathbb{M}\tilde{\xi}_k \quad \text{and} \quad \tilde{\sigma}_k^2 = \mathbb{D}\tilde{\xi}_k, \quad (k = 1, 2, \ldots).$$

Dispersion and Concentration of Random Variables. The variance $\mathbb{D}\xi = \mathbb{M}(\xi - \mathbb{M}\xi)^2$ serves as the simplest measure of dispersion of the variable $\xi = \xi(\omega)$ as a function of the outcome ω. But there may be no variance. A *degree of dispersion* of the random variable ξ can be defined as [55]

$$\delta_\xi = -\log \int_{-\infty}^{\infty} \int_{-\infty}^{\infty} e^{-|x_1 - x_2|} \mathbb{P}_\xi(dx_1) \mathbb{P}_\xi(dx_2) = -\log \frac{1}{\pi} \int_{-\infty}^{\infty} \frac{|\varphi_\xi(u)|^2}{1+u^2} du$$

where $\mathbb{P}_\xi$ is the probability distribution and φ_ξ the characteristic function of the random variable ξ; logarithms are taken with respect to the basis e.

The degree of dispersion δ_ξ has the following properties. First, the equation $\delta_\xi = 0$ is equivalent to the fact that the random variable ξ is constant with probability 1. Secondly, the existence of the limit $\lim_{n\to\infty} \delta_{\xi_n} = 0$ for a sequence of random variables $\xi_1, \xi_2, \ldots$ is equivalent to the fact that for some constants a_n the sequence $\xi_n - a_n$ converges stochastically to zero. Third, $\delta_{\xi_n} \to \infty$ for $n \to \infty$ if and only if the *concentration function*

$$Q_{\xi_n}(l) = \sup_a \mathbb{P}\{a - l \leq \xi_n \leq a + l\}$$

of the random variables ξ_n is such that $Q_{\xi_n}(l) \to 0$ for every finite l. Fourth, the degree of dispersion of the sum $\xi = \xi_1 + \xi_2$ of independent random variables ξ_1 and ξ_2 is never smaller than the degree of each term:

$$\delta_\xi \geq \max(\delta_{\xi_1}, \delta_{\xi_2}),$$

and equality holds if and only if one of the terms ξ_1 or ξ_2 is constant with probability 1.

Centered Series of Independent Terms. Suppose that $\xi_1, \xi_2, \ldots$ is a sequence of independent random variables, and let

$$\eta_n = \sum_{k=1}^{n} \xi_k \quad (n = 1, 2, \ldots).$$

The condition

$$\delta = \lim_{n\to\infty} \delta_{\eta_n} < \infty$$

---

[55] *Ito, K.*, On stochastic processes, I. Jap. J. Math. 18, 261—301 (1942).

is necessary and sufficient for the existence with probability 1 of the limit

$$\eta = \lim_{n \to \infty} (\eta_n - b_n)$$

where $b_1, b_2, \dots$ are certain *centering constants*. In this case we have

$$\delta_\eta = \lim_{n \to \infty} \delta_{\eta n}.$$

The centering constants b_n can be determined, for example, from the relations $\mathbb{M} \arctan(\eta_n - b_n) = 0$ $(n = 1, 2, \dots)$.

If, however,

$$\lim_{n \to \infty} \delta_{\eta n} = \infty ,$$

then we have

$$\lim_{n \to \infty} \sup_{1 \le m \le n} |\eta_m| = \infty$$

with probability 1.

Strengthened Law of Large Numbers. Let ξ_1, ξ_2 be independent identically distributed random variables with a finite expectation $a = \mathbb{M} \xi_k$. Then

$$\lim_{n \to \infty} \frac{1}{n} \sum_{k=1}^{n} \xi_k = a$$

with probability 1.

Let ξ_1, ξ_2 be independent random variables with finite expectations $a_k = \mathbb{M} \xi_k$ and variances $\sigma_k^2 = \mathbb{D} \xi_k$ and $b_1, b_2, \dots$ a monotone increasing sequence of positive numbers such that $b_n \to \infty$ for $n \to \infty$ and

$$\sum_{k=1}^{\infty} \frac{\sigma_k^2}{b_k^2} < \infty .$$

Then

$$\lim_{n \to \infty} \frac{1}{b_n} \sum_{k=1}^{n} (\xi_k - a_k) = 0$$

with probability 1.

Law of the Iterated Logarithm. Let ξ_1, ξ_2 be independent random variables with finite expectations $a_k = \mathbb{M} \xi_k$ and variances $\sigma^2 = \mathbb{D} \xi_k$, and suppose that

$$\frac{1}{B_n} (\xi_n - a_n) = o \left\{ \frac{1}{\sqrt{\log \log B_n^2}} \right\},$$

where $B_n^2 = \sum\limits_{k=1}^{n} \sigma_k^2$. Then we have

$$\varlimsup_{n \to \infty} \frac{\sum\limits_{k=1}^{n} (\xi_k - a_k)}{B_n \sqrt{2 \log \log B_n^2}} = 1 .$$

with probability 1.

2. The Brownian Motion Process

A Gaussian process with independent increments on a finite or infinite interval $T = [a, b]$ such that

$$\mathbb{M}[\xi(t) - \xi(s)] = 0 , \qquad \mathbb{D}[\xi(t) - \xi(s)] = t - s$$

for any $s, t \in T$, $s \leq t$ is termed a *Brownian motion* or a *Wiener process*.

Brownian Motion Considered as a Continuous Random Walk. Let $\xi = \xi(t)$ be a Brownian motion process on the interval $T = [0, 1]$, and $\xi(0) = 0$. Consider the values $\xi(t)$ at the discrete moments $t = k/n$, $k = 0, 1, \ldots, n$ only. Set

$$\Delta \xi(t) = \xi\left(t + \frac{1}{n}\right) - \xi(t) ,$$

and let $\xi_n = \xi_n(t)$ be the random process which is obtained by linear interpolation between the neighboring values $\xi(k - 1/n)$ and $\xi(k/n)$; thus we have:

$$\xi_n(t) = \sum_{m=0}^{k-1} \Delta \xi\left(\frac{m}{n}\right) + (nt - k) \Delta \xi\left(\frac{k}{n}\right)$$

where $k = [nt]$ is the integral part of the number nt; if $0 \leq t < 1/n$, then $\xi_n(t) = nt \, \Delta \xi(0)$.

Each trajectory $\xi_n(\omega, t)$ of the random process $\xi_n = \xi_n(t)$ represents a continuous broken line with vertices $t = k/n$, $\xi = \xi(\omega, k/n)$ (Fig. 24).

Consider the sequence of random processes $\xi_n(t)$, $n = 1, 2, \ldots$ of the form described above. Then with probability 1

$$\xi_n(t) \to \xi(t) \quad \text{for} \quad n \to \infty$$

uniformly with respect to $t \in T$.

Let ξ_{mn}, $m = 0, \ldots, n - 1$ be identically distributed independent random variables such that

$$\mathbb{M} \xi_{mn} = 0 , \qquad \mathbb{D} \xi_{mn} = \frac{1}{n} \quad (n = 1, 2, \ldots) .$$

Consider the continuous random process $\xi_n = \xi_n(t)$ of the form

$$\xi_n(t) = \sum_{m=0}^{k-1} \xi_{mn} + (nt - k)\, \xi_{kn}$$

where $k = [nt]$ is the integral part of the number nt; if $0 \le t < 1/n$, then $\xi_n(t) = nt\, \xi_{on}$.

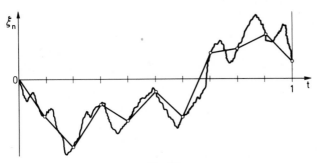

Fig. 24

Let $\mathbb{P}_n = \mathbb{P}_n(A)$ be the corresponding probability distribution defined on a σ-algebra of all Borel sets A in the space $C[0, 1]$ of all real functions $x = x(t)$ which are continuous on the interval $T = [0, 1]$. Then for $n \to \infty$ there exists the limit probability distribution $\mathbb{P} = \mathbb{P}(A)$:

$$\mathbb{P}_n \Rightarrow \mathbb{P} .$$

The directly given process $\xi = \xi(t)$ with the limit distribution $\mathbb{P} = \mathbb{P}(A)$ is a Brownian motion process, the so-called *standard Wiener process*. Given any function $\varphi = \varphi(t)$ which is continuous almost everywhere in the interval $T = [0, 1]$ with respect to Lebesgue measure, the probability distributions of the random variables

$$\eta_n = \frac{1}{n} \sum_{k=1}^{n} \varphi\left[\xi_n\left(\frac{k}{n}\right)\right]$$

converge weakly to the distribution of the random variable

$\eta = \int_0^1 \varphi[\xi(t)]\, dt$:

$$\mathbb{P}_{\eta_n} \Rightarrow \mathbb{P}_\eta$$

for $n \to \infty$.

The Wiener Process as a Curve in Hilbert Space. The Wiener process $\xi = \xi(t)$ on the interval $T = [0, 1]$ can be defined as a Gaussian random process with expectation zero and correlation function

$$B(s, t) = \min(s, t) .$$

Example. Let $\xi = \xi(t)$ be a Wiener process. Then the random process $\xi_1 = \xi_1(t)$ of the form

$$\xi_1(t) = \begin{cases} 0 & \text{for } t = 0, \\ t\xi\left(\dfrac{1}{t}\right) & \text{for } 0 < t \leq 1 \end{cases}$$

has the correlation function

$$B_1(s, t) = st \cdot \min\left(\frac{1}{s}, \frac{1}{t}\right) = \min(s, t),$$

and is a Wiener process, too. The same is true for the random process $\xi_2 = \xi_2(t)$ of the form

$$\xi_2(t) = \sigma \cdot \xi\left(\frac{t}{\sigma^2}\right).$$

As a function with values in the Hilbert space $L^2(\Omega)$ the Wiener process $\xi = \xi(t)$ admits the following *canonical representation:*

$$\xi(t) = \sum_{k=0}^{\infty} \Phi_k \varphi_k(t)$$

where the Φ_k are independent Gaussian variables:

$$\mathbb{M}\,\Phi_k = 0, \quad \mathbb{D}\Phi_k = \frac{1}{\left[\dfrac{\pi}{2}(2k+1)\right]^2} \quad (k = 0, 1, \ldots),$$

and

$$\varphi_k(t) = \sin\left[\frac{\pi}{2}(2k+1)t\right] \quad (k = 0, 1, \ldots)$$

are the eigenfunctions of the operator B defined by the formula

$$B\varphi(t) = \int_0^1 B(s, t)\,\varphi(s)\,ds$$

in the Hilbert space $L^2[0, 1]$ of all square integrable functions $\varphi = \varphi(t)$ with respect to the Lebesgue measure in the interval $[0, 1]$.

Brownian Motion as a Markov Random Process. The Brownian motion $\xi = \xi(t)$, $t \geq 0$ can be defined as a homogeneous Markov process with transition function $P(t, x, B) = \int_B p(t, x, y)\,dy$, where the transition density $p(t, x, y)$ is the fundamental solution of the parabolic differential equation

$$\frac{\partial p}{\partial t} = \frac{1}{2}\frac{\partial^2 p}{\partial x^2},$$

and is given by the formula

$$p(t, x, y) = \frac{1}{\sqrt{2\pi t}} e^{-\frac{(y-x)^2}{2t}}.$$

The transition function $P(t, x, B)$ and the conditional probability distribution $\mathbb{P}_x = \mathbb{P}_x(A)$ on the σ-algebra of events $\mathfrak{A}(0, \infty)$ are invariant with respect to the shift transformations in the phase space:

$$\mathbb{P}_{x+a}\{\xi(t_1) + a \in B_1, \ldots, \xi(t_n) + a \in B_n\} = \mathbb{P}_x\{\xi(t_1) \in B_1, \ldots, \xi(t_n) \in B_n\}$$

for any x, for all $t_1, \ldots, t_n \geq 0$, and all Borel sets $B_1, \ldots, B_n$.

The Time of Hitting a Fixed Point First. Let τ_a be the moment when a point a is reached for the first time by the Brownian motion process $\xi = \xi(t)$. Then

$$\begin{aligned}
\mathbb{P}_x\{\tau_a \leq t\} &= \mathbb{P}_{x-a}\{\tau_0 \leq t\}, \\
\mathbb{P}_0\{\tau_y - \tau_x \leq t\} &= \mathbb{P}_0\{\tau_{y-x} \leq t\} \quad (y \geq x \geq 0), \\
\mathbb{P}_0\{\tau_a \leq a^2 t\} &= \mathbb{P}_0\{\tau_1 \leq t\} \quad (a > 0).
\end{aligned}$$

Let

$$\varphi(x) = \begin{cases} 1 & \text{for} \quad x \geq a, \\ 0 & \text{for} \quad x < a. \end{cases}$$

Then we have

$$\int_0^\infty e^{-\lambda t} \mathbb{P}_0\{\xi(t) \geq a\} \, dt = \mathbb{M}_0 \int_{\tau_a}^\infty e^{-\lambda t} \varphi[\xi(t)] \, dt$$

$$= (\mathbb{M}_0 e^{-\lambda \tau_a}) \left(\mathbb{M}_a \int_0^\infty e^{-\lambda t} \varphi[\xi(t)] \, dt \right) = \tfrac{1}{2} \int_0^\infty e^{-\lambda t} \mathbb{P}_0\{\tau_a \leq t\} \, dt$$

for every $\lambda \geq 0$, where $\mathbb{M}_x$ stands for the mathematical expectation which corresponds to the conditional distribution $\mathbb{P}_x$, and

$$\mathbb{P}_0\{\tau_a \leq t\} = 2\mathbb{P}_0\{\xi(t) \geq a\} = \frac{2}{\sqrt{2\pi t}} \int_a^\infty e^{-\frac{x^2}{2t}} \, dx$$

$$= 1 - \sqrt{\frac{2}{\pi}} \int_0^{\frac{a}{\sqrt{t}}} e^{-\frac{x^2}{2}} \, dx = \frac{a}{\sqrt{2\pi}} \int_0^t s^{-\frac{3}{2}} e^{-\frac{a^2}{2s}} \, ds \quad (0 \leq t < \infty).$$

Distribution of the Maximum. For $a > 0$ we have

$$\mathbb{P}_0\left\{ \max_{0 \leq s \leq t} \xi(s) \geq a \right\} = \mathbb{P}_0\{\tau_a \leq t\} = 2\mathbb{P}_0\{\xi(t) \geq a\} = \frac{2}{\sqrt{2\pi t}} \int_a^\infty e^{-\frac{y^2}{2t}} \, dy.$$

Let $\xi_a = \xi_a(t)$ be the random process of the form

$$\xi_a(t) = \begin{cases} \xi(t) & \text{for } t \leq \tau_a, \\ 2a - \xi(t) & \text{for } t \geq \tau_a. \end{cases}$$

This continuous process with independent Gaussian increments is a Brownian motion process. The following relation holds:

$$\left\{ \max_{0 \leq s \leq t} \xi(s) \geq a, \ \xi(t) \in [c, d] \cap (-\infty, a) \right\} = \{ \xi_a(t) \in [2a - d, 2a - c] \cap [a, \infty) \},$$

and for $a > 0$ we have

$$\mathbb{P}_0 \left\{ \max_{0 \leq s \leq t} \xi(s) \geq a, \ \xi(t) \in [c, d] \right\}$$

$$= \frac{1}{\sqrt{2\pi t}} \int_{\max(c, a)}^{\max(d, a)} e^{-\frac{x^2}{2t}} \, dx + \frac{1}{\sqrt{2\pi t}} \int_{\max(2a - d, a)}^{\max(2a - c, a)} e^{-\frac{x^2}{2t}} \, dx .$$

For $a > 0$ and $[c, d] \subseteq [-a, a]$ the equation

$$\mathbb{P}_0 \left\{ \max_{0 \leq s \leq t} |\xi(s)| < a, \ \xi(t) \in [c, d] \right\} = \int_c^d \frac{1}{\sqrt{2\pi t}} \sum_{k = -\infty}^{\infty} (-1)^k e^{-\frac{(x - 2ka)^2}{2t}} \, dx$$

takes place.

Crossing an Upper Bound. Consider the bounds in the (t, x)-plane described by the equations

$$x_1(t) = \gamma_1 + \delta_1 t, \qquad x_2(t) = \gamma_2 + \delta_2 t,$$

where $\gamma_1 > 0$, $\gamma_2 < 0$ and $x_1(t) \geq x_2(t)$, $t \geq 0$. Let $\tau_1 + \tau_1(\omega)$ be the moment when the trajectory $\xi(\omega, t)$ of the Brownian motion crosses the upper bound for the first time, $\tau_2 = \tau_2(\omega)$ the moment when it crosses the lower bound first (Fig. 25). Then the formula [56]

$$P_0\{\tau_1 \leq \min(t, \tau_2)\} = 1 - \Phi\left(\frac{\delta_1 t + \gamma_1}{\sqrt{t}}\right)$$

$$+ \sum_{k=1}^{\infty} \left\{ e^{-2[k\gamma_1 - (k-1)\gamma_2][k\delta_1 - (r-1)\delta_2]} \Phi\left(\frac{\delta_1 t + 2(k-1)\gamma_2 - 2(k-1)\gamma_1}{\sqrt{t}}\right) \right.$$

$$- e^{-2[k^2(\gamma_1\delta_2 + \gamma_2\delta_2) - k(k-1)\gamma_1\delta_2 - k(k+1)\gamma_2\delta_1]} \Phi\left(\frac{\delta_1 t + 2k\gamma_2 - (2k-1)\gamma_1}{\sqrt{t}}\right)$$

$$- e^{-2[(k-1)\gamma_1 - k\gamma_2][(k-1)\delta_1 - k\delta_2]} \left[1 - \Phi\left(\frac{\delta_1 t - 2k\gamma_2 + (2k-1)\gamma_1}{\sqrt{t}}\right)\right]$$

$$\left. + e^{-2[k^2(\gamma_1\delta_1 + \gamma_2\delta_2) - k(k-1)\gamma_2\delta_1 - k(k+1)\gamma_1\delta_2]} \left[1 - \Phi\left(\frac{\delta_1 t + (2k+1)\gamma_1 - 2k\gamma_2}{\sqrt{t}}\right)\right] \right\}$$

---

[56] *Anderson, T. W.*, A modification of the sequential probability ratio test to reduce the sample size. Ann. Math. Stat. **31**, 1 (1960), 165—198.

holds, where

$$\Phi(x) = \int_{-\infty}^{x} \frac{1}{\sqrt{2\pi}} e^{-\frac{u^2}{2}} du.$$

The Time of Hitting a Fixed Point Last. Let τ_a^* be the greatest root of the equation $\xi(s) = a$ on the interval $0 \leq s \leq t$, that is, the last moment

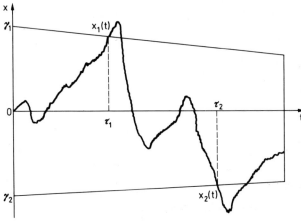

Fig. 25

when the point a is reached during the interval of time $[0, t]$. Then

$$\mathbb{P}_a\{\tau_a^* \leq s\} = \int_{-\infty}^{\infty} \mathbb{P}_x\{\tau_a > t - s\} P(a, s, dx)$$

$$= \frac{1}{\pi} \int_{0}^{s} \frac{du}{\sqrt{u(t - u)}} = \frac{2}{\pi} \arcsin \sqrt{\frac{s}{t}} \quad (0 \leq s \leq t).$$

The Method of Differential Equations[57]. Consider the variable

$$\int_{0}^{t} \varphi[\xi(s)] ds$$

where $\varphi = \varphi(x)$ is some real function. Under some restrictions on $\varphi(x)$ the function

$$u_\lambda(t, x) = \mathbb{M}_x \exp\left\{\lambda \int_{0}^{t} \varphi[\xi(s)] ds\right\}$$

---

[57] *Gichman, I. I.*, and *A. V. Skorochod*, An Introduction to the Theory of Random Processes (Russian). Moscow, Nauka 1965.

which depends on the parameter λ satisfies the differential equation

$$\frac{\partial u_\lambda}{\partial t} = \frac{1}{2} \frac{\partial^2 u}{\partial x^2} + \lambda \, \varphi(x) \, u_\lambda$$

with the initial condition $u_\lambda(0, x) \equiv 1$ (see § 5.1 of this chapter). The parameter λ either takes all purely imaginary values: $\lambda = i\alpha$, $-\infty < \alpha < \infty$ or, in the case of a non-negative function $\varphi(x)$, all non-positive values $\lambda = -\alpha$, where $\alpha \geq 0$. Let

$$v_{\lambda,\mu}(x) = \int\limits_0^\infty e^{-\mu t} \, u_\lambda(t, x) \, dt \, .$$

The function $v_{\lambda,\mu}$ is a bounded solution of the differential equation

$$\frac{1}{2} v''_{\lambda,\mu}(x) + [\lambda \varphi(x) - \mu] \, v_{\lambda,\mu}(x) = -1$$

obtained by multiplying by $e^{-\mu t}$ and integrating with respect to t both sides of the differential equation for $u_\lambda(t, x)$. If $\varphi(x)$ is a piece-wise continuous function, $v_{\lambda,\mu}(x)$ continuously differentiable, it has a second derivative at all points of continuity of the function $\varphi(x)$ and satisfies the equation above.

Example. *The Time Spent on the Positive Half-Line.* Let

$$\varphi(x) = \begin{cases} 1 & \text{for} \quad x \geq 0 \\ 0 & \text{for} \quad x < 0 \, . \end{cases}$$

Then the random variable

$$\tau = \int\limits_0^t \varphi[\xi(s)] \, ds$$

represents the "time spent" on the positive half-line $x \geq 0$ within an interval of time $[0, t]$. The bounded solution of the differential equation

$$\frac{1}{2} v''_{-\lambda,\mu}(x) - [\lambda \varphi(x) + \mu] \, v_{-\lambda,\mu}(x) = -1$$

has the property that for $x = 0$ and $\lambda \geq 0$

$$v_{-\lambda,\mu}(0) = \frac{1}{\sqrt{(\lambda + \mu) \mu}} = \int\limits_0^\infty e^{-\mu t} \frac{1}{\pi} \int\limits_0^t \frac{e}{\sqrt{s(t - s)}} \, ds \, dt \, .$$

Thus the corresponding function

$$u_{-\lambda}(t, 0) = \mathsf{M}_0 \, e^{-\lambda \tau} = \int\limits_0^t e^{-\lambda s} \, p_\tau(s) \, ds \, ,$$

where $p_\tau(s)$ is the distribution density of the random variable τ, has the form

$$u_{-\lambda}(t,0) = \frac{1}{\pi} \int\limits_0^t \frac{e^{-\lambda s}}{s(t-s)} \, ds \,.$$

Hence

$$p_\tau(s) = \frac{1}{\pi \sqrt{s(t-s)}} \qquad (0 \le s \le t)\,,$$

$$\mathbb{P}_0\{\tau \le s\} = \frac{1}{\pi} \int\limits_0^s \frac{du}{\sqrt{u(t-u)}} = \frac{2}{\pi} \arcsin \sqrt{\frac{s}{t}} \qquad (0 \le s \le t)\,.$$

Let $\tau_{(a,b)}$ be the moment of the first exit from the interval (a, b) and $\varphi = \varphi(x)$ a real function. Consider the random variable

$$\int\limits_0^{\tau_{(a,b)}} \varphi[\xi(t)] \, dt \,.$$

Under some restrictions imposed on $\varphi(x)$ the function

$$u_\lambda(x) = \mathbb{M}_x \exp\left\{\lambda \int\limits_0^{\tau_{(a,b)}} \varphi[\xi(t)] \, dt\right\}$$

satisfies the differential equation

$$\frac{1}{2} u_\lambda''(x) + \lambda \varphi(x) \, u_\lambda(x) = 0$$

with the boundary conditions $u_\lambda(a) = u_\lambda(b) = 1$; if $a = -\infty$ or $b = \infty$, then these conditions have to be replaced by boundedness conditions on the solution for $x \to a$, or $x \to b$, respectively (see § 5.1 of this chapter).

Example. *Period of Stay.* Let τ_a be the moment when the point a is reached for the first time and let

$$\varphi(x) = \begin{cases} 1 & \text{for} \quad x \ge 0\,, \\ 0 & \text{for} \quad x < 0\,. \end{cases}$$

Then the random variable $\tau = \int\limits_0^{\tau_a} \varphi[\xi(t)] \, dt$ represents the "time spent" on the positive half-line until the point $a < 0$ is reached for the first time. The bounded solution of the differential equation

$$\frac{1}{2} u_{-\lambda}''(x) - \lambda \varphi(x) \, u_{-\lambda}(x) = 0\,, \qquad u_{-\lambda}(a) = 1\,,$$

leads for $x = 0$ and $\lambda \geq 0$ to the relations [58]

$$u_{-\lambda}(0) = \mathbb{M}_0 \, e^{-\lambda \tau} = \lambda \int\limits_0^\infty e^{-\lambda t} \, \mathbb{P}_0\{\tau \leq t\} \, dt = \frac{1}{1 - a\sqrt{\lambda}},$$

$$\mathbb{P}_0\{\tau \leq t\} = 1 - \frac{2e^{\frac{t}{a^2}}}{\sqrt{\pi}} \int\limits_{\frac{\sqrt{t}}{a}}^\infty e^{-s^2} \, ds \qquad (0 \leq t < \infty).$$

In the case of a positive point $a > 0$ the distribution $\mathbb{P}_0\{\tau \leq t\}$ looks quite different. In particular, for $a = 1$ the corresponding solution $u_{-\lambda}(x)$ fulfills [59]

$$u_{-\lambda} = \frac{1}{ch\sqrt{2\pi}}.$$

Modes of Continuity. The following equation holds for almost all trajectories of the Brownian motion process:

$$\lim_{h \to +0} \sup_{0 \leq t \leq \delta - h} \frac{|\xi(t + h) - \xi(t)|}{\sqrt{2h \log \frac{\delta}{h}}} = 1 \, ;$$

moreover

$$\lim_{h \to \infty} \sum_{k=0}^{n-1} [\Delta \xi(kh)]^2 = \delta$$

where $h = \delta/n$, $\Delta \xi(t) = \xi(t + h) - \xi(t)$.

Law of the Iterated Logarithm. For almost all trajectories with respect to the conditional distribution $\mathbb{P}_0$ we have

$$\overline{\lim_{h \to \infty}} \frac{\xi(h)}{\sqrt{2h \log \log \frac{1}{h}}} = 1 \, .$$

Applying the law of the iterated logarithm to the Brownian motion process $\xi_1(t) = t \xi(1/t)$ we can also write it in another form:

$$\overline{\lim_{t \to \infty}} \frac{\xi(t)}{\sqrt{2t \log \log t}} = 1 \, .$$

---

[58] *Has'minskiĭ, R. Z.*, Probability distribution for functionals of the trajectory of a random diffusion process. Doklady AN SSSR, **104**, 1 (1955), 22—25 (Russian).

[59] *Ito, K.*, and *H. McKean*, Diffusion Processes and their Sample Paths. Berlin: Springer 1965.

Local Time. Let

$$\varphi_B(x) = \begin{cases} 1 & \text{for} \quad x \in B, \\ 0 & \text{for} \quad x \notin B, \end{cases}$$

and consider the function

$$\varphi_0^t(B) = \int_0^t \varphi_B[\xi(u)]\, du\,.$$

For each fixed trajectory of the Brownian motion process, $\varphi_0^t(B)$ considered as a function of the variable B represents a measure on the σ-algebra of Borel sets of the real line.

This measure is absolutely continuous for almost all trajectories:

$$\varphi_0^t(B) = \int_B \tau(t, x)\, dx\,.$$

The corresponding density $\tau(t, x)$ is called the *local time* at the point x. The variable $\tau(t, x)$ considered as a function of t represents a random process which is continuous with probability 1.

3. Structure of Random Processes with Independent Increments

Centering of Random Process with Independent Increments. Consider a random process $\xi(t)$ with independent increments and a continuous parameter t on a finite or infinite interval $T = [a, b]$. The degree of dispersion $\delta(t) = \delta[\xi(t) - \xi(a)]$ of this process is a monotone non-decreasing function of t and has only a countable set of points of discontinuity. Moreover the limits

$$\delta(t - 0) = \lim_{s \to t - 0} \delta(s) \quad \text{and} \quad \delta(t + 0) = \lim_{s \to t + 0} \delta(s)$$

exist for all t. Consequently, there is a *centering function* $b(t)$, for example, the one satisfying the condition

$$\mathsf{M} \text{ arc tg}\,[\eta(t) - b(t)] = 0\,,$$

such that for each fixed t the limits $\lim_{s \to t \pm 0} [\eta(s) - b(s)]$ exist for the process with independent increments $\eta(t) - b(t)$. In order to avoid a change of notations we assume that the process $\eta(t)$ has already this property, that is, $b(t) \equiv 0$. Under this convention the equation

$$\eta(t - 0) = \eta(t) \quad \text{or} \quad \eta(t + 0) = \eta(t)$$

is satisfied with probability 1 if and only if

$$\delta(t - 0) = \delta(t) \quad \text{or} \quad \delta(t + 0) = \delta(t)\,, \quad \text{respectively.}$$

The jumps $\eta(s) - \eta(s-0)$ and $\eta(s+0) - \eta(s)$ of the random process $\eta(t)$ at fixed points s do not depend on the behavior of the process $\eta(t)$ until the time $s-0$ and s, respectively; more precisely, they do not depend on the family of random variables $\eta(t)$, $t < s$, and $\eta(t)$, $t \leqq s$, and may be studied separately. In particular, if we number the points of discontinuity of the function $\delta(t)$, that is, the fixed points of discontinuity of the random process $\eta(t)$, we can define a sequence of random processes $\eta_d^{(n)}(t)$ with independent increments of the form

$$\eta_d^{(n)}(t) = \sum_{\substack{1 \leqq k \leqq n \\ s_k \leqq t}} [\eta(s_k + 0) - \eta(s_k - 0)] - c^{(n)}(t) .$$

It is understood that if t is a point of discontinuity $t = s_k$, then we take $\eta(s_k)$ instead of $\eta(s_k + 0)$; the centering constants $c^{(n)}(t)$ are chosen in such a way that the limit

$$\eta_d(t) = \lim_{n \to \infty} \eta_d^{(n)}(t) .$$

exists with probability 1.

Roughly spoken the random process $\eta_d(t)$ is, up to the centering function, the sum of the jumps of the initial process $\eta(t)$ at fixed points of discontinuity until the present time t, and hence is a process with independent increments. The degree of dispersion $\delta_d(t) = \delta[\eta_d(t) - \eta_d(a)]$ of this process coincides with the discontinuity functions in the decomposition of the monotone function $\delta(t)$ into a continuous component $\delta_c(t)$ and a pure jump function $\delta_d(t)$:

$$\delta(t) = \delta_c(t) + \delta_d(t) .$$

To the continuous component of the degree of dispersion $\delta(t)$ of the initial process there corresponds a stochastically continuous random process $\eta_c(t)$ of the form $\eta_c(t) = \eta(t) - \eta_d(t) - c(t)$, where the centering function $c(t)$ is taken in such a way that, for example, the condition

$$\mathsf{M} \, \text{arc tg} \, [\eta(t) - \eta_d(t) - c(t)] = 0$$

is satisfied; in this case the degree of dispersion $\delta_c(t) = \delta[\eta_c(t) - \eta_c(a)]$ coincides with the continuous component $\delta_c(t)$ in the decomposition of the monotone function $\delta(t)$. The random process $\eta_c(t)$ has independent increments which do not depend on the increments of the "jump" process $\eta_d(t)$.

Let $\xi(t)$ be a stochastically continuous separable process with independent increments on an interval $T = [a, b]$. For fixed t we have

$$\lim_{s \to t} \xi(s) = \xi(t)$$

with probability 1. This does not mean, of course, that the trajectories of the process $\xi(\omega, t)$ are continuous. However, almost all trajectories $\xi(\omega, t)$ will have at most discontinuities of the first kind, that is, for almost all ω the limits

$$\xi(\omega, t - 0) = \lim_{s \to t-0} \xi(\omega, s), \quad \xi(\omega, t + 0) = \lim_{s \to t+0} \xi(\omega, s)$$

exist for any t. It amounts to the same to say that, given any fixed $\varepsilon > 0$, there is on any bounded interval Δ only a finite number of oscillations of the trajectory $\xi(\omega, t)$ larger than ε; by the *number of oscillations* of the function $x = x(t)$ we mean the largest n such that there exist points $t_0 \leq t_1 \leq \cdots \leq t_n$ in the interval in question which satisfy the inequalities $|x(t_k) - x(t_{k-1})| \geq \varepsilon$, $k = 1, 2, \ldots, n$.

There is a random process $\xi(t)$ which is equivalent to the initial one and has right continuous trajectories, this with probability 1:

$$\xi(\omega, t + 0) = \xi(\omega, t).$$

Poisson Process. A random process with independent increments and satisfying

$$\mathbb{P}\{\xi(t) - \xi(s) = k\} = \frac{[\lambda(t - s)]^k}{k!} e^{-\lambda(t-s)}$$

for any $s, t \in T$, $s \leq t$ is termed a *Poisson process*. This is a stochastically continuous process with independent increments whose sample functions are simple monotone functions of the parameter t with a finite number of jumps of size 1 in any bounded interval; in fact the increments take only non-negative integral values. Moreover

$$\mathbb{M}[\xi(t) - \xi(s)] = \lambda(t - s)$$

for any $s, t \in T$, $s \leq t$. The increments $\xi(t) - \xi(s)$ obey the Poisson law with parameter $a = \lambda(t - s)$.

Stochastic Measures Constructed from the Discontinuities of Random Processes. Let $\xi(t)$ be a process with independent increments which is stochastically continuous and continuous from the right with probability 1. Consider a Borel set B on the line which has a positive distance from the origin, and an interval of time Δ. We denote by $v(\Delta \times B)$ the number of jumps of the process $\xi(t)$ during the interval Δ which fall into B, that is,

$$\xi(\omega, t) - \xi(\omega, t - 0) \in B.$$

For each bounded interval Δ the random variable $v(\Delta \times B)$ is finite with probability 1. Random variables $v(\Delta_1 \times B)$ and $v(\Delta_2 \times B)$ which correspond to non-intersecting intervals Δ_1 and Δ_2 are independent. Moreover we have

$$\mathbb{P}\{v(\Delta \times B) > 1\} = o(|\Delta|)$$

where $|\Delta|$ is the length of the interval Δ. Thus the random variable $v(\Delta \times B)$ has a Poisson distribution:

$$\mathbb{P}\{v(\Delta \times B) = k\} = \frac{[N(\Delta \times B)]^k}{k!} e^{-N(\Delta \times B)}$$

where $N(\Delta \times B) = \mathbb{M} v(\Delta \times B)$.

The random variable $v(\Delta \times B)$ considered as a set function can be extended to a finite generalized σ-measure in the (t, x)-plane; $v(A)$ and $N(A)$ may take the value $+\infty$ for sets A contiguous to the axis $x = 0$.

Structure of Processes with Independent Increments. Suppose that the interval $T = [a, b]$ is finite. We introduce random processes $\zeta_B(t)$ of the form

$$\zeta_B(t) = \int_B x \, v([a, t] \times dx)$$

which represent nothing else but the sum of the jumps of the initial process $\xi(t)$ with values in the set B occuring up to the time t. The following formulas hold:

$$\mathbb{M} \zeta_B(t) = \int_B x \, N([a, t] \times dx),$$
$$\mathbb{D} \zeta_B(t) = \int_B x^2 \, N([a, t] \times dx).$$

If the sets B_1 and B_2 do not intersect, the random processes $\zeta_{B_1}(t)$ and $\zeta_{B_2}(t)$ are mutually independent.

Consider the sequence of random processes $\xi_n(t) = \zeta_{B_n}(t)$ which correspond to the sets $B_n = \{|x| \geq \varepsilon_n\}$, and represent the sum of the jumps of size at least ε_n of the initial process $\xi(t)$ in the interval $[a, t]$. It is worthwhile to remark that if we exclude from the process $\xi(t)$ all jumps whose absolute value is larger than a fixed level (for example one), then the random process $\xi(t) - \xi_1(t)$ obtained in this way has moments of any order. In particular,

$$\int_{-1}^{1} x^2 N([a, b] \times dx) = \mathbb{D}[\xi(t) - \xi_1(t)] < \infty.$$

Excluding all discontinuities from $\xi(t)$ we obtain a random process with continuous trajectories. In fact, a process of this kind will be given by

$$\xi_c(t) = \xi(t) - \xi_1(t) - \lim_{n \to \infty} \{[\xi_n(t) - \xi_1(t)] - \mathbb{M}[\xi_n(t) - \xi_1(t)]\}$$

where the sequence ε_n is chosen in such a way that

$$\sum_{n=1}^{\infty} \int_{-\varepsilon_n}^{\varepsilon_n} x^2 N([a,b] \times dx) < \infty ;$$

this condition guarantees the uniform convergence with respect to t when going to the limit as described before.

The almost surely continuous process $\xi_c(t)$ has independent increments and, in addition, does not depend on the Poisson measure $v(dt \times dx)$.

The random process $\xi_c(t)$ with independent increments and almost surely continuous trajectories represents virtually a (non-homogeneous) Brownian motion, that is, a random process with independent Gaussian increments whose mathematical expectation $A(t) = \text{M} \xi_c(t)$ and variance $D(t) = \text{D} \xi_c(t)$ are continuous functions of t; every separable Gaussian process with independent increments and continuous mean value and variance has continuous trajectories with probability 1.

Thus the structure of an arbitrary stochastically continuous random process $\xi(t)$ with independent increments can be clearly recognized from its following representation:

$$\xi(t) = \xi_c(t) + \int_{|x| \leq 1} x[v([a,t] \times dx) - N([a,t] \times dx)] + \int_{|x| > 1} x v([a,t] \times dx) .$$

where $\xi_c(t)$ is a continuous Gaussian process with independent increments which does not depend on the Poisson measure $v(dt \times dx)$ and is constructed from the discontinuities of the initial process $\xi(t)$.

Probability Distributions of Random Processes with Independent Increments. Given a stochastically continuous process with independent increments the probability distribution of the variable $\xi(t) - \xi(s)$ is, of course, infinitely divisible. In some sense the converse statement holds, too: for fixed t and s there is always a stochastically continuous random process with independent increments such that the variable $\xi(t) - \xi(s)$ has a given infinitely divisible distribution which may be arbitrary. The natural logarithm of the characteristic function of the increment $\xi(t) - \xi(s)$ looks like this:

$$\log \text{M} \exp\{iu[\xi(t) - \xi(s)]\} = iu[A(t) - A(s)] - \frac{1}{2} u^2[D(t) - D(s)]$$

$$+ \int_{|x| \leq 1} (e^{iux} - 1 - iux) N([s,t]) \times dx) + \int_{|x| > 1} (e^{iux} - 1) N([s,t] \times dx)$$

where $A(t)$ is the continuous function which equals the expectation of the continuous Gaussian component $\xi_c(t)$ in the representation of the process $\xi(t)$; $D(t)$ and $D(t) - D(s)$ are the variances of $\xi_c(t)$ and the difference

$\xi_c(t) - \xi_c(s)$, respectively; $N([s, t] \times B)$ is the expectation of the Poisson measure $v([s, t] \times B)$ constructed from the jumps of the process $\xi(t)$:

$$A(t) = \mathbb{M}\,\xi_c(t)\,, \qquad D(t) = \mathbb{D}\,\xi_c(t)\,,$$
$$N([s, t] \times B) = \mathbb{M}\,v([s, t] \times B)\,.$$

If we set

$$G([s, t] \times B) = \int_B \frac{x^2}{1 + x^2}\, N([s, t] \times dx)\,,$$

$$\gamma(t) = A(t) + \int_{|x| > 1} \frac{x}{1 + x^2}\, N([a, t] \times dx) - \int_{|x| \le 1} x\,G([a, t] \times dx)\,,$$

we obtain

$$\log \mathbb{M}\{iu[\xi(t) - \xi(s)]\} = iu[\gamma(t) - \gamma(s)] - \frac{1}{2}\,u^2[D(t) - D(s)]$$

$$+ \int_{-\infty}^{\infty} \left(e^{iux} - 1 - \frac{iux}{1 + x^2} \right) \frac{1 + x^2}{x}\, G([s, t] \times dx)\,.$$

Homogeneous Processes. A process $\xi(t)$ with independent increments is called *homogeneous* if the probability distribution of the increments $\xi(t) - \xi(s)$ depends only on the difference $t - s$, that is, if it does not depend on the origin of the time scale. A necessary and sufficient condition for homogeneity is

$$A(t) = at\,, \qquad D(t) = \sigma^2 t\,,$$
$$N(dt \times dx) = N(dx)dt\,.$$

The class of homogeneous processes with independent increments coincides with the class of homogeneous Markov processes whose transition function is invariant with respect to shifts in the phase space, that is, on the real line $-\infty < x < \infty$:

$$\mathbb{P}(t, x, B) = \mathbb{P}(t, 0, B - x)$$

where $B - x$ denotes the set of all points $y - x$, $y \in B$.

A homogeneous process $\xi(t)$ with independent increments is called *stable* if the distributions of its increments are stable (see § 7, ch. IV). The measure $N(dx)$ connected with the jumps of the stable process $\xi(t)$ has the form

$$N(B) = C_1 \int_{B \cap (-\infty, 0)} \frac{dx}{|x|^{\alpha + 1}} + C_2 \int_{B \cap (0, \infty)} \frac{dx}{|x|^{\alpha + 1}}$$

where as a consequence of the conditions $\int\limits_{|x|\leq 1} x^2 N(dx) < \infty$ and $\int\limits_{|x|>1} N(dx) < \infty$ the parameter α lies within the limits $0 < \alpha < 2$. The parameter β determined by

$$\beta = \frac{C_2 - C_1}{C_2 + C_1} \quad (-1 \leq \beta \leq 1)$$

is another important characteristic of the stable process. For example, in the case of extreme values $\beta = \pm 1$ the process $\xi(t)$ has jumps of the same sign as β only.

Example. *The Time of the First Hit of a Fixed Point.* Let $\xi = \xi(t)$ be a Brownian motion process, $\tau = \tau(a)$ the instant when the point $a > 0$ is hit for the first time. If we consider the point a as a parameter, then the random process $\tau = \tau(a)$ on the halfline $a \geq 0$ is stable with parameters $\alpha = 1/2, \beta = 1$. Its probability distribution satisfies for $b \geq a \geq 0$ the relation

$$\mathbb{P}_0\{\tau_b - \tau_a \leq t\} = \int\limits_0^t \frac{b-a}{\sqrt{2\pi}} s^{-\frac{3}{2}} e^{-\frac{(b-a)^2}{2s}} ds$$

$$= 1 - \sqrt{\frac{2}{\pi}} \int\limits_0^{\frac{a}{\sqrt{t}}} e^{-\frac{x^2}{2}} dx \quad (0 \leq t < \infty).$$

Properties of the Trajectories. The process $\xi(t)$ is continuous with probability 1 if and only if it is Gaussian, that is,

$$N(dx) \equiv 0.$$

An important rôle among the discontinuous processes is played by the so-called "step" processes whose trajectories take with probability 1 during any bounded period of time only a finite number of values, each of them being taken on a corresponding interval of the type $[s, t)$. In order that $\xi(t)$ be a "step" process it is necessary and sufficient that there is no Gaussian component and that the measure $N(dx)$ is bounded:

$$\sigma^2 = 0, \quad \int\limits_{-1}^1 N(dx) < \infty.$$

The analogous condition

$$\sigma^2 = 0, \quad \int\limits_{-1}^1 |x| N(dx) < \infty$$

is necessary and sufficient in order that almost all trajectories of $\xi(t)$ be functions of bounded variation. A process of bounded variation can be represented like this:

$$\xi(t) = \xi(s) + a(t-s) + \int_{-\infty}^{\infty} x\, v([s,t] \times dx);$$

here the constant a differs from the speed of the drift $A'(t)$ by the term $\int_{|x| \leq 1} x N(dx)$. Such a process $\xi(t)$ is differentiable at each fixed point s:

$$\lim_{t \to s} \frac{\xi(t) - \xi(s)}{t - s} = a$$

with probability 1. For processes with unbounded variation we have

$$\lim_{t \to s} \frac{|\xi(t) - \xi(s)|}{t - s} = \infty .$$

§ 4. Diffusion Processes

1. Differential and Stochastic Equations

Coefficients of Drift and Diffusion. By a diffusion process $\xi(t)$ whose phase space is the real line we usually mean a continuous Markov process with transition function $P(s, x, t, B)$ satisfying the following conditions: for $\varepsilon > 0$ we have

$$\left.\begin{aligned}
&\lim_{\Delta t \to 0} \frac{1}{\Delta t} \int_{|y-x|>\varepsilon} P(s, x, s+\Delta t, dy) = 0, \\
&\lim_{\Delta t \to 0} \frac{1}{\Delta t} \int_{|y-x|\leq\varepsilon} (y-x) P(s, x, s+\Delta t, dy) = a(s, x), \\
&\lim_{\Delta t \to 0} \frac{1}{\Delta t} \int_{|y-x|\leq\varepsilon} (y-x)^2 P(s, x, s+\Delta t, dy) = \sigma^2(s, x).
\end{aligned}\right\} \quad (4.1)$$

The quantity $a(s, x)$ characterizes the average trend of evolution of the random process $\xi(s)$ in a short interval of time from s to $s + \Delta t$ under the condition that $\xi(s) = x$, and is called the *drift coefficient*. The quantity $\sigma(s, x)$ determines the mean square deviation of the process $\xi(t)$ from its expected value and is termed the *diffusion coefficient*:

$$\xi(s + \Delta t) \sim \xi(s) + a[s, \xi(s)] \Delta t + \sigma[s, \xi(s)] \Delta\eta(s),$$

where $\Delta\eta(s)$ is a random variable such that

$$\mathbb{M}\{\Delta\eta(s) | \xi(u), u \leq s\} \sim 0, \quad \mathbb{D}\{\Delta\eta(s) | \xi(u), u \leq s\} \sim \Delta t.$$

The most important representative of this class of processes is the Brownian motion which was first investigated as a mathematical model of processes of diffusion; hence the name "diffusion processes". This class also contains the general continuous Gaussian process $\xi(t)$ with independent increments and smoothly varying moments $A(t) = \mathbb{M}\xi(t)$ and $D(t) = \mathbb{D}\xi(t)$; these are connected with the drift coefficient $a(t, x) \equiv a(t)$ and the diffusion coefficient $\sigma(t, x) \equiv \sigma(t)$ by the relations:

$$A(t) - A(t_0) = \int_{t_0}^{t} a(s)\, ds, \qquad D(t) - D(t_0) = \int_{t_0}^{t} \sigma^2(s)\, ds.$$

For this process the corresponding variable

$$\Delta\eta(s) = \frac{\xi(s + \Delta t) - \xi(s) - a(s)\,\Delta t}{\sigma(s)}$$

is Gaussian and does not depend on the evolution of the process until the time s.

The probability distribution of $\xi(t)$ is the same as that of the process $\tilde{\xi}(t)$ constructed with the help of the stochastic integral:

$$\tilde{\xi}(t) = \xi(t_0) + \int_{t_0}^{t} a(s)\, ds + \int_{t_0}^{t} \sigma(s)\, d\eta(s) \qquad (t \geq t_0)$$

where $\eta(t) = \dfrac{\xi(t) - \xi(t_0) - [A(t) - A(t_0)]}{\sqrt{D(t) - D(t_0)}}$ is a Brownian motion process.

The Kolmogorov Differential Equations. Suppose that the limit relations (4.1) are satisfied uniformly with respect to s and that $\varphi(x)$ is a bounded continuous function. We define $\varphi(s, x)$ by the formula

$$\varphi(s, x) = \int \varphi(y)\, P(s, x, t, dy) \qquad (s < t).$$

Assume that the function $\varphi(s, x)$ and its first two derivatives $\dfrac{\partial}{\partial x}\varphi(s, x)$ and $\dfrac{\partial^2}{\partial x^2}\varphi(s, x)$ are bounded and continuous. Then $\varphi(s, x)$ has a derivative $\dfrac{\partial}{\partial s}\varphi(s, x)$ and satisfies the following differential equation:

$$\frac{\partial}{\partial s}\varphi(s, x) = -a(s, x)\frac{\partial}{\partial x}\varphi(s, x) - \frac{1}{2}\sigma^2(s, x)\frac{\partial^2}{\partial x^2}\varphi(s, x)$$

with the "final" condition

$$\lim_{s \to t} \varphi(s, x) = \varphi(x).$$

17*

If the transition density

$$p(s, x, t, y) = \frac{P(s, x, t, dy)}{dy}$$

exists and is continuous with respect to s together with its derivatives $\frac{\partial}{\partial x} p(s, x, t, y)$ and $\frac{\partial^2}{\partial x^2} p(s, x, t, y)$, then it represents a fundamental solution of the differential equation

$$\frac{\partial}{\partial s} p(s, x, t, y) = -a(s, x) \frac{\partial}{\partial x} p(s, x, t, y) - \frac{1}{2} \sigma^2(s, x) \frac{\partial^2}{\partial x^2} p(s, x, t, y),$$

which is called the *backward Kolmogorov equation*.

In the homogeneous case where the drift coefficient $a(t, x) \equiv a(x)$ and the diffusion coefficient $\sigma(t, x) \equiv \sigma(x)$ do not depend on the time t the backward Kolmogorov equation for the transition density $p(s, x, t, y) = p(t - s, x, y)$ has the form

$$\frac{\partial}{\partial t} p(t, x, y) = a(x) \frac{\partial}{\partial x} p(t, x, y) + \frac{1}{2} \sigma^2(x) \frac{\partial^2}{\partial x^2} p(t, x, y).$$

A solution of this equation exists and is unique, and is also a transition density of the homogeneous diffusion process, if, for example, the coefficients $a(x)$ and $\sigma(x)$ are bounded and satisfy the Lipschitz condition

$$|a(x) - a(y)| \leq C|x - y|,$$
$$|\sigma(x) - \sigma(y)| \leq C|x - y|,$$

and if, moreover,

$$\sigma(x) \geq \sigma > 0$$

for all x.

Suppose that the relations (4.1) are satisfied uniformly with respect to s and x, and that $Q(dx)$ is a generalized measure with the continuous density $q(x) = \frac{Q(dx)}{dx}$. Define $Q(t, A)$ by the formula

$$Q(t, A) = \int Q(dx) P(s, x, t, A) \qquad (t > s).$$

We assume that for each t the generalized measure $Q(t, dx)$ has a density $q(t, x)$, that the derivatives

$$\frac{\partial}{\partial t} q(t, x), \qquad \frac{\partial}{\partial x} [a(t, x) q(t, x)] \quad \text{and} \quad \frac{\partial^2}{\partial x^2} [\sigma^2(t, x) q(t, x)]$$

exist, and that the first one is continuous with respect to t and x and the second one continuous with respect to x. Then the function $q(t, x)$

satisfies the following differential equation:

$$\frac{\partial}{\partial t} q(t, x) = - \frac{\partial}{\partial x} [a(t, x) q(t, x)] + \frac{1}{2} \frac{\partial^2}{\partial x^2} [\sigma^2(t, x) q(t, x)]$$

with the initial condition

$$\lim_{t \to s} q(t, x) = q(x).$$

If the transition density $p(s, x, t, y)$ exists, if it has a derivative $\frac{\partial}{\partial t} p(s, x, t, y)$ which is continuous with respect to t and y, and if the functions

$$\frac{\partial}{\partial y} [a(t, y) p(s, x, t, y)] \quad \text{and} \quad \frac{\partial^2}{\partial y^2} [\sigma^2(t, y) p(s, x, t, y)]$$

are continuous with respect to y, then $p(t, x, t, y)$ is a fundamental solution of the differential equation

$$\frac{\partial}{\partial t} p(s, x, t, y) = - \frac{\partial}{\partial y} [a(t, y) p(s, x, t, y)] + \frac{1}{2} \frac{\partial^2}{\partial y^2} [\sigma^2(t, y) p(s, x, t, y)].$$

This equation is called the *Fokker-Planck equation* or the *forward Kolmogorov equation.*

Stochastic Ito Equations. Let $\xi(t)$ be a diffusion process such that with probability 1

$$\mathbf{M}\{|\xi(t)|^2 \,|\, \xi(s)\} \leq \eta_s, \quad \mathbf{M} \eta_s < \infty$$

for $t_0 \leq s < t < t_1$ and

$$\left| \mathbf{M}\{\xi(t + \Delta t) - \xi(t) \,|\, \xi(t)\} - \int_t^{t+\Delta t} a[s, \xi(t)] | ds \right| \leq [1 + \xi(t)^2] \, \Delta t \, \delta(\Delta t),$$

$$\left| \mathbf{M}\{[\xi(t + \Delta t) - \xi(t)]^2 \,|\, \xi(t)\} - \int_t^{t+\Delta t} \sigma[s, \xi(t)]^2 \, ds \right| \leq [1 + \xi(t)^2] \, \Delta t \, \delta(\Delta t)$$

where $a(t, x)$ and $\sigma(t, x)$ are the corresponding drift and diffusion coefficients, and $\delta(h) \to 0$ monotonically for $h \to 0$. In this case we have

$$\mathbf{M}\{\xi(t) - \xi(s) \,|\, \xi(u), \ u \leq s\} = \mathbf{M}\left\{ \int_s^t a[u, \xi(u)] \, du \,|\, \xi(u), \ u \leq s \right\},$$

so that the process $\eta^*(t)$ of the form

$$\eta^*(t) = \xi(t) - \xi(t_0) - \int_{t_0}^t a[s, \xi(s)] \, ds \qquad (t_0 \leq t \leq t_1)$$

is a continuous martingale.

The stochastic integral

$$\eta(t) = \int_{t_0}^{t} \frac{1}{\sigma[s, \xi(s)]} \, d\eta^*(s) \qquad (t_0 \leq t \leq t_1)$$

where it is assumed that $\sigma(t, x) > 0$, defines a Brownian motion process $\eta(t)$ of the following kind: its evolution after the time t does not depend on the behavior of the initial process $\xi(s)$ until this time t if the state $\xi(t)$ is fixed.

The diffusion process $\xi(t)$ has a stochastic differential of the form

$$d\xi(t) = a[t, \xi(t)] \, dt + \sigma[t, \xi(t)] \, d\eta(t),$$

that is, for any t in the interval $t_0 \leq t \leq t_1$ we have

$$\xi(t) = \xi(t_0) + \int_{t_0}^{t} a[s, \xi(s)] \, ds + \int_{t_0}^{t} \sigma[s, \xi(s)] \, d\eta(s).$$

Conversely, if we start with some auxiliary Brownian motion process $\eta(t)$, then given some functions $a(t, x)$ and $\sigma(t, x) \geq 0$ we can construct a diffusion process $\xi(t)$ with drift coefficient $a(t, x)$ and diffusion coefficient $\sigma(t, x)$ as a solution of the *stochastic Ito differential equation*

$$d\xi(t) = a[t, \xi(t)] \, dt + \sigma[t, \xi(t)] \, d\eta(t).$$

In other words, we can construct a diffusion process $\xi(t)$ which satisfies the *stochastic integral equation*

$$\xi(t) = \xi(t_0) + \int_{t_0}^{t} a[s, \xi(s)] \, ds + \int_{t_0}^{t} \sigma[s, \xi(s)] \, d\eta(s) \qquad (t_0 \leq t \leq t_1).$$

A solution $\xi(t)$ of this equation exists and determines a diffusion process if, for example, the coefficients $a(t, x)$ and $\sigma(t, x)$ satisfy the following conditions: first, the functions $a(t, x)$ and $\sigma(t, x)$ do not increase too fast for $x \to \infty$ in the sense that

$$|a(t, x)| \leq C(1 + x^2)^{1/2}, \qquad |\sigma(t, x)| \leq C(1 + x^2)^{1/2};$$

secondly, the functions $a(t, x)$ and $\sigma(t, x)$ satisfy a Lipschitz condition in x uniformly with respect to t and x in each bounded interval, that is,

$$|a(t, x_1) - a(t, x_2)| \leq C|x_1 - x_2|,$$
$$|\sigma(t, x_1) - \sigma(t, x_2)| \leq C|x_1 - x_2|.$$

Given such coefficients $a(t, x)$ and $\sigma(t, x)$ the solution of the stochastic integral equation can be obtained by successive approximations. In fact, let $\xi_0(t)$ be an arbitrary random process with continuous trajectories whose increments $\xi(t) - \xi(s)$ do not depend on the increments $\eta(t') - \eta(s')$, $s \leq t \leq s' \leq t'$ of the initial Brownian motion process, and such that

$$\xi_0(t_0) = \xi(t_0), \quad \int_{t_0}^{t} \mathbf{M} |\xi_0(t)|^2 \, dt < \infty.$$

Then we may choose as a "zero approximation" for example the variable $\xi_0(t) \equiv \xi(t_0)$ which is constant in time. The successive approximations are determined with the help of stochastic integrals of the form

$$\xi_n(t) = \xi(t_0) + \int_{t_0}^{t} a[s, \xi_{n-1}(s)] \, ds + \int_{t_0}^{t} \sigma[s, \xi_{n-1}(s)] \, d\eta(s) \quad (n = 1, 2, \ldots).$$

On each bounded interval $t_0 \leq t \leq t_1$ this sequence of random processes converges with probability 1 to the solution $\xi(t)$ uniformly with respect to t_0, and the mean square deviation of $\xi_n(t)$ from $\xi(t)$ decreases exponentially fast:

$$\int_{t_0}^{t_1} \mathbf{M} |\xi_n(t) - \xi(t)|^2 \, dt \leq C e^{-cn}.$$

Discrete Diffusion Model. An approximate discrete model of the diffusion process $\xi(t)$ consists in the following scheme of a random walk, where $\xi(t)$ denotes the position of the wandering particle at the present time t. At the discrete moments of time divisible by Δt the particle can change its state in such a way that it passes from $\xi(t) = x$ to the neighboring point $x + \Delta x$ with probability $p(t, x) \sim \dfrac{1}{2} + \dfrac{a(t, x)}{2\sigma(t, x)} \sqrt{\Delta t}$ and to the point $x - \Delta x$, $\Delta x \sim \sigma(t, x) \sqrt{\Delta t}$ with probability $1 - p(t, x)$; this transition takes place independently of the behavior of the particle until the time t where $\xi(t) = x$.

Let $P(s, x, t, B)$ be the transition function of the random walk described above. The formula of complete probabilities yields the following finite difference equation for the function $u(s, x) = P(s, x, t, B)$:

$$u(s, x) = p(s, x) u(s + \Delta t, x + \Delta x) + [1 - p(s, x)] u(s + \Delta t, x - \Delta x).$$

In the case of smoothly varying $u(s, x)$, $a(s, x)$ and $\sigma(s, x)$ this turns for $\Delta t \to 0$ into a differential equation of the form

$$\frac{\partial}{\partial s} u(s, x) = -a(s, x) \frac{\partial}{\partial x} u(s, x) - \frac{1}{2} \sigma^2(s, x) \frac{\partial^2}{\partial x^2} u(s, x).$$

Let $\xi = \xi(t)$ be a diffusion process which is a solution of the stochastic equation

$$\xi(t) = \xi(0) + \int_0^t a[s, \xi(s)] \, ds + \int_0^t \sigma[s, \xi(s)] \, d\eta(s),$$

where $\xi(0)$ does not depend on the Brownian motion $\eta(t)$, $0 \le t \le 1$, and $a(t, x)$ and $\sigma(t, x)$ are continuous with respect to all variables and satisfy a Lipschitz condition with respect to x. Let ξ_{kn}, $k = 0, \ldots, n$ be random variables forming a Markov chain with the transition function $P_n(s, x, t, B)$, $n = 1, 2, \ldots$, and let

$$a_n(kh, x) = \frac{1}{h} \int_{-\infty}^{\infty} (y - x) P_n(kh, x, (k+1)h, dy),$$

$$\sigma_n(kh, x) = \frac{1}{h} \int_{-\infty}^{\infty} (y - x)^2 P_n(kh, x, (k+1)h, dy)$$

where $k = 0, 1, \ldots, n$ and $h = 1/n$.

Let $\mathbb{P}_n = \mathbb{P}_n(A)$ be the probability distribution on the Borel sets A of the space $C[0, 1]$ of all continuous real functions $x = x(t)$ on the interval $[0, 1]$ which corresponds to the random process $\xi_n = \xi_n(t)$ of the form

$$\xi_n(t) = \sum_{k=0}^{m-1} \xi_{k, n} + (nt - m) \xi_{m, n}$$

where $m = [nt]$ is the integral part of the number nt and $\xi_n(t) = nt\xi_{on}$ if $0 \le t \le 1/n$. We assume that for $n \to \infty$ the following conditions are satisfied:

$$\overline{\lim}\, a_n(kh, x) < \infty, \qquad \underline{\lim}\, \sigma_n(kh, x) > 0,$$

$$h \sum_{k=0}^{n} \mathbb{M}\{|a_n(kh, \xi_{kn}) - a(kh, \xi_{kn})|^2 + |\sigma_n(kh, \xi_{kn}) - \sigma(kh, \xi_{kn})|^2\} \to 0,$$

$$\mathbb{M}|\xi_{k+1, n} - \xi_{k, n}|^{2 + \delta} \to 0 \quad \text{for some} \quad \delta > 0,$$

$$\sup_k \sum_{j=k}^{n} \mathbb{M}\{|\xi_{j+1, n} - \xi_{j, n}|^2 | \xi_{k, n}\} \to 0 \quad \text{stochastically}.$$

We further assume that the probability distributions of the random variables ξ_{on} converge weakly to the probability distribution of $\xi(0)$. Let $\mathbb{P}_n = \mathbb{P}_n(A)$ be the probability distribution on the Borel sets A of the space $C[0, 1]$ of all continuous real-valued functions $x = x(t)$ on the interval $[0, 1]$ which corresponds to the process $\xi_n = \xi_n(t)$ given by

$$\xi_n(t) = \sum_{k=0}^{m-1} \xi_{k, n} + (nt - m) \xi_{m, n}$$

where $m = [nt]$ is the integral point of the number nt, and $\xi_n(t) = nt\xi_{on}$ for $0 \le t < 1/n$. Then for $n \to \infty$ the distributions $\mathbb{P}_n$ converge weakly to the distribution $\mathbb{P} = \mathbb{P}(A)$ which corresponds to the diffusion process $\xi = \xi(t)$.

2. The Behavior of Homogeneous Diffusion Processes on the Boundary Ergodic Properties

Suppose that the transition density $p(t, x, y)$ of a homogeneous diffusion process $\xi = \xi(t)$ on the half-line $[0, \infty)$ satisfies in the neighborhood of each inner point x of the closed interval $[r_1, r_2]$ the *backward Kolmogorov equation*:

$$\frac{\partial}{\partial t} p = Lp, \qquad L = a(x) \frac{\partial}{\partial x} + b(x) \frac{\partial^2}{\partial x^2}$$

where the coefficients $a(x)$ and $b(x)$ are continuous and $b(x) > 0$. Roughly speaking, the random process $\xi(t)$ is governed by the stochastic differential equation

$$d\xi(t) = a[\xi(t)|dt + \sigma[\xi(t)] d\eta(t), \qquad \frac{1}{2} \sigma^2(x) = b(x).$$

Boundary Barriers. Consider the behavior of the process $\xi(t)$ in the immediate neighborhood of the boundary r where r is either r_1 or r_2. The condition that the trajectories be continuous on the entire closed interval $[r_1, r_2]$ admits only three possibilities. Namely, three phenomena are possible on the boundary r: absorption *(absorbing barrier)*, reflection *(reflecting barrier)*, and the so-called *elastic barrier* which is a combination of absorption and reflection.

The phenomenon of absorption is a very simple one. If we consider $\xi(t)$ as a random walk of a particle, then absorption at the point $x = r$ means that once the particle hits the point r it stays there forever. The corresponding boundary condition on the transition density $p(t, x, y)$ considered as a solution of the differential equation $\dfrac{\partial p}{\partial t} = Lp$ can be expressed in the following way:

$$\lim_{x \to r} Lp(t, x, y) = 0.$$

The phenomenon of reflection is more complicated. We can confine ourselves to the half-line $[r, \infty]$ and interpret this phenomenon geometrically. We extend $a(x)$ and $\sigma(x)$ to all values of x as symmetric functions with respect to the boundary r. The coefficients of drift $\tilde{a}(x)$ and and diffusion $\tilde{\sigma}(x)$ obtained this way determine a diffusion process $\tilde{\xi}(t)$ with a transition density $\tilde{p}(t, x, y)$. The process $\xi(t)$ is obtained geometrically from $\xi(t)$ by means of the reflected image with respect to r:

$$\xi(t) = \begin{cases} \tilde{\xi}(t) & \text{if } \tilde{\xi}(t) \geq r, \\ 2r - \tilde{\xi}(t) & \text{if } \tilde{\xi}(t) < r. \end{cases}$$

The transition density $p(t, x, y)$ of the process with reflection is connected with the transition density $\tilde{p}(t, x, y)$ of the auxiliary process $\tilde{\xi}(t)$ by the relation

$$p(t, x, y) = \tilde{p}(t, x, y) + \tilde{p}(t, 2r - x, y).$$

Considered as a solution of the differential equation $\dfrac{\partial p}{\partial t} = Lp$ the transition density $p(t, x, y)$ satisfies the boundary condition

$$\lim_{x \to r} \frac{\partial}{\partial x} p(t, x, y) = 0.$$

From the point of view of boundary conditions on the transition density $p(t, x, y)$, the elastic barrier is simply defined by a linear combination of the conditions of absorption and reflection:

$$\lim_{x \to r} \left[Lp(t, x, y) - \lambda \frac{\partial}{\partial x} p(t, x, y) \right] = 0$$

where $0 \leq \lambda \leq \infty$ is some constant. For $\lambda = 0$ we have pure absorption; if $\lambda = \infty$ we have a reflection on the boundary $x = r$.

The elastic barrier can be interpreted probabilistically if we refer to an approximate model of the diffusion process $\xi(t)$, namely, to the discrete random walk constructed accordingly by stipulating that a particle passes during an interval of time t from a point x to its neighboring points $x \pm \Delta x$, $\Delta x \sim \sigma(x) \sqrt{\Delta t}$, in the positive direction with probability $p(x) \sim \dfrac{1}{2} + \dfrac{a(x)}{2\sigma(x)} \sqrt{\Delta t}$ and in the negative direction with probability $1 - p(x)$.

If, having hit the boundary r, the particle stays there with probability 1 at the next step, too, we are dealing with absorption. If the particle is bound to make a transition from the state r to its neighboring state $x = r + \Delta r$, we are confronted with reflection. If, however, having hit the boundary $x = r$ at the time t the particle stays there with probability $1 - \delta$ at the next step, too, and passes to the neighboring state $x = r + \Delta r$ with probability $\delta \sim \lambda \dfrac{\sqrt{\Delta t}}{\sigma(x)}$, then we are confronted with an elastic barrier.

The transition function $P(t, x, y)$ of the random walk described above is the solution of the finite difference equation

$$P(t + \Delta t, x, y) = p(x) P(t, x + \Delta x, y) + [1 - p(x)] P(t, x - \Delta x, y)$$

with the boundary conditions

$$P(t + \Delta t, r, y) = (1 - \delta) P(t, r, y) + \delta P(t, r + \Delta r, y).$$

For $\Delta t \to 0$ this equation turns into the differential equation $\dfrac{\partial p}{\partial t} = Lp$, and the boundary conditions turn into the boundary conditions of the elastic barrier with parameter λ for a continuous diffusion process.

Recurrent and Non-Recurrent Processes. Let $\xi = \xi(t)$ be a diffusion process in an *open* interval (r_1, r_2), $[c, d]$ a closed interval which lies entirely inside (r_1, r_2), and $\tau_{[c,d]}$ the instant of the first exit from this interval. According to its definition the first exit time from the interval (r_1, r_2) is the random variable

$$\tau_{(r_1, r_2)} = \lim_{n \to \infty} \tau_{[c_n, d_n]},$$

where $\tau_{[c_n, d_n]}$ is the sequence of the first exit times from the closed intervals $[c_n, d_n]$ which converge increasingly to the entire phase space (r_1, r_2).

Any point x with $\sigma(x) > 0$ has a neighborhood (c, d) such that the first exit time $\tau_{(c, d)}$ will be finite with probability 1; moreover, given any ε we can choose the neighborhood (c, d) in such a way that

$$\mathbb{M}_x \tau_{(c, d)} \leq \varepsilon.$$

The trajectory leaves the point x itself instantaneously:

$$\mathbb{P}_x \{\tau_{[x, x]} = 0\} = 1,$$

but also

$$P_x \{\tau_{[c, x]} = \tau_{[x, d]} = 0\} = 1$$

for arbitrary $c \leq x$ and $d \geq x$.

By τ we denote the exit time from the interval (r_1, r_2), that is, $\tau = \tau_{(r_1, r_2)}$. The diffusion process $\xi(t)$ is called *regular* if

$$\mathbb{P}_x \{\tau_{(r_1, c]} < \tau\} > 0, \qquad \mathbb{P}_x \{\tau_{[d, r_2)} < \tau\} > 0,$$

that is, if the trajectory leaves any set of the form $(r_1, c]$ or $[d, r_2)$ with positive probability by passing through the inner points c or d of the interval (r_1, r_2). If this happens with probability 1, the process $\xi(t)$ is called *recurrent*.

The diffusion process $\xi(t)$ will be regular if the diffusion coefficients $\sigma(x)$ do not vanish on (r_1, r_2). If the process $\xi(t)$ is recurrent, then we have with probability 1

$$\varliminf_{t \to \tau} \xi(t) = r_1, \qquad \varlimsup_{t \to \tau} \xi(t) = r_2.$$

If $\xi(t)$ is non-recurrent, then the limit

$$\lim_{t \to \tau} \xi(t) = r$$

exists with probability 1 where r is a boundary point of the interval (r_1, r_2); thus r is either r_1 or r_2.

The boundary point r_i is called *attracting* if the limit r in this context is actually equal to r_i with positive probability; in the opposite case r_i is called a *repelling* boundary. If the process $\xi(t)$ is recurrent, then r_1 and r_2 are both repelling. For a non-recurrent process $\xi(t)$ at least one of the points r_1 and r_2 is repelling.

The character of a boundary point is entirely determined by the behavior of the drift coefficient $a(x)$ and the diffusion coefficient $\sigma(x)$ in its neighborhood. In fact the boundary r_i is attracting if and only if the function

$$R(x) = \exp\left\{ -\int_{x_0}^{x} \frac{a(y)}{b(y)} \, dy \right\}$$

is integrable in the neighborhood of the point $x = r_i$:

$$\left| \int_{x_0}^{r_i} R(x) \, dx \right| < \infty .$$

This analytic condition results from the following facts. If we start with $\xi(t_0) = x, r_1 < c < x < d < r_2$, then the probability that $u(x) = u(x, c, d)$ hits the point c earlier than d represents a solution of the differential equation

$$Lu = 0, \qquad L = a(x) \frac{\partial}{\partial x} + b(x) \frac{\partial^2}{\partial x^2}$$

with the boundary values $u(c) = 1, u(d) = 0$ (see Section 4 of this paragraph). The general solution of this equation is the function

$$u(x) = C_1 \int_{x_0}^{x} R(y) \, dy + C_2$$

where C_1 and C_2 are arbitrary constants. The condition that r_i (say, $r_i = r_1$) is a repelling boundary is tantamount to saying that the probability $u(x, r_1, d) = \lim_{c \to r_1} u(x, c, d)$ of hitting r_1 earlier than d vanishes identically, and this is equivalent to the non-integrability of the function $R(x)$ in the neighborhood of the point r_1. The boundary point r_1 is repelling if and only if the equation $Lu = 0$ has no bounded solution in the interval (r, c) satisfying a given condition $u(c) = u_1$.

In the case of an attracting boundary r_1 the probability $u(x, r_1, d)$ that r_1 is hit earlier than d represents a positive solution of this differential equation with the boundary conditions $u(r_1) = 1, u(d) = 0$.

Example. Assume that the interval (r_1, r_2) is the entire infinite line: $r_1 = -\infty, r_2 = +\infty$, that the diffusion coefficient is uniformly bounded and positive: $0 < \sigma \le \sigma(x) \le C$, and that the drift coefficient $a(x)$ is negative on the positive half-line $x \ge 0$ and positive on the negative half-line $x \le 0$, in other words, the deterministic motion of the process $\xi(t)$ takes always place towards the origin:

$$a(x) \le 0 \quad \text{for} \quad x > 0,$$
$$a(x) \ge 0 \quad \text{for} \quad x < 0.$$

Then the diffusion process $\xi(t)$ will be recurrent since

$$\int_{-\infty}^{x_0} R(x)\,dx = \int_{x_0}^{\infty} R(x)\,dx = \infty.$$

If, however, the drift coefficient $a(x)$ has the same sign as the state x:

$$a(x) \ge 0 \quad \text{for} \quad x > 0,$$
$$a(x) \le 0 \quad \text{for} \quad x < 0,$$

and if $|a(x)|$ does not decrease too fast:

$$\int_{-\infty}^{x_0} R(x)\,dx < \infty \quad \text{and} \quad \int_{x_0}^{\infty} R(x)\,dx < \infty,$$

then $r_1 = -\infty$ and $r_2 = +\infty$ are both attracting boundaries.

Attainable and Unattainable Boundaries. The attracting boundary r_i is called *attainable* if with positive probability the trajectory $\xi(\omega, t)$ passes beyond the boundary r_i after a finite time, that is, the corresponding exit time τ from the interval (r_1, r_2) is finite with positive probability

$$\mathbb{P}_x\left\{\lim_{t \to \tau} \xi(t) = r_i,\ \tau < \infty\right\} > 0.$$

In the opposite case the boundary is called *unattainable.*

If the boundary r_i is attainable, then it can be reached after a finite time by almost all trajectories $\xi(\omega, t)$ that pass by the boundary r_i:

$$\mathbb{P}_x\left\{\lim_{t \to \tau} \xi(t) = r_i,\ \tau < \infty\right\} = \mathbb{P}_x\left\{\lim_{t \to \tau} \xi(t) = r_i\right\}.$$

The boundary r_i is attainable if and only if the function

$$R_1(x) = R(x) \int_{x_0}^{x} \frac{dy}{b(y)\,R(y)} \quad \text{with} \quad R(x) = \exp\left\{-\int_{x_0}^{x} \frac{a(y)}{b(y)}\,dy\right\}$$

is integrable in the neighborhood of the point $x = r_i$:

$$\left|\int_{x_0}^{r_i} R_1(x)\,dx\right| < \infty.$$

This result can be obtained if we investigate the diffusion process $\xi(t)$ which differs from the original process by the fact that at some point $d > r_1$ a reflecting barrier is established. The boundary point r_1 will be attainable or unattainable simultaneously for both processes; also the differential operator L will be the same:

$$L = a(x) \frac{\partial}{\partial x} + b(x) \frac{\partial^2}{\partial x^2}.$$

The boundary point r_1 is attainable if and only if there exists a finite T such that the exit time τ from the half-interval $(r_1, d]$ satisfies the relation

$$\inf_{r_1 < x \leq d} \mathbb{P}_x\{\tau \leq T\} = \mathbb{P}_d\{\tau \leq T\} = p > 0.$$

Then, however, we have

$$\sup_{r_1 < x \leq d} \mathbb{P}_x\{\tau > T\} \leq 1 - p, \quad \mathbb{P}_x\{\tau > nT\} \leq \mathbb{P}_x\{\tau > (n-1)\,T\}\,(1-p),$$

hence

$$\sup_{r_1 < x \leq d} \mathbb{P}_x\{\tau > t\} \leq C e^{-Dt}$$

for some positive constants C and D.

This means, in particular, that the boundary r_1 is attainable if and only if the average time the process with the reflecting barrier takes to reach the boundary is finite:

$$\sup_{r_1 < x \leq d} \mathbb{M}_x \tau < \infty.$$

The function $u(x) = \mathbb{M}_x \tau$, however, is a solution of the equation $Lu = -1$ with the boundary condition $u(r_1) = 0$ which has the general solution

$$u(x) = - \int_{x_0}^{x} R_1(y)\,dy + C_1 \int_{x_0}^{x} R(y)\,dy + C_2$$

(see Section 4 of this paragraph).

Example. Let $r = r_2 = \infty$. If $0 < \sigma < \sigma(x) \leq C$ and if, moreover,

$$|a(x)| \leq C,$$

then the boundary $r_2 = \infty$ is unattainable. If, however, the drift coefficient $a(x)$ increases sufficiently fast for $x \to \infty$, say

$$a(x) \geq C x^{1+\delta} \quad (\delta > 0),$$

then the corresponding function $R_1(x)$ will be integrable on the half-line $[x_0, \infty)$ and hence the boundary r_2 will be attainable.

Example. Let the interval (r_1, r_2) be finite, $a(x) \equiv 0$ and $b(x) > 0$. The boundary r is attainable if and only if the coefficient $b(x)$ does not degenerate too fast when x approaches r in the sense that the function

$$R_1(x) = \int\limits_{x_0}^{x} \frac{dy}{b(y)}$$ is integrable in the neighborhood of this point. In particu-

lar, this will be the case if $b(x) \geq b_0 > 0$.

Ergodic Properties. Let $\xi(t)$ be a recurrent diffusion process in the open interval (r_1, r_2), that is, the trajectory of the process $\xi(t)$ leaves a set $(r_1, c]$ or $[d, r_2)$ with probability 1 via an inner point c or d. This means that r_1 and r_2 are both repelling boundaries.

The condition that both boundaries r_1 and r_2 are repelling can be formulated in terms of the differential operator $L = a(x) \dfrac{\partial}{\partial x} + b(x) \dfrac{\partial^2}{\partial x^2}$

as follows: for any interval (c, d) which is together with its boundary points c and d included in the phase space $E = (r_1, r_2)$ there exists in the open set $E \setminus [c, d]$ only one bounded solution of the equation $Lu = 0$ with given boundary conditions $u(c) = u_1$, $u(d) = u_2$. On each of the half-intervals $(r_1, c]$ and $[d, r_2)$ this solution coincides with the constants $u(x) \equiv u_1$ and the constant $u(x) \equiv u_2$, respectively.

The diffusion process $\xi = \xi(t)$ returns instantaneously to each initial point x:

$$\mathbb{P}_x \left\{ \inf_{\substack{t > \tau_{[x,x]} \\ \xi(t) = x}} t = \tau_{[x,x]} \right\} = 1 .$$

Let τ_1 be the time of the first return to the point x after some point d, $d > x$, was reached, τ_2 the time of the second return to the point x after the point d was reached etc.; thus τ_{n+1} has the same meaning with respect to τ_n as τ_1 has with respect to the initial time $t = 0$. The entire process can be decomposed into cycles which are completed successively during the period of time from τ_n to τ_{n+1}, $n = 0, 1, \ldots$ where $\tau_0 = 0$. The behavior of the process on each interval $\tau_n \leq t \leq \tau_{n+1}$ is subject to one and the same probabilistic law for all $n = 0, 1, \ldots$, and the evolution of the process for $\tau_n \leq t \leq \tau_{n+1}$ does not depend on its behavior until τ_n and after τ_{n+1}.

We denote by $\tau(B)$ the time spent by the trajectory of the process $\xi(t)$ in the Borel set B during one cycle, that is, until it returns at the time τ to the initial point x:

$$\tau(B) = \int\limits_0^{\tau} \varphi_B[\xi(t)] \, dt$$

where

$$\varphi_B(x) = \begin{cases} 1 & \text{for } x \in B, \\ 0 & \text{for } x \notin B. \end{cases}$$

If the set B and its boundary are completely contained in the interval (r_1, r_2), then

$$\mathbb{Q}^0(B) = \mathbb{M}\tau(B) < \infty .$$

This relation defines a σ-finite measure on the interval (r_1, r_2) which is invariant:

$$\mathbb{Q}^0(B) = \int\limits_{r_1}^{r_2} \mathbb{Q}^0(dx)\, P(t, x, B) .$$

Any invariant measure differs from $\mathbb{Q}^0(dx)$ only by a constant factor. For $\mathbb{Q}(B_2) > 0$ we have with probability 1

$$\lim_{T \to \infty} \frac{\int\limits_0^T \varphi_{B_1}[\xi(t)]\, dt}{\int\limits_0^T \varphi_{B_2}[\xi(t)]\, dt} = \frac{\mathbb{Q}^0(B)}{\mathbb{Q}^0(B_2)} ,$$

that is, the ratio of the times the process spends during a large interval $0 \le t \le T$ in the sets B_1 and B_2 of the phase space, respectively, equals approximately the ratio of the measures $\mathbb{Q}^0(B_1)$ and $\mathbb{Q}^0(B_2)$ of these sets.

Stationary Distributions. Suppose that the invariant measure is finite. Then there exists a stationary probability distribution $\mathbb{P}$ on the phase space (r_1, r_2):

$$\mathbb{P}(B) = \int\limits_{r_1}^{r_2} \mathbb{P}(dx)\, P(t, x, B) .$$

In this case the transition function $P(t, x, B)$ of the process $\xi(t)$ has the property that

$$\lim_{t \to \infty} P(t, x, B) = \mathbb{P}(B)$$

for any Borel set B and all $x \in (r_1, r_2)$. This means that after a long period of time the process $\xi(t)$ is subject to *stationary* probability laws. The stationary limit process $\xi = \xi(t)$ is the same as if we would have started with a stationary initial probability distribution $\mathbb{P}(dx)$.

A necessary and sufficient condition in order that a finite invariant measure, that is, a stationary probability distribution $\mathbb{P}$ exists, consists in the fact that the waiting time for a return to the initial point x be finite:

$$\mathbb{M}\tau < \infty .$$

This relation is true or false simultaneously for all inner points x of the interval (r_1, r_2).

An analytical condition for the existence of a stationary distribution consists in the integrability of the function

$$R_2(x) = \frac{1}{b(x)\, R(x)} \quad \text{with} \quad R(x) = \exp\left\{-\int_{x_0}^{x} \frac{a(y)}{b(y)}\, dy\right\} : \int_{r_1}^{r_2} R_2(x)\, dx < \infty.$$

This condition is obtained in the following way. The function $u(x) = \mathbb{M}_x \tau_d$ where τ_d denotes the instant when the point d is reached for the first time, is a solution of the differential equation

$$Lu = -1, \quad L = a(x)\frac{\partial}{\partial x} + b(x)\frac{\partial^2}{\partial x^2}$$

with the boundary condition $u(d) = 0$ (see Section 4 of this paragraph). The general solution of this equation has the form

$$u(x) = -\int_{x_0}^{x} R_1(y)\, dy + C_1 \int_{x_0}^{x} R(y)\, dy + C_2$$

where

$$R_1(x) = R(x) \int_{x_0}^{x} \frac{dy}{b(y)\, R(y)}$$

and C_1, C_2 are arbitrary constants.

The expectation $\mathbb{M}\tau$ of the return time to x under consideration will be finite if and only if

$$\varlimsup_{c \to r_1} u(x, c, d)\mathbb{M}_c \tau_d < \infty, \quad \varlimsup_{d \to r_2} u(x, d, c)\mathbb{M}_d \tau_c < \infty,$$

where

$$u(x, c, d) = \mathbb{P}_x\{\tau_c < \tau_d\}$$

stands for the probability of reaching the point c earlier than d, and is given by the formula

$$u(x, c, d) = \int_{c}^{x} R(y)\, dy \left/ \int_{c}^{d} R(y)\, dy\right. .$$

The relations stated above are equivalent to the integrability of the function $R_2(x)$.

Assume that the stationary distribution $\mathbb{P}$ is define by a density $p = p(x)$. Then

$$p(y) = \int_{r_1}^{r_1} p(x)\, p(t, x, y)\, dx .$$

If differentiation with respect to t and two-fold differentiation with respect to x is possible under the integral sign, then the density of the stationary distribution $p(x)$ satisfies the following differential equation:

$$L^* p \equiv -\frac{\partial}{\partial x}[a(x)\,p(x)] + \frac{\partial^2}{\partial x^2}[b(x)\,p(x)] = 0 .$$

Example. Let the phase space be the entire infinite line ($r_1 = -\infty$ and $r_2 = +\infty$), and assume that the coefficients $a(x)$ and $b(x)$ have the following form:

$$a(x) = a_0 + a_1 x , \qquad b(x) = b_0 + b_1 x + b_2 x^2$$

where a_0, a_1 and b_0, b_1, b_2 are some constants ($a_1 < 0, b_2 > 0$). In this case a stationary probability distribution exists with a density $p(x)$ which satisfies the equation

$$\frac{p'(x)}{p(x)} = \frac{x - c_0}{d_0 + d_1 x + d_2 x^2}$$

where

$$c_0 = \frac{b_1 - a_0}{a_1 - 2b_2} , \quad d_0 = \frac{b_0}{a_1 - 2b_2} , \quad d_1 = \frac{b_1}{a_1 - 2b_2} , \quad d_2 = \frac{b_2}{a_1 - 2b_2} .$$

Its solutions for various c_0 and d_0, d_1, d_2 are the densities of the so-called *Pearson distributions*.

3. Transformations of Diffusion Processes

Transformations of the Phase Space. By a one-to-one transformation $\tilde{x} = \varphi(x)$ of the phase space a Markov process $\xi = \xi(t)$ with the transition function $P(s, x, t, B)$ is transformed into a random process $\tilde{\xi} = \tilde{\xi}(t)$ which is again a Markov process with a transition function $\tilde{P}(s, \tilde{x}, t, \tilde{B})$:

$$\tilde{\xi}(t) = \varphi[\xi(t)] , \qquad \tilde{P}(s, \tilde{x}, t, \tilde{B}) = P(s, x, t, \{\varphi \in \tilde{B}\}) .$$

In the homogeneous case such a transformation always enables us to pass from a diffusion process $\xi(t)$ with arbitrary drift coefficient $a(x)$ and diffusion coefficient $\sigma(x)$ to a diffusion process $\tilde{\xi}(t)$ with corresponding coefficients $\tilde{a}$ and $\tilde{\sigma}$. As functions of the original variable x these coefficients have the form

$$\tilde{a}(x) = a(x)\,\varphi' + b(x)\,\varphi'' , \qquad b(x) = \frac{1}{2}\sigma^2(x) ,$$
$$[\tilde{\sigma}(x)]^2 = \sigma^2(x)\,[\varphi'(x)]^2 .$$

If, in particular, we choose the transformation $\tilde{x} = \varphi(x)$ in such a way that the equation

$$\varphi'(x) = R(x) = \exp\left\{-\int_{x_0}^{x} \frac{a(y)}{b(y)}\, dy\right\}$$

holds, then we obtain a process $\tilde{\xi}(t)$ with a vanishing drift coefficient:

$$\tilde{a}(x) \equiv 0 .$$

Setting

$$\varphi'(x) = \frac{1}{\sigma(x)}$$

we obtain a process $\tilde{\xi}(t)$ with the diffusion coefficient 1:

$$\tilde{\sigma}(x) \equiv 1 .$$

Random Substitution of Time. Consider the trajectories $\xi(\omega, t)$ of the diffusion process $\xi = \xi(t)$ individually. They describe the motion of a particle along a single trajectory $\xi(\omega, t)$ chosen at random. Having chosen a trajectory we change the speed of motion of the particle by introducing a new scale of time as follows. For each outcome ω, that is, each trajectory $\xi(\omega, t)$ we introduce a transformation of time $\tau = \tau(\omega, t)$ by the formula

$$\frac{d\tau}{dt} = \frac{1}{V[t, \xi(\omega, \tau)]}$$

where $V = V(t, x)$ is a positive function, and we define the random process $\tilde{\xi} = \tilde{\xi}(t)$ by setting

$$\tilde{\xi}(\omega, t) = \xi[\omega, \tau(\omega, t)] .$$

The process $\tilde{\xi} = \tilde{\xi}(t)$ obtained by means of such a *random time substitution* will be Markovian. Roughly speaking, the difference between the new process $\tilde{\xi} = \tilde{\xi}(t)$ and the initial process $\xi = \xi(t)$ is that when the particle on its random walk leaves a point x at the time t it moves $\dfrac{1}{V(t, x)}$ times faster during the next infinitely small interval of time Δt. The drift coefficient $\tilde{a}(t, x)$ and the diffusion coefficient $\tilde{\sigma}(t, x)$ of the new process $\tilde{\xi} = \tilde{\xi}(t)$ are connected with the corresponding coefficients of the original diffusion process as follows:

$$\tilde{a}(t, x) = \frac{a(t, x)}{V(t, x)}, \quad \tilde{\sigma}(t, x) = \frac{\sigma(t, x)}{\sqrt{V(t, x)}} .$$

Transformations Connected with Additive Functionals. Let $\xi = \xi(t)$ be a diffusion process with the transition function $P(s, x, t, B)$, and $\mathfrak{A}(s, t)$ the σ-algebra generated by the events of the form $\{\xi(u) \in B\}$, $s \leq u \leq t$. Denote by $\mathbb{P}_{s,x} = \mathbb{P}_{s,x}(A)$ the corresponding conditional probability distributions on $\mathfrak{A}(s, \infty)$ and by $\mathbb{M}_{s,x}(\cdot)$ the corresponding expectations.

A family of real or complex-valued variables $\varphi = \varphi_s^t(\omega)$ which depend on the parameters $s \leq t$ determines a so-called *additive functional* of the process $\xi = \xi(t)$ if each $\varphi_s^t = \varphi_s^t(\omega)$ is measurable with respect to the corresponding σ-algebra $\mathfrak{A}(s, t)$ and if for any $s \leq u \leq t$ we have with probability 1

$$\varphi_s^u + \varphi_u^t = \varphi_s^t.$$

Let $\varphi = \varphi_s^t(\omega)$ be an arbitrary additive functional such that

$$\mathbb{M}_{s,x} \exp\{-\varphi_s^t(\omega)\} < \infty$$

for all s and t. Then the relations

$$\tilde{P}(s, x, t, B) = \int_{\{\xi(t) \in B\}} \exp\{-\varphi_s^t(\omega)\} \, \mathbb{P}_{s,x}(d\omega) \qquad (4.2)$$

define a family of generalized distributions on the Borel sets B in the phase space which satisfy the Chapman-Kolmogorov equation:

$$\tilde{P}(\tilde{s}, x, t, B) = \int_{-\infty}^{\infty} \tilde{P}(s, x, u, dy) \, \tilde{P}(u, y, t, B) \qquad (s \leq u \leq t).$$

Like the transition functions of a Markov process, the "transition functions" $\tilde{P}(s, x, t, B)$, too, define generalized distributions $\tilde{\mathbb{P}}_{s,x} = \tilde{\mathbb{P}}_{s,x}(A)$ on the σ-algebra $\mathfrak{A}(s, \infty)$:

$$\tilde{\mathbb{P}}_{s,x}\{\xi(t_1) \in B_1, \ldots, \xi(t_n) \in B_n\}$$
$$= \int_{B_1} \cdots \int_{B_{n-1}} \tilde{P}(s, x, t_1, dx_1) \, \tilde{P}(t_1, x_1, t_2, dx_2) \ldots \tilde{P}(t_{n-1}, x_{n-1}, t_n, B_n).$$

The generalized distribution $\tilde{\mathbb{P}}_{s,x} = \tilde{\mathbb{P}}_{s,x}(A)$ considered on the σ-algebra of events $\mathfrak{A}(s, t)$ for finite s and t is absolutely continuous with respect to the original probability distribution $\mathbb{P}_{s,x} = \mathbb{P}_{s,x}(A)$, and the corresponding density $p(\omega) = \dfrac{\tilde{\mathbb{P}}_{s,x}(d\omega)}{\mathbb{P}_{s,x}(d\omega)}$ has the form $p(\omega) = \exp\{-\varphi_s^t(\omega)\}$.

Change of the Drift Coefficient. Let $\xi = \xi(t)$ be a diffusion process described by the Ito stochastic differential equation

$$d\xi(t) = a[t, \xi(t)] \, dt + \sigma[t, \xi(t)] \, d\eta(t),$$

and let $\varphi = \varphi_s^t(\omega)$ be an additive functional of the form

$$\varphi_s^t(\omega) = \int_s^t \frac{\tilde{a}[u, \xi(u)] - a[u, \xi(u)]}{\sigma[u, \xi(u)]} \, d\eta(u)$$

$$- \frac{1}{2} \int_s^t \left\{ \frac{\tilde{a}[u, \xi(u)] - a[u, \xi(u)]}{\sigma[u, \xi(u)]} \right\}^2 du \, .$$

Then the transformation (4.2) defines the transition functions $\tilde{P}(s, x, t, B)$ of a diffusion process $\tilde{\xi} = \tilde{\xi}(t)$ with the drift coefficient $\tilde{a}(t, x)$ and the same diffusion coefficient $\sigma(t, x)$ as the original process $\xi = \xi(t)$. The corresponding probability distribution $\tilde{\mathbb{P}}_{s,x} = \tilde{\mathbb{P}}_{s,x}(A)$ on the σ-algebra $\mathfrak{A}(s, t)$ is absolutely continuous with respect to the original distribution $\mathbb{P}_{s,x} = \mathbb{P}_{s,x}(A)$, and the density $p(\omega) = \dfrac{\tilde{\mathbb{P}}_{s,x}(d\omega)}{\mathbb{P}_{s,x}(d\omega)}$ has the form

$$p(\omega) = \exp \left\{ - \int_s^t \frac{\tilde{a}[u, \xi(u)] - a[u, \xi(u)]}{\sigma[u, \xi(u)]} \, d\eta(u) \right.$$

$$\left. + \frac{1}{2} \int_s^t \left\{ \frac{\tilde{a}[u, \xi(u)] - a[u, \xi(u)]}{\sigma[u, \xi(u)]} \right\}^2 du \right\} .$$

Thus by the transformation of the probability distribution described before the diffusion process $\xi = \xi(t)$ can be converted into another diffusion process $\tilde{\xi} = \tilde{\xi}(t)$ with an arbitrary drift coefficient $\tilde{a}(t, x)$ and the same diffusion coefficient $\tilde{\sigma}(t, x) = \sigma(t, x)$. It is impossible to pass by a similar transformation to a process $\tilde{\xi} = \tilde{\xi}(t)$ whose diffusion coefficient $\tilde{\sigma}(t, x)$ differs from the initial coefficient $\sigma(t, x)$. Any diffusion process can be obtained from the Brownian motion process by transforming the probability distribution in the way described above and then substituting the time at random.

Terminating a Process. Suppose that we are given a diffusion process $\xi = \xi(t)$, and that $\tau = \tau(\omega)$ is the exit time from the interval (r_1, r_2). We define an additive functional $\varphi = \varphi_s^t(\omega)$ as follows:

$$\varphi_s^t(\omega) = \begin{cases} \infty , & \text{if } \ t > \tau(\omega) , \\ 0 , & \text{if } \ t \leq \tau(\omega) . \end{cases}$$

The transformation (4.2) which corresponds to this functional can be rewritten in a more suitable form:

$$\tilde{P}(s, x, t, B) = \int_{\{\xi(t) \in B\}} \varphi_{t \leq \tau}(\omega) \, \mathbb{P}_{s,x}(d\omega) = \int_{\{\xi(t) \in B, \, t \leq \tau\}} \mathbb{P}_{s,x}(d\omega)$$

where

$$\varphi_{t \le \tau}(\omega) = \begin{cases} 0, & \text{if } t > \tau(\omega), \\ 1, & \text{if } t \le \tau(\omega). \end{cases}$$

This transformation defines the transition functions of a new process $\tilde{\xi} = \tilde{\xi}(t)$ which is obtained by terminating $\xi = \xi(t)$ after the instant τ. The probability distributions $\tilde{\mathbb{P}}_{s,x} = \tilde{\mathbb{P}}_{s,x}(A)$ are absolutely continuous with respect to the original distribution $\mathbb{P}_{s,x} = \mathbb{P}_{s,x}(A)$ on each of the σ-algebras $\mathfrak{A}(s, t)$, $t < \infty$, and the density $p(\omega) = \dfrac{\tilde{\mathbb{P}}_{s,x}(d\omega)}{\mathbb{P}_{s,x}(d\omega)}$ has the form

$$p(\omega) = \varphi_{t \le \tau}(\omega).$$

The terminated diffusion process $\tilde{\xi} = \tilde{\xi}(t)$ has the same drift and diffusion coefficients:

$$\tilde{a}(t, x) = a(t, x), \qquad \tilde{\sigma}(t, x) = \sigma(t, x)$$

for all t and $x \in (r_1, r_2)$. The transition function $\tilde{P}(s, x, t, B)$ is given by $\tilde{P}(s, x, t, B) \equiv 0$ for $x \notin (r_1, r_2)$.

A termination time of another kind can be defined in the following way. Each trajectory $\xi(\omega, t)$ of the original process $\xi = \xi(t)$, when taking the value $\xi(\omega, t) = x$ terminates during the following period of time Δt with probability $V(t, x) \Delta t + o(\Delta t)$ where $V = V(t, x) \ge 0$ is the so-called *termination-density*. The random process $\tilde{\xi} = \tilde{\xi}(t)$ obtained in this way terminates at some random instant τ. We get the transition function of this process $\tilde{\xi} = \tilde{\xi}(t)$ by a transformation of the type (4.2) with an additive functional of the form

$$\varphi_s^t(\omega) = \int_s^t V[u, \xi(u)] \, du.$$

The random process $\tilde{\xi} = \tilde{\xi}(t)$ terminates at the random instant τ, which we can find by looking at the extended space of elementary events $\tilde{\Omega} = \Omega \times (-\infty, \infty)$ whose points are the pairs $\tilde{\omega} = (\omega, \lambda)$ with $\omega \in \Omega$, $-\infty < \lambda < \infty$. To this end we set $\tau(\tilde{\omega}) = \lambda$ for $\tilde{\omega} = (\omega, \lambda)$, and define the conditional distribution by the formula

$$\tilde{\mathbb{P}}\{\tau > t \,|\, \xi(u), \, s \le u \le t\} = \exp\left\{ -\int_s^t V[u, \xi(u)] \, du \right\}.$$

On the extended space $\tilde{\Omega}$ the terminated process $\tilde{\xi} = \tilde{\xi}(t)$ can be defined by

$$\tilde{\xi}(\tilde{\omega}, t) = \xi(\omega, t) \quad \text{for} \quad \tilde{\omega} = (\omega, \lambda)$$

where $t < \lambda$. Given this definition we have

$$\tilde{P}(s, x, t, B) = \tilde{\mathbb{P}}_{s,x}\{\xi(t) \in B, \tau > t\}$$
$$= \int_{\{\xi(t) \in B\}} \exp\left\{ -\int_s^t V[u, \xi(u)] \, du \right\} \mathbb{P}_{s,x}(d\omega).$$

Let

$$L = a(s, x) \frac{\partial}{\partial x} + b(s, x) \frac{\partial}{\partial x^2}, \qquad b(s, x) = \frac{1}{2} \sigma^2(s, x)$$

be the differential operator in the backward Kolmogorov equation for the diffusion process $\xi = \xi(t)$. Under the conditions defined above (see Section 1 of this paragraph) the function $u(s, x) = \int \varphi(y) P(s, x, t, dy)$ satisfies the differential equation

$$-\frac{\partial u}{\partial s} = a(s, x) \frac{\partial u}{\partial x} + b(s, x) \frac{\partial^2 u}{\partial x^2} .$$

We set

$$\tilde{u}(s, x) = \int \varphi(y) \, \tilde{P}(s, x, t, dy)$$

where $\tilde{P}(s, x, t, B)$ is the transition function of the terminated diffusion process $\tilde{\xi} = \tilde{\xi}(t)$ with the termination density $V = V(t, x)$. If termination density V is bounded and continuous at the point (s, x), the corresponding function $\tilde{u} = \tilde{u}(s, x)$ satisfies the differential equation

$$-\frac{\partial \tilde{u}}{\partial s} = a(s, x) \frac{\partial \tilde{u}}{\partial x} + b(s, x) \frac{\partial^2 \tilde{u}}{\partial x^2} - V(s, x) \tilde{u} ,$$

that is, the differential operator $\tilde{L}$ corresponding to the process $\tilde{\xi} = \tilde{\xi}(t)$ equals $\tilde{L} = L - V$.

We can gain an insight in to this transformation of the differential operator if we consider again the discrete model of the diffusion process $\xi = \xi(t)$ (see Section 1 of this paragraph). In fact, suppose that at the time s the wandering particle moves from the point x by the quantity $\Delta x \sim \sigma(s, x) \sqrt{\Delta t}$ with probability $p(s, x) \sim \frac{1}{2} + \frac{a(s, x)}{2\sigma(s, x)} \sqrt{\Delta t}$, by the quantity $-\Delta x$ with probability $1 - p(s, x) - V(s, x) \Delta t$ and vanishes from the phase space under consideration with probability $V(s, x) \Delta t$. Then the finite difference relation

$$\tilde{u}(s, x) \sim p(s, x) \tilde{u}(s + \Delta t, x + \Delta x)$$
$$+ [1 - p(s, x)] \tilde{u}(s + \Delta t, x - \Delta x) - V(s, x) \tilde{u}(s, x) \Delta t$$

is the analogue to the differential equation $-\dfrac{\partial \tilde{u}}{\partial s} = \tilde{L}\tilde{u}$.

4. The Kolmogorov Backward Equation and the Probability Distribution of Some Functionals of a Diffusion Process

Let $\xi = \xi(t)$ be a diffusion process in the finite or infinite interval (r_1, r_2) whose transition density $p(s, x, t, y)$ satisfies the backward Kolmogorov equation:

$$- \frac{\partial p}{\partial s} = Lp, \qquad L = a(s, x) \frac{\partial}{\partial x} + b(s, x) \frac{\partial^2}{\partial x^2},$$

where $a(s, x)$ and $b(s, x)$ are continuous and $b(s, x) > 0$. Let τ be the exit time from some interval (c, d) in the phase space, and $\varphi(x)$ a function on its boundary. The mean value

$$u(s, x) = \mathbb{M}_{s, x} \varphi[\xi(\tau)],$$

where $\mathbb{M}_{s, x}(\cdot)$ is the expectation which corresponds to the conditional distribution $\mathbb{P}_{s, x}$, satisfies the differential equation

$$- \frac{\partial u}{\partial s} = Lu$$

with the boundary conditions

$$u(s, c) = \varphi(c), \qquad u(s, d) = \varphi(d).$$

If $\varphi(c) = 1$ and $\varphi(d) = 0$, the solution $u(s, x) = u(s, x, c, d)$ coincides with the probability that the point c is reached earlier than d.

The differential equation for $u(s, x)$ follows from the functional relation

$$u(s, x) = \int_{r_1}^{r_2} u(t, y) \, P(s, x, t, dy)$$

where $P(s, x, t, B)$ is the transition function of the diffusion process $\xi = \xi(t)$ for which the boundary points c and d are absorbing, that is, the process $\xi = \xi(t)$ stops when leaving the interval under consideration.

Differential Equations for Characteristic Functions. Let $V(t, x)$ be a real or complex-valued bounded function. The variable

$$u(s, x) = \mathbb{M}_{s, x} \exp \left[- \int_s^\tau V[t, \xi(t)] \, dt \right] \varphi[\xi(\tau)]$$

where τ is the exit time from the interval (c, d), satisfies the functional relation

$$u(s, x) = \int_{r_1}^{r_2} u(t, y) \, \tilde{P}(s, x, t, dy)$$

in which $\tilde{P}(s, x, t, B)$ denotes the "transition function" of the form

$$\tilde{P}(s, x, t, B) = \int_{\{\xi(t) \in B, t \le \tau\}} \exp \left\{ - \int_s^t V[u, \xi(u)] \, du \right\} \mathbb{P}_{s, x}(d\omega).$$

Under certain conditions (see Section 1 of this paragraph) the function $u(s, x)$ also satisfies the differential equation

$$-\frac{\partial u}{\partial s} = a(s, x)\frac{\partial u}{\partial x} + b(s, x)\frac{\partial^2 u}{\partial x^2} - V(s, x)\,u$$

with the boundary conditions

$$u(s, a) = \varphi(c)\,, \qquad u(s, b) = \varphi(d)\,.$$

If $V(t, x) = -i\lambda\psi(t, x)$ where $\psi(t, x)$ is a real function, then

$$u(s, x, \lambda) = \mathbb{M}_{s,x}\exp\left\{i\lambda\int_s^\tau \psi[t, \xi(t)]\,dt\right\}$$

considered as a function of λ, $-\infty < \lambda < \infty$, is the characteristic function of the variable $\Psi = \int_s^\tau \psi[t, \xi(t)]\,dt$, and satisfies for fixed λ the differential equation

$$-\frac{\partial u}{\partial s} = a(s, x)\frac{\partial u}{\partial x} + b(s, x)\frac{\partial^2 u}{\partial x^2} + i\lambda\psi(s, x)\,u,$$

$$u(s, c, \lambda) = u(s, d, \lambda) = 1\,.$$

All that had been said before remains true if the time τ appearing in the expressions for the various functions $u(s, x)$ is not the exit time from some interval but simply a constant variable $\tau = t$. In this case the boundary conditions on the functions $u(s, x)$ have to be replaced by the corresponding "final" values:

$$u(t, x) = \varphi(x)\,.$$

The same remains also true for the exit time τ from an interval (c, d) whose boundary points may coincide with the boundary points r_1 and r_2 of the phase space provided that c and d are both attainable.

Differential Equations for Mathematical Expectations. Let

$$v(s, x) = \mathbb{M}_{s,x}\int_s^\tau \psi[u, \xi(u)]\,du$$

where τ is either the exit time from some interval (c, d) or a constant $\tau \geq s$. The following functional relation holds:

$$v(s, x) = \int_{r_1}^{r_2} v(t, y)\,\tilde{P}(s, x, t, dy) + \tilde{\mathbb{M}}_{s,x}\int_s^t \psi[u, \xi(u)]\,du$$

where $\tilde{P}(s, x, t, B)$ is the transition function of the process $\tilde{\xi} = \tilde{\xi}(t)$ obtained from the original diffusion process $\xi = \xi(t)$ by stopping after the instant τ. Under certain conditions (the function ψ is bounded and continuous) the function $v(s, x)$ has bounded and continuous derivatives $\dfrac{\partial v}{\partial x}$ and $\dfrac{\partial^2 v}{\partial x^2}$ and the differential relation

$$-\frac{\partial v}{\partial s} = a(s, x)\frac{\partial v}{\partial x} + b(s, x)\frac{\partial^2 v}{\partial x^2} + \psi(s, x)$$

holds with the boundary conditions

$$v(s, c) = v(s, d) = 0$$

if τ is the exist time from the interval (c, d), or

$$v(t, x) = 0$$

if $\tau = t$ is a constant.

5. Multi-Dimensional Diffusion Processes

By a *multi-dimensional diffusion process* we usually mean a continuous Markov process

$$\xi(t) = \{\xi_1(t), \xi_2(t), \ldots, \xi_n(t)\}$$

whose phase space is the n-dimensional vector space E^n and whose transition function $P(s, x, t, B)$ satisfies the following conditions: for any $\varepsilon > 0$

$$\lim_{t \to 0} \frac{1}{\Delta t} \int_{|y-x|>\varepsilon} P(t, x, t+\Delta t, dy) = 0,$$

$$\lim_{t \to 0} \frac{1}{\Delta t} \int_{|y-x|<\varepsilon} (y_k - x_k) P(t, x, t+\Delta t, dy) = a_k(t, x) \quad (k = 1, \ldots, n),$$

$$\lim_{t \to 0} \frac{1}{\Delta t} \int_{|y-x|<\varepsilon} (y_k - x_k)(y_j - x_j) P(t, x, t+\Delta t, dy) = 2b_{kj}(t, x) \quad (k, j = 1, \ldots, n).$$

The vector $a = \{a_1(t, x), \ldots, a_n(t, x)\}$ characterizes the local drift of the process $\xi(t)$, and the matrix $\sigma^2 = (2b_{kj}(t, x))$, $j, k = 1, \ldots, n$, describes the mean square deviation of the random process $\xi(t)$ from the original position x during a short period of time from t to $t + \Delta t$.

Under additional restrictions the transition density $p(s, x, t, y)$ of the diffusion process satisfies the *backward and forward Kolmogorov differential equation*:

$$\frac{\partial p}{\partial s} = -\sum_{k=1}^{n} a_k(s, x)\frac{\partial p}{\partial x_k} - \sum_{k,j=1}^{n} b_{kj}(s, x)\frac{\partial^2 p}{\partial x_k \partial x_j},$$

$$\frac{\partial p}{\partial t} = -\sum_{k=1}^{n} \frac{\partial}{\partial y_k}[a_k(t, y) p] + \sum_{k,j=1}^{n} \frac{\partial^2}{\partial y_k \partial y_j}[b_{kj}(t, y) p].$$

The local behavior of the diffusion process $\xi(t)$ can be described in terms of the Ito stochastic differential equations:

$$d\xi_k(t) = a_k[t, \xi(t)]\, dt + \sum_{j=1}^{n} \sigma_{kj}[t, \xi(t)]\, d\eta_j(t) \quad (k = 1, \ldots, n)$$

where $\eta_1(t), \ldots, \eta_n(t)$ are mutually independent Brownian motion processes, and the vectors

$$\sigma_j = \{\sigma_{1j}(t, x), \ldots, \sigma_{nj}(t, x)\} \quad (j = 1, \ldots, n)$$

are eigenvectors of the matrix $\sigma^2 = (2b_{kj}(t, x))$.

Example. *Stationary Gaussian Processes with Rational Spectral Densities.* Let $\xi_0(t)$ be a stationary Gaussian process with the rational spectral density $f(\lambda) = |Q(\lambda)|^{-2}$. The multi-dimensional stationary process $\xi(t) = \{\xi_k(t)\}_{\overline{k=0,\ldots,n-1}}$ whose components are the original process $\xi_0(t)$ and all its derivatives $\xi_k(t) = \xi^{(k)}(t)$, $k = 1, \ldots, n-1$ is a homogeneous Markov process. Its transition function $P(t, x, B)$ represents for fixed t and x a Gaussian probability distribution with the mean values

$$A(t, x) = C(t)\, x = \left\{ \sum_{j=0}^{n-1} C_{kj}(t)\, x_j \right\}_{k = \overline{0, n-1}}$$

and a correlation matrix $(B_{kj}(t))$ which coincides with the correlation matrix of the components of the vector $\xi(t) - C(t)\, \xi(0)$, where $C(t) = (C_{kj}(t))$ is the matrix yielding the *best prediction*. In other words the differences $\xi_k(t) - \sum_{j=0}^{n-1} C_{kj}(t)\, \xi_j(0)$ are orthogonal to all values $\xi_0(s)$, $s \leq 0$.

Let $z_1, z_2, \ldots, z_n$ be the zeros of the polynomial $|Q(\lambda)|^2$ in the upper half-plane $\operatorname{Im} z \geq 0$. If they are all different of each other, the elements of the matrix $C(t) = (C_{kj}(t))$ can be obtained from the following system of linear equations:

$$\sum_{j=0}^{n-1} (i z_q)^{j-k}\, C_{kj} = e^{i z_q t} \quad (q = 1, \ldots, n; \; k = 0, \ldots, n-1).$$

The local drift coefficients of the afore-mentioned multi-dimensional diffusion process $\xi = \xi(t)$ are

$$a_k(x) = \sum_{j=0}^{n-1} c_{kj} x_j \quad (k = 0, 1, \ldots, n-1)$$

where the coefficients $c_{kj} = C'_{kj}(0)$ satisfy systems of linear equations of the form

$$\sum_{j=0}^{n-1} (i z_q)^{j-k-1}\, c_{kj} = 1 \quad (q = 1, \ldots, n; \; k = 0, \ldots, n-1).$$

The diffusion matrix $\sigma^2(x) = 2(b_{kj}(x))$ of the process $\xi = \xi(t)$ is degenerate; only the last diagonal element $b = b_{n-1,n-1}$ differs from zero:

$$b = \frac{1}{2} B'_{n-1,n-1}(0).$$

The stochastic differential equations have the form

$$d\xi_k(t) = a_k(x)\,dt \quad (k = 0, \ldots, n-2),$$
$$d\xi_{n-1}(t) = a_{n-1}(x)\,dt + \sigma\,d\eta(t), \quad \sigma = \sqrt{B'_{n-1,n-1}(0)}.$$

The corresponding differential operator in the backward Kolmogorov equation is

$$L = \sum_{k=0}^{n-1} a_k(x) \frac{\partial}{\partial x_k} + b \frac{\partial^2}{\partial x_{n-1} \partial x_{n-1}}.$$

Conditional Markov Processes. Let $\xi_1(t)$ be a diffusion process controlled by the stochastic differential equation

$$d\xi_1(t) = a_1[\xi_1(t), t]\,dt + \sigma_{11}[\xi_1(t), t]\,d\eta_1(t)$$

and suppose that the process $\xi_2(t)$ is connected with $\xi_1(t)$ as follows:

$$d\xi_2(t) = a_2[\xi_1(t), \xi_2(t), t]\,dt + \sigma_{21}[\xi_1(t), \xi_2(t), t]\,d\eta_1(t)$$
$$+ \sigma_{22}[\xi_1(t), \xi_2(t), t]\,d\eta_2(t)$$

where $\eta_1(t)$ and $\eta_2(t)$ are independent Brownian motion processes. Then $\xi_1(t)$ and $\xi_2(t)$ form a two-dimensional Markov process $\{\xi_1(t), \xi_2(t)\}$.

We assume that for some reasons the random process $\xi_2(t)$ cannot be observed by the investigator and that its behavior can be judged only from observations of the process $\xi_1(t)$. Then we may regard as a characteristic of the non-observed process either the conditional transition function

$$P(s, x, t, B, \omega) = \mathbb{P}\{\xi_2(t) \in B \mid \xi_2(s) = x, \xi_1(u), s \leq u \leq t\}$$

or the so-called *a posteriori probability distribution* of the unknown variable $\xi_2(t)$ at the present time t which is defined like this:

$$\pi(s, t, B, \omega) = \int_E \mathbb{P}_s(dx)\, P(s, x, t, B, \omega)$$

where $\mathbb{P}_s(dx)$ is the *(a priori)* distribution of the initial variable $\xi_2(s)$. We are mainly interested in the evolution of the a posteriori distribution $\pi(s, t, B, \omega)$ in the course of time t.

We assume that for each elementary event ω connected with the behavior of the process $\xi_1(t)$ under observation the conditional transition function $P(s, x, t, B, \omega)$ has the density

$$p(s, x, t, y, \omega) = \frac{P(s, x, t, dy, \omega)}{dy}.$$

The investigation of the evolution of the function $p(s, x, t, ...)$ in the course of time t like that of the ordinary transition function can be based on the following functional relation:

$$p(s, x, t_1 + t_2, y, \omega) = \int p(s, x, t_1, y_1, \omega) \, p(t_1, y_1, t_1 + t_2, y, \omega) \, dy_1.$$

Assuming that the processes under consideration are homogeneous with respect to the a posteriori distribution density

$$\pi(t, y, \omega) = \int_E \mathbb{P}_s(dx) \, p(s, x, t, y, \omega)$$

of the unobserved variable $\xi_2(t)$ we obtain the following stochastic equation:

$$
\begin{aligned}
d\pi(t, y) = {} & \frac{1}{2} \frac{\partial^2}{\partial y_2} \{[\sigma_{21}^2(\xi_1(t), y) + \sigma_{22}^2(\xi_1(t), y)] \, \pi(t, y)\} \, dt \\
& - \frac{\partial}{\partial y} \{a_2(\xi_1(t), y) \, \pi(t, y)\} \, dt \\
& - \frac{\partial}{\partial y} \{\sigma_{21}(\xi_1(t), y) \, \pi(t, y)\} \, d\eta_1(t).
\end{aligned}
$$

For fixed y the conditional density $\pi(t, y)$ as a random function of t forms together with $\xi_1(t)$ a two-dimensional diffusion process which we call a conditional Markov process.

Let $\xi_1(t)$ be a Markov process which takes only a finite number of states numbered from 1 to n. Suppose that the transition densities $\lambda_{ij}(t)$ from a state i to a state j do not depend on the behavior of a certain random process $\xi_2(t)$ which is controlled by a stochastic differential equation of the form

$$d\xi_2(t) = a[t, \xi_1(t), \xi_2(t)] \, dt + \sigma[t, \xi_2(t)] \, d\eta(t)$$

where $\eta(t)$ is a Brownian motion process which does not depend on the process $\xi_1(t)$. We assume that for some reasons the random process $\xi_1(t)$ cannot be observed by the investigator and that conclusions on its state at the time t can only be drawn from observations of the process $\xi_2(t)$, $s \leq t$, where $\xi_2(s)$ and $\xi_1(t)$ form a two-dimensional Markov process $\{\xi_1(t), \xi_2(t)\}$.

If $P_s(k) = \mathbb{P}\{\xi_1(s) = k\}$, $k = 1, ..., n$ is the probability distribution of the non-observed process $\xi_1(s)$ at the initial moment s, then the a posteriori probabilities

$$\pi_j(t) = \sum_{k=1}^{n} P_s(k) \, \mathbb{P}\{\xi_1(t) = j \mid \xi_1(s) = k, \xi_2(s), s \le t\} \qquad (j = 1, \ldots, n)$$

together with the observed process $\xi_2(t)$ form a so-called *conditional Markov process*, whose evolution in the course of time t is described by the following stochastic differential equations:

$$d\pi_j(t)$$
$$= \left\{ \sum_{k=1}^{n} \pi_k(t) \lambda_{kj}(t) - \pi_j(t) \frac{a_j[t, \xi_2(t)] - \sum_{k=1}^{n} \pi_k(t) a_k[t, \xi_2(t)]}{\sigma^2[t, \xi_2(t)]} \sum_{k=1}^{n} \pi_k(t) a_k[t, \xi_2(t)] \right\} dt$$

$$+ \pi_j(t) \frac{a_j[t, \xi_2(t)] - \sum_{k=1}^{n} \pi_k(t) a_k[t, \xi_2(t)]}{\sigma^2[t, \xi_2(t)]} d\xi_2(t)$$

where $a_k(t, x_2) = a(t, k, x_2)$.

If $\pi_1(t), \ldots, \pi_n(t)$ and $\xi_2(t)$ are fixed, then the further evolution of the probabilities $\pi_1, \ldots, \pi_n$ takes place independently of the behavior of the processes $\xi_1(s), \xi_2(s)$ and $\pi_1(s), \ldots, \pi_n(s)$ for $s \le t$.

If the drift and diffusion coefficients of the observed process $\xi_2(t)$ depend only on the time and the state of the process $\xi_1(t)$, that is, $a_k(t, x_2) \equiv a_k(t)$ and $\sigma(t, x_2) \equiv \sigma(t)$, then all a posteriori probabilities $\{\pi_1(t), \ldots, \pi_n(t)\}$ together represent a multi-dimensional diffusion process which is controlled by the afore-mentioned stochastic differential equations[60].

§ 5. General Markov Processes and their Characteristics

1. Semigroups Corresponding to Transition Functions and their Infinitesimal Operators

Let $\xi(t)$, $t \ge 0$ be a homogeneous Markov process with the transition function $P(t, x, B)$ in the compact phase space E with a countable base. Assume that the transition function $P(t, x, B)$ is stochastically continuous:

$$\lim_{t \to 0} \int_E \varphi(y) \, P(t, x, dy) = \varphi(x)$$

for any continuous bounded function $\varphi(x)$ on E and, moreover, that the so-called *Feller condition* is satisfied: the distributions $P(t, x, B)$

---

[60] *Shiryaev, A. N.*, Stochastic equations of non-linear filtration of Markov jump processes. Problems of the transmission of information, Nr. 3 (1966), 1—22 (Russian).

in the phase space E converge weakly to $P(t, x_0, B)$ for $x \to x_0$:

$$P(t, x, B) \Rightarrow P(t, x_0, B) .$$

Let $C(E)$ be the space of all continuous functions $\varphi(x)$ on the phase space E endowed with the norm $\|\varphi\| = \max_x |\varphi(x)|$. The relation

$$T_t \varphi(x) = \int_E \varphi(y) \, P(t, x, dy)$$

defines a semigroup of linear transformations $T_t, t \geq 0$ of the space $C(E)$:

$$T_s \cdot T_t = T_{s+t}, \qquad T_0 = I .$$

The condition that the transition function $P(t, x, B)$ is stochastically continuous is equivalent to the condition that the semigroup of the operators T_t is continuous:

$$\lim_{s \to t} T_s \varphi = T_t \varphi , \qquad \varphi \in C(E) .$$

Within some linear and everywhere dense (but in general not closed) subspace D_A the limit

$$A \varphi = \lim_{t \to 0} \frac{T_t \varphi - \varphi}{t} \qquad (\varphi \in D_A) \tag{5.1}$$

exists and determines the so-called *infinitesimal operator* A of the semigroup T_t.

Differential Equations of the Semigroup. Assume that the infinitesimal operator A is bounded and defined in the entire space $C(E)$, and that the limit relation (5.1) is satisfied uniformly with respect to φ for $\|\varphi\| \leq 1$. Then the operator function T_t is differentiable with respect to t in the sense of convergence with respect to the operator norm and satisfies the differential equation

$$\frac{dT_t}{dt} = A T_t , \qquad T_0 = I ,$$

whose solution is the operator function

$$T_t = e^{At} .$$

In the general case the function $T_t \varphi$ is differentiable and satisfies the following differential equation:

$$\frac{dT_t \varphi}{dt} = A T_t \varphi , \qquad T_0 = I .$$

The Resolvent. The infinitesimal operator A determines the corresponding semigroups T_t uniquely. In particular, for any element $\varphi \in C(E)$ the Laplace transform $R_\lambda \varphi$ of the function $T_t \varphi$ of t, that is, the so-called *resolvent*

$$R_\lambda \varphi = \int_0^\infty e^{-\lambda t} T_t \varphi \, dt \qquad (\lambda > 0)$$

belongs to the domain D_A of the infinitesimal operator A and is the unique solution of the equation

$$\lambda (R_\lambda \varphi) - A(R_\lambda \varphi) = \varphi \qquad (\lambda > 0).$$

The semigroup of operators T_t determines the corresponding family of transition functions $P(t, x, B)$ of the Markov process $\xi(t)$ uniquely.

Which properties should a linear operator A on a linear and everywhere dense subspace $D_A \subseteq C(E)$ have in order to be the infinitesimal operator of some Markov process $\xi(t)$ in the phase space E? In the case of a compact phase space E the following conditions are necessary and sufficient. First, if a function $\varphi(x)$ on D_A reaches its minimum at some point x_0, then $(A\varphi)(x_0) \geq 0$ *(principle of minimum)*; in particular, $A \cdot 1 \equiv 0$. Secondly, for $\lambda > 0$ the equation $\lambda \psi - A \psi = \varphi$ has a solution $\psi \in C(E)$ for any element $\varphi \in C(E)$. In fact, under these conditions the linear functional $T_t \varphi(x)$ of φ where t and x are fixed is bounded and positive, and can thus be written in the form

$$T_t \varphi(x) = \int_E \varphi(y) \, P(t, x, dy),$$

where $P(t, x, B)$ is a distribution depending on t and x, that is, a transition function.

The Adjoint Semigroup. By T_t^* we denote the semigroup of operators adjoint to T_t which operates in the adjoint space $C^*(E)$ of all generalized distributions $\mathbb{Q} = \mathbb{Q}(B)$ on the phase space E. The adjoint semigroup T_t^* is given by the formula

$$T_t^* \mathbb{Q}(B) = \int_E P(t, x, B) \, \mathbb{Q}(dx)$$

where B is any Borel set of E. The infinitesimal operator of this semigroup coincides with the adjoint operator A^* of A. The differential equation for T_t^* has the form

$$\frac{d T_t^* \mathbb{Q}}{dt} = A^* T_t^* \mathbb{Q}, \qquad T_0^* = I.$$

Example. Let $\xi(t)$, $t \geq 0$ be a Markov process with a finite number of states; say, E consists of the points $x = 1, \ldots, n$. Then $C(E)$ is the n-

dimensional euclidean space of vectors $\varphi = \varphi(x)$, $x \in E$, with coordinates $\varphi(x)$, $x = 1, \ldots, n$, in which the operators T_t are determined by the corresponding matrices $\{p_{ij}(t)\}$ of the transition probability of the process under consideration:

$$T_t \varphi(i) = \sum_{j=1}^{n} \varphi(j) \, p_{ij}(t) \, .$$

The infinitesimal operator A is defined for all $\varphi \in C(E)$ by the formula

$$A \varphi(i) = \lim_{h \to 0} \left[\sum_{j \neq i} \varphi(j) \frac{p_{ij}(h)}{h} + \varphi(i) \frac{p_{ij}(h) - 1}{h} \right] = \sum_{j=1}^{n} \varphi(j) \, \lambda_{ij} \, ,$$

that is, A is given by the matrix $\{\lambda_{ij}\}$ of the transition densities. The equation $dT_t \varphi/dt = A T_t \varphi$ is equivalent to the system of backward differential equations

$$\sum_{j=1}^{n} \varphi(j) \, p'_{ij}(t) = \sum_{k=1}^{n} \lambda_{ik} \sum_{j=1}^{n} \varphi(j) \, p_{kj}(t) \, .$$

In the phase space E each generalized measure $\mathbb{Q} = \mathbb{Q}(B)$ is determined by some function $q = q(x)$, $x \in E$ via the equation $\mathbb{Q}(B) = \sum_{x \in B} q(x)$. Hence the adjoint space of $C(E)$ is practically the n-dimensional euclidean space of all vectors $q = q(x)$ with components $q(x)$, $x = 1, \ldots, n$. The adjoint operators are determined by the corresponding matrices in such a way that the equation $dT_t^* q \, dt = A^* T_t^* q$ is equivalent to the system of forward differential equations

$$\sum_{i=1}^{n} q(i) \, p'_{ij}(t) = \sum_{k=1}^{n} \lambda_{kj} \sum_{i=1}^{n} q(i) \, p_{ik}(t) \, .$$

2. Infinitesimal Operators, Harmonic and Excessive Functions

Let $\xi(t)$ be a right-continuous Markov process in the compact phase space E with a countable base whose transition function $P(t, x, B)$ is stochastically continuous and satisfies the Feller condition. For the infinitesimal operator A of the process $\xi(t)$ the following formula holds:

$$A \varphi(x) = \lim_{V \to x} \frac{\mathbb{M}_x \varphi[\xi(\tau)] - \varphi(x)}{\mathbb{M}_x \tau}$$

where V denotes a neighborhood of the point x, the limit is taken with respect to a system of monotone decreasing neighborhoods V contracting themselves to x in the sense that their intersection consists of x only, and $\tau = \tau_V$ is the exit time of $\xi(t)$ from V.

Example. Assume that $\xi(t)$ is a diffusion process in a closed interval $[r_1, r_2]$ with the drift coefficient $a(x)$ and diffusion coefficient $\sigma(x)$ where $a(x)$ and $b'(x)$ are continuous and $b(x) = 1/2\,\sigma^2(x) > 0$. Given an inner point x we take an interval $V = (x - \Delta x, x + \Delta x)$ such that $M_x \tau \sim \Delta t$ up to infinitely small terms of higher orders. To this end we have to choose $\Delta x \sim \sigma(x)\sqrt{\Delta t}$. If we choose Δt and Δx in this way, the process $\xi(t)$ leaves the interval V via the point $x + \Delta x$ with probability

$$p(x) = \frac{1}{2} + \frac{a(x)}{2\sigma(x)}\sqrt{\Delta t}$$ and via the point $x - \Delta x$ with probability $q(x) = 1 - p(x)$.

Hence

$$A\varphi(x) = \lim_{\Delta t \to 0} \frac{\varphi(x + \Delta x)\,p(x) + \varphi(x - \Delta x)\,q(x) - \varphi(x)}{\Delta t}$$

where the limit exists and defines a continuous function $A\varphi(x)$ in some neighborhood of x if and only if $\varphi(x)$ is twice continuously differentiable at the point x:

$$A\varphi(x) = a(x)\,\varphi'(x) + \frac{1}{2}\,\sigma^2(x)\,\varphi''(x).$$

If $x = r$ is a boundary point, the condition that the function $A\varphi(x)$ be continuous on the entire interval $[r_1, r_2]$ implies

$$A\varphi(r) = \lim_{x \to r} A\varphi(x).$$

Hereby we obtain for various kinds of boundary points the following restrictions on functions $\varphi(x)$ in the domain D_A of the infinitesimal operator A:

$$A\varphi(r) = 0 \quad \text{in the case of absorption at the point } x = r,$$
$$\varphi'(r) = 0 \quad \text{in the case of reflection at the point } x = r.$$

General Form of the Infinitesimal Operator A of a Regular Markov Process on a Closed Interval $[r_1, r_2]$. The regularity of the process $\xi(t)$ consists in the fact that for any inner point x the process leaves the interval (r_1, x) as well as the interval (x, r_2) with positive probability through this point.

Let $[c, d]$ be any interval of the phase space and $u(x, c, d)$ the probability that the process $\xi(t)$, when starting from x, $c \leq x \leq d$ hits the point c earlier than d. There exists a monotone increasing continuous function

$u(x)$ which is unique up to a linear transformation such that we have

$$u(x, d, c) = \frac{u(x) - u(c)}{u(d) - u(c)}$$

for any interval $[c, d]$.

Moreover, the expectation $\mathbb{M}_x \tau_{[c,d]}$ of the exit time from the interval $[c, d]$ when starting at x, considered as a function of x, is convex from below with respect to the monotone function $u(x)$, that is, when the variable x is replaced by $u = u(x)$. The function $v(x)$ given by

$$v(x) = - \frac{d \mathbb{M}_x \tau_{[c,d]}}{du(x)}$$

is monotone increasing but not necessarily continuous. The function $v(x)$ is the same for all intervals $[c, d]$ up to a constant term.

We define the differential operators D_u^+ and D_v by the formulas

$$D_u^+ \varphi(x) = \lim_{h \to 0} \frac{\varphi(x + h) - \varphi(x)}{u(x + h) - u(x)},$$

$$D_v \varphi(x) = \lim_{h_1, h_2 \to 0} \frac{\varphi(x + h_1) - \varphi(x - h_1)}{v(x + h_2) - v(x - h_2)}.$$

It turns out that at each inner point x the infinitesimal operator A has the form

$$A \varphi(x) = D_v D_u^+ \varphi(x).$$

In any absorbing point $x = r$ the infinitesimal operator equals

$$A \varphi(r) = 0.$$

If we denote by Δt the expectation of the exit time of the process $\xi(t)$ from the half-interval $[r, r + \Delta x)$, starting from the original position $x = r$, then at a boundary point r which is not absorbing the infinitesimal operator is given by the formula

$$A \varphi(r) = \lim_{\Delta x \to 0} \frac{\varphi(r + \Delta x) - \varphi(r)}{\Delta t}.$$

The domain D_A of the infinitesimal operator consists of all functions $\varphi(x)$ which are continuous together with the function $A \varphi(x)$ determined at each point x by the local operator A described above. This continuity requirement imposes certain differential conditions on the function $\varphi(x) \in D_A$ and certain boundary conditions for $x = r_1, r_2$.

Harmonic Functions. A function $u(x) \in C(E)$ is called *harmonic* with respect to the process $\xi(t)$ if

$$u(x) = \mathbb{M}_x u[\xi(\tau)]$$

19*

for any constant τ. This equation is then automatically satisfied for any Markov time τ.

Let $\xi(t)$ be a process with continuous trajectories. A function $u(x)$ defined in a domain G is called *harmonic* in G if it is continuous on G (including the boundary) and if $u(x) = \mathbb{M}_x u[\xi(\tau)]$ for all $x \in G$. If $u(x)$ is harmonic in G, it satisfies the equation

$$A u(x) = 0 \quad (x \in G). \tag{5.2}$$

Moreover, if the process $\xi(t)$ stopped when passing beyond the boundary of G satisfies the assumptions of Section 1, then the function $u(x)$ is harmonic in G if and only if it is included in the domain D_A of the infinitesimal operator A of the process described above, and if it satisfies the equation (5.2).

If some continuous function $\varphi(x)$ is given on the boundary of the domain G, then the formula

$$u(x) = \mathbb{M}_x \varphi[\xi(\tau)]$$

determines a harmonic function in G which coincides with $\varphi(x)$ on the boundary, and thus yields a solution of the equation (5.2) with this boundary conditions.

Example. Suppose that $\xi(t)$ represents a multi-dimensional diffusion process $\xi(t) = \{\xi_k(t)\}_{k=1,\dots,n}$ with mutually independent components where each of them is a Brownian motion with expectation zero and diffusion coefficient one. Then the infinitesimal operator A of the process $\xi(t)$ coincides with the Laplace operator:

$$A = \frac{1}{2} \sum_{k=1}^{n} \frac{\partial^2}{\partial x_k^2}$$

and the harmonic functions $u = u(x)$ with respect to $\xi(t)$ are the ordinary harmonic functions, these being the solutions of the Laplace equation:

$$\sum_{k=1}^{n} \frac{\partial^2 u}{\partial x_k^2} = 0.$$

A function $u(x) \in C(E)$ is called *superharmonic* with respect to the Markov process $\xi(t)$ if

$$u(x) \geq \mathbb{M}_x u[\xi(\tau)]$$

for any constant τ. This inequality is then automatically also satisfied for any *Markov time* τ. A positive superharmonic function is called *excessive*.

§ 6. Controlled Markov Processes

1. Controlled Markov Sequences

Assume that a change of the position of some system in the course of time t, where t runs through integers, takes place in the following way: if the system is in state $\xi(t) = x$ at the time t, then at the next moment $t+1$ it passes to a state y independently of its behavior until the time t with a probability $P(t, x, y, d)$ which depends on a parameter d to be chosen arbitrarily by the observer. The observer's decision to choose this or that parameter d is, generally speaking, based on the observation of the entire behavior of the system until the time t, which amounts to the fact that the *decision* d is a function of $\xi^{[t_0, t]}$, that is, of the section of the process observed during the period from t_0 to t.

Let $W(t, x)$ be some function of the two variables t and x which represents the profit resulting from the "utilization" of the system considered during a unit of time from t to $t+1$ under the condition that at the instant t the system is in state $\xi(t) = x$. Let τ be the time until which the system is utilized and which does not depend on the future; $\tau = \infty$ is not excluded. It is convenient to assume that the process $\xi(t)$ under consideration stops after the instant τ. Then the average total profit is given by the expression

$$V = \mathbb{M} \sum_{t_0}^{\tau} W[t, \xi(t)] .$$

The expectation $\mathbb{M} \sum_{t_0}^{\tau} W[t, \xi(t)]$ depends on the decisions $d = d(t, \xi^{[t_0, t]})$ taken by the observer at each step t, and finally on the accepted *strategy* $d^{[t_0, \infty]}$ which is a function of the two "variables" t and $\xi^{[t_0, t]}$, $t \geq t_0$. The observer's acceptance of the strategy $d^{[t_0, \infty]}$ means that at the time t he decides for $d(t, \xi^{[t_0, t]})$ if the behavior of the system until this instant is described by the trajectory $\xi^{[t_0, t]}$. Thus we have

$$V = V(d^{[t_0, \infty]}) .$$

The quantity

$$V^* = \sup_{d^{[t_0, \infty]}} V(d^{[t_0, \infty]})$$

is called the *value;* it is the value obtained by "exploiting" the system under consideration. The strategy $d^{[t_0, \infty]}$ is called *optimal* if

$$V(d^{[t_0, \infty]}) = V^* ,$$

and ε-*optimal* if

$$V(d^{[t_0, \infty]}) \geq V^* - \varepsilon .$$

Markov Strategies. The strategy $d^{[t_0, \infty]}$ is called a *Markov* strategy if at each instant t the corresponding decisions $d(t, \xi^{[t_0, t]})$ are taken merely in dependance of t and of the state $x = \xi(t)$, regardless of the behavior of the system until the time t: $d(t, \xi^{[t_0, t]}) = d[t, \xi(t)]$. For any strategy $d^{[t_0, \infty]}$ there exists a Markov strategy $\tilde{d}^{[t_0, \infty]}$ which guarantees the same average profit:

$$V(d^{[t_0, \infty]}) = V(\tilde{d}^{[t_0, \infty]}).$$

The Bellman Equation. In the following we consider Markov strategies only. By $V(t, x, d^{[t_0, \infty]})$ we denote the average profit obtained by the utilization of the system during the period of time starting from the instant t under the condition that $\xi(t) = x$:

$$V(t, x, d^{[t_0, \infty]}) = \mathbb{M}\left\{ \sum_{s=t}^{\tau} W[s, \xi(s)] \mid \xi(t) = x \right\}.$$

This profit is determined by the Markov strategy $d^{[t_0, \infty]}$ in the considered period of time $[t, \infty]$ alone:

$$V(t, x, d^{[t_0, \infty]}) = V(t, x, d^{[t, \infty]}).$$

Moreover,

$$V(t, x, d^{[t, \infty]}) = \sum_{y} P(t, x, y, d) V(t+1, y, d^{[t+1, \infty]}).$$

The corresponding value

$$V(t, x) = \sup_{d^{[t, \infty]}} V(t, x, d^{[t, \infty]})$$

satisfies the *Bellman* functional *equation:*

$$V(t, x) = W(t, x) + \sup_{d} \sum_{y} P(t, x, y, d) V(t+1, y).$$

If we start from the initial position (t_0, x_0), the strategy $d^{[t_0, \infty]}$ is optimal if and only if it is optimal in any period of time $[t, \infty]$ for any initial position (t, x) attainable from (t_0, x_0).

If for each $\varepsilon > 0$ an ε-optimal strategy $d^{[t, \infty]}$ exists in some period of time $[t, \infty]$, that is, for any x

$$V(t, x, d^{[t, \infty]}) \geq V(t, x) - \varepsilon$$

where the initial moment t may depend on ε, then there is also for each $\varepsilon > 0$ an ε-optimal strategy on the entire interval $[t_0, \infty]$. If for some t there exists an optimal strategy $d^{[t, \infty]}$ and if the least upper bound in the Bellman equation is always attained at some point $d = d(t, x)$, then an optimal strategy $d^{[t_0, \infty]}$ also exists on the entire interval $[t_0, \infty]$. It coincides with the initial optimal strategy after the instant t, and for each $s \leq t$ the corresponding optimal solutions $d(s, x)$ are successively determined simultaneously with the value $V(s, x)$: $d(s, x)$ is a point of a maximum of the expression

$$\sum_y P(s, x, y, d)\, V(s + 1, y).$$

In particular, if the *stopping time* $\tau = t$ is finite and not random, then any strategy $d^{[t, \infty]}$ will be optimal; the corresponding value equals

$$V(t, x) \equiv W(t, x)$$

and an optimal strategy during the period of time $[t_0, t]$ can be obtained in the way described above.

Example. *The Problem of Best Choice.* Suppose that we are given a collection of n objects out of which we are to select the best possible one. When comparing any two of them we can always decide which is the better one, but the act of choice is complicated by the fact that when objects have been tried successively and rejected one cannot return to them once more. Imagine for instance a girl particular in her choice of a husband who chooses a bridegroom out of n candidates; the rejected bridegroom will never return any more, and the choice terminates when the girl accepts the proposal of marriage of any candidate.

It is assumed that the objects are inspected at random in such a way that depending on chance and following some rule we can stop at the best or the worst object. If k first objects have already been tried and rejected, then the following one may be compared with all preceding objects; on this basis we can either decide to terminate the procedure by selecting this object, or reject it and go on seeking a better one.

We confine ourselves to observations of the following type. Let $\xi(0) = 1$ be the first object to be tried. It is either accepted or rejected. In case of rejection the same happens automatically with all following objects which are worse than $\xi(0)$, and the next decision is taken only when an object better than $\xi(0)$ occurs. Let $\xi(1)$ be the serial number of this object in the process of inspection. The object numbered $\xi(1)$ is accepted with a certain probability or rejected; in the latter case all following objects worse than $\xi(1)$ are automatically rejected and the next object $\xi(2)$ can be accepted only if it is better than $\xi(1)$ etc.

If the choice terminates at the k-th object, then the probability $W(k)$ that the object selected is the best of all equals k/n where n is the number of all objects; this number is known in advance. If the best object in a row occurs after k objects had been tried, that is, $\xi(t - 1) = k$, then by the decision to stop here the choice is terminated; if, however, depending on $\xi(0), \ldots, \xi(t-1)$ we decide to continue the inspection, then the probability that j will be the following best object (that is, $\xi(t)=j$) equals $\dfrac{k}{(j-1)j}$:

$$p(k, j, d) = \begin{cases} 0 & \text{if } d = \text{ to accept the } k\text{-th object} \\ \dfrac{k}{(j-1)j} & \text{if } d = \text{ to continue the inspection .} \end{cases}$$

The average value for the chosen strategy $d^{[0, \infty]}$ is

$$V(d^{[0, \infty]}) = \mathbb{M} \, W[\xi(\tau)]$$

where $\xi(\tau)$ is the serial number of the object accepted. The stopping time τ does not exceed n, hence an optimal strategy exists for which the average value equals the prize:

$$V = \max_{d^{[0, \infty]}} V(d^{[0, \infty]}) .$$

By $V(k)$ we denote the prize under the condition that the first $k-1$ objects were rejected and the next k-th object turns out to be the best one among those that appeared so far. If this object is the last one, that is, $k = n$, then according to the condition it is the absolutely best one and is, of course, accepted:

$$V(n) = W(n) = 1 .$$

Let m_n be a number with the property that if a best object with a serial number $\xi(t) \geq m_n$ turns up it must be accepted and the choice terminates (such a number $m_n \leq n$ obviously exists). Then for $k \geq m_n$ the prize equals

$$V(k) = W(k) = \frac{k}{n} .$$

The Bellman equation permits to determinate the number m_n. In fact, we have for $k \geq m_n$

$$V(k) = \max \left\{ W(k), \ \sum_{j=k+1}^{n} p(k, j) \, V(j) \right\}$$

where $p(k, j) = \dfrac{k}{(j-1)j}, j > k$, and m_n is the smallest integer k for which

$$\sum_{j=k+1}^{n} p(k, j) \, V(j) = \frac{k}{n} \left(\frac{1}{k} + \frac{1}{k+1} + \cdots + \frac{1}{n-1} \right) \leq W(k) = \frac{k}{n} ,$$

that is, $\dfrac{1}{k} + \dfrac{1}{k+1} + \cdots + \dfrac{1}{n-1} \leq 1$.

If we select an object with a serial number $k < m_n$, then the average value will be smaller than in the case where this object is rejected and the choice is made later under the optimal strategy. Thus the optimal strategy for choosing the best object consists in examining the first $m_n - 1$ objects and then accepting the first one which is better than all preceding objects. For large n the number m_n is approximately equal to $n/3$, more precisely

$$\lim_{n \to \infty} \frac{m_n}{n} = \frac{1}{e}, \qquad e = 2.718, \dots .$$

Optimal Stopping of a Markov Process. On each step t one of two alternative decisions is taken: either to stop the process ($\tau = t$) or not. The random stopping time τ is a Markov time. The prize is determined by the formula

$$V = \sup_{\tau} \mathbb{M} \, W[\xi(\tau)] .$$

If the function of profit $W(x)$ is an excessive function, then for any initial position x we have

$$\mathbb{M}_x \, W[\xi(\tau)| \leq W(x),$$

so that the process must stop immediately. In the general case we have to look at the *excessive majorant* of the function $W(x)$, that is, the excessive function $U(x)$ such that for all x

$$U(x) \geq W(x)$$

and such that $U(x)$ is the smallest excessive function larger than or equal to $W(x)$. It can be determined by successive approximations as the limit

$$U(x) = \lim_{n \to \infty} T^n W(x), \qquad TW(x) = \max \{W(x), \mathbb{M}_x W[\xi(1)]\} .$$

Let $U(x)$ be the excessive majorant of the function $W(x)$; then stopping the process at the time τ when the set $\Gamma_\varepsilon = \{x : W(x) \geq U(x) - \varepsilon\}$ is reached for the first time is an ε-optimal strategy. In the case where the phase space consists of a finite number of points x, there exists an optimal strategy. It consists in stopping the process at the moment when the function $W[\xi(t)]$ becomes equal to $U[\xi(t)]$, that is, when the set $\Gamma_0 = \{x : W(x) = U(x)\}$ is reached. A point x_0 belongs to Γ_0 if and only if an excessive function $U(x_0, x)$ exists which majorizes $W(x)$ and coincides at x_0 with the profit function $W(x_0)$; such a function $U(x_0, x)$ is called a "*barrier*" [61].

---

[61] *Dynkin, E. B.*, Controlled random sequences. Teor. veroyatn. i primen. X, **1** (1965), 3—18 (Russian).

Example. In the problem of best choice considered before the set Γ_0 consists of the points $m_n, m_{n+1}, \ldots, n$ and can be obtained by determining the corresponding barriers $U(x_0, x)$; they are the functions

$$U(k, x) = \min\left(\frac{k}{n}, \frac{x}{n}\right), \quad k \geqq m_n.$$

2. Control in the Case of Incomplete Data

Assume that for some reasons the state $\xi(t)$ of the system under consideration is observed merely partially. Let us say that the state $\xi(t) = \{\xi_1(t), \xi_2(t)\}$ is described by two components $\xi_1(t)$ and $\xi_2(t)$ of which only $\xi_2(t)$ is observed. For definiteness suppose that the possible values of the non-observed component $\xi_1(t)$ are the integers $0, 1, 2, \ldots$, and let $P_{kj}(t, d)$ be the probability that the process $\xi_1(t)$ passes from the state k to the state j if at the same time t the observer takes the *decision* d. This decision $d = d(t, \xi_2^{[t_0, t]})$ is based on the values of the second component ξ_2 observed until the time t.

Suppose that the process $\xi_2(t)$ behaves in such a way that under the conditions $\xi_1(t) = k$ and $\xi_2(t) = x$ the probability of a transition into the state y equals $P_k(t, x, y, d)$, and this transition takes place independently of the behavior of the process until the time t. The state of the non-observed component is characterized by the a posteriori probabilities

$$\pi_j(t) = \sum_k \pi_k^0 \cdot \mathbb{P}\{\xi_1(t) = j \,|\, \xi_1(t_0) = k, \ \xi_2^{[t_0, t]}\} \qquad (j = 0, 1, \ldots)$$

where π_k^0, $k = 0, 1, \ldots$ is the distribution of the initial variable $\xi_1(t_0)$. The profit function $W[t, \xi(t)]$ depends on the observed component $\xi_2(t)$ as well as on the non-observed component $\xi_1(t)$; we set

$$W(t, \{k, x\}) = W_k(t, x).$$

The strategy $d^{[t_0, \infty]}$ is called *Markovian* if at each time t the decision $d = d(t, \xi_2^{[t_0, t]})$ merely depends on the observed state $\xi_2(t)$ of the process and the a posteriori distribution $\pi(t) = \{\pi_1(t), \pi_2(t), \ldots\}$:

$$d = d[t, \pi(t), \xi_2(t)].$$

For any strategy $d^{[t_0, \infty]}$ there exists a Markov strategy $\tilde{d}^{[t_0, \infty]}$ which yields the same average profit:

$$V(d^{[t_0, \infty]}) = V(\tilde{d}^{[t_0, \infty]}).$$

Bellman Equation. The evolution of the a posteriori probabilities $\pi_1(t), \pi_2(t), \ldots$ can be described like this:

$$\pi_k(t+1) = \frac{\sum_j \pi_j(t)\, P_j\{t, \xi_2(t), \xi_2(t+1), d\}\, P_{jk}(t, d)}{\sum_j \pi_j(t)\, P_j\{t, \xi_2(t), \xi_2(t+1), d\}}$$

$$(k = 0, 1, \ldots).$$

By $V(t, \pi, x, d^{[t_0, \infty]})$ we denote the average profit obtained by utilizing the system during a period of time starting at the instant t under the condition that $\pi(t) = \pi$ and $\xi_2(t) = x$:

$$V(t, \pi, x, d^{[t_0, \infty]}) = \mathbb{M}_{t, \pi, x} \sum_{s=t}^{\tau} W[s, \xi(s)].$$

This profit is determined by the Markov strategy $d^{[t_0, t]}$ restricted to the period of time $[t, \infty]$ under consideration:

$$V(t, \pi, x, d^{[t_0, \infty]}) = V(t, \pi, x, d^{[t, \infty]});$$

moreover

$$V(t, \pi, x, d^{[t, \infty]}) = \sum_k \pi_k\, W_k(t, x) + \sum_k \pi_k \sum_y P_k(t, x, y, d)\, V(t+1, \pi^*, y, d^{[t+1, \infty]}),$$

where

$$\pi^* = \pi_k(t+1) = \frac{\sum_j \pi_j P_j(t, x, y, d)\, P_{jk}(t, d)}{\sum_j \pi_j P_j(t, x, y, d)} \qquad (k = 0, 1, \ldots).$$

The corresponding prize

$$V(t, \pi, x) = \sup_{d^{[t, \infty]}} V(t, \pi, x, d^{[t, \infty]})$$

satisfies the *Bellman equation:*

$$V(t, \pi, x) = \sum_k \pi_k\, W_k(t, x) + \sup_d \sum_k \pi_k \sum_y P_k(t, x, y, d)\, V(t+1, \pi^*, y).$$

As in the case of a control of the system $\xi(t)$ by means of direct observations of its behavior, in this case, too, where the system is controlled by observations of the process $\xi_2(t)$, the optimal and ε-optimal Markov strategies on the entire interval of time $[t_0, \infty]$ can be constructed on the basis of the optimal and ε-optimal strategies $d^{[t, \infty]}$ on the interval $[t, \infty]$. In fact, if $d^{[s+1, \infty]}$, $s < t$, is an optimal strategy and $V(s+1, \pi^*, y)$ the prize corresponding to some distribution π^* and position y, then the optimal solution $d = d(s, \pi, x)$ on the step s is the point where the expression

$$\sum_k \pi_k \sum_y P_k(s, x, y, d) V(s+1, \pi^*, y)$$

reaches its maximum.

In the case when the *stopping time* τ is a constant, that is, $\tau = T < \infty$, all strategies $d^{[t, \infty]}$ after the instant T are optimal. The corresponding prize $V(t, \pi, x)$ equals

$$V(t, \pi, x) = \begin{cases} 0 & \text{for} \quad t > T. \\ \sum_k \pi_k W_k(t, x) & \text{for} \quad t = T. \end{cases}$$

Example. *The Problem of Two Types of Weapons.* Assume that we are given some target and that we may launch n bullets in order to destroy it. Moreover we have two guns numbered 0 and 1, and one of them is better than the other one. More precisely, the probability that one hits the target equals P, and the probability that the other will do so equals p, $p < P$, but it is not known which of them is indeed superior. By ξ_1 we denote the unknown property of the gun carrying the number 1. We convene to regard ξ_1 as a random variable which takes two values; say, the value 0 if the probability of hitting the target equals p and 1 if this probability equals P.

The outcome $\xi_2(t)$ of the shot number t is random; with probability p or P we have $\xi_2(t) = 0$ (*failure*), and with probability $1 - p$ or $1 - P$ we have $\xi_2(t) = 1$ (*success*). The outcomes are being observed in such a way that at the time of the shot number t the results of all preceding shots $\xi_2(1), \ldots, \xi_2(t-1)$ are known, in other words, the random sequence $\xi_2(t)$ is the one under observation. The probability of success on each step depends on the choice of the gun d and on its nature (that is, the state ξ_1). We set

$$P_k(x, d) = \mathbb{P}\{\xi_2(t) = x \mid \xi_1 = k\} .$$

We have:

$$\begin{aligned} P_0(0, 0) &= 1 - P, & P_0(0, 1) &= 1 - p, \\ P_0(1, 0) &= P, & P_0(1, 1) &= p, \\ P_1(0, 0) &= 1 - p, & P_1(0, 1) &= 1 - P, \\ P_1(1, 0) &= p, & P_1(1, 1) &= P. \end{aligned}$$

On the basis of the result of observing the shooting we have to choose the gun d at each step in such a way that the average number of good shots is maximal. This strategy is optimal with respect to the profit function $W(x)$ of the form

$$W(x) = \begin{cases} 0 & \text{if } x = 0 \quad \text{(failure)} \\ 1 & \text{if } x = 1 \quad \text{(success)}. \end{cases}$$

Let $\pi = \{\pi_0, \pi_1\}$ be the a posteriori probability that the gun number 1 has the property 0 or 1, and $V(t, \pi, x)$ the prize of the shooting during the period from t to n shots under the condition that the shot t yielded the result x. Obviously we have

$$V(n, \pi, x) = W(x),$$
$$V(n-1, \pi, x) = W(x) + \max_d \{\pi_0 P_0(1, d) + \pi_1 P_1(1, d)\}.$$

Hence for the last remaining bullet the optimal solution is to shoot with the gun that will be the better one with largest a posteriori probability: $d = 0$ if $\pi_0 \geq \pi_1$ and $d = 1$, if $\pi_0 \leq \pi_1$.

The Bellman equation

$$V(t, \pi, x) = W(x) + \max_d \left\{ \sum_{k=0}^{1} \pi_k P_k(y, d) V(t+1, \pi^*, y) \right\}$$

permits to obtain the optimal solution successively at each step t. In fact, what we have to do is to choose always the gun which has better quality with largest a posteriori probability: $d(t, \pi) = 0$ if $\pi_0(t) \geq \pi_1$ and $d(t, \pi) = 1$ if $\pi_0(t) \leq \pi_1(t)$.

3. Controlled Diffusion Processes

Let $\xi = \xi(t)$ be a Markov diffusion process controlled by a stochastic differential equation of the form

$$d\xi(t) = a[t, \xi(t), u] \, dt + \sigma[t, \xi(t), u] \, d\eta(t) \quad (t > t_0)$$

where the drift coefficient $a(t, x, u)$ and diffusion coefficient $\sigma(t, x, u)$ depend on the control parameter $u = u(t, \cdot)$ which is, say, numerical or vector-valued. The control $u^{[t_0, \infty]}$ is called *Markovian* if for each t the control parameter $u(t, \cdot)$ depends only on t and the state $x = \xi(t)$ under observation:

$$u(t, \cdot) = u(t, x).$$

Under certain restrictions on the control function $u = u(t, x)$ of the two variables t, x and the coefficients $a(t, x, u)$, $b(t, x, u)$ the afore-mentioned stochastic differential equation has a unique solution.

Suppose that the average profit from the utilization of the system which is in state $\xi(t)$ at the time t is determined like this:

$$V(u^{[t_0, \infty]}) = \mathbb{M}\left\{\int_{t_0}^\tau W[t, \xi(t)]\, dt + W_0[\tau, \xi(\tau)]\right\}$$

where $W(t, x)$ and $W_0(t, x)$ are some profit functions, and τ a certain random Markov time. It is convenient to assume that the process stops after the time τ.

The prize for the "utilization of the system ξ" after the time t is determined by

$$V(t, x) = \sup \mathbb{M}_{t, x}\left\{\int_t^\tau W[s, \xi(s)]\, ds + W_0[\tau, \xi(\tau)]\right\}.$$

The control $u^{[t, \infty]}$ is called *optimal after t* if the corresponding profit

$$V(t, x, u^{[t, \infty]}) = \mathbb{M}_{t, x}\left\{\int_t^\tau W[s, \xi(s)]\, ds + W_0[\tau, \xi(\tau)]\right\}$$

equals the prize $V(t, x)$. The control $u^{[t_0, \infty]}$ after the instant t_0 is optimal if and only if for every $t \geq t_0$ the corresponding control $u^{[t, \infty]}$ is optimal with the same control parameters $u[s, \xi(s)]$ as the original control $u^{[t_0, \infty]}$.

Assume that an optimal control $u^{[T, \infty]}$ after some instant $T \leq \tau$ exists. A discrete model of the diffusion process $\xi(t)$, $t_0 \leq t \leq T$ is given by the following controlled random walk: a particle passes at each step of duration Δt from the corresponding point x to the neighboring point $x + \Delta x$ with probability $p(t, x, u) = \dfrac{1}{2} + \dfrac{a(t, x, u)}{2\sigma(t, x, u)}\sqrt{\Delta t}$ and to the point $x - \Delta x$ with probability $q(t, x, u) = 1 - p(t, x, u)$, where $\Delta x = \sigma(t, x, u)\sqrt{\Delta t}$; the transition probabilities p and q depend also on the control parameter u. For such a discrete model the average profit has to be defined as

$$V^*(t, x, u^{[t, T]}) = \mathbb{M}_{t, x}\left\{\sum_t^{T-1} W[s, \xi(s)]\, \Delta t + V[T, \xi(T)]\right\}.$$

The prize for the utilization of the discrete model during a period of time from t to T satisfies the Bellman equation:

$$V^*(t, x) = W(t, x)\, \Delta t$$
$$+ \sup_u [p(t, x, u)\, V(t + \Delta t, x + \Delta x) + q(t, x, u)\, V(t + \Delta t, x - \Delta x)],$$

$$V^*(T, x) \equiv V(T, x).$$

If $\Delta t \to 0$, then at the limit the Bellman equation may be written as

$$-\frac{\partial V^*}{\partial t} = \sup_u \left[a(t, x, u) \frac{\partial V^*}{\partial u} + \frac{1}{2} \sigma^2(t, x, u) \frac{\partial^2 V^*}{\partial x^2} \right] + W(t, x),$$

$$V^*(T, x) \equiv V(T, x).$$

If this equation has a unique sufficiently smooth solution $V^*(t, x)$, then this solution will also be the prize: $V^*(t, x) \equiv V(t, x)$. Moreover, if a function $u_0 = u_0(t, x)$ exists which is admissible as a control of the system under consideration and satisfies

$$a[t, x, u_0(t, x)] \frac{\partial V}{\partial u} + \frac{1}{2} \sigma^2[t, x, u_0(t, x)] \frac{\partial^2 V}{\partial x^2}$$

$$= \sup_u \left[a(t, x, u) \frac{\partial V}{\partial u} + \frac{1}{2} \sigma^2(t, x, u) \frac{\partial^2 V}{\partial x^2} \right],$$

then this function $u_0 = u_0(t, x)$ also yields an optimal control [62].

---

[62] *Fleming, W. H.*, The Cauchy problem for degenerate parabolic equations. J. Math. and Mech., **13** (1964), 987—1008.

CHAPTER VI

Stationary Processes

§ 1. Spectral Theory of Harmonizable Processes

1. Linear Transformations

Spectral Representation. Any stationary real or complex random process

$$\xi = \xi(t),$$

considered as a function of the parameter t with values in the Hilbert space $L^2(\Omega)$ of all real or complex-valued random variables $\eta = \eta(\omega)$, $M|\eta|^2 < \infty$ with the scalar product $(\eta_1, \eta_2) = M\eta_1\bar{\eta}_2$ can be represented in the form

$$\xi(t) = \int e^{i\lambda t}\,\Phi(d\lambda). \tag{1.1}$$

On the right side of (1.1) we integrate within the limits $-\pi \leq \lambda \leq \pi$ in the case of a discrete parameter running through all integers, and within in the limits $-\infty < \lambda < \infty$ in the case of a continuous t running through all real values. The function $\Phi = \Phi(\Delta)$ is a *stochastic spectral measure*, that is, a generalized orthogonal measure with values in $L^2(\Omega)$:

$$M\Phi(\Delta_1)\,\overline{\Phi(\Delta_2)} = 0$$

for any two disjoint sets Δ_1 and Δ_2 in the σ-algebra of the measurable sets with respect to the spectral measure $F = F(\Delta)$; see § 2.1, Chapter III.
The spectral measure and the covariance function

$$B(t) = M\xi(s + t)\,\overline{\xi(s)}$$

are connected by the relation

$$B(t) = \int e^{i\lambda t}\,F(d\lambda) \qquad (-\infty < t < \infty),$$

and $F(\Delta) = M|\Phi(\Delta)|^2$.

Let $H(T)$ be the closed linear space generated by the values $\xi(t)$, $t \in T$, in the Hilbert space $L^2(\Omega)$, and L_T^2 the Hilbert space of functions

$\varphi = \varphi(\lambda)$ with the scalar product $(\varphi_1, \varphi_2) = \int \varphi_1(\lambda)\,\overline{\varphi_2(\lambda)}\,F(d\lambda)$ which is the closure of all functions of the form

$$\varphi(\lambda) = \sum_{k=1}^{n} c_k e^{i\lambda t_k} \qquad (t_1, \ldots, t_n \in T)$$

where $c_1, \ldots, c_n$ are real or complex coefficients. Every element $h \in H(T)$ admits the *spectral representation*

$$h = \int \varphi(\lambda)\,\Phi(d\lambda)$$

where $\varphi = \varphi(\lambda)$ is an element of the space L_T^2, and for any $\varphi \in L_T^2$ the stochastic integral $h = \int \varphi(\lambda)\,\Phi(d\lambda)$ defines an element $h \in H(T)$. Moreover, we have

$$\mathsf{M}[\int \varphi_1(\lambda)\,\Phi(d\lambda) \int \overline{\varphi_2(\lambda)\,\Phi(d\lambda)}] = \int \varphi_1(\lambda)\,\overline{\varphi_2(\lambda)}\,F(d\lambda),$$

that is, the spaces $H(T)$ and L_T^2 are *isometric*. The function $\varphi = \varphi(\lambda)$ is called the *spectral characteristic* of the corresponding element $h \in H(T)$.

Inversion Formulas. For any interval $\Delta = (\lambda_1, \lambda_2)$ let

$$\varphi_\Delta(\lambda) = \begin{cases} 1 & \text{for} \quad \lambda_1 < \lambda < \lambda_2, \\ \frac{1}{2} & \text{for} \quad \lambda = \lambda_1 \quad \text{or} \quad \lambda = \lambda_2, \\ 0 & \text{for} \quad \lambda < \lambda_1 \quad \text{or} \quad \lambda > \lambda_2. \end{cases}$$

Then, if

$$F(\lambda_1) = F(\lambda_2) = 0$$

and the parameter t is discrete, the function $\varphi_\Delta(\lambda)$ considered as an element of the space L_T^2 can be expanded into a series

$$\varphi_\Delta(\lambda) = \frac{1}{2\pi}(\lambda_2 - \lambda_1) + \frac{1}{2\pi} \sum_{t \neq 0} \frac{e^{-i\lambda_2 t} - e^{-i\lambda_1 t}}{-it} e^{i\lambda t}.$$

In the continuous case, however, $\varphi_\Delta(\lambda)$ can be represented by the integral

$$\varphi_\Delta(\lambda) = \frac{1}{2\pi} \int_{-\infty}^{\infty} \frac{e^{-i\lambda_2 t} - e^{-i\lambda_1 t}}{-it} e^{i\lambda t}\,dt.$$

Accordingly, the variable $\Phi(\Delta) = \int \varphi_\Delta(\lambda)\,\Phi(d\lambda)$ can be represented by

$$\Phi(\Delta) = \frac{1}{2\pi}(\lambda_2 - \lambda_1)\,\xi(0) + \frac{1}{2\pi} \sum_{t \neq 0} \frac{e^{-i\lambda_2 t} - e^{-i\lambda_1 t}}{-it}\,\xi(t) \qquad \text{(for discrete t)}$$

and by

$$\Phi(\Delta) = \frac{1}{2\pi} \int_{-\infty}^{\infty} \frac{e^{-i\lambda_2 t} - e^{-i\lambda_1 t}}{-it}\,\xi(t)\,dt \qquad \text{(for continuous t)}.$$

Let

$$\Phi(\lambda) = \begin{cases} 1 & \text{for } \lambda = \lambda_0 \\ 0 & \text{for } \lambda \neq \lambda_0 . \end{cases}$$

In the discrete case the function $\varphi_{\lambda_0}(\lambda)$ as an element of the space L_T^2 is the limit

$$\varphi_{\lambda_0}(\lambda) = \lim_{T \to \infty} \frac{1}{T} \sum_{t=0}^{T-1} e^{i(\lambda - \lambda_0)t} ,$$

and in the continuous case

$$\varphi_{\lambda_0}(\lambda) = \lim_{T \to \infty} \frac{1}{T} \int_0^T e^{i(\lambda - \lambda_0)t} \, dt .$$

Accordingly the variable $\Phi(\lambda_0) = \int \varphi_{\lambda_0}(\lambda)\, \Phi(d\lambda)$ can be written as

$$\Phi(\lambda_0) = \lim_{T \to \infty} \sum_{t=0}^{T-1} e^{-i\lambda_0 t}\, \xi(t)$$

in the discrete case, and

$$\Phi(\lambda_0) = \lim_{T \to \infty} \frac{1}{T} \int_0^T e^{-i\lambda_0 t}\, \xi(t)\, dt$$

in the continuous case.

Analytic Representation of Processes with a Bounded Spectrum. Let $\xi = \xi(t)$ be a stationary process with continuous time t and a bounded spectrum, that is, the spectral measure $F = F(\Delta)$ is concentrated on some bounded interval $(-W, W)$: $F(-W, W) = F(-\infty, \infty)$. The function $\varphi(\lambda) = e^{i\lambda t}$ considered as an element of L_T^2 can be represented by

$$e^{i\lambda t} = \sum_{n=-\infty}^{\infty} \frac{\sin\left[W\left(t - \frac{\pi}{W} n\right)\right]}{W\left(t - \frac{\pi}{W} n\right)} e^{i\frac{\pi}{W} n\lambda} .$$

Accordingly, the process $\xi(t) = \int\limits_{-\infty}^{\infty} e^{i\lambda t}\, \Phi(d\lambda)$ has the form

$$\xi(t) = \sum_{n=-\infty}^{\infty} \frac{\sin\left[W\left(t - \frac{\pi}{W} n\right)\right]}{W\left(t - \frac{\pi}{W}\right) n}\, \xi\left(\frac{\pi}{W} n\right) .$$

Linear Transformations. By a linear transformation of the process $\xi = \xi(t)$ we mean a transformation of the form

$$\eta(t) = \int e^{i\lambda t} \, \varphi(\lambda) \, \Phi(d\lambda).$$

The function $\varphi \in L^2_{(-\infty, \infty)}$ is called the *spectral characteristic* of this linear transformation. It gives rise to the wide sense stationary process $\eta = \eta(t)$ with spectral measure

$$G(\varDelta) = \int_\varDelta |\varphi(\lambda)|^2 \, F(d\lambda).$$

defined above.

If the original stationary process $\xi = \xi(t)$ has a spectral density $f = f(\lambda)$, that is, if its spectral measure $F = F(\varDelta)$ is absolutely continuous and $F(\varDelta) = \int_\varDelta f(\lambda) \, d\lambda$, then the corresponding process $\eta = \eta(t)$ has the spectral density

$$g(\lambda) = |\varphi(\lambda)|^2 \, f(\lambda).$$

Like every wide sense stationary process, the process $\eta = \eta(t)$ admits a spectral representation

$$\eta(t) = \int e^{i\lambda t} \, \Psi(d\lambda)$$

where the stochastic spectral measure Ψ is related to the corresponding stochastic spectral measure Φ in the following way:

$$\Psi(\varDelta) = \int_\varDelta \varphi(\lambda) \, \Phi(d\lambda).$$

The stationary process $\xi = \xi(t)$, in turn, can be obtained by the "inverse" linear transformation

$$\xi(t) = \int e^{i\lambda t} \, \psi(\lambda) \, \Psi(d\lambda)$$

if and only if the spectral characteristic $\varphi = \varphi(\lambda)$ is unequal zero for almost all λ with respect to the spectral measure F. The spectral characteristic $\psi = \psi(\lambda)$ of the "inverse" transformation is given by the formula

$$\psi(\lambda) = \frac{1}{\varphi(\lambda)}.$$

Example. *Differentiation.* Let $\xi = \xi(t)$ be a stationary process with a continuous time t such that its spectral measure F satisfies the condition

$$\int_{-\infty}^{\infty} \lambda^2 \, F(d\lambda) < \infty.$$

Then there is a well-defined transformation with the spectral characteristic

$$\varphi(\lambda) = i\lambda.$$

20*

The corresponding stationary process $\eta = \eta(t)$ represents the derivative of the original process $\xi = \xi(t)$:

$$\eta(t) = \int_{-\infty}^{\infty} i\lambda \, e^{i\lambda t} \, \Phi(d\lambda) = \xi'(t).$$

Here we have in mind the differentiation of $\xi = \xi(t)$ as a function with values in the Hilbert space $L^2(\Omega)$, that is, differentiation in the sense of square means.

Being a primitive function of the function $\xi' = \xi'(t)$ which is integrable on each finite interval, the random process $\xi = \xi(t)$ has the form

$$\xi(t) = \xi(t_0) + \int_{t_0}^{t} \xi'(s) \, ds$$

where $\xi'(s), t_0 \leq s \leq t$, is integrated as a function with values in $L^2(\Omega)$; in particular, for each fixed t this equation is satisfied with probability 1. The random process $\xi' = \xi'(t)$ is stochastically continuous, and without loss of generality may be assumed to be measurable. If the random process $\xi = \xi(t)$ is separable and square mean differentiable, then it is continuous with probability 1, and almost all trajectories have the form

$$\xi(\omega, t) = \xi(\omega, t_0) + \int_{t_0}^{t} \xi'(\omega, s) \, ds .$$

Example. *Integration.* Let $\xi = \xi(t)$ be a stationary process whose spectral measure satisfies the condition

$$\int_{-\infty}^{\infty} \frac{1}{\lambda^2} F(d\lambda) < \infty .$$

Then the linear transformation with the spectral characteristic

$$\varphi(\lambda) = \frac{1}{i\lambda}$$

is well defined and yields the stationary process

$$\eta(t) = \int_{-\infty}^{\infty} e^{i\lambda t} \frac{1}{i\lambda} \Phi(d\lambda)$$

which is differentiable in the square mean such that

$$\eta'(t) = \xi(t) .$$

Example. *Moving Averages.* Let $\varphi = \varphi(\lambda)$ be the Fourier transform of some integrable function $c(t)$:

$$\varphi(\lambda) = \int_{-\infty}^{\infty} e^{-i\lambda t} c(t)\, dt\,.$$

Then the linear transformation with the spectral characteristic $\varphi = \varphi(\lambda)$ is well defined. The corresponding stationary process $\eta = \eta(t)$ is given by

$$\eta(t) = \int_{-\infty}^{\infty} e^{i\lambda t} \varphi(\lambda)\, \Phi(d\lambda) = \int_{-\infty}^{\infty} c(t-s)\, \xi(s)\, ds\,.$$

Physically Realizable Linear Transformations. The linear transformation with the spectral characteristic $\varphi = \varphi(\lambda)$ is called *physically realizable* if φ belongs to the space $L^2_{(-\infty,0]}(F)$. Roughly speaking the physical realizability of the linear transformation means that at a given instant t the values of the process $\eta(t) = \int e^{i\lambda t} \varphi(\lambda)\, \Phi(d\lambda)$ are built from the values $\xi(s)$ of the original process at instances $s \leq t$.

Example. Assume that $c = c(t)$ is a function which vanishes for negative t: $c(t) = 0$ if $t < 0$, and such that

$$\sum_{0}^{\infty} |c(t)| < \infty \qquad \text{(for discrete } t)$$

$$\int_{0}^{\infty} |c(t)|\, dt < \infty \quad \text{(for continuous } t)\,.$$

Then the linear transformation with the corresponding spectral characteristic

$$\varphi(\lambda) = \sum_{0}^{\infty} e^{-i\lambda t} c(t) \quad \text{(in the discrete case)}$$

$$\varphi(\lambda) = \int_{0}^{\infty} e^{-i\lambda t} c(t)\, dt \quad \text{(in the continuous case)}$$

is physically realizable. The stationary process

$$\eta(t) = \int e^{i\lambda t} \varphi(\lambda)\, \Phi(d\lambda)$$

has the form

$$\eta(t) = \sum_{-\infty}^{t} c(t-s)\, \xi(s) \qquad \text{(for discrete } t)$$

$$\eta(t) = \int_{-\infty}^{t} c(t-s)\, \xi(s)\, ds \quad \text{(for continuous } t)\,.$$

2. Regular Stationary Processes

The "White Noise" Process. The discrete time stationary process with the simplest structure is the process $\zeta = \zeta(t)$ with *uncorrelated* values:

$$\mathbb{M}\zeta(t) = 0, \quad \mathbb{M}|\zeta(t)|^2 = 1,$$
$$\mathbb{M}\zeta(t_1)\,\overline{\zeta(t_2)} = 0 \quad (t_1 \neq t_2).$$

In the case of a continuous time t an analogue of this process is the so-called "*white noise*", which is the generalized stationary process $\zeta = \langle u, \zeta \rangle$ of the form

$$\langle u, \zeta \rangle = \int u(t)\,\zeta(dt)$$

where $\zeta = \zeta(\varDelta)$ is a stochastic measure such that

$$\mathbb{M}\zeta(\varDelta) = 0, \quad \mathbb{M}|\zeta(\varDelta)|^2 = t - s \quad \text{for} \quad \varDelta = (s, t),$$
$$\mathbb{M}\zeta(\varDelta_1)\,\overline{\zeta(\varDelta_2)} = 0$$

for any two disjoint sets $\varDelta_1$ and $\varDelta_2$; recall that the parameter $u = u(t)$ is an infinitely differentiable function, see § 2.1, Chapter III, and Section 6 of this paragraph.

Regularity. The stationary process $\xi = \xi(t)$, $\mathbb{M}\xi(t) = 0$, is called *linearly regular* if

$$\bigcap_t H(-\infty, t) = 0$$

where $H(s, t)$ is the closed linear subspace of the space $L^2(\Omega)$ spanned by the values $\xi(u)$, $s \leq u \leq t$. The stationary process $\xi = \xi(t)$ with the spectral measure F is linearly regular if and only if $F = F(\varDelta)$ is absolutely continuous: $F(\varDelta) = \int_\varDelta f(\lambda)\,d\lambda$, and the spectral density $f = f(\lambda)$ satisfies the condition

$$\int_{-\pi}^{\pi} \log f(\lambda)\,d\lambda > -\infty \qquad \text{(for discrete } t\text{)}$$

$$\int_{-\infty}^{\infty} \log f(\lambda)\frac{d\lambda}{1 + \lambda^2} > -\infty \quad \text{(for continuous } t\text{)}.$$

The stationary process $\xi = \xi(t)$ is linearly regular if and only if it is obtained by means of a physically realizable linear transformation from the process $\zeta = \zeta(t)$ with uncorrelated values in the case of discrete t:

$$\xi(t) = \sum_{-\infty}^{t} c(t-s)\,\zeta(s), \quad \sum_{0}^{\infty} |c(t)|^2 < \infty,$$

and from the "white noise" process $\zeta = \langle u, \zeta \rangle$ in the case of continuous t:

$$\xi(t) = \int_{-\infty}^{t} c(t-s)\,\zeta(ds), \qquad \int_{0}^{\infty} |c(t)|^2\,dt < \infty$$

(see § 2.1, Chapter III).

In the case of a discrete time t the spectral characteristic $\varphi = \varphi(\lambda)$ of this linear transformation has the form

$$\varphi(\lambda) = \sum_{0}^{\infty} e^{-i\lambda t}\,c(t)$$

and is the boundary value of the analytic function $\gamma(z) = \sum_{0}^{\infty} z^t c(t)$ in the unit circle $|z| < 1$; the boundary value is given by the formula $\varphi(\lambda) = \gamma(e^{-i\lambda})$. In the case of continuous t the spectral characteristic $\varphi = \varphi(\lambda)$ has the form

$$\varphi(\lambda) = \int_{0}^{\infty} e^{-i\lambda t}\,c(t)\,dt$$

and is the boundary value of the analytic function $\gamma(z) = \int_{0}^{\infty} e^{-izt}\,c(t)\,dt$ on the lower half-plane $\operatorname{Im} z < 0$; in fact $\varphi(\lambda) = \gamma(\lambda)$. The spectral density $f(\lambda)$ of the stationary process $\xi(t)$ equals

$$f(\lambda) = \frac{1}{2\pi}\,|\varphi(\lambda)|^2 \,.$$

The corresponding process $\zeta = \zeta(t)$ or stochastic measure $\zeta = \zeta(\Delta)$ with uncorrelated values can be obtained by means of the "inverse transformation"

$$\zeta(t) = \int_{-\pi}^{\pi} e^{i\lambda t}\,\varphi^{-1}(\lambda)\,\Phi(d\lambda) \qquad \text{(for discrete t)},$$

$$\zeta(\Delta) = \int_{-\infty}^{\infty} \left[\int_{\Delta} e^{i\lambda t}\,dt \right] \varphi^{-1}(\lambda)\,\Phi(d\lambda) \qquad \text{(for continuous t)}.$$

Among all functions $\varphi = \varphi(\lambda)$ of this type there exists, uniquely up to the constant factor, a function $\varphi_0 = \varphi_0(\lambda)$ which is the boundary value of the *maximal analytic function* $\gamma_0 = \gamma_0(z)$:

$$|\gamma_0(z)| \geq |\gamma(z)|$$

for each analytic function $\gamma(z)$ that satisfies the same boundary condition $|\gamma(z)|^2 = \dfrac{1}{2\pi}\,f(\lambda)$ as the function $\varphi_0(z)$. To this and only this function

$\varphi_0(\lambda)$ there corresponds a physically realizable linear transformation whose spectral characteristic $\varphi_0^{-1}(\lambda)$ is contained in the class $L^2_{[-\infty, 0]}(F)$. The corresponding process $\zeta = \zeta(t)$ or $\zeta = \langle u, \zeta \rangle$ and the stochastic measure $\zeta = \zeta(\varDelta)$ are called *fundamental* for the stationary process $\xi = \xi(t)$.

The maximal analytic function $\gamma = \gamma(z)$ can be expressed by the spectral density $f = f(\lambda)$ of the process $\xi = \xi(t)$:

$$\gamma(z) = 2\pi \exp \left\{ \frac{1}{4\pi} \int_{-\pi}^{\pi} \log f(\lambda) \frac{e^{-i\lambda} + z}{e^{-i\lambda} - z} \, d\lambda \right\}$$

in the discrete case and

$$\gamma(z) = \sqrt{\pi} \exp \left\{ \frac{1}{2\pi i} \int_{-\infty}^{\infty} \log f(\lambda) \frac{1 + \lambda z}{z - \lambda} \cdot \frac{d\lambda}{1 + \lambda^2} \right\}$$

in the continuous case.

Processes with Rational Spectral Densities. Stationary processes with rational spectral densities represent an important class. Let

$$f(\lambda) = \frac{\Sigma \, c_k \, e^{-i\lambda k}}{\Sigma \, d_k \, e^{-i\lambda k}}$$

be a rational function of $e^{-i\lambda}$ which is non-negative and integrable on the interval $-\pi \leq \lambda \leq \pi$; the numerator and denominator have no common divisors. The zeros of the polynomial in $e^{-i\lambda}$ in the numerator on the boundary of the unit circle must occur with an even multiplicity, whereas the polynomial in $e^{-i\lambda}$ in the denominator has no such zeros.

The function $f(\lambda)$ can always be represented in the following form:

$$f(\lambda) = \frac{1}{2\pi} \frac{|P(e^{-i\lambda})|^2}{|Q(e^{-i\lambda})|^2},$$

where the polynomial

$$P(z) = \sum_{k=1}^{m} a_k z^k = a_m(z - p_1) \dots (z - p_m)$$

has zeros outside of the unit circle or on its boundary, whereas the polynomial

$$Q(z) = \sum_{k=1}^{n} b_k z^k = (z - q_1) \dots (z - q_n)$$

has zeros outside of the unit circle.

The function

$$\gamma(z) = \frac{P(Q)}{Q(z)}, \qquad |\gamma(e^{-i\lambda})|^2 = \frac{1}{2\pi} f(\lambda),$$

is a maximal analytic function in the unit circle $|z| < 1$, and in the discrete case the stationary process $\xi(t)$ with the spectral density $f(\lambda)$ is obtained from the fundamental process with uncorrelated values by means of the linear transformation with the spectral characteristic $\varphi(\lambda) = \gamma(e^{-i\lambda})$. The connection between the processes $\xi = \xi(t)$ and $\zeta = \zeta(t)$ can be described by

$$\sum_{k=0}^{n} b_k \, \xi(t-k) = \sum_{k=0}^{m} a_k \, \zeta(t-k).$$

Let

$$f(\lambda) = \frac{\Sigma \, c_k \lambda^k}{\Sigma \, d_k \lambda^k}$$

be a rational function of λ which is non-negative and integrable on the real line $-\infty < \lambda < \infty$, and assume that the denumerator and denominator have no common divisors. On the real line the zeros of the polynomial in the numerator must have an even multiplicity whereas the polynomial in the denominator has no such zeros. The function $f(\lambda)$ can always be expressed in the following form:

$$f(\lambda) = \frac{1}{2\pi} \frac{|P(\lambda)|^2}{|Q(\lambda)|^2}$$

where the polynomial

$$P(z) = \sum_{k=1}^{m} a_k z^k = a_m(z - p_1) \dots (z - p_m)$$

has zeros in the upper half-plane or on the real line, and the polynomial

$$Q(z) = \sum_{k=1}^{n} b_k z^k = (z - q_1) \dots (z - q_n)$$

has zeros in the upper half-plane.

The function

$$\gamma(z) = \frac{P(z)}{Q(z)}, \qquad |\gamma(\lambda)|^2 = \frac{1}{2\pi} f(\lambda)$$

is a maximal analytic function on the lower half-plane $\operatorname{Im} z < 0$, and in the continuous case the stationary process $\xi(t)$ with the spectral density $f(\lambda)$ is obtained from the fundamental "white noise" process $\zeta = \langle u, \zeta \rangle$, by means of the linear transformation with the spectral characteristic $\varphi(\lambda) = \gamma(\lambda)$. The connection between the generalized processes $\xi = \langle u, \xi \rangle$ and $\zeta = \langle u, \zeta \rangle$ can be expressed like this:

$$\sum_{k=0}^{n} b_k \, \xi^{(k)} = \sum_{k=0}^{m} a_k \, \zeta^{(k)}.$$

Complete Regularity. Consider a linearly regular stationary process $\xi = \xi(t)$, $\mathbb{M}\, \xi(t) \equiv 0$ which satisfies the condition of complete linear regularity:

$$r(t - s) = \sup \mathbb{M}\, h_1 \, \overline{h_2} \to 0$$

for $t - s \to \infty$, where sup is taken with respect to all $h_1 \in H(-\infty, s)$ and $h_2 \in H(t, \infty)$ with $\mathbb{M}\, h_1 = \mathbb{M}\, h_2 = 1$.

Let us pause at the case of a discrete time t. If the stationary process $\xi = \xi(t)$ satisfies the condition mentioned above, then its spectral density $f = f(\lambda)$ can be represented by

$$f(\lambda) = |P(\lambda)|^2 \, g(\lambda)$$

where $P = P(\lambda)$ is a trigonometrical polynomial and the function $g = g(\lambda)$ has no zeros; more precisely, for each λ_0 we have

$$\lim_{\lambda \to \lambda_0} \frac{g(\lambda)}{|\log|\lambda - \lambda_0||} = \infty.$$

Moreover the primitive function $G = G(\lambda)$ of g has the property that

$$\omega(h) = \sup_{\mu \leq h} \sup_{\lambda} \frac{|G(\lambda + \mu) - 2G(\lambda) + G(\lambda - \mu)|}{|G(\lambda + \mu) - G(\lambda)|} \to 0$$

for $h \to 0$.

If the spectral density $f = f(\lambda)$ of the stationary process $\xi = \xi(t)$ can be represented in the form described above where

$$\sum_{k=1}^{\infty} [\omega(2^{-k})]^2 < \infty,$$

then the stationary process $\xi = \xi(t)$ satisfies the condition of complete linear regularity. The relation

$$r(t - s) = 0\{(t - s)^{-n-\alpha}\},$$

where n is a positive integer and $0 < \alpha < 1$, holds if and only if the corresponding function $g(\lambda)$ has an n-th derivative $g^{(n)}(\lambda)$ which satisfies the Hölder condition with the exponent α:

$$\sup_{\lambda} |g^{(n)}(\lambda + h) - g^{(n)}(\lambda)| = 0\{h^{\alpha}\}$$

for $h \to 0$.

The relation

$$r(t - s) = 0\{e^{-c(t-s)}\} \qquad (c > 0)$$

is satisfied if and only if the spectral density $f(\lambda)$ can be extended analytically into the stripe $-c < \text{Im}\,\lambda < c$ of the complex λ-plane. In particular stationary processes with rational spectral densities have this property.

Analogous results hold in the continuous case. In particular, let the spectral density $f = f(\lambda)$ be represented in the form

$$f(\lambda) = |P(\lambda)|^2 \, g(\lambda)$$

where $P = P(\lambda)$ is an analytic function of exponential type: $P(\lambda) = \int_{-\tau}^{\tau} a(t) e^{i\lambda t}\, dt$, $\int_{-\infty}^{\infty} |a(t)|^2\, dt < \infty$, and let $g = g(\lambda)$ have the following properties: $\int_{-\infty}^{\infty} \dfrac{|\log g(\lambda)|}{1 + \lambda^2} < \infty$, and the function $\log g(\lambda)$ has an n-th derivative which satisfies the Hölder condition with exponent α. Then [63]

$$r(t - s) = 0\{(t - s)^{-n-\alpha}\} \, .$$

3. Linear Prediction of Stationary Processes

The Prediction Problem. Suppose that we are interested in the value of some variable η, $\text{M}|\eta|^2 < \infty$, but we know only the values of the stationary process $\xi = \xi(t)$ at the instants of time t of some set T. In other words, we are interested in the prediction of the variable η on the basis of the values $\xi(t)$, $t \in T$.

The prediction $\hat{\eta} = \hat{\eta}[\xi(t), t \in T]$ is a functional of $\xi(t)$, $t \in T$. The prediction is called *linear* if the variable $\hat{\eta}$ is an element of the subspace $H(T)$, that is, an element of the closed linear space spanned by the values $\xi(t)$, $t \in T$. A linear prediction $\hat{\eta}$ is called a *best* linear prediction if

$$\varepsilon^2 = \text{M}|\eta - \hat{\eta}|^2 = \inf_{h \in H(T)} \text{M}|\eta - h|^2 \, .$$

Geometrically speaking, the problem of best linear prediction consists in the following. We are given an element η of the Hilbert space

[63] *Ibragimov, I. A.,* On conditions of strong mixture for stationary Gaussian processes. Dokl. AN SSSR, **161**, 1 (1965), 33—36 (Russian).

$L^2(\Omega)$ and a subspace $H(T)$. We are to draw the orthogonal projection of η onto this subspace. The base of this projection will then be the best linear prediction of the variable η.

When solving the prediction problem it is natural to assume that we know the correlations between η and the "observed" variables $\xi(t)$, $t \in T$, that is, the function $\mathbb{M}[\eta \xi(t)]$ of $t \in T$, and the correlation function $B = B(t)$ or the spectral measure $F = F(\Delta)$ of the stationary process $\xi = \xi(t)$. On the basis of these data we are to find the spectral characteristic $\hat{\varphi}(\lambda)$ of the variable

$$\hat{\eta} = \int \hat{\varphi}(\lambda) \, \Phi(d\lambda)$$

which yields the best linear prediction; here $\Phi = \Phi(\Delta)$ is the spectral stochastic measure of the stationary process $\xi = \xi(t)$.

The orthogonal projection of η onto $H(T)$ is uniquely determined by the following two conditions: first, we have $\hat{\eta} \in H(T)$, and secondly, the difference $\eta - \hat{\eta}$ is orthogonal to all variables $\xi(t)$, $t \in T$. This is equivalent to the fact that the spectral characteristic $\hat{\varphi}(\lambda)$ of the variables $\hat{\eta}$ belongs to the space L_T^2 and satisfies the integral equation

$$\int e^{-i\lambda t} \, \hat{\varphi}(\lambda) \, F(d\lambda) = \mathbb{M}[\eta \, \xi(t)] \qquad (t \in T).$$

A solution of this equation always exists and is unique in the class $L_T^2(F)$.

Example. Let T be a finite set. Then the spectral characteristic $\hat{\varphi} = \hat{\varphi}(\lambda)$ is a function of the form

$$\hat{\varphi}(\lambda) = \sum_{t \in T} a(t) \, e^{i\lambda t},$$

and the integral equation reduces to a system of linear equations for the unknown coefficients $a(t)$, $t \in T$:

$$\sum_{s \in T} a(s) \, B(s - t) = \mathbb{M}[\eta \cdot \xi(t)] \qquad (t \in T),$$

where $B = B(t)$ is the correlation function of the process $\xi = \xi(t)$.

Linear Extrapolation. In the following the most important problem will be that of the prediction of the process $\xi = \xi(t)$. Suppose that all values $\xi(s)$ are known until the instant t, that is, $s \leq t$, and it is required to give the best prediction of the unknown variables $\xi(t + \tau)$, $\tau > 0$. When dealing with this problem it seems natural to single out the class of processes for which a correct linear prediction is possible: for any $\tau > 0$ we have

$$\hat{\xi}(t + \tau) = \xi(t + \tau).$$

These processes are called *linearly singular*. The singularity condition is equivalent to the fact that for all t we have

$$H[-\infty, t] = H[-\infty, \infty].$$

Example. Any process with a *bounded spectrum*

$$\xi(t) = \int_{-W}^{W} e^{i\lambda t}\, \Phi(d\lambda) \quad (W < \infty)$$

is singular; here the time t is continuous. Such a process $\xi(t)$ is analytical, and hence for any t

$$\xi(t) = \sum_{0}^{\infty} \frac{1}{n!}\, \xi^{(n)}(t_0)\, (t - t_0)^n\,.$$

Example. Every stationary process with a *discrete spectrum* is singular:

$$\xi(t) = \sum_{\lambda \in \Lambda} e^{i\lambda t}\, \Phi(\lambda)$$

where the summation is extended over some finite or countably infinite set Λ of points λ, in fact the points of the spectrum of the process $\xi(t)$. With probability 1 each trajectory of $\xi(t)$ is an almost periodic function and can be completely restored from its values on a half-line of the time axis.

In order that a stationary process $\xi = \xi(t)$ with the spectral measure F be linearly singular it is necessary and sufficient that

$$\int \log \frac{F(d\lambda)}{d\lambda} \cdot \frac{d\lambda}{1 + \lambda^2} = -\infty\,;$$

here we set $\log[F(d\lambda)/d\lambda] = -\infty$ for $F(d\lambda)/d\lambda = 0$. In particular, if the density $F(d\lambda)/d\lambda$ of a stationary process vanishes on some set of positive Lebesgue measure, the process is singular.

Every stationary process $\xi(t)$ can be written as a sum of two uncorrelated stationary processes, a regular process $\xi_r(t)$ and a singular process $\xi_s(t)$, each of them being obtained from $\xi(t)$ by a physically realizable linear transformation:

$$\xi(t) = \xi_r(t) + \xi_s(t)\,,$$
$$\mathsf{M}\,\xi_r(t_1)\,\xi_s(t_2) = 0 \quad \text{for all } t_1 \text{ and } t_2\,.$$

If in this decomposition both components $\xi_r = \xi_r(t)$ and $\xi_s = \xi_s(t)$ are present, then the spectral measure $F_r = F_r(\Delta)$ of the regular part equals $F_r(\Delta) = \displaystyle\int_{\Delta} \frac{F(d\lambda)}{d\lambda}\, d\lambda$, and the spectral measure $F_s = F_s(\Delta)$ coincides with the singular part of the measure $F = F(\Delta)$. Moreover, if Δ "carries" the singular part $F_s : F_s(\Delta) = F_s(-\infty, \infty)$, then for $F_r(\Delta) = 0$ we have

$$\xi_r(t) = \int e^{i\lambda t}[1 - \varphi_\Delta(\lambda)]\, \Phi(d\lambda)$$
$$\xi_s(t) = \int e^{i\lambda t}\, \varphi_\Delta(\lambda)\, \Phi(d\lambda)\,,$$

where

$$\varphi_\Delta(\lambda) = \begin{cases} 1 & \text{if } \lambda \in \Delta , \\ 0 & \text{if } \lambda \notin \Delta . \end{cases}$$

The problem of predicting a stationary process $\xi = \xi(t)$ is reduced to the prediction of its regular part $\xi_r = \xi_r(t)$:

$$\hat{\xi}(t + \tau) = \hat{\xi}_r(t + \tau) + \hat{\xi}_s(t + \tau) .$$

The General Formula of Extrapolation (Discrete Case). Let $\xi = \xi(t)$ be a linearly regular stationary process with discrete time and $\zeta = \zeta(t)$ its corresponding fundamental process with uncorrelated values:

$$\xi(t) = \sum_{-\infty}^{t} c(t - s) \zeta(s) .$$

The fundamental process has the property that for arbitrary t the closed linear hull of the values $\zeta(s)$, $s \leq t$ coincides with the corresponding hull $H(-\infty, t)$ of the values $\xi(s)$, $s \leq t$. Therefore the best prediction for $\xi(t + \tau)$ is

$$\hat{\xi}(t + \tau) = \sum_{-\infty}^{t} c(t + \tau - s) \zeta(s) ,$$

and the mean square error of this prediction can be expressed like this:

$$\varepsilon^2 = \mathbf{M} |\xi(t + \tau) - \hat{\xi}(t + \tau)|^2 = \sum_{0}^{\tau - 1} |c(s)|^2 .$$

The stationary process $\hat{\xi} = \hat{\xi}(t + \tau)$, $-\infty < t < \infty$ which is the best prediction of the process $\xi = \xi(t)$ by τ "steps" forward can be obtained by the physically realizable linear transformation with the spectral characteristic

$$\hat{\varphi}(\lambda, \tau) = e^{i\lambda\tau} \left[\varphi(\lambda) - \sum_{0}^{\tau-1} c(s) e^{-i\lambda s} \right] \varphi^{-1}(\lambda) ,$$

$$\hat{\xi}(t + \tau) = \int_{-\pi}^{\pi} e^{i\lambda t} \hat{\varphi}(\lambda, \tau) \Phi(d\lambda) ,$$

where $\varphi(\lambda) = \gamma(e^{-i\lambda})$ is the boundary value of the maximal analytic function $\gamma(z) = \sum_{0}^{\infty} c(t) z^t$ in the unit circle with the boundary condition $|\gamma(e^{-i\lambda})|^2 = \dfrac{1}{2\pi} f(\lambda)$, f the spectral density of the stationary process $\xi = \xi(t)$, and Φ its spectral stochastic measure.

Example. Suppose that the stationary process $\xi = \xi(t)$ has the correlation function

$$B(t) = \sigma^2 e^{-\alpha |t|} \qquad (\alpha > 0).$$

Its spectral density $f(\lambda)$ equals

$$f(\lambda) = \frac{\sigma^2}{2\pi} \frac{1 - \beta^2}{|1 - \beta e^{i\lambda}|^2}, \qquad \beta = e^{-\alpha}$$

hence

$$\varphi(\lambda) = \sigma \sqrt{1 - \beta^2} \, \frac{1}{1 - \beta e^{-i\lambda}} = \sigma \sqrt{1 - \beta^2} \sum_0^\infty \beta^k e^{-i\lambda k},$$

$$\hat{\varphi}(\lambda, \tau) = e^{i\lambda \tau} \sum_\tau^m \beta^s e^{-i\lambda s} \, \frac{1}{1 - \beta e^{-i\lambda}} = \beta^\tau .$$

Thus the formula

$$\hat{\xi}(t + \tau) = \int_{-\pi}^\pi e^{i\lambda t} \, \hat{\varphi}(\lambda, \tau) \, \Phi(d\lambda) = \beta^\tau \xi(t)$$

yields the best linear prediction for $\xi(t + \tau)$.

Example. Suppose that the stationary process $\xi(t)$ has a spectral density of the form

$$f(\lambda) = \frac{1}{2\pi} \cdot \frac{1}{|Q(e^{-i\lambda})|^2}$$

where the polynomial $Q(z) = \sum_0^n b_k z^k$ has no zeros within the unit circle. Then

$$\varphi(\lambda) = \frac{1}{Q(e^{-i\lambda})} \sum_0^\infty c_k e^{-i\lambda k},$$

$$\hat{\varphi}(\lambda, \tau) = e^{i\lambda \tau} \left[1 - Q(e^{-i\lambda}) \sum_0^{\tau - 1} c_k e^{-i\lambda k} \right] = \sum_0^{n-1} a_{k+\tau} e^{-i\lambda k},$$

$$a_m = \sum_{\substack{k+r=m \\ k \leq \tau - 1}} c_k b_r .$$

In this way the best linear prediction is given by

$$\hat{\xi}(t + \tau) = \int_{-\pi}^\pi e^{i\lambda t} \, \hat{\varphi}(\lambda, \tau) \, \Phi(d\lambda) = \sum_0^{n-1} a_{k+\tau} \xi(t - k).$$

In the case of a stationary process with a spectral density which is rational with respect to $e^{-i\lambda}$, the spectral characteristic $\hat{\varphi}(\lambda, \tau)$ of the best prediction by τ steps forward is also a rational function of $e^{-i\lambda}$.

The General Formula of Extrapolation (Continuous Case). Let $\xi = \xi(t)$ be a linearly regular stationary process with continuous time and $\zeta = \zeta(\varDelta)$ its corresponding fundamental stochastic measure:

$$\xi(t) = \int_{-\infty}^{t} c(t-s)\,\zeta(ds).$$

The fundamental stochastic measure has the property that for arbitrary t the closed linear hull of the values $\zeta(\varDelta)$ for intervals $\varDelta \subseteq (-\infty, t]$ coincides with the closed linear hull $H(-\infty, t)$ of the values $\xi(s)$, $s \leq t$. Thus the best prediction for $\xi(t+\tau)$ is equal to

$$\hat{\xi}(t+\tau) = \int_{-\infty}^{t} c(t+\tau-s)\,\zeta(ds),$$

and the "mean square error" of this prediction is given by

$$\varepsilon^2 = \mathbf{M}\,|\xi(t+\tau) - \hat{\xi}(t+\tau)|^2 = \int_{0}^{\tau} |c(s)|^2\,ds.$$

For fixed τ the best linear prediction $\hat{\xi} = \hat{\xi}(t+\tau)$ of the stationary process $\xi = \xi(t)$ is a stationary process which can be obtained by the physically realizable linear transformation with the spectral characteristic

$$\hat{\varphi}(\lambda, \tau) = e^{i\lambda\tau}\left[\varphi(\lambda) - \int_{0}^{\tau} e^{-i\lambda s} c(s)\,ds\right]\varphi^{-1}(\lambda).$$

This prediction is given by the formula

$$\hat{\xi}(t+\tau) = \int_{-\infty}^{\infty} e^{i\lambda t}\,\hat{\varphi}(\lambda, \tau)\,\Phi(d\lambda)$$

where $\varphi(\lambda) = \gamma(\lambda)$ is the boundary value of the analytic function $\gamma(z) = \int_{0}^{\infty} e^{-izt} c(t)\,dt$ in the lower half-plane with the boundary condition $|\gamma(\lambda)|^2 = \dfrac{1}{2\pi}\,f(\lambda)$.

Example. Let the stationary process $\xi(t)$ have the correlation function

$$B(t) = \sigma^2\,e^{-\alpha|t|} \qquad (\alpha > 0).$$

Its spectral density $f(\lambda)$ equals

$$f(\lambda) = \frac{\alpha^2}{\pi}\,\frac{\alpha^2}{|\alpha + i\lambda|^2},$$

hence

$$\varphi(\lambda) = \sigma \sqrt{2\alpha} \, \frac{1}{\alpha + i\lambda} = \sigma \sqrt{2\alpha} \int_0^\infty e^{-i\lambda t} \, e^{-\alpha t} \, dt,$$

$$\hat{\varphi}(\lambda, \tau) = e^{i\lambda \tau} \int_\tau^\infty e^{-i\lambda t} \, e^{-\alpha t} \, dt \cdot \frac{1}{\alpha + i\lambda} = e^{-\alpha \tau}.$$

In this way the best linear prediction for $\xi(t + \tau)$ is given by

$$\hat{\xi}(t + \tau) = \int_{-\infty}^\infty e^{i\lambda t} \, \hat{\varphi}(\lambda, \tau) \, \Phi(d\lambda) = e^{-\alpha \tau} \, \xi(t).$$

Extrapolation Formula for Processes with Rational Spectral Densities.
Suppose that the spectral density of a stationary process is rational with respect to λ:

$$f(\lambda) = \frac{1}{2\pi} \frac{|P(\lambda)|^2}{|Q(\lambda)|^2}.$$

Then the spectral characteristic $\hat{\varphi}(\lambda, \tau)$ of the best prediction by the time τ ahead is also a rational function which is analytic in the lower half-plane:

$$\hat{\varphi}(\lambda, \tau) = \frac{\sum\limits_0^v x_k \lambda^k}{P(\lambda)}$$

where the degree v is smaller than the degree n of the polynomial $Q(\lambda)$. The indefinite coefficients x_k can be obtained from the condition that the function

$$\varphi(\lambda, \tau) = \frac{e^{i\lambda \tau} P(\lambda) - \sum\limits_0^v x_k \lambda^k}{P(\lambda)} f(\lambda)$$

is analytic in the upper half-plane.

If q_j are the zeros of the polynomial $Q(z)$, each of them with multiplicity n_j, then the coefficients x_k satisfy the system of linear equations

$$\frac{d^m}{d\lambda^m} \left[e^{i\lambda \tau} P(\lambda) - \sum_{k=0}^v x_k \lambda^k \right] \Bigg|_{\lambda = q_j} = 0$$

where $m = 0, 1, \ldots, n_j$ and $\Sigma n_j = n$.

Example. Let the stationary process $\xi(t)$ have a spectral density $f(\lambda)$ of the form

$$f(\lambda) = \frac{1}{2\pi} \cdot \frac{1}{|Q(\lambda)|^2}$$

where the polynomial $Q(z) = \sum_{0}^{n} b_k z^k$ has no zeros in the lower half-plane. Then the spectral characteristic $\hat{\varphi}(\lambda, \tau)$ is just a polynomial

$$\hat{\varphi}(\lambda, \tau) = \sum_{0}^{v} x_k \lambda^k$$

where the x_k are obtained from the system of linear equations

$$\frac{d^m}{d\lambda^m}\left[e^{i\lambda\tau} - \sum_{0}^{v} x_k \lambda^k\right]\Bigg|_{\lambda=q_j} = 0\,;$$

here the q_j are the roots of $Q(z)$ with corresponding multiplicities n_j, $m = 0, \ldots, n_j$, $\Sigma n_j = n$. Thus the formula of best prediction of $\xi(t+\tau)$ has the form

$$\xi(t+\tau) = \int_{-\infty}^{\infty} e^{i\lambda t}\, \hat{\varphi}(\lambda, \tau)\, \Phi(d\lambda) = \sum_{0}^{v} (-1)^k x_k\, \xi^{(k)}(t)\,.$$

Stationarily Connected Processes. The stationary processes $\xi = \xi(t)$ and $\eta = \eta(t)$ are called *stationarily connected* if their *joint correlation function* $B_{\xi\eta}(s, t) = \mathbb{M}\,\xi(s)\,\overline{\eta(t)}$ does not depend on the origin of the time scale:

$$B_{\xi\eta}(s, t) = B_{\xi\eta}(s - t)\,.$$

If $\Phi_\xi = \Phi_\xi(\Delta)$ and $\Phi_\eta = \Phi_\eta(\Delta)$ are the stochastic spectral measures of the stationarily connected processes $\xi = \xi(t)$ and $\eta = \eta(t)$, then for any two disjoint intervals Δ_1 and Δ_2 we have

$$\mathbb{M}\,\Phi_\xi(\Delta_1)\,\overline{\Phi_\eta(\Delta_2)} = 0\,,$$

and

$$F_{\xi\eta}(\Delta) = \mathbb{M}\,\Phi_\xi(\Delta)\,\overline{\Phi_\eta(\Delta)}$$

is a generalized bounded measure on the Borel sets Δ which we call the *joint spectral measure* of $\xi = \xi(t)$ and $\eta = \eta(t)$. It is connected with the joint correlation function by

$$B_{\xi\eta}(t) = \int e^{i\lambda t} F_{\xi\eta}(d\lambda)\,.$$

If the generalized measure $F_{\xi\eta}$ is absolutely continuous, then the derivative $f_{\xi\eta}(\lambda) = \dfrac{F_{\xi\eta}(d\lambda)}{d\lambda}$ is called the *joint spectral density* of $\xi = \xi(t)$ and $\eta = \eta(t)$.

Linear Filtration. Let $\xi = \xi(t)$ and $\eta = \eta(t)$ be stationarily connected processes, where $\xi = \xi(t)$ is the process "under observation". It is required to give the best linear prediction $\hat{\eta}(t+\tau)$ of the unknown values $\eta(t+\tau)$ from the values $\xi(s)$, $s \leq t$; here, τ may be positive and negative as well. The best linear prediction $\hat{\eta} = \hat{\eta}(t + \tau)$, $-\infty < t < \infty$ is a stationary process which can be obtained by a physically realizable linear transformation:

$$\hat{\eta}(t + \tau) = \int e^{i\lambda t} \hat{\varphi}(\lambda, \tau) \, \Phi_\xi(d\lambda).$$

Consider now the case of a discrete time t and a linearly regular stationary process $\xi = \xi(t)$. The spectral characteristic $\hat{\varphi}(\lambda, \tau)$ can be expressed in the following way:

$$\hat{\varphi}(\lambda, \tau) = \left[\sum_{s=0}^{\infty} a(s + \tau) e^{-i\lambda s} \right] \varphi^{-1}(\lambda)$$

where

$$a(k) = \frac{1}{2\pi} \int_{-\pi}^{\pi} e^{i\lambda k} \, \varphi(\lambda) \frac{f_{\eta\xi}(\lambda)}{f_{\xi\xi}(\lambda)} \, d\lambda,$$

and where $\varphi(\lambda) = \gamma(e^{-i\lambda})$ is the boundary value of the maximal analytic function satisfying the boundary condition $|\gamma(e^{-i\lambda})|^2 = \frac{1}{2\pi} f_{\xi\xi}(\lambda)$; here $f_{\xi\xi}(\lambda)$ stands for the spectral density of the process $\xi = \xi(t)$ and $f_{\eta\xi}(\lambda)$ for the joint spectral density of $\eta = \eta(t)$ and $\xi = \xi(t)$.

Example. Suppose that the stationary processes $\xi(t)$ and $\eta(t)$ satisfy

$$f_{\xi\xi}(\lambda) = \frac{a^2}{2\pi} \cdot \frac{|1 - \alpha e^{-i\lambda}|^2}{|1 - \beta e^{-i\lambda}|^2}, \qquad f_{\eta\xi}(\lambda) = \frac{b e^{-i\lambda}(1 - \alpha e^{-i\lambda})}{e^{-i\lambda} - \beta}$$

where $\alpha > 0$, $\beta < 1$. Then

$$\varphi(\lambda) = a \frac{1 - \alpha e^{-i\lambda}}{1 - \beta e^{-i\lambda}},$$

$$\frac{1}{2\pi} \varphi(\lambda) \frac{f_{\eta\xi}(\lambda)}{f_{\xi\xi}(\lambda)} = \frac{b}{a} \cdot \frac{1 - \alpha e^{-i\lambda}}{1 - \alpha e^{i\lambda}} = \frac{b}{a} \left[-\alpha e^{-i\lambda} + (1 - \alpha^2) \sum_{k=0}^{\infty} \alpha^k e^{i\lambda k} \right];$$

thus the coefficients $a(k)$ in the formula for the spectral characteristic $\hat{\varphi}(\lambda, \tau)$ are equal to

$$a(0) = \frac{b}{a}(1 - \alpha^2), \qquad a(1) = -\frac{b\alpha}{a}, \qquad a(2) = a(3) = \cdots = 0.$$

Therefore the best linear prediction for $\tau = 0$ will be given by

$$\hat{\eta}(t, 0) = \frac{b}{a^2} \int_{-\pi}^{\pi} e^{i\lambda t} \frac{(1 - \alpha^2 - \alpha e^{-i\lambda})(1 - \beta e^{-i\lambda})}{1 - \alpha e^{-i\lambda}} \, \Phi_\xi(d\lambda)$$

$$= \frac{b}{a^2} \left[(1 - \alpha^2) \xi(t) - (\alpha^3 + \beta(1 - \alpha^2)) \xi(t - 1) + \alpha(\beta - \alpha) \sum_{k=2}^{\infty} \alpha^k \xi(t - k) \right].$$

21*

Next let the time t be continuous. Then the spectral characteristic $\hat{\varphi}(\lambda, \tau)$ can be expressed in the following way:

$$\hat{\varphi}(\lambda, \tau) = \left[\int_0^\infty e^{-i\lambda s} a(s + \tau) \, ds \right] \varphi^{-1}(\lambda)$$

where

$$a(t) = \frac{1}{2\pi} \int_{-\infty}^\infty e^{i\lambda t} \, \varphi(\lambda) \, \frac{f_{\eta\xi}(\lambda)}{f_{\xi\xi}(\lambda)} \, d\lambda,$$

and $\varphi(\lambda) = \gamma(\lambda)$ is the boundary value of the maximal analytic function $\gamma = \gamma(z)$ in the lower half-plane satisfying the boundary condition $|\gamma(\lambda)|^2 = \dfrac{1}{2\pi} f(\lambda)$.

Let the spectral densities $f_{\xi\xi}(\lambda) = \dfrac{1}{2\pi} \cdot \dfrac{|P(\lambda)|^2}{|Q(\lambda)|^2}$ and $f_{\eta\xi}(\lambda)$ be rational with respect to λ. In this case the spectral characteristic $\hat{\varphi}(\lambda, \tau)$ is also rational with respect to λ and can be represented in the form

$$\hat{\varphi}(\lambda, \tau) = \frac{Q(\lambda)}{P(\lambda)} \cdot \frac{\sum\limits_0^v x_k \lambda^k}{(\lambda - r_1) \dots (\lambda - r_n)},$$

where $r_1, \dots, r_n$ are the poles of the joint spectral density $f_{\eta\xi}(\lambda)$ in the upper half-plane, and the degree v of the polynomial in the denominator is smaller than the number n of these poles, each of them being counted with its multiplicity. The coefficients $x_1, \dots, x_v$ can be obtained from the condition that the function

$$\psi(\lambda, \tau) = e^{i\lambda\tau} f_{\eta\xi}(\lambda) - \hat{\varphi}(\lambda, \tau) f_{\xi\xi}(\lambda)$$

be analytic in the upper half-plane. This condition amounts to the fact that the expression

$$e^{i\lambda\tau} f_{\eta\xi}(\lambda) \left[(\lambda - r_1) \dots (\lambda - r_n) \right] - \frac{Q(\lambda)}{P(\lambda)} f_{\xi\xi}(\lambda) \sum_{k=0}^v x_k \lambda^k$$

and its derivatives up to the order $n_j - 1$ inclusively must vanish at each point λ, $\operatorname{Im} \lambda > 0$, which is a pole of the order n_j of the function $f_{\eta\xi}(\lambda)$.

Example. Suppose that the stationary processes $\xi(t)$ and $\eta(t)$ satisfy

$$f_{\xi\xi}(\lambda) = \frac{a^2(\lambda^2 + \alpha^2)}{2\pi(\lambda^2 + \beta^2)(\lambda^2 + \gamma^2)}, \qquad f_{\eta\xi}(\lambda) = \frac{b}{\lambda^2 + \gamma^2}$$

where α, β, $\gamma > 0$. Then the corresponding polynomials $P(\lambda)$ and $Q(\lambda)$ are given by the formulas

$$P(\lambda) = a(\lambda - i\alpha), \qquad Q(\lambda) = (\lambda - i\beta)(\lambda - i\gamma),$$

respectively, so that the spectral characteristic $\hat{\varphi}(\lambda, \tau)$ has the form

$$\hat{\varphi}(\lambda, \tau) = x \frac{\lambda - i\beta}{\lambda - i\alpha}$$

where the coefficient x is determined by the condition that the function $\psi(\lambda, \tau)$ be analytic. In the present case this condition amounts to the equation

$$e^{-\gamma\tau} \frac{b}{2i\gamma} + \frac{ia(\gamma + a)}{(\gamma + \beta) 2\gamma} x = 0.$$

Thus

$$\hat{\eta}(t, \tau) = \int_{-\infty}^{\infty} e^{i\lambda t} \left[\frac{b}{a} e^{-\gamma\tau} \frac{\beta + \gamma}{\alpha + \gamma} \cdot \frac{\lambda - i\beta}{\lambda - i\alpha} \right] \Phi_\xi(d\lambda)$$

$$= \frac{b}{a} e^{-\gamma\tau} \frac{\beta + \gamma}{\alpha + \gamma} \left[\xi(t) + (\beta - \alpha) \int_0^{\infty} e^{-\alpha s} \xi(t - s)\, ds \right].$$

Linear Interpolation. Consider the problem of best linear prediction of the unknown values $\xi(t)$ of a stationary process on the interval $\tau_1 \leq t \leq \tau_2$ from the remaining values $\xi(t)$ which correspond to $t < \tau_1$ and $t > \tau_2$. For the solution of this problem we can assume without loss of generality that $\tau_1 = -\tau$ and $\tau_2 = \tau$, and that the process $\xi = \xi(t)$ itself has a spectral density $f = f(\lambda)$.

From the point of view of the problem of linear interpolation it seems natural to single out the class of processes which can be exactly interpolated, that is, processes with the property that for any τ the best linear prediction $\hat{\xi}(t)$ of the unknown values $\xi(t)$, $-\tau \leq t \leq \tau$, coincides with $\xi(t)$. Geometrically speaking, the condition of an exact interpolation of $\xi = \xi(t)$ looks like this: for any τ we have

$$H(T) = H(-\infty, \infty)$$

where $T = (-\infty, -\tau) \cup (\tau, \infty)$, and $H(T)$ denotes the closed linear hull of the values $\xi(t)$, $t \in T$. This is equivalent to the following analytic condition:

$$\int \frac{|P(\lambda)|^2}{f(\lambda)}\, d\lambda = \infty$$

in the case of discrete t for any trigonometric polynomial $P(\lambda) = \sum_k a_k e^{i\lambda k}$, and in the case of continuous t for any analytic function of exponential type $P(\lambda) = \int_{-\tau}^{\tau} a(t) e^{i\lambda t} \, dt$, where $P(\lambda) \not\equiv 0$.

Let us consider the case of discrete time t. A number λ_0 is called a *zero of order k* for the function $f(\lambda)$ if

$$\int_{-\pi}^{\pi} \frac{|\lambda - \lambda_0|^{k-1}}{f(\lambda)} \, d\lambda = \infty, \qquad \int_{-\pi}^{\pi} \frac{|\lambda - \lambda_0|^k}{f(\lambda)} \, d\lambda < \infty.$$

The stationary process $\xi(t)$ cannot be exactly interpolated if and only if its spectral density $f(\lambda)$ has only a finite number of zeros, each of them of finite order. Let $\lambda_1, \ldots, \lambda_n$ be the zeros of the spectral density of such a process $\xi(t)$, and let λ_j have the order k_j. We set

$$P_0(\lambda) = \prod_{j=1}^{n} (e^{i\lambda} - e^{i\lambda_j})^{m_j}$$

where $m_j = [k_j + 1/2]$ is the integral part of the number $(k_j + 1)/2$.

The trigonometric polynomial $P_0(\lambda)$ has the property that

$$\int_{-\pi}^{\pi} \frac{|P_0(\lambda)|^2}{f(\lambda)} \, d\lambda < \infty,$$

and every trigonometric polynomial $P(\lambda)$ with this property is divisible by $P_0(\lambda)$:

$$P(\lambda) = P_0(\lambda) \sum_k a_k e^{i\lambda k}.$$

The values $\xi(t)$, $-\tau \leq t \leq \tau$ admit an exact linear interpolation for a given τ if and only if $2\tau \leq m$ where $m = \sum_{j=1}^{n} m_j$ is the degree of the minimal trigonometric polynomial $P_0(\lambda)$.

Assume that $2\tau > m$. The best linear prediction $\hat{\xi}(t)$ of the variable $\xi(t)$ is the orthogonal projection of $\xi(t)$ to the subspace $H(T)$ where $T = (-\infty, \tau) \cup (\tau, \infty)$. It admits the spectral representation

$$\hat{\xi}(t) = \int_{-\pi}^{\pi} \hat{\varphi}(\lambda) \, \Phi(d\lambda),$$

and the spectral characteristic is expressed by

$$\hat{\varphi}(\lambda) = e^{i\lambda t} - e^{-i\lambda \tau} \frac{P_0(\lambda)}{f(\lambda)} \sum_{k=0}^{2\tau - m} x_k e^{i\lambda k}.$$

The indefinite coefficients $x_k, k = 0, \ldots, 2\tau - m$ can be obtained from the system of linear equations

$$\sum_{k=0}^{2\tau-m} x_k a_{k-j} = \begin{cases} 0 & \text{if } j \neq t + \tau, \\ 1 & \text{if } j = t + \tau, \end{cases}$$

where $j = 0, \ldots, 2\tau - m$, and

$$a_k = \frac{1}{2\pi} \int_{-\pi}^{\pi} \frac{P_0(\lambda)}{f(\lambda)} e^{i\lambda k} d\lambda.$$

Example. Assume that the spectral density $f = f(\lambda)$ has no zeros in the sense discussed above, and that $\tau = 0$. The best prediction of the variable $\xi(0)$ on the basis of the remaining values $\xi(t), t \neq 0$ can be written like this:

$$\hat{\xi}(0) = \int_{-\pi}^{\pi} \left\{ 1 - \frac{2\pi}{f(\lambda)} \left[\int_{-\pi}^{\pi} \frac{d\mu}{f(\mu)} \right]^{-1} \right\} \Phi(d\lambda);$$

the mean square error of this prediction equals

$$\varepsilon = (\mathbb{M}|\xi(0) - \hat{\xi}(0)|^2)^{1/2} = 2\pi \left(\int_{-\pi}^{\pi} \frac{d\lambda}{f(\lambda)} \right)^{-1/2}.$$

Integral Equation of the Linear Prediction Problem. Consider the following integral equation arising in problems of best linear prediction:

$$\int e^{-i\lambda t} \varphi(\lambda) F(d\lambda) = A(t) \qquad (t \in T)$$

where $F = F(\Delta)$ is a bounded measure, $A = A(t)$ some function defined on the set T, and $\varphi = \varphi(\lambda)$ an unknown function in the space L_T^2. This equation has a solution (which is unique) if and only if

$$\inf \int \left| \sum_{t_k \in T} c_k e^{i\lambda t} \right|^2 F(d\lambda) > 0$$

where inf is taken with respect to all $c_1, c_2, \ldots$ such that

$$\sum_{t_k \in T} c_k A(t_k) = 1;$$

here we exclude the trivial case $A(t) \equiv 0$ in which $\varphi(\lambda) \equiv 0$ is the unique solution in $L_T^2(F)$.

Let us investigate a method of finding the solution $\varphi(\lambda)$ when the corresponding process $\xi = \xi(t)$ is real with a rational spectral density $f(\lambda)$. Let the time t be continuous and the set T be an interval

$T = (-\tau, 0)$. We assume that the spectral density $f = f(\lambda)$ vanishes nowhere on the real axis. Such a spectral density can be written in the form

$$f(\lambda) = \frac{|P(i\lambda)|^2}{|Q(i\lambda)|^2}$$

where

$$P(z) = \sum_{k=1}^{m} a_k z^k, \qquad Q(z) = \sum_{k=0}^{n} b_k z^k$$

are polynomials with real coefficients. All zeros of these polynomials lie in the left half-plane.

If $\varphi = \varphi(\lambda)$ is the solution sought for, then the function

$$x(t) = \int_{-\infty}^{\infty} e^{-i\lambda t} \varphi(\lambda) \frac{1}{|Q(i\lambda)|^2} d\lambda,$$

which is defined for all real t, is the solution of the differential equation with constant coefficients

$$P\left(\frac{d}{dt}\right) P\left(-\frac{d}{dt}\right) x(t) = A(t) \qquad (-\tau < t < 0)$$

where the boundary conditions are given by the equations

$$Q\left(-\frac{d}{dt}\right) x^{(k)} (-\tau + 0) = 0,$$
$$Q\left(\frac{d}{dt}\right) x^{(k)} (-0) \quad\; = 0 \qquad (k = 0, 1, \ldots, m-1).$$

We then have

$$Q\left(\frac{d}{dt}\right) Q\left(-\frac{d}{dt}\right) x(t) = \int_{-\infty}^{\infty} e^{-i\lambda t} \varphi(\lambda) d\lambda,$$

so that the solution $\varphi = \varphi(\lambda)$ sought for is the Fourier transform of the generalized function $y(t) = Q\left(\frac{d}{dt}\right) Q\left(-\frac{d}{dt}\right) x(t)$. As regards "generalized components" this function contains only δ-functions and their derivatives in the endpoints of the interval $(-\tau, 0)$.

The solution $\varphi = \varphi(\lambda)$ can be written explicitly in the form

$$\varphi(\lambda) = e^{-i\lambda\tau} \sum_{k=0}^{n-m-1} (c_k' + c_k'') (i\lambda)^k + \int_{-\tau}^{0} e^{i\lambda t} c(t) dt$$

where

$$c(t) = \frac{1}{2\pi} Q\left(\frac{d}{dt}\right) Q\left(-\frac{d}{dt}\right) x(t),$$

$$c_k' = \frac{1}{2\pi} \sum_{j=m+k+1}^{n} b_j \left[Q\left(-\frac{d}{dt}\right) x^{(j-k-1)}(-\tau+0)\right],$$

$$c_k'' = \frac{1}{2\pi} \sum_{j=m+k+1}^{n} (-1)^j b_j \left[Q\left(\frac{d}{dt}\right) x^{(j-k-1)}(-0)\right].$$

An analogous method is employed in the case of discrete t.

4. Physical Interpretation of the Spectral Representation

Let $\xi = \xi(t)$ be a real stationary process. The spectral representation (1.1) can be rewritten in real form by using the fact that the spectral stochastic measure $\Phi = \Phi(\Delta)$ of a real stationary process satisfies the condition

$$\Phi(-\Delta) = \overline{\Phi(\Delta)}$$

where $-\Delta$ is the set of points $-\lambda, \lambda \in \Delta$. In fact,

$$\xi(t) = \int \cos(\lambda t)\, \Phi_1(d\lambda) + \int \sin(\lambda t)\, \Phi_2(d\lambda)$$

where we integrate either within the limits $0 \leq \lambda \leq \pi$ (for discrete t), or within the limits $0 \leq \lambda < \infty$ (for continuous t); here $\Phi_1 = \Phi_1(\Delta)$ and $\Phi_2 = \Phi_2(\Delta)$ are real stochastic measures such that

$$\Phi_1(\Delta) = 2\,\mathrm{Re}\,\Phi(\Delta), \qquad \Phi_2(\Delta) = -2\,\mathrm{Im}\,\Phi(\Delta),$$
$$\mathrm{M}\,\Phi_1(\Delta')\,\Phi_2(\Delta'') = 0$$

for any Δ' and Δ''.

The formula (1.1) yields the expansion of a stationary process into a "continuous" sum of harmonic oscillations $\Phi(d\lambda)\,e^{i\lambda t}$ with frequencies λ, amplitudes $|\Phi(d\lambda)|$ and phases $\arg\Phi(\lambda)$; the amplitudes and phases are random. The spectral measure $F = F(\Delta)$ describes the energy distribution of $\xi = \xi(t)$ to the various components $\Phi(d\lambda)\,e^{i\lambda t}$. The mean energy belonging to harmonic components with a frequency λ in the interval Δ equals up to a constant factor the corresponding value $F(\Delta)$.

Linear transformations. The spectral characteristic $\varphi = \varphi(\lambda)$ of the linearly transformed stationary process is closely connected with the so-called transmission function $\psi = \psi(p)$ of the corresponding linear system by means of which the given transformation is carried out. In fact, if at the input of the linear system with transmission function $\psi = \psi(p)$ we have a stationary process $\xi = \xi(t)$ (Fig. 26), then after stationary conditions have been established the output will be a stationary process $\eta = \eta(t)$ of the form $\eta(t) = \int_{-\infty}^{\infty} e^{i\lambda t} \varphi(\lambda) \, \Phi(d\lambda)$, where

$$\varphi(\lambda) = \psi(i\lambda)$$

is the spectral characteristic.

Regularity. Stationary processes occuring in reality arise as a rule from a random stationary perturbation $\zeta = \zeta(t)$ of the "white noise" type. The process $\zeta = \zeta(t)$ undergoes some physically realizable linear transformation which is often completely inaccessible to the observer's eye who deals only with the final result of this transformation, that is,

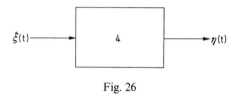

Fig. 26

the stationary process $\xi = \xi(t)$. The spectral density $f = f(\lambda)$ of the latter process in the spectral band ($-\pi \leq \lambda \leq \pi$ for an integer-valued time, and $-\infty < \lambda < \infty$ for continuous t) cannot vanish identically on any interval. In the opposite case the stationary process $\xi(t)$ would be singular, that is, it could be completely restored from the values on the half-line of time $(-\infty, t_0)$ until any instant t_0 alone. This may often seem to be paradox. Processes whose spectra are practically concentrated in some frequency interval $-W < \lambda < W$, and which do not at all share the properties of singular processes are widely spread in technics and other fields. From the point of view of energy these processes actually have a bounded spectrum in so far as the energy of their elementary harmonic oscillations $\Phi(d\lambda) e^{i\lambda t}$ with frequencies λ outside the interval $(-W, W)$ is weak; but these oscillations make themselves especially felt when we consider the problem of linear prediction of the values $\xi(t + \tau)$ from the values $\xi(s)$ on the half-line of time $s \leq t$.

Filtration and Smoothing. When considering problems of linear prediction, filtration and the like it often happens that under real conditions we have to fix our attention to one important factor, namely, the linear systems employed for the solution of one or the other problem must have a completely determined time constant T; this constant is also called the *time of the transition processes*. Precisely speaking, this means that the weight function $h = h(t)$ of the linear system under consideration, which is associated with the corresponding transmission function $\psi = \psi(p)$ by the equation

$$\psi(p) = \int_0^\infty e^{-pt}\, h(t)\, dt\,,$$

has to satisfy the requirement

$$h(t) = 0 \quad \text{for} \quad t > T\,.$$

Let us now consider the linear filtration problem in the case that to start with we are given a process $\xi = \xi(t)$ of the form

$$\xi(t) = \eta(t) + \zeta(t)\,,$$

where we usually call $\eta = \eta(t)$ the "effective signal" and the stochastic process $\zeta = \zeta(t)$ which we assume to be independent of $\eta = \eta(t)$, the "noise". The linear system with the time constant T has to be chosen in such a way that the output process $\hat{\xi} = \hat{\xi}(t)$ comes as close as possible to the input "effective signal" $\eta = \eta(t)$, more precisely, that under stationary working conditions

$$\mathsf{M}\,|\hat{\xi}(t) - \eta(t)|^2 = \min\,;$$

here it is assumed that $\eta = \eta(t)$ is a stationary random process. The linear system which satisfies these requirements must have a transmission function $\psi = \psi(p)$ with the property that the corresponding spectral characteristic $\varphi(\lambda) = \psi(i\lambda)$ is a solution of the integral equation

$$\int_{-\infty}^{\infty} e^{i\lambda t}\, \varphi(\lambda)\, f_{\xi\xi}(\lambda)\, d\lambda = B_{\eta\eta}(t) \quad (-T < t < 0)\,,$$

where $f_{\xi\xi}(\lambda) = f_{\eta\eta}(\lambda) + f_{\zeta\zeta}(\lambda)$ is the spectral density of the input process $\xi(t)$, and $B_{\eta\eta}(t)$ the correlation function of the "effective signal" $\eta(t)$.

Suppose that the "effective signal" $\eta(t)$ has the form

$$\eta(t) = \sum_{k=0}^{m} a_k\, e^{i\omega_k t} + \sum_{k=0}^{n} b_k\, t^k\,.$$

Under stationary working conditions every linear system with the transmission function $\psi(p)$ transforms the input function $\eta(t)$ into a function $\hat{\eta}(t)$ of the same type:

$$\hat{\eta}(t) = \sum_{k=0}^{m} \hat{a}_k\, e^{i\omega_k t} + \sum_{k=0}^{n} \hat{b}_k\, t^k\,,$$

where

$$\hat{a}_k = a_k\, \psi(i\omega_k) \quad (k = 0, \ldots, m)\,,$$

$$\hat{b}_k = \sum_{j=k}^{n} (-1)^j\, \frac{j!}{k!\,(j-k)!}\, b_j\, \psi^{(j-k)}(0) \quad (k = 0, \ldots, n)\,.$$

Let us imagine that the purpose of the linear system is to produce under stationary working conditions an output "signal" $\hat{\eta}(t)$ of a given type and to smooth at the same time the "disturbing noise" $\zeta(t)$ as much as possible, that is,

$$\mathbf{M}\,|\hat{\xi}(t) - \eta(t)|^2 = \min .$$

For example we may want to extract the "effective signal" $\eta(t)$ itself; in this case all coefficients a_k and b_k must coincide with the corresponding coefficients $\hat{a}_k$ and $\hat{b}_k$. The spectral characteristic $\varphi(\lambda) = \psi(i\lambda)$ of such a linear system is a solution of the integral equation

$$\int_{-\infty}^{\infty} e^{-i\lambda t}\,\varphi(\lambda)\,f_{\zeta\zeta}(\lambda)\,d\lambda = \sum_{k=0}^{m} c_k\,e^{i\omega_k t} + \sum_{k=0}^{n} d_k\,t^k ,$$

where the indefinite coefficients $c_0, \ldots, c_m$ and $d_0, \ldots, d_n$ can be obtained from the afore-mentioned relations between the coefficients a_k and $\hat{a}_k$ $(k = 0, \ldots, m)$, and b_k and $\hat{b}_k$ $(k = 0, \ldots, n)$, respectively.

5. Multi-Dimensional Stationary Processes

Spectral Representation. By a multi-dimensional wide sense stationary process $\xi = \xi(t)$ we understand a set of stationary and stationarily connected processes, say $\xi_1(t), \ldots, \xi_n(t)$; their number n is called the dimension of the process $\boldsymbol{\xi}(t) = \{\xi_1(t), \ldots, \xi_n(t)\}$.

The matrix $\boldsymbol{B}(t) = \{B_{kj}(t)\}$ $(k, j = 1, \ldots, n)$ whose elements $B_{kj}(t)$ are the corresponding joint correlation functions of the single components $\xi_k(t), k = 1, \ldots, n$, is called the *correlation function* of the multi-dimensional process $\boldsymbol{\xi}(t)$. The matrix function $\boldsymbol{F}(\varDelta) = \{F_{kj}(\varDelta)\}$ $(k, j = 1, \ldots, n)$ whose elements $F_{kj}(\varDelta)$ are the corresponding joint spectral measures of the components $\xi_k(t)$ is called the *spectral measure* of $\boldsymbol{\xi}(t)$. In the following we assume that all components of $\boldsymbol{\xi}(t)$ have spectral densities so that $\boldsymbol{\xi} = \boldsymbol{\xi}(t)$ also has a spectral density $\boldsymbol{f}(\lambda)$; by this we mean the matrix function $\boldsymbol{f} = \{f_{kj}\}$ $(k, j = 1, \ldots, n)$ consisting of the elements $f_{kj}(\lambda) = F_{kj}(d\lambda)/d\lambda$.

We denote by H the Hilbert subspace of the random variables h, $\mathbf{M}\,|h|^2 < \infty$, spanned by the values $\xi_k(t)$, $k = 1, 2, \ldots, n$; $-\infty < t < \infty$. Let $L^2(F)$, or simply L^2 be the set of all vector functions $\boldsymbol{\varphi} = \{\varphi_1, \ldots, \varphi_n\}$ such that

$$\int [\boldsymbol{\varphi}\,\boldsymbol{f}\,\boldsymbol{\varphi}^*(\lambda)]\,d\lambda = \int \left[\sum_{k,j} \varphi_k(\lambda)\,\overline{\varphi_j(\lambda)}\,f_{kj}(\lambda)\right]\,d\lambda < \infty ,$$

where

$$\boldsymbol{\varphi}^* = \left\{\begin{array}{c} \overline{\varphi}_1 \\ \vdots \\ \overline{\varphi}_n \end{array}\right\}$$

represents the column vector which is conjugate in the Hermitian sense to the row vector $\varphi = \{\varphi_1, \ldots, \varphi_n\}$. If we introduce the scalar product

$$(\varphi_1, \varphi_2) = \int [\varphi_1 \, f \, \varphi_2^*(\lambda)] \, d\lambda$$

in L^2, then we can establish an isometry between the space H and L^2 under which the vector function $e^{i\lambda k} \, \delta_k$ where the k-th component of δ_k equals 1 and the others equal 0, corresponds to the value $\xi_k(t)$.

Each element h of H can be represented in the form

$$h = \int (\varphi(\lambda) \, \Phi^*(d\lambda)) = \int \sum_{k=1}^{n} \varphi_k(\lambda) \, \Phi_k(d\lambda),$$

where $\varphi = \{\varphi_1, \ldots, \varphi_n\}$ is the function in the space L^2 which corresponds to the element h, and Φ_k is the spectral stochastic measure of the process $\xi_k(t)$, $k = 1, \ldots, n$. The vector function $\Phi = \{\Phi_1, \ldots, \Phi_n\}$ is called the stochastic spectral measure of the process $\xi(t) = \{\xi_1(t), \ldots, \xi_n(t)\}$. Moreover we have

$$\mathbb{M} h_1 h_2 = \int [\varphi_1 \, f \, \varphi_2^*(\lambda)] \, d\lambda$$

where the functions φ_1 and φ_2 in the space L^2 correspond to the elements h_1 and h_2.

Two functions φ_1 and φ_2 in the space $L^2(F)$ represent the same element of this space if their difference $\varphi = \varphi_1 - \varphi_2$ satisfies the condition

$$\varphi(\lambda) \, f(\lambda) \, \varphi^*(\lambda) \equiv \sum_{k,j=1}^{n} \varphi_k(\lambda) \, \overline{\varphi_j(\lambda)} \, f_{kj}(\lambda) = 0.$$

If for almost all λ the spectral density $f(\lambda)$ is a non-degenerate matrix, then φ_1 and φ_2 coincide if and only if $\varphi_1(\lambda) = \varphi_2(\lambda)$ almost everywhere. However, it is also possible that one and the same element is represented by two apparently different functions $\varphi_1(\lambda)$ and $\varphi_2(\lambda)$; for example, if all components $\xi_1(t), \ldots, \xi_n(t)$ of the multi-dimensional stationary process coincide, then for all $k = 1, \ldots, n$ the function $e^{i\lambda t} \, \delta_k$ represents the same element of the space $L^2(F)$ which corresponds to the general value $\xi_1(t) = \cdots = \xi_n(t)$.

Linear transformations. The stationary process

$$\eta(t) = \{\eta_1(t), \ldots, \eta_m(t)\}$$

with m components is obtained from the n-dimensional stationary process

$$\xi(t) = \{\xi_1(t), \ldots, \xi_n(t)\}$$

by a linear transformation if

$$\eta(t) = \int e^{i\lambda t} \, \varphi(\lambda) \, \Phi^*(d\lambda),$$

where $\varphi = \{\varphi_{jk}\}$ $(j=1, ..., m; k=1, ..., n)$ is an $m \times n$-dimensional matrix function such that every row

$$\varphi_j = \{\varphi_{j1}, ..., \varphi_{jn}\}$$

represents an element of the space L^2.

The process $\xi(t)$, in turn, can be obtained from $\eta(t)$ by an "inverse" linear transformation if there exists a matrix function $\psi = \{\psi_{kj}\}$ $(k=1, ..., n; j=1, ..., m)$ such that the product $\psi(\lambda)\, \varphi(\lambda)$ represents a matrix whose k-th row is an element of the space L^2 and coincides with the vector δ_k:

$$\psi(\lambda)\, \varphi(\lambda) = I_n$$

where I_n is the unit matrix of order n. This function ψ serves as the *spectral characteristic* of the "inverse" linear transformation. In particular, if the matrix $\varphi(\lambda)$ is regular almost everywhere, then

$$\psi(\lambda) = \varphi^{-1}(\lambda).$$

The spectral density

$$g(\lambda) = \{g_{ij}(\lambda)\} \qquad (i,j = 1, ..., m)$$

of the process $\eta(t)$ obtained from $\xi(t)$ by the linear transformation with the spectral characteristic $\varphi(\lambda) = \{\varphi_{jk}(\lambda)\}$ $(j=1, ..., m; k=1, ..., n)$ is given by

$$g(\lambda) = \varphi(\lambda)\, f(\lambda)\, \varphi^*(\lambda)$$

where φ^* is the conjugate matrix to φ in the Hermitian sense.

The Rank of a Multi-Dimensional Process. Regularity. We say, that the n-dimensional stationary process $\xi(t)$ has *rank* m if for almost all λ its spectral density $f(\lambda) = \{f_{kj}(\lambda)\}$ $(k,j = 1, ..., n)$ has one and the same rank m. In the case of a discrete time each component $\xi_k(t)$ of such a process can be represented by

$$\xi_k(t) = \sum_{j=1}^{m} \sum_{-\infty}^{\infty} c_{kj}(t-s)\, \zeta_j(s) \qquad (k=1, ..., n)$$

where we have

$$\mathrm{M}\, \zeta_i(t_1)\, \overline{\zeta_j(t_2)} = 0$$

for $i \neq j$ and any t_1 and t_2, but also for $i=j$ and $t_1 \neq t_2$. If, however, the time t is continuous, then

$$\xi_k(t) = \sum_{j=1}^{m} \int_{-\infty}^{\infty} c_{kj}(t-s)\, \zeta_j(ds) \qquad (k=1, ..., n)$$

where

$$\mathbb{M}\zeta_i(\varDelta_1)\overline{\zeta_j(\varDelta_2)} = 0$$

for arbitrary intervals $\varDelta_1$ and $\varDelta_2$ if $i \neq j$, and for disjoint intervals $\varDelta_1$ and $\varDelta_2$ if $i = j$.

In particular, all linearly regular n-dimensional stationary processes $\xi(t)$ are processes of this type. From the point of view of physics they represent linearly transformed stationary perturbations of the "white noise" type:

$$\xi_k(t) = \sum_{j=1}^{n} \sum_{-\infty}^{t} c_{kj}(t-s)\,\zeta_j(s) \qquad (k = 1, \ldots, n)$$

for discrete time and

$$\xi_k(t) = \sum_{j=1}^{n} \int_{-\infty}^{t} c_{kj}(t-s)\,\zeta_j(ds) \qquad (k = 1, \ldots, n)$$

for continuous time.

From the point of view of applications the most interesting case is the one where all components $\xi_k(t)$ of the stationary n-dimensional process $\xi(t)$ under consideration result from one and the same stationary perturbation (case of processes of rank 1), or where all components $\xi_k(t)$ are practically very little connected with each other so that the stationary process $\xi(t)$ has maximal rank $m = n$.

The spectral characteristics of these transformations are given by

$$\varphi(\lambda) = \sum_{0}^{\infty} c(t)\,e^{-i\lambda t} \qquad \text{for discrete } t$$

$$\varphi(\lambda) = \int_{0}^{\infty} c(t)\,e^{-i\lambda t}\,dt \qquad \text{for continuous } t,$$

where

$$c(t) = \{c_{kj}(t)\} \qquad (k = 1, \ldots, n;\; j = 1, \ldots, m),$$

$$\sum_{0}^{\infty} \sum_{k,j} |c_{kj}(t)|^2\,dt < \infty \qquad \text{for discrete time}$$

$$\int_{0}^{\infty} \sum_{k,j} |c_{kj}(t)|^2\,dt < \infty \qquad \text{for continuous time}.$$

Here the spectral density $f(\lambda)$ of the n-dimensional process $\xi(t)$ can be represented in the form

$$f(\lambda) = \frac{1}{2\pi}\,\varphi(\lambda)\,\varphi^*(\lambda);$$

it is customary to say that $f(\lambda)$ admits a *factorization*.

The matrix functions $\varphi(\lambda)$ are the boundary values of functions which are analytic $\gamma(z)$ in the unit circle or the lower half-plane, respectively. Among all such functions $\gamma(z)$ there exists a so-called *maximal function* $\gamma_0 = \gamma_0(z)$, unique up to a constant factor, which is a unitary matrix of order m with the property that the difference $\gamma_0 \gamma_0^* - \gamma \gamma^*$ is a positive definite matrix:

$$\gamma_0(z) \gamma_0^*(z) - \gamma(z) \gamma^*(z) \geq 0$$

where z lies within the unit circle or on the lower half-plane.

The stationary n-dimensional process $\xi(t)$ is linearly regular if and only if its spectral density $f(\lambda)$ can be factorized. For example, all processes with rational spectral densities, that is, all processes whose spectral densities are matrices with rational elements f_{kj} are regular.

Suppose that t is discrete and the elements of the spectral density $f(\lambda)$ are rational in $e^{-i\lambda}$. Then $f(\lambda)$ may be written in the form

$$f(\lambda) = \frac{1}{2\pi} \gamma(e^{-i\lambda}) \gamma^*(e^{-i\lambda})$$

where

$$\gamma(z) = \{\gamma_{kj}(z)\} \qquad (k = 1, \ldots, n; \; j = 1, \ldots, m)$$

is a matrix function whose elements are rational in z and analytic within the unit circle, and the rank of $\gamma(z)$ equals the rank m of the stationary process $\xi(t)$ for all z with $|z| < 1$. This matrix function $\gamma(z)$ is also maximal.

Next let t be continuous. If the elements of the spectral density $f(\lambda)$ are rational in λ, then $f(\lambda)$ can be written in the form

$$f(\lambda) = \frac{1}{2\pi} \gamma(\lambda) \gamma^*(\lambda)$$

where

$$\gamma(z) = \{\gamma_{kj}(z)\} \qquad (k = 1, \ldots, n; \; j = 1, \ldots, m)$$

is a matrix function whose elements are rational in z and analytic in the lower half-plane, and the rank of $\gamma(z)$ equals the rank m of the stationary process $\xi(t)$ for all z with $\operatorname{Im} z < 0$. This matrix function $\gamma(z)$ is also maximal.

A condition for the regularity of a process with maximal rank $m = n$ consists in

$$\int_{-\pi}^{\pi} \log[\det f(\lambda)] \, d\lambda > -\infty \qquad \text{for discrete time},$$

$$\int_{-\infty}^{\infty} \log[\det f(\lambda)] \frac{d\lambda}{1 + \lambda^2} > -\infty \quad \text{for continuous time}$$

where $\det f(\lambda)$ is the determinant of the matrix

$$f(\lambda) = \{f_{kl}(\lambda)\} \qquad (k, l = 1, \ldots, n).$$

In the general case where the rank of the spectral density $f(\lambda)$ equals m, $1 \leq m < n$, for all λ, let us replace $\det f(\lambda)$ by the product of all positive eigenvalues of the matrix $f(\lambda)$. Then for the regularity of the process it is necessary and sufficient that the condition above be satisfied and that the linear subspace $E^m(\lambda)$ spanned by the vectors

$$f_l(\lambda) = \{f_{1l}(\lambda), \ldots, f_{nl}(\lambda)\} \qquad (l = 1, \ldots, n)$$

be analytic. By the latter requirement we mean the following: there exists a matrix function

$$\varphi(\lambda) = \{\varphi_{kj}(\lambda)\} \qquad (k = 1, \ldots, n; \ j = 1, \ldots, m)$$

which is the boundary value of an analytic matrix $\gamma(z)$ such that the linear space spanned by the vectors

$$\varphi_j(\lambda) = \{\varphi_{1j}(\lambda), \ldots, \varphi_{nj}(\lambda)\} \qquad (j = 1, \ldots, m)$$

coincides with the subspace $E^m(\lambda)$ for almost all λ. For example, if the spectral density $f(\lambda)$ has rational elements $f_{kl}(\lambda)$, then we can take as the matrix $\varphi(\lambda)$ the matrix function

$$D(\lambda)\{f_{k,l_j}(\lambda)\} \qquad (k = 1, \ldots, n; \ j = 1, \ldots, m)$$

where $D(\lambda)$ is the least common multiple of the denominators of all $f_{k,l_j}(\lambda)$, and

$$\left\{ \begin{matrix} f_{1,l_1}(\lambda)\ f_{1,l_2}(\lambda) \ldots f_{1,l_m}(\lambda) \\ \cdots\cdots\cdots\cdots\cdots\cdots \\ f_{n,l_1}(\lambda)\ f_{n,l_2}(\lambda) \ldots f_{n,l_m}(\lambda) \end{matrix} \right\}$$

are m linearly independent columns of the matrix $f(\lambda)$.

By the example of processes of rank 1 we can illustrate in how complicated a way the maximal matrix $\gamma(z)$ depends on the corresponding density in the multi-dimensional case. Assuming the time to be discrete such a process is regular if and only if

$$\int_{-\pi}^{\pi} \log f_{jj}(\lambda)\, d\lambda > -\infty$$

for some j, and the functions $\gamma_{kj}(e^{-i\lambda}) = \dfrac{f_{kj}(\lambda)}{f_{jj}(\lambda)}$ are the boundary values of some functions of a complex variable $\gamma_{kj}(z)$ which can be written as ratios of two bounded analytic functions in the unit circle. Such functions are uniquely determined by their boundary values.

Let $z_j^{(1)}, z_j^{(2)}, \ldots$ be all poles of the various functions $\gamma_{kj}(z)$, each of them being counted with their maximal multiplicity, let m_j be the maximal multiplicity of the pole $z = 0$, $z_{k,j}^{(1)}, z_{k,j}^{(2)}, \ldots$ the poles of the single functions $\gamma_{kj}(z)$ counted with their multiplicity, and m_{kj} the multiplicity of the pole $z = 0$. We set

$$\alpha_{kj}(z) = \gamma_{kj}(z) \frac{\gamma_{jo}(z)\,\beta_{kj}(z)}{\gamma_{ko}(z)\,\beta_{jk}(z)},$$

$$\beta_{kj}(z) = z^{m_{kj}} \prod_p \frac{z_{kj}^{(p)} - z}{1 - z_{kj}^{(p)} z} \cdot \frac{|z_{kj}^{(p)}|}{z_{kj}^{(p)}},$$

$$\gamma_{ko}(z) = \exp\left\{ \frac{1}{4\pi} \int_{-\pi}^{\pi} \log f_{kk}(\lambda) \frac{e^{-i\lambda} + z}{e^{-i\lambda} - z}\, d\lambda \right\}.$$

The relation

$$\sigma_{kj}(\Delta) = \lim_{\varrho \to 1} \int_{\lambda_1}^{\lambda_2} \log |\alpha_{kj}(\varrho\, e^{-i\lambda})|\, d\lambda$$

defines a real generalized measure $\sigma_{kj}(d\lambda)$ on the intervals $\Delta = (\lambda_1, \lambda_2)$ such that $\sigma_{kj}(\lambda_1) = \sigma_{kj}(\lambda_2) = 0$.

Let

$$\sigma_{kj}(d\lambda) = \sigma_{kj}^+(d\lambda) - \sigma_{kj}^-(d\lambda)$$

be the decomposition of the measure $\sigma_{kj}(d\lambda)$ into its positive part $\sigma_{kj}^+(d\lambda)$ and its negative part $\sigma_{kj}^-(d\lambda)$. We set

$$\sigma_j(d\lambda) = p_j(\lambda) \sum_k \sigma_{kj}^+(d\lambda),$$

$$p_{kj}(\lambda) = \frac{\sigma_{kj}(d\lambda)}{\sum_k \sigma_{kj}^+(d\lambda)}, \qquad p_j(\lambda) = \max_k \{p_{kj}(\lambda)\}.$$

Then the component $\gamma_j(z)$ of the maximal matrix

$$\boldsymbol{\gamma}(z) = \{\gamma_k(z)\} \qquad (k = 1, \ldots, n)$$

can be represented in the form

$$\gamma_j(z) = \gamma_{jo}(z)\, z^{m_j} \left(\prod_p \frac{z_j^{(p)} - z}{1 - z_j^{(p)} z} \cdot \frac{|z_j^{(p)}|}{z_j^{(p)}} \right) \exp \times \left\{ -\frac{1}{2\pi} \int_{-\pi}^{\pi} \frac{e^{-i\lambda} + z}{e^{-i\lambda} - z}\, \sigma_j(d\lambda) \right\}.$$

The remaining components can be obtained in the same way, or by the formula

$$\gamma_k(z) = \gamma_{kj}(z)\, \gamma_j(z) \qquad (k = 1, \ldots, n)$$

where $\gamma_{kj}(z)$ are the afore-mentioned functions in the unit circle which are ratios of bounded analytic functions and equal to $f_{kj}(\lambda)/f_{jj}(\lambda)$ for $z = e^{-i\lambda}$.

6. Generalized Stationary Processes
and Processes with Stationary Increments

Linear Transformations. Let $\xi = \langle u, \xi \rangle$ be a generalized stationary process and

$$\langle u, \xi \rangle = \int_{-\infty}^{\infty} \tilde{u}(\lambda)\, \Phi(d\lambda) \quad (u \in U)$$

its spectral representation (see § 2.1, Chapter III). The linear transformation of the process $\xi = \langle u, \xi \rangle$ with the spectral characteristic $\varphi = \varphi(\lambda)$ is defined to be the generalized stationary process $\eta = \langle u, \eta \rangle$ of the form

$$\langle u, \eta \rangle = \int_{-\infty}^{\infty} \tilde{u}(\lambda)\, \varphi(\lambda)\, \Phi(d\lambda)$$

where the function $\varphi(\lambda)$ does not increase faster than $|\lambda|^p$ for $\lambda \to \infty$. The spectral measure $G = G(\Delta)$ of the generalized stationary process $\eta = \langle u, \eta \rangle$ is connected with the spectral measure $F = F(\Delta)$ of the initial process $\xi = \langle u, \xi \rangle$ by the relation

$$G(\Delta) = \int_{\Delta} |\varphi(\lambda)|^2\, F(d\lambda).$$

Example. Let $\varphi = \varphi(\lambda)$ be the Fourier transform of an integrable function in the interval $(-\tau, \tau)$:

$$\varphi(\lambda) = \int_{-\tau}^{\tau} e^{-i\lambda t}\, c(t)\, dt .$$

The linear transformation of the linear generalized stationary process $\xi = \langle u, \xi \rangle$ with the spectral characteristic φ yields the stationary generalized process $\eta = \langle u, \eta \rangle$

$$\langle u, \eta \rangle = \left\langle \int_{-\infty}^{\infty} c(t - s) u(s)\, ds, \xi \right\rangle .$$

Differentiation. Let $\xi = \langle u, \xi \rangle$ be a generalized random process with mean value

$$A(u) = \mathbb{M} \langle u, \xi \rangle$$

and covariance functional

$$B(u, v) = \mathbb{M} \{ \langle u, \xi \rangle\, \overline{\langle v, \xi \rangle} \} .$$

The generalized random process $\xi' = \langle u, \xi' \rangle$ defined by

$$\langle u, \xi' \rangle = - \langle u', \xi \rangle$$

is called the *derivative* of the process. It is obtained by the linear transformation with spectral characteristic $\varphi(\lambda) = i\lambda$. Its mean value and correlation functional are given by $-A(u')$ and $B(u', v')$, respectively, where $u' = u'(t)$ and $v' = v'(t)$ denote the derivatives of infinitely differentiable functions $u = u(t)$ and $v = v(t)$ belonging to the space U.

If the generalized random process $\xi = \langle u, \xi \rangle$ has the form

$$\langle u, \xi \rangle = \int_{-\infty}^{\infty} u(t)\, \xi(t)\, dt$$

and $\xi = \xi(t)$ represents an ordinary random process, then we denote by $\xi = \xi(t)$ the generalized process, too, and by $\xi^{(n)} = \xi^{(n)}(t)$ its derivatives, $n = 0, 1, \ldots$.

"*White Noise*". Let $\zeta = \zeta(\Delta)$ be a stochastic measure with non-correlated values such that for $\Delta = (s, t)$ we have

$$\mathsf{M}\zeta(\Delta) = 0, \qquad \mathsf{M}|\zeta(\Delta)|^2 = t - s.$$

With this measure we can associate the generalized process $\zeta = \langle u, \zeta \rangle$ defined by

$$\langle u, \zeta \rangle = \int_{-\infty}^{\infty} u(t)\, \zeta(dt).$$

The mean value of this process equals zero, and the correlation functional equals

$$B(s, t) = \delta(s - t)$$

where $\delta(s - t)$ is the generalized function of two arguments determined by

$$\int_{-\infty}^{\infty} \int_{-\infty}^{\infty} u_1(s)\, u_2(t)\, \delta(s - t)\, ds\, dt = \int_{-\infty}^{\infty} u_1(t)\, u_2(t)\, dt.$$

The generalized process described in this way is stationary and is called "white noise". Its *spectral* measure $F = F(\Delta)$ is absolutely continuous: $F(\Delta) = \int_{\Delta} f(\lambda)\, d\lambda$, and its *spectral density* $f(\lambda)$ equals $f(\lambda) = \dfrac{1}{2\pi}$.

Example. Let $\xi = \xi(t)$ be a Poisson process with mean values $A(t) = a t$ and $\xi(t) \equiv 0$ for $t < 0$. The derivative $\xi' = \xi'(t)$ is a generalized process of of the form

$$\xi'(t) = \sum_{k} \delta(t - \tau^k),$$

where $\tau_1, \tau_2, \ldots$ are random times, namely, the instances of the jumps of the Poisson process $\xi(t)$, and $\delta(t - \tau)$ denotes the δ-function with the singularity at the point τ: $\langle u, \xi' \rangle = \sum_{k} u(\tau_k)$. The mean value of this process equals the constant

$$\mathsf{M} \sum_{k} u(\tau_k) = a \int_{0}^{\infty} u(t)\, dt.$$

The correlation function of the Poisson process is equal to

$$B(s, t) = a \min(s, t),$$

hence the correlation functional of the derivative $\xi' = \xi'(t)$ equals $a\delta(s-t)$, that is,

$$\mathbb{M} \sum_k u(\tau_k) \overline{\sum_l v(\tau_l)} = a \int_0^\infty u(t) \overline{v(t)} \, dt.$$

Example. Suppose that $\xi = \xi(t)$, $\mathbb{M}\xi(t) = 0$ is a Brownian motion process. Its covariance function equals

$$B(s, t) = \min(s, t).$$

The derivative $\xi' = \xi'(t)$ of the Brownian motion process has the covariance functional $\delta(s-t)$ and turns out to be the "white noise" process.

Integration. Let $u_1 = u_1(t)$, $u_1 \in U$ be a fixed function such that

$$\int_{-\infty}^\infty u_1(t) \, dt = 1.$$

Then an arbitrary function $u = u(t)$, $u \in U$ can be represented in the form

$$u(t) = u_1(t) \int_{-\infty}^\infty u(s) \, ds + u_0(t), \qquad \int_{-\infty}^\infty u_0(s) \, ds = 0.$$

If $\xi = \langle u, \xi \rangle$ is a given generalized process, then its "primitive" function $\eta = \langle u, \eta \rangle$, $\eta' = \xi$ can be represented in the form

$$\langle u, \eta \rangle = \left\langle \int_{-\infty}^t u_0(s) \, ds, \xi \right\rangle + C$$

where C is a constant. Here, all primitive processes of ξ coincide on the subspace $U^{(1)}$ of the elements $u \in U$ which satisfy the condition

$$\int_{-\infty}^\infty u(t) \, dt = 0.$$

Analogously, all generalized processes $\eta = \langle u, \eta \rangle$ with a given n-th derivative $\xi = \langle u, \xi \rangle$, $\eta^{(n)} = \xi$ coincide on the subspace $U^{(n)}$ of all elements $u \in U$ which satisfy the condition

$$\int_{-\infty}^\infty t^k u(t) \, dt = 0 \qquad (k = 0, \ldots, n-1)$$

and differ from each other only by terms of the type $\sum_0^{n-1} C_k t^k$. More precisely,

$$\langle u, \eta \rangle = \langle u, \eta_0 \rangle + \int_{-\infty}^\infty u(t) \sum_{k=0}^{n-1} C_k t^k \, dt.$$

If

$$\langle u, \xi \rangle = \int\limits_{-\infty}^{\infty} \tilde{u}(\lambda)\, \Phi(d\lambda)$$

is the spectral decomposition of the given process $\xi = \langle u, \xi \rangle$, then

$$\langle u, \xi \rangle = \int\limits_{-\infty}^{\infty} \tilde{u}(\lambda)\, (i\lambda)^{-n}\, \Phi(d\lambda)$$

for $u \in U^{(n)}$.

Processes with Stationary Increments. A random process is called a *process with stationary n-th increments* if its n-th derivative is stationary. In the case of an ordinary process $\eta = \eta(t)$ this is equivalent to the requirement that the n-th finite difference

$$\Delta_k^n \eta(t) = \sum_{k=0}^{n} C_n^k (-1)^{k+1}\, \eta(t + hk)$$

is a stationary process for any h.

Every generalized stationary process $\xi = \langle u, \xi \rangle$ is the n-th derivative of some ordinary (non-generalized) process with stationary n-th increments where n is chosen in such a way that

$$\int\limits_{-\infty}^{\infty} (1 + \lambda^2)^{-n}\, F(d\lambda) < \infty\,;$$

here, F denotes the spectral measure of the process ξ under consideration.

Let

$$\langle u, \xi \rangle = \int\limits_{-\infty}^{\infty} \tilde{u}(\lambda)\, \Phi(d\lambda)$$

be the spectral decomposition of such a process. The corresponding process $\eta = \eta(t)$ with n-th stationary increments can be constructed as follows. The generalized process $\eta = \langle u, \eta \rangle$ restricted to the functions $u = u(t)$, $u \in U^{(n)}$, is obtained by an n-fold integration

$$\langle u, \eta \rangle = \int\limits_{-\infty}^{\infty} \tilde{u}(\lambda)\, (i\lambda)^{-n}\, \Phi(d\lambda) = \int\limits_{-\infty}^{\infty} \tilde{u}(\lambda)\, \Psi(d\lambda)\,.$$

The stochastic measure Ψ in the spectral decomposition of the generalized process $\eta = \langle u, \eta \rangle$ has the property that the spectral measure $G(\Delta) = \mathbb{M}\,|\Psi(\Delta)|^2$ satisfies the following condition: for any $\varepsilon > 0$

$$\int\limits_{-\infty}^{\varepsilon} G(d\lambda) < \infty\,, \qquad \int\limits_{-\varepsilon}^{\varepsilon} \lambda^{2n}\, G(d\lambda) < \infty\,, \qquad \int\limits_{-\varepsilon}^{\infty} G(d\lambda) < \infty\,.$$

The ordinary (non-generalized) process $\eta = \eta(t)$ with stationary n-th increments associated with the generalized process $\eta = \langle u, \eta \rangle$ by the relation

$$\langle u, \eta \rangle = \int_{-\infty}^{\infty} u(t)\,\eta(t)\,dt$$

which has the n-th derivative $\xi = \langle u, \xi \rangle$ can be represented by

$$\eta(t) = \int_{-\infty}^{\infty} \left[e^{i\lambda t} - \frac{1}{1+\lambda^n} \sum_{k=0}^{n-1} \frac{(i\lambda t)^k}{k!} \right] \Psi(d\lambda).$$

The general form of a process with stationary n-th increments [64] whose n-th derivative coincides with the generalized process $\xi = \langle u, \xi \rangle$ is $\eta(t) + \sum_0^{n-1} c_k t^k$, where $\sum_0^{n-1} c_k t^k$ is an arbitrary polynomial of degree $n-1$.

Regularity. Let

$$\langle u, \xi \rangle = \int_{-\infty}^{\infty} \tilde{u}(\lambda)\,\Phi(d\lambda)$$

be a generalized stationary process with the spectral measure F, and $H(s,t)$ the closed linear hull in the Hilbert space $L^2(\Omega)$ of the values $\langle u, \xi \rangle$ where u runs through all functions of U which vanish outside of the interval $[s,t]$. Every element h of $H(-\infty, \infty)$ admits the spectral representation

$$\eta = \int_{-\infty}^{\infty} \varphi(\lambda)\,\Phi(d\lambda)$$

where the *spectral characteristic* $\varphi = \varphi(\lambda)$ is the corresponding element of the functional space L^2. Moreover

$$M h_1 \bar{h}_2 = \int_{-\infty}^{\infty} \varphi_1(\lambda)\,\overline{\varphi_2(\lambda)}\,F(d\lambda).$$

The generalized stationary process $\xi(t)$ with mean zero is called *linearly regular* if

$$\bigcap_t H(-\infty, t) = 0,$$

and *linearly singular* if for all t

$$H(-\infty, t) = H.$$

A necessary and sufficient condition for the linear regularity of the process is that its spectral measure F be absolutely continuous and the

[64] Yaglom, A. M., Correlation theory of processes with stationary n-th increments. Matem. Sbornik, **37**, 1 (1955) (Russian).

spectral density $f(\lambda)$ satisfies

$$\int\limits_{-\infty}^{\infty} \log f(\lambda) \frac{d\lambda}{1+\lambda^2} > -\infty \,.$$

Linear Prediction. The variable $\langle u, \hat{\xi}\rangle \in H(-\infty, t)$ which satisfies the requirement

$$\mathbb{M}|\langle u, \xi\rangle - \langle u, \hat{\xi}\rangle|^2 = \min_{h \in H(-\infty, t)} \mathbb{M}|\langle u, \xi\rangle - h|^2$$

is called the best linear prediction of the generalized stationary process $\xi = \langle u, \xi\rangle$ on the basis of the values $\langle v, \xi\rangle$ where v runs only through the set of all functions which vanish outside the half-line $[-\infty, t]$.

For a singular process we have $\langle u, \hat{\xi}\rangle = \langle u, \xi\rangle$. In the case of a regular process the quantity $\langle u, \hat{\xi}\rangle$ is given by

$$\langle u, \hat{\xi}\rangle = \int\limits_{-\infty}^{\infty} \varphi(\lambda)\, \Phi(d\lambda)$$

where

$$\varphi(\lambda) = \frac{1}{2\pi} \gamma^{-1}(\lambda) \int\limits_{-\infty}^{t} e^{i\lambda s} \left[\int\limits_{-\infty}^{-\infty} e^{-i\mu s} \tilde{u}(\mu)\, \gamma(\mu)\, d\mu\right] ds \,,$$

and $\gamma = \gamma(\lambda)$ is the boundary value of the analytic function in the lower half-plane

$$\gamma(z) = \sqrt{\pi} \exp\left\{\frac{1}{2\pi i} \int\limits_{-\infty}^{\infty} [\log f(\lambda)] \frac{1+\lambda z}{z-\lambda} \cdot \frac{d\lambda}{1+\lambda^2}\right\}.$$

The error of the prediction

$$\varepsilon^2 = \mathbb{M}|\langle u, \hat{\xi}\rangle - \langle u, \xi\rangle|^2$$

can be expressed in the following way:

$$\varepsilon^2 = \frac{1}{4\pi^2} \int\limits_{t}^{\infty} \left|\int\limits_{-\infty}^{\infty} e^{-i\lambda s} \tilde{u}(\lambda)\, \gamma(\lambda)\, d\lambda\right|^2 ds \,.$$

7. Harmonizable Random Processes. Some Non-Linear Transformations

Harmonizable processes. The random process $\xi = \xi(t)$ with continuous time t, $-\infty < t < \infty$, is called *harmonizable* if it can be represented in the form

$$\xi(t) = \int\limits_{-\infty}^{\infty} e^{i\lambda t}\, \Phi(d\lambda) \tag{1.2}$$

where $\Phi = \Phi(\Delta)$ is a generalized measure with values in the Hilbert space $L^2(\Omega)$. As in the stationary case we have

$$\Phi(\lambda_0) = \lim_{T \to \infty} \frac{1}{2T} \int_{-T}^{T} \xi(t) e^{-i\lambda_0 t} \, dt \quad (-\infty < \lambda_0 < \infty),$$

$$\Phi(\Delta) = \lim_{T \to \infty} \int_{-T}^{T} \frac{e^{-i\lambda_2 t} - e^{-i\lambda_1 t}}{-it} \, \xi(t) \, dt$$

for any interval $\Delta = (\lambda_1, \lambda_2)$ such that $\Phi(\lambda_1) = \Phi(\lambda_2) = 0$.

Example. Let $\xi = \xi(t)$ be a wide sense stationary process, $c(t) = \int_{-\infty}^{\infty} e^{i\lambda t} m(d\lambda)$ where $m = m(\Delta)$ is some complex measure of bounded variation, and define the random process $\eta = \eta(t)$ like this

$$\eta(t) = c(t) \, \xi(t).$$

Such a process $\eta = \eta(t)$ is harmonizable:

$$\eta(t) = \int_{-\infty}^{\infty} e^{i\lambda t} \, \Psi(d\lambda)$$

where the stochastic measure $\Psi = \Psi(\Delta)$ is given by

$$\Psi(\Delta) = \int_{\Delta} m(\Delta - \lambda) \, \Phi(d\lambda);$$

$\Delta - \lambda$ is the set of all points $\mu - \lambda$, $\mu \in \Delta$.

Example. Let $\xi = \xi(t)$ be a harmonizable stochastic process of the form (1.2), A a linear bounded operator on the linear closed subspace H of the Hilbert space $L^2(\Omega)$ generated by the values $\xi(t)$, $-\infty < t < \infty$ and define the stochastic process $\eta = \eta(t)$ by

$$\eta(t) = A \, \xi(t).$$

Such a process $\eta(t)$ is harmonizable:

$$\eta(t) = \int_{-\infty}^{\infty} e^{i\lambda t} \, \Psi(d\lambda)$$

where the stochastic measure $\Psi = \Psi(\Delta)$ is given by

$$\Psi(\Delta) = A \, \Phi(\Delta).$$

Covariance Function of a Harmonizable Process. We assume that the function

$$F(\Delta_1 \times \Delta_2) = \mathbb{M} \, \Phi(\Delta_1) \, \overline{\Phi(\Delta_2)}$$

of Borel sets $\Delta_1 \times \Delta_2$ in the real plane defines a complex measure F of bounded variation. The stochastic process $\xi = \xi(t)$ is harmonizable and has the spectral measure F if and only if its covariance function $B(s, t) = \mathbb{M}\, \xi(s)\, \overline{\xi(t)}$ admits a representation of the form

$$B(s, t) = \int_{-\infty}^{\infty} \int_{-\infty}^{\infty} e^{i(\lambda s - \mu t)}\, F(d\lambda\, d\mu).$$

Spectral Moments. The stochastic process $\xi = \xi(t)$ belongs to the class $\Phi^{(2n)}$, $n \geq 1$ if $\mathbb{M}\,|\xi(t)|^{2n} < \infty$ and if for all $k + l \leq 2n$ the moments

$$M^{(k, l)}(s, t) = \mathbb{M}\, \xi(s_1) \ldots \xi(s_k)\, \overline{\xi(t_1)} \ldots \overline{\xi(t_l)}$$

$$(s = (s_1, \ldots, s_k), \qquad t = (t_1, \ldots, t_l))$$

can be represented in the form

$$M^{(k, l)}(s, t) = \int_{E^{k+l}} e^{i(\lambda s - \mu t)}\, \mathscr{M}^{(k, l)}(d\lambda\, d\mu)$$

$$\left(\begin{array}{ll} \lambda = (\lambda_1, \ldots, \lambda_k), & \mu = (\mu_1, \ldots, \mu_l); \\ \lambda s = \lambda_1 s_1 + \cdots + \lambda_k s_k, & \mu t = \mu_1 t_1 + \cdots + \mu_l t_l \end{array} \right)$$

where $\mathscr{M}^{(k, l)}$ is a complex measure of bounded variation [65] on the $(k + l)$-dimensional real space E^{k+l}.

Let $\xi = \xi(t)$ be a harmonizable stochastic process, and define the random function $\Phi^{(k, l)} = \Phi^{(k, l)}(\Delta)$ on the sets of the form $\Delta = \Delta_1 \times \cdots \times \Delta_k \times \Delta'_1 \times \cdots \times \Delta'_l$ of the real $(k + l)$-dimensional space E^{k+l} by the formula

$$\Phi^{(k, l)}(\Delta) = \Phi(\Delta_1) \ldots \Phi(\Delta_k)\, \overline{\Phi(\Delta'_1)} \ldots \overline{\Phi(\Delta'_l)}.$$

The stochastic process $\xi = \xi(t)$ belongs to the class $\Phi^{(2n)}$ if and only if $\mathbb{M}\,|\Phi^{(k, l)}(\Delta)|^2 < \infty$ for any Δ and $k + l \leq 2n$. Then the *spectral moments*

$$\mathscr{M}^{(k, l)}(\Delta) = \mathbb{M}\, \Phi^{(k, l)}(\Delta)$$

define complex measure $\mathscr{M}^{(k, l)}$ of bounded variation which coincide with the generalized measures appearing in the spectral representation of the moments $M^{(k, l)}(s, t)$.

Within the class $\Phi^{(2n)}$ the random functions $\Phi^{(k, l)}$ with $k, l \leq n$ are generalized measures with values in $L^2(\Omega)$. These measures are called *stochastic spectral measures.*

Spectral Semi-Invariants. Suppose that $\xi = \xi(t)$ is a real stochastic process in the class $\Phi^{(2n)}$. The semi-invariants of this process

$$S^{(k)}(t) = \frac{\partial^k}{\partial u_1 \ldots \partial u_k}\, \mathbb{M}\, \exp\{i u\, \xi(t)\}$$

$$(t = (t_1, \ldots, t_k), \qquad u = (u_1, \ldots, u_k), \qquad u\, \xi(t) = u_1\, \xi(t_1) + \cdots + u_k\, \xi(t_k),$$

---

[65] *Shiryaev, A. N.*, Some problems of spectral theory of leading instants. Teor. veroyat. i primen. V, **3** (1960), 293—313 (Russian).

are connected with the moments

$$M^{(k)}(I) = \mathbf{M}\,\xi(t_1)\ldots\xi(t_k)$$

$$= \int_{E^k} \exp\left\{i\left(\sum_{r=1}^{p}\lambda_r t_r - \sum_{l=1}^{q}\mu_l t_{p+l}\right)\right\}\mathscr{M}^{(p,q)}(d\lambda\,d\mu)^{66}$$

$$(\lambda = (\lambda_1,\ldots,\lambda_p)\,,\ \mu = (\mu_1,\ldots,\mu_q)\,,\ p+q=k)$$

by the following relations:

$$S^{(k)}(I) = \sum_{\substack{q\\ \bigcup_{p=1}^{q} I_p = I}} (-1)^{q-1}[(q-1)!]\prod_{p=1}^{q} M^{(p)}(I_p)\,,$$

$$M^{(k)}(I) = \sum_{\substack{q\\ \bigcup_{p=1}^{q} I_p = I}} \prod_{p=1}^{q} S^{(p)}(I_p)\,.$$

Here

$$I = (t_1,\ldots,t_k)\,,\qquad I_p = (t_{i_1},\ldots,t_{i_p})\subseteq I\,,$$

and the summation is extended over all partitions of I into disjoint subsets I_p.

The semi-invariants $S^{(k)}(I)$ can be represented in the form

$$S^{(k)}(I) = \int_{E^k} \exp\left\{i\left(\sum_{k=1}^{p}\lambda_k t_k - \sum_{l=1}^{q}\mu_l t_{p+l}\right)\right\}\mathscr{S}^{(p,q)}(d\lambda\,d\mu)$$

where the *spectral semi-invariants* $\mathscr{S}^{(p,q)}$ are connected with *the spectral moments* $\mathscr{M}^{(p,q)}$ by relations of the afore-mentioned type. In particular, we have

$$S^{(1)}(t) = M^{(1)}(t)\quad\text{and}\quad \mathscr{S}^{(1,0)}(\Delta) = \mathscr{M}^{(1,0)}(\Delta)$$

where $M^{(1)}(t) = \mathbf{M}\,\xi(t) = a(t)$ is the mean value of the process $\xi(t)$, $\mathscr{M}^{(1,0)}(\Delta) = \mathbf{M}\,\Phi(\Delta)$ the mean value of its stochastic spectral measure

$$\Phi = \Phi(\Delta)\,,$$

$$S^{(2)}(t_1, t_2) = M^{(2)}(t_1, t_2) - M^{(1)}(t_1)\,M^{(2)}(t_2)\,,$$

$$\mathscr{S}^{(1,1)}(\Delta_1\times\Delta_2) = \mathscr{M}^{(1,1)}(\Delta_1\times\Delta_2) - \mathscr{M}^{(1,0)}(\Delta_1)\,\mathscr{M}^{(0,1)}(\Delta_2)\,,$$

and $M^{(2)}(t_1, t_2) = \mathbf{M}\,\xi(t_1)\,\overline{\xi(t_2)} = B(t_1, t_2)$ is the correlation function of the process, $\mathscr{M}^{(1,1)}(\Delta_1\times\Delta_2) = \mathbf{M}\,\Phi(\Delta_1)\,\overline{\Phi(\Delta_2)} = F(\Delta_1\times\Delta_2)$ its spectral measure.

When looking at the semi-invariant it is convenient to consider the so-called *characteristic functional* $\varphi_\xi = \varphi_\xi(u)$ of the process $\xi = \xi(t)$

---

[66] This representation of the moment $M^{(k)}(I)$ holds identically with respect to all non-negative integers p and q such that $p+q=k$. This remark applies as well to the representation of the semi-invariant $S^{(k)}(I)$ given below.

defined by

$$\varphi_\xi(u) = \mathbb{M} \exp\left\{ i \int_{-\infty}^{\infty} \xi(t) u(dt) \right\}$$

where $u = u(\varDelta)$ runs through the normed space U of all real generalized measure with $\|u\| = \operatorname{Var} u$. For harmonizable processes

$$\varphi_\xi(u) = \mathbb{M} \exp\left\{ i \int_{-\infty}^{\infty} \tilde{u}(\lambda) \Phi(d\lambda) \right\}$$

where

$$\tilde{u}(\lambda) = \int_{-\infty}^{\infty} e^{i\lambda t} u(dt).$$

In some neighborhood of the point $u = 0$, that is, for all u whose norm does not exceed some $\varepsilon > 0$, we have the following expansion of the characteristic functional:

$$\log \varphi_\xi(u) = \sum_{k=1}^{2n-1} \frac{i^k}{k!} \int_{E^k} S^{(k)}(t) u(dt_1) \dots u(dt_k) + O(\|u\|^{2n})$$

$$= \sum_{k=1}^{2n-1} \frac{i^k}{k!} \int_{E^k} \tilde{u}(\lambda_1) \dots \tilde{u}(\lambda_k) \mathscr{S}^{(k)}(d\lambda) + O(\|\tilde{u}\|^{2n})$$

where $\|\tilde{u}\| = \sup |u(\lambda)|$.

Example. Let $\xi = \xi(t)$ be a real Gaussian process with expectation $A(t) = \mathbb{M} \xi(t)$ and covariance function $B(s, t) = \mathbb{M} \xi(s) \xi(t)$. Then

$$\log \varphi_\xi(u) = i \int_{E^1} A(t) u(dt) - \tfrac{1}{2} \int_{E^2} [B(s, t) - A(s) A(t)] u(ds) u(dt).$$

In the stationary case if the mean value equals zero and $F = F(\varDelta)$ denotes the spectral measure, we have

$$\log \varphi_\xi(u) = -\tfrac{1}{2} \int_{-\infty}^{\infty} |\tilde{u}(\lambda)|^2 F(d\lambda).$$

Example. Let

$$\xi(t) = \int_{-\infty}^{\infty} c(t, s) \zeta(ds)$$

where $\zeta = \zeta(\varDelta)$ is a stochastic measure such that for each interval $\varDelta$ the variable $\zeta(\varDelta)$ obeys the Poisson law of distribution:

$$\log \mathbb{M} \exp\{iu\zeta(\varDelta)\} = (e^{iu} - 1) \sigma(\varDelta).$$

Here $\sigma = \sigma(\varDelta)$ is a finite positive measure on the time axis $-\infty < t < \infty$. Such a stochastic process $\xi = \xi(t)$ is called a "*shot effect*" process. Its characteristic functional $\varphi_\xi = \varphi_\xi(u)$ is given by the following formula:

$$\log \varphi_\xi(u) = \int_{-\infty}^{\infty} \left[\exp\left\{ i \int_{-\infty}^{\infty} c(t, s) u(ds) \right\} - 1 \right] \sigma(dt).$$

If $c(t, s) = c(t - s)$ and the weight function $c(t)$ can be written as

$$c(t) = \int_{-\infty}^{\infty} e^{i\lambda t} m(d\lambda),$$

then the shot effect process $\xi = \xi(t)$ is harmonizable:

$$\xi(t) = \int_{-\infty}^{\infty} e^{i\lambda t} \Phi(d\lambda)$$

where

$$\Phi(\Delta) = \int_{\Delta} \left[\int_{-\infty}^{\infty} e^{-i\lambda s} \zeta(ds) \right] m(d\lambda).$$

Its first two spectral semi-invariants are given by

$$\mathscr{S}^{(1)}(\Delta) = \int_{\Delta} f(\lambda) m(d\lambda),$$

$$\mathscr{S}^{(1, 1)}(\Delta_1 \times \Delta_2) = \int_{\Delta_1} \int_{\Delta_2} f(\lambda - \mu) m(d\lambda) m(d\mu),$$

where

$$f(\lambda) = \int_{-\infty}^{\infty} e^{-i\lambda t} \sigma(dt).$$

Some Transformations of Harmonizable Processes. Suppose that the harmonizable process $\xi = \xi(t)$ is linearly transformed into the process

$$\eta(t) = \int_{-\infty}^{\infty} e^{i\lambda t} \varphi(\lambda) \Phi(d\lambda).$$

Then the spectral moments $\mathscr{M}_\eta^{(k, l)}$ of $\eta = \eta(t)$ are connected with the corresponding moments of the original process $\xi = \xi(t)$ in the following way:

$$\mathscr{M}^{(k, l)}(\Delta_1 \times \Delta_2) = \int_{\Delta_1} \int_{\Delta_2} \varphi(\lambda_1) \ldots \varphi(\lambda_k) \overline{\varphi(\mu_1)} \ldots \overline{\varphi(\mu_l)} \mathscr{M}_\xi^{(k, l)}(d\lambda \, d\mu).$$

In the case of real processes $\xi = \xi(t)$ and $\eta = \eta(t)$ analogous formulas holds for the spectral semi-invariants:

$$\mathscr{S}^{(k, l)}(\Delta_1 \times \Delta_2) = \int_{\Delta_1} \int_{\Delta_2} \varphi(\lambda_1) \ldots \varphi(\lambda_k) \overline{\varphi(\mu_1)} \ldots \overline{\varphi(\mu_l)} \mathscr{S}_\xi^{(k, l)}(d\lambda \, d\mu).$$

A very large family of transformations of random processes $\xi = \xi(t)$ in the class $\Phi^{(2n)}$ can be described by the formula

$$\eta(t) = \sum_{k+l \leq n} \int_{E^{k+l}} \exp\left\{ it\left(\sum_{p=1}^{k} \lambda_p - \sum_{q=1}^{l} \mu_q \right) \right\} \times \varphi_{k, l}(\lambda, \mu) \Phi^{(k, l)}(d\lambda \, d\mu)$$

where $\lambda = (\lambda_1, \ldots, \lambda_k)$, $\mu = (\mu_1, \ldots, \mu_l)$, and the $\Phi^{(k,l)}$ are the stochastic spectral measures of the harmonizable process $\xi = \xi(t)$. These transformations include the operation of raising to a power with a subsequent linear transformation.

Each process $\eta = \eta(t)$ of this form is harmonizable:

$$\eta(t) = \int_{-\infty}^{\infty} e^{i\lambda t}\, \Psi(d\lambda),$$

where

$$\Psi(\Delta) = \sum_{k+l \leq n} \int_{E^{k+l}} \varphi_\Delta(\lambda_1 + \cdots + \lambda_k - \mu_1 - \cdots - \mu_l) \times \varphi_{k,l}(\lambda, \mu)\, \Phi^{(k,l)}(d\lambda\, d\mu),$$

and the function $\varphi_\Delta(\lambda)$ has the form

$$\varphi_\Delta(\lambda) = \begin{cases} 1 & \text{for } \lambda \in \Delta, \\ 0 & \text{for } \lambda \notin \Delta. \end{cases}$$

§ 2. Stationary Processes in the Strict Sense

1. Ergodic Properties

Let $(\Omega, \mathfrak{A}, \mathbb{P})$ be a space of elementary events with the probability measure $\mathbb{P}$, S_t the family of measure preserving shift transformations of the sets A of the σ-algebra $\mathfrak{A} = \mathfrak{A}(-\infty, \infty)$ which correspond to a strict sense stationary stochastic process $\xi = \xi(t)$, and let U_t be the corresponding family of shift transformations of the random variables $\eta = \eta(\omega)$ which are measurable with respect to $\mathfrak{A}$ (see § 2.5, Chapter III). Assume that $\xi = \xi(t)$ is measurable.

Theorem of Birkhoff and Hinčin. Ergodicity. A set $A \in \mathfrak{A}$ is termed *invariant* if for any t the sets $S_t A$ and A coincide up to a set of probability zero. A random variable $\eta = \eta(\omega)$ which is measurable with respect to $\mathfrak{A}$ is called *invariant* if for any t we have $U_t \eta = \eta$ with probability 1. The set $\hat{\mathfrak{A}}$ of all invariant sets is a σ-algebra. A random variable η is invariant if and only if it is measurable with respect to the σ-algebra $\hat{\mathfrak{A}}$ of invariant sets.

Let $\eta = \eta(\omega)$ be an arbitrary random variable which is measurable with respect to the σ-algebra $\mathfrak{A}$ and has a mathematical expectation. Then we have the following

Theorem of Birkhoff-Hinčin (law of large numbers):

$$\lim_{T \to \infty} \frac{1}{T} \sum_{0}^{T-1} \eta(t) = \hat{\eta} \qquad (\textit{for discrete } t),$$

$$\lim_{T \to \infty} \frac{1}{T} \int_{0}^{T} \eta(t)\, dt = \hat{\eta} \qquad (\textit{for continuous } t)$$

where $\eta = \eta(t)$ is the *stationary process generated by the transformations* $U_t : \eta(t) = U_t \eta$, and $\hat{\eta} = \mathbb{M}(\eta \mid \hat{\mathfrak{A}})$ is the *conditional expectation of the original random variable* η *with respect to* $\hat{\mathfrak{A}}$. In addition, if $\mathbb{M}|\eta|^p < \infty$ for some $p \geq 1$, then in these limit relations the convergence takes also place in the space $L^p(\Omega)$.

The stationary process $\xi = \xi(t)$ is called *ergodic* or *metrically transitive* if for any random variable $\eta = \eta(\omega)$ the corresponding limit $\hat{\eta}$ turns out to be equal to the expectation of this random variable: $\hat{\eta} = \mathbb{M}\eta$. The stationary process $\xi = \xi(t)$ is ergodic if and only if every invariant set has the probability 0 or 1 or, what amounts to the same, if every invariant variable η is constant with probability 1.

For any real λ the following relations

$$\lim_{T \to \infty} \frac{1}{T} \sum_{0}^{T-1} e^{-i\lambda t} \eta(t) = \hat{\eta}(\lambda) \qquad \text{(for discrete } t)$$

$$\lim_{T \to \infty} \frac{1}{T} \int_{0}^{T} e^{-i\lambda t} \eta(t) \, dt = \hat{\eta}(\lambda) \qquad \text{(for continuous } t)$$

are satisfied with probability 1, and in the case $\mathbb{M}|\eta|^p < \infty$ for some $p \geq 1$ in the sense of convergence in $L^p(\Omega)$, too. The limit variable $\hat{\eta}(\lambda)$ has the property that with probability 1

$$U_t \hat{\eta}(\lambda) = e^{i\lambda t} \hat{\eta}(\lambda)$$

for all t, that is, $\hat{\eta}(\lambda)$ is an eigenfunction of the operator group U_t corresponding to the eigenvalue λ provided that $\hat{\eta}(\lambda) \neq 0$.

Consider U_t as a group of unitary operators in the Hilbert space $L^2(\Omega)$. In order that the stationary process $\xi(t)$ be ergodic it is necessary and sufficient that every eigenvalue λ is simple, that is, the dimension of the subspace of eigenfunctions $\hat{\eta}(\lambda)$ equals 1. This is equivalent to the requirement that the eigenvalue $\lambda = 0$ is simple, that is, every eigenfunction $\hat{\eta}$ corresponding to the eigenvalue $\lambda = 0$ is a constant.

Decomposition into Ergodic Components. Let the stationary process $\xi = \xi(t)$ have the property that the σ-algebra $\mathfrak{A} = \mathfrak{A}(-\infty, \infty)$ is separable and the probability measure $\mathbb{P} = \mathbb{P}(A)$, $A \in \mathfrak{A}$, is complete. Then there exists a decomposition of the space Ω into disjoint invariant sets $A_\alpha \in \hat{\mathfrak{A}}$:

$$\Omega = \bigcup_\alpha A_\alpha,$$

and a family of probability measures $\mathbb{P}_\alpha = \mathbb{P}_\alpha(A)$, $A \in \mathfrak{A}$, where the parameter α runs through some set of real numbers such that

$$\mathbb{P}_\alpha(A_\alpha) = 1,$$
$$\mathbb{P}(A) = \int_\Omega \mathbb{P}_{\alpha(\omega)}(A) \, \mathbb{P}(d\omega)$$

for any $A \in \mathfrak{A}$, where $\alpha(\omega) = \alpha$ for $\omega \in A_\alpha$, and $\xi = \xi(t)$ is a stationary ergodic process with respect to each of the probability measures $\mathbb{P}_\alpha$.

Ergodicity, Mixing, and Regularity. The ergodicity of the stationary process $\xi(t)$ is equivalent to the fact that for any two events $A_1, A_2 \in \mathfrak{A}$ we have

$$\lim_{T \to \pm\infty} \frac{1}{T} \sum_0^{T-1} \mathbb{P}\{(S_t A_1) \cap A_2\} = \mathbb{P}(A_1) \mathbb{P}(A_2)$$

in the case of discrete t, and

$$\lim_{T \to \pm\infty} \frac{1}{T} \int_0^T \mathbb{P}\{S_t A_1) \cap A_2\} = \mathbb{P}(A_1) \mathbb{P}(A_2)$$

in the case of continuous t.

The stationary process $\xi(t)$ is called *mixing* if for any two sets $A_1, A_2 \in \mathfrak{A}$ we have

$$\lim_{t \to \pm\infty} \mathbb{P}\{(S_t A_1) \cap A_2)\} = \mathbb{P}(A_1) \mathbb{P}(A_2).$$

This relation expresses a property which, roughly speaking, can be described as follows: for $t \to \infty$ the points ω of the set $S_t A_1$ are "uniformly mixed", or uniformly distributed over the entire space Ω in the sense that for any set of this space the points ω of $S_t A$ falling into it have a measure which is proportional to the measure of this set; note that the total measure of the points $\omega \in S_t A$ is preserved for all t.

The mixing property is weaker than the property of *regularity* of the stochastic process $\xi = \xi(t)$ which means that for any fixed $A_2 \in \mathfrak{A}(t, \infty)$ we have

$$\sup_{A_1 \in \mathfrak{A}(-\infty, s)} |\mathbb{P}\{A_1 \cap A_2\} - \mathbb{P}\{A_1\} \mathbb{P}\{A_2\}| \to 0$$

for $t - s \to \infty$.

The property of regularity of $\xi = \xi(t)$, in turn, is weaker than the property of *complete regularity* which is also called *strong mixing*, and is defined by

$$\sup_{\substack{A_1 \in \mathfrak{A}(-\infty, s) \\ A_2 \in \mathfrak{A}(t, \infty)}} |\mathbb{P}\{A_1 \cap A_2\} - \mathbb{P}\{A_1\} \mathbb{P}\{A_2\}| \to 0$$

for $t - s \to \infty$.

There is one important difference between ergodicity and mixing on the one hand, and regularity on the other. In fact, ergodicity and mixing are preserved under a transition from $\xi(t)$ to any other stationary process $\eta(t)$ which is a function of $\xi(t)$: $\eta(t) = U_t \eta$ where the random variable η is measurable with respect to the σ-algebra $\mathfrak{A} = \mathfrak{A}(-\infty, \infty)$; however, regularity may be lost under such a transition.

Central Limit Theorem. Under certain regularity conditions on $\xi = \xi(t)$ the type of approximation of the expectation $\hat{\eta} = \mathbb{M}\eta$ by the "temporal means"

$$
\eta_T = \begin{cases} \dfrac{1}{T} \displaystyle\sum_0^{T-1} \eta(t) & \text{for discrete } t, \\[2ex] \dfrac{1}{T} \displaystyle\int_0^T \eta(t)\, dt & \text{for continuous } t \end{cases}
$$

can be described by the *central limit theorem*. This theorem states that the probability distributions of the normalized differences

$$
\Delta_T = \frac{\eta_T - \mathbb{M}\eta}{\sigma_T}, \qquad \sigma_T^2 = \mathbb{D}\eta_T,
$$

converge weakly to the Gaussian distribution with expectation zero and variance 1:

$$
\mathbb{P}\{\Delta_T \leq x\} \to \frac{1}{\sqrt{2\pi}} \int_{-\infty}^x e^{-\frac{1}{2}u^2}\, du.
$$

Various kinds of conditions for the central limit theorem are connected with various regularity properties of the process $\xi(t)$. For example, suppose that

$$
\alpha(t) = \sup_{\substack{A \in \mathfrak{A}(-\infty, 0) \\ B \in \mathfrak{A}(t, \infty)}} |\mathbb{P}(A\,B) - \mathbb{P}(A)\,\mathbb{P}(B)| = O(t^{-1-\varepsilon}).
$$

Then the limit theorem holds at least for all random variables $\eta = \eta(\omega)$ which satisfy the following conditions: η is measurable with respect to some σ-algebra $\mathfrak{A}(s_0, t_0)$ and has a finite absolute moment of order $2 + \delta$, where $\delta \geq 4/\varepsilon$:

$$
\mathbb{M}|\eta|^{2+\delta} < \infty;
$$

the quantity σ_T^2 increases like T for $T \to \infty$:

$$
\sigma_T^2 \asymp T,
$$

that is, $0 < \underline{\lim}(\sigma_T^2/T) \leq \overline{\lim}(\sigma_T^2/T) < \infty$.

2. General Ergodic Properties. Their Application to Markov Processes

Measure preserving transformations. Let $(\Omega, \mathfrak{A}, \mathbb{Q})$ be a measure space with a positive measure $\mathbb{Q}(d\omega)$ where $\mathbb{Q}(\Omega) = \infty$ is not excluded; more precisely $\mathbb{Q}$ is assumed to be σ-finite. Let S be a one-to-one mapping of the space Ω onto itself which preserves $\mathbb{Q}$, that is,

$$
\mathbb{Q}(S\,A) = \mathbb{Q}(A)
$$

for any $A \in \mathfrak{A}$.

A set $A \in \mathfrak{A}$ is called a *wandering* set if its intersection with each of its images $S_t A$ has measure zero:

$$\mathbb{Q}(A \cap S_t A) = 0 \qquad (t = 1, 2, \ldots) .$$

We say that the system $(\Omega, \mathfrak{A}, \mathbb{Q}, S)$ has no *dissipative* part if there is no wandering set of positive measure.

For any measurable real function $\eta = \eta(\omega)$ we set

$$\eta(\omega), t) = \eta(S_t \omega) \qquad (t = 1, 2, \ldots) .$$

Assume that the system $(\Omega, \mathfrak{A}, \mathbb{Q}, S)$ has not dissipative part. Then for every positive measurable function $\zeta = \zeta(\omega)$ the relation

$$\lim_{T \to \infty} \sum_0^T \zeta(\omega, t) = \infty$$

holds for almost all ω. For any $\eta = \eta(\omega)$ and any positive $\zeta = \zeta(\omega)$ from $L^1(\Omega)$ the limit

$$\lim_{T \to \infty} \frac{\displaystyle\sum_0^T \eta(\omega, t)}{\displaystyle\sum_0^T \zeta(\omega, t)} = \hat\eta(\omega)$$

exists for almost all η. The function $\hat\eta = \hat\eta(\omega)$ which depends, of course, on ζ, is invariant with respect to S, and

$$\int_\Omega \eta(\omega) \, \mathbb{Q}(d\omega) = \int_\Omega \hat\eta(\omega) \, \zeta(\omega) \, \mathbb{Q}(d\omega) .$$

In particular, if $\mathbb{Q}(\Omega) < \infty$, then for almost all

$$\lim_{T \to \infty} \frac{1}{T} \sum_0^{T-1} \eta(\omega, t) = \hat\eta(\omega) .$$

If $\mathbb{Q}(\Omega) = \infty$ and if, in addition, there exist no invariant sets of positive finite measure, then for almost all ω

$$\lim_{T \to \infty} \frac{1}{T} \sum_0^{T-1} \eta(\omega, t) = 0 .$$

In case of a metrically transitive system $(\Omega, \mathfrak{A}, \mathbb{Q}, S)$, that is, if every invariant function $\hat\eta = \hat\eta(\omega)$ coincides almost everywhere with a constant, the limit function $\hat\eta = \hat\eta(\omega)$ equals

$$\hat\eta = \frac{\displaystyle\int_\Omega \eta(\omega) \, \mathbb{Q}(d\omega)}{\displaystyle\int_\Omega \zeta(\omega) \, \mathbb{Q}(d\omega)} .$$

Analogous results hold for a system $(\Omega, \mathfrak{A}, \mathbb{Q}, S_t)$ with a continuous parameter t, where S_t, $t \geq 0$ is a semigroup of $\mathbb{Q}$-measure preserving one-to-one transformations of Ω onto itself.

Invariant Distributions of Homogeneous Markov Processes. Let $\xi = \xi(t)$, $t \geq 0$ be a homogeneous discrete time Markov process in the phase space $(E, \mathfrak{B})$ with the transition function $P(x, B)$ which gives the transition probability "in one step" from the point $x \in E$ to the set $B \in \mathfrak{B}$. A positive σ-finite measure $\mathbb{Q}^0 = \mathbb{Q}^0(B)$ in the phase space $(E, \mathfrak{B})$ is called *invariant* if

$$\mathbb{Q}^0(B) = \int_E \mathbb{Q}^0(dx)\, P(x, B)$$

for any $B \in \mathfrak{B}$.

We assume that an invariant measure $\mathbb{Q}^0$ exists for the Markov process $\xi = \xi(t)$. Let $P_x = P_x(A)$ be the conditional probability distributions on the σ-algebra $\mathfrak{A} = (\mathfrak{A}(0, \infty)$ of the space of elementary events Ω. Then the formula

$$\mathbb{Q}(A) = \int_E \mathbb{Q}^0(dx)\, P_x(A) \qquad (A \in \mathfrak{A})$$

defines a σ-finite measure $\mathbb{Q} = \mathbb{Q}(A)$ on $\mathfrak{A}$ which is invariant under the shift transformation. Given any initial probability distribution $\mathbb{P}^0 = \mathbb{P}^0(B)$ in the phase space $(E, \mathfrak{B})$ which is absolutely continuous with respect to the invariant measure $\mathbb{Q}^0 = \mathbb{Q}^0(B)$, the corresponding probability distribution $\mathbb{P} = \mathbb{P}(A)$ in the space $(\Omega, \mathfrak{A})$ defined by

$$\mathbb{P}(A) = \int_E \mathbb{P}^0(dx)\, P_x(A)$$

is absolutely continuous with respect to the invariant measure $\mathbb{Q} = \mathbb{Q}(A)$.

The system $(\Omega, \mathfrak{A}, \mathbb{Q}, S)$ will have no dissipative part if the following condition is satisfied: for any set $B \in \mathfrak{B}$ with $\mathbb{Q}^0(B) > 0$ we have

$$P_x\{\xi(t) \in B \quad \text{for an infinite number of values } t\} = 1$$

for almost all $x \in B$ with respect to the measure $\mathbb{Q}^0$. If we interpret the process $\xi = \xi(t)$ as describing a random walk of a particle, then this condition means the following: starting at a point x of the set B the wandering particle returns to B infinitely often with probability 1. Under this condition the limit

$$\lim_{T \to \infty} \frac{\displaystyle\sum_0^T \eta(\omega, t)}{\displaystyle\sum_0^T \zeta(\omega, t)} = \hat{\eta}(\omega)$$

exists with probability 1 for any random variable $\eta = \eta(\omega)$ and any positive variable $\zeta = \zeta(\omega)$ which are measurable with respect to $\mathfrak{A}$ and satisfy

$$\int_\Omega |\eta(\omega)| \, \mathbb{Q}(d\omega) < \infty \,, \qquad \int_\Omega \zeta(\omega) \, \mathbb{Q}(d\omega) < \infty \,.$$

If the condition given above for the absence of a dissipative part is satisfied not only for almost all x of the corresponding set B, but in the case $\mathbb{Q}^0(B) > 0$ for almost all $x \in E$, too, then the system $(\Omega, \mathfrak{A}, \mathbb{Q}, S)$ will be metrically transitive. Hence the limit variable $\hat{\eta}$ will be constant

$$\hat{\eta} = \frac{\int_\Omega \eta(\omega) \, \mathbb{Q}(d\omega)}{\int_\Omega \zeta(\omega) \, \mathbb{Q}(d\omega)} \,.$$

A condition for the existence of an invariant σ-finite measure $\mathbb{Q}^0 = \mathbb{Q}^0(B)$ for the Markov process $\xi = \xi(t)$ can be stated as follows [67]. Let $m = m(B)$ be some σ-finite measure in the phase space $(E, \mathfrak{B})$. The Markov process $\xi = \xi(t)$ is called m-singular if for almost all x relative to m there exists a set $B_x \in \mathfrak{B}$ of measure $m(B_x) = 0$ such that

$$P_x\{\xi(t) \in B_x \quad \text{for all } t\} = 1 \,.$$

If the process $\xi(t)$ is not m-singular and if, in addition, the inequality $m(B) > 0$ implies

$$P_x\{\xi(t) \in B \quad \text{for infinitely many } t\} = 1$$

for almost all $x \in E$ with respect to m, then there exists an invariant σ-finite measure $\mathbb{Q}^0 = \mathbb{Q}^0(B)$ which is absolutely continuous with respect to the original measure $m = m(B)$. This invariant measure $\mathbb{Q}^0$ is unique up to a constant factor; in general, different invariant measures $\mathbb{Q}^0$ can correspond to the various measures m.

Conditions for the existence of an invariant probability measure, that is, conditions for the existence of a *stationary probability distribution*, expressed directly in terms of the transition functions $P(n, x, B)$, can be stated as follows. Suppose that the measure $m = m(B)$ is finite, and for any measurable set B the equation $m(B) = 0$ implies the equation $P(x, B) = 0$ for almost all x with respect to m. Then in order that a finite invariant measure $\mathbb{Q}^0 = \mathbb{Q}^0(B)$ exists it is necessary and sufficient that for any B with $m(B) > 0$ the relation

$$\varlimsup_{T \to \infty} \frac{1}{n} \sum_{k=1}^{n} P(k, x, B) > 0$$

---

[67] *Ito, K.*, Invariant measures for Markov processes. Trans. Amer. Math. Soc. 110, 1 (1964), 152—184.

holds for all x in some set B_0 with $m(B_0) > 0$. Moreover, the measure $\mathbb{Q}^0$ is equivalent to the measure m.

Suppose that $m = m(B)$ defines a probability distribution:

$$m(B) = \mathbb{P}_0(B) .$$

Then the corresponding stationary probability distribution $\mathbb{Q}^0 = \mathbb{Q}^0(B)$ can be explicitly expressed in terms of the corresponding probability distributions "*at the n-th step*":

$$\mathbb{P}_n(B) = \int_E P(n, x, B) \, \mathbb{P}_0(dx) .$$

In fact,

$$\mathbb{Q}^0(B) = \lim_{n \to \infty} \frac{1}{n} \sum_{k=1}^{n} \mathbb{P}_k(B)$$

for any measurable set B.

We say that the Markov process $\xi = \xi(t)$ with the transition function $P(n, x, B)$ satisfies *Doeblin's condition* if there exists a finite measure $m = m(B)$, an integer $n \geq 1$, and an $\varepsilon > 0$ such that

$$P(n, x, B) \leq 1 - \varepsilon \quad \text{for} \quad m(B) \leq \varepsilon .$$

If this condition is fulfilled, then for each $x \in E$ the limit

$$\lim_{n \to \infty} \frac{1}{n} \sum_{k=1}^{n} P(k, x, B) = \mathbb{Q}^0(x, B)$$

exists. The function $\mathbb{Q}^0(x, B)$ of $B \in \mathfrak{B}$ yields a stationary probability distribution.

Example. Suppose that the phase space E consists of a finite number of points. Then Doeblin's condition is satisfied for the measure $m = m(B)$ which is equal to the number of points x in the corresponding set B, $n = 1$ and $\varepsilon \leq 1$. In fact, if $m(B) < 1$ the set B must be empty and $P(x, B) = 0$.

Example. Suppose that the phase space E is a multi-dimensional Euclidean space and the transition function $P(x, B)$ is given by a density

$$P(x, B) = \int_B p(x, y) \, m(dy)$$

where $m = m(B)$ is some finite measure. If the density $p(x, y)$ is uniformly bounded: $p(x, y) \leq K$, then Doeblin's condition is satisfied with $m = m(B)$, $n = 1$ and $\varepsilon \leq 1/(K + 1)$.

Consider a homogeneous Markov process $\xi = \xi(t)$ which satisfies Doeblin's condition. A set $B \in \mathfrak{B}$ of the phase space E is called *invariant* if

$$P(x, B) = 1 \quad \text{for all} \quad x \in B .$$

The measure $m(B)$ of a non-empty invariant set B must be at least equal to the positive number ε appearing in Doeblin's condition. An invariant set B is called *minimal* if it does not contain other invariant sets. Any two minimal invariant sets B_1 and B_2 either do not intersect each other, or coincide up to a set of m-measure zero. Altogether, there are not more than $m(E)/\varepsilon$ essentially different minimal invariant sets in the phase space E.

Let $B_1, \dots, B_N$ be the system of the disjoint minimal invariant sets of E. Then for each $x \in E$ we have

$$\lim_{n \to \infty} P\left(n, x, \bigcup_k B_k\right) = 1 \; ;$$

the convergence in this asymptotic relation is exponentially fast. The relation can be visualized in the following way: starting from any point $x \in E$ the wandering particle hits after a finite number of steps one of the invariant sets $B_1, \dots, B_N$ with probability 1, and then stays there forever. The stationary limit distribution $\mathbb{Q}^0(x, B)$ is the same for all x in the same minimal invariant set B_k:

$$\mathbb{Q}^0(x, B) = \mathbb{Q}^0_k(B) \quad (B \in \mathfrak{B})$$

for $x \in B_k$, $k = 1, \dots, N$. Every invariant measure $\mathbb{Q}^0$ in the phase space $(E, \mathfrak{B})$ is finite and can be written as a linear combination of mutually perpendicular stationary probability distributions $\mathbb{Q}^0_k = \mathbb{Q}^0_k(B)$, $k = 1, \dots, N$:

$$\mathbb{Q}^0_k(B_k) = 1, \quad B_k \cap B_j = \emptyset \quad \text{for} \quad k \neq j.$$

A set of states B of the phase space E is called a *null set* if for all $x \in E$

$$\lim_{n \to \infty} P(n, x, B) = 0.$$

The system of disjoint minimal invariant sets $B_1, \dots, B_N$ is uniquely determined up to null sets. The sets B_k are also called *ergodic classes*. They can be chosen in such a way that each B_k can be partitioned into disjoint *cyclic subclasses* $C_{k1}, \dots C_{kd_k}$, that is, sets of states of the phase space with the property that

$$P(x, C_{k, i+1}) = 1 \quad \text{for} \quad x \in C_{ki} \quad (i = 1, \dots, d_k).$$

In other words the sets C_{ki} follow each other in cyclic order. The asymptotic relations

$$\lim_{n \to \infty} P(n d_k + i_0, x, B) = \mathbb{Q}^0_{kj}(B) \quad (x \in C_{ki}, \; j = i + i_0 (\operatorname{mod} d_k))$$

define probability distributions $\mathbb{Q}^0_{kj} = \mathbb{Q}^0_{kj}(B)$, $j = 1, \dots, d_k$ which are connected with the stationary probability distribution $\mathbb{Q}^0_k = \mathbb{Q}^0_k(B)$ by

$$\mathbb{Q}^0_k(B) = \frac{1}{d_k} \sum_{j=1}^{d_k} \mathbb{Q}^0_{kj}(B) \quad (B \in \mathfrak{B}).$$

Here the convergence takes place in such a way that

$$\operatorname{Var}\{P(n\,d_k + i_0, x, B) - \mathbb{Q}^0_{kj}(B)\} \leqq C\,e^{-Dn}$$

with some positive constants C and D.

The cyclic property of the subclasses $C_{k1}, \dots, C_{kd_k}$ can be described in terms of a random walk: from any point x of the set C_{ki} the wandering particle passes with probability 1 at the next step to a point of the set C_{ki+1} which follows C_{ki} in cyclic order. The probability distribution $\mathbb{Q}^0_{kj} = \mathbb{Q}^0_{kj}(B), j = 1, \dots, d_k$ as well as the stationary distribution $\mathbb{Q}^0_k = \mathbb{Q}^0_k(B)$, $k = 1, \dots, N$ are uniquely determined; moreover

$$\mathbb{Q}^0_{kj}(C_{kj}) = 1 , \qquad C_{ki} \cap C_{kj} = \emptyset \quad \text{for} \quad i \neq j .$$

If we are given a Markov process $\xi = \xi(t)$ with only one ergodic class and no cyclic subclasses, then we have only one stationary probability distribution $\mathbb{Q}^0 = \mathbb{Q}^0(B)$. Hence for any initial distribution $\mathbb{P}_0 = \mathbb{P}_0(B)$ the corresponding probability distribution $\mathbb{P}_n = \mathbb{P}_n(B)$ "after n steps":

$$\mathbb{P}_n(B) = \int\limits_E \mathbb{P}_0(dx)\, P(n, x, B) = \mathbb{P}\{\xi(n) \in B\}$$

has the property that

$$\lim_{n \to \infty} \mathbb{P}_n(B) = \mathbb{Q}^0(B) \qquad (B \in \mathfrak{B}) ,$$

that is, for $n \to \infty$ it converges to the stationary probability distribution $\mathbb{Q}^0 = \mathbb{Q}^0(B)$. This convergence takes place uniformly exponentially fast:

$$\operatorname{Var}\{\mathbb{P}_n - \mathbb{Q}^0\} \leqq C\,e^{-Dn}$$

with some positive constants C and D.

Analogous results hold also in the case of a continuous time t; in a certain sense these results are even simpler since there are no cyclic subclasses.

We will now introduce different conditions for the existence of a stationary probability distribution [68]. Assume that $\xi = \xi(t)$, $t \geqq 0$ is a homogeneous Markov process with continuous time, and its transition function $P(t, x, B)$ satisfies the following requirements: for any $\varepsilon > 0$ there exists a finite measure $m = m(B)$ in the phase space $(E, \mathfrak{B})$, a set $B_0 \in \mathfrak{B}$ and positive numbers t_0 and δ such that for $t \geqq t_0$ and $B \subseteq B_0$ we have

$$P(t_0, x, B) \geqq \delta m(B) \qquad (x \in B_0) ,$$
$$\mathbb{P}_t(B) = \int\limits_E P(t, x, B)\, \mathbb{P}_0(dx) \leqq m(B) + \varepsilon ,$$
$$\mathbb{P}_t(B_0) \geqq 1 - \varepsilon$$

[68] *Sevastianov, B. A.*, An ergodic theorem for Markov processes and its applications to telephone systems with refusals. Teor. veroyatn. i primen. II, 1 (1957), 106—115 (Russian).

for any initial distribution $\mathbb{P}_0 = \mathbb{P}_0(B)$, $B \in \mathcal{B}$. Then there exists a unique stationary probability distribution $\mathbb{Q}^0 = \mathbb{Q}^0(B)$ in the phase space $(E, \mathcal{B})$, and

$$\lim_{t \to \infty} \text{Var}(\mathbb{P}_t - \mathbb{Q}^0) = 0$$

for any initial distribution $\mathbb{P}_0$.

Regularity and the Central Limit Theorem. Let $\xi = \xi(t)$ be a Markov process satisfying Doeblin's condition. Given a stationary probability distribution the process $\xi = \xi(t)$ is ergodic if and only if there is only one ergodic class without cyclic subclasses. In this case for any initial distribution the process $\xi = \xi(t)$ fulfills the following regularity condition: if $t - s \to \infty$

$$\beta(t - s) = \sup_{A \in \mathfrak{A}(t, \infty)} |\mathbb{P}\{A \mid \mathfrak{A}(-\infty, s)\} - \mathbb{P}\{A\}| \leq C e^{-D(t-s)}$$

with probability 1 with some constants $C >$ and $D > 0$.

Suppose that the variable $\eta = \eta(\omega, t)$ is measurable with respect to the σ-algebra $\mathfrak{A}(s_0, t_0)$, $\mathbb{M}|\eta|^2 < \infty$ and $\mathbb{D} \sum_0^{T-1} \eta(t) \to \infty$. Then the deviation of the temporal means $\eta_T = \dfrac{1}{T} \sum_0^{T-1} \eta(t)$ from the expectation $\hat{\eta} = \mathbb{M}\eta$ is subject to the central limit theorem: for $T \to \infty$

$$\mathbb{P}\{\Delta_T \leq x\} \to \frac{1}{\sqrt{2\pi}} \int_{-\infty}^{x} e^{-\frac{1}{2}u^2}\, du,$$

$$\Delta_T = \frac{\eta_T - \hat{\eta}}{\sigma_T}, \qquad \sigma_T^2 = \mathbb{D}\eta_T.$$

Analogous results hold in the case of a continuous time t.

3. Spectral Conditions for the Ergodicity of Some Stationary Processes

General Spectral Conditions. Let $\xi = \xi(t)$ be a stationary ergodic process and U_t the corresponding group of unitary operators in the space $L^2(\Omega)$. If $\hat{\eta} = \hat{\eta}(\lambda)$ is an eigenfunction, that is,

$$U_t \hat{\eta}(\lambda) = e^{i\lambda t} \hat{\eta}(\lambda)$$

for all t, then the absolute value $\varrho(\lambda) = |\hat{\eta}(\lambda)|$ is constant with probability 1, and the argument $\theta(\lambda) = \arg \hat{\eta}(\lambda)$ is a random variable which is uniformly distributed in the interval $-\pi \leq \theta(\lambda) \leq \pi$. If

$$\hat{\eta}(\lambda) = \varrho(\lambda)\, e^{i\theta(\lambda)},$$

then

$$U_t \hat{\eta}(\lambda) = \varrho(\lambda) \, e^{i[\theta(\lambda) + \lambda t]} \, .$$

Assume that with some finite number of eigenvalues λ the relations

$$\left.\begin{array}{ll} \sum_\lambda \lambda m(\lambda) \equiv 0 \, (\mathrm{mod}\, 2\pi), & \text{if } t \text{ is discrete} \\[2mm] \sum_\lambda \lambda m(\lambda) = 0, & \text{if } t \text{ is continuous} \end{array}\right\} \tag{2.1}$$

are satisfied where the coefficients $m(\lambda)$ are integers.

Then we have with probability 1

$$\sum_\lambda m(\lambda)\, \theta(\lambda) \equiv \theta \, (\mathrm{mod}\, 2\pi) \tag{2.2}$$

with some constant θ.

If the stationary process $\xi = \xi(t)$ has the mixing property, then $\lambda = 0$ is the only eigenvalue, and corresponds to the eigenfunction $\hat{\eta} \equiv 1$.

Process with Discrete Spectrum. We say that a complex stationary process $\xi = \xi(t)$ with $\mathbb{M}\,|\xi(t)|^2 < \infty$ has a discrete spectrum if it can be written as

$$\xi(t) = \sum_{\lambda \in \Lambda} e^{i\lambda t} \, \Phi(\lambda)$$

where the summation is extended over a finite or countable set Λ of points λ of the spectrum of λ, and $\Phi = \Phi(\lambda)$ is a family of non-correlated random variables. Each variable $\Phi(\lambda)$ is an eigenfunction of the operators U_t corresponding to the eigenvalue λ.

Such a stationary process $\xi = \xi(t)$ is ergodic if and only if the absolute value $\varrho(\lambda) = |\Phi(\lambda)|$ of each variable $\Phi(\lambda)$ is a constant and the variables $\theta(\lambda) = \arg \Phi(\lambda)$ have the property that for any finite number of points $\lambda \in \Lambda$ and corresponding integers $m(\lambda)$ satisfying (2.1) the relation (2.2) holds.

Consider the set M of all possible sequences $m = m(\lambda)$, $\lambda \in \Lambda$, with integer components $m(\lambda)$ which differ from zero only for a finite number of points $\lambda \in \Lambda$. Define the addition of sequences $m = m(\lambda)$ and their multiplication by integers α by

$$m = \alpha_1 m_1 + \alpha_2 m_2, \qquad m(\lambda) = \alpha_1 m_1(\lambda) + \alpha_2 m_2(\lambda) \, .$$

Let M_0 be the set of all sequences $m = m(\lambda)$ which fulfil the relations (2.1). From the entire set M_0 of sequences $m = m(\lambda)$ we select a linearly independent subset $m_1 = m_1(\lambda)$, $m_2 = m_2(\lambda), \dots$. In other words the equation

$$\sum_{k=1}^{n} \alpha_k m_k = 0$$

with integers $\alpha_1, \alpha_2, \ldots, \alpha_n$ implies

$$\alpha_1 = \alpha_2 = \cdots = \alpha_n = 0.$$

As mentioned above there exist constants $\theta_1, \theta_2, \ldots$ such that

$$\left.\begin{array}{c} \sum_\lambda m_1(\lambda)\,\theta(\lambda) \equiv \theta_1\,(\mathrm{mod}\,2\pi), \\[4pt] \sum_\lambda m_2(\lambda)\,\theta(\lambda) \equiv \theta_2\,(\mathrm{mod}\,2\pi), \\ \cdots\cdots\cdots\cdots\cdots\cdots\cdots\cdots \end{array}\right\}$$

The probability distribution of an ergodic stationary process $\xi = \xi(t)$ with a discrete spectrum $\varLambda$ is uniquely defined by the positive variables $\varrho(\lambda)$:

$$\sum_\lambda [\varrho(\lambda)]^2 < \infty,$$

and the integers $\theta_1, \theta_2, \ldots (-\pi \leq \theta_k \leq \pi)$ corresponding to the element $m_k = m_k(\lambda)$ of the chosen system of linearly independent elements of M_0. In fact, the σ-algebra $\mathfrak{A} = \mathfrak{A}(-\infty, \infty)$ coincides with the σ-algebra generated by the random variables $\theta(\lambda) = \arg \Phi(\lambda)$, $\lambda \in \varLambda$, and completed by the events of probability zero. The finite-dimensional distributions of these variables can be described as follows. If the points $\lambda_1, \ldots, \lambda_n \in \varLambda$ have the property that the relations (2.1) hold for no choice of integers $m(\lambda), \lambda = \lambda_1, \ldots, \lambda_n$, then the random variables $\theta(\lambda_1), \ldots, \theta(\lambda_n)$ are mutually independent and uniformly distributed in the interval $[-\pi, \pi]$. If however, the points $\lambda_1, \ldots, \lambda_n$ satisfy the condition (2.1) with integers $m(\lambda)$, $\lambda = \lambda_1, \ldots, \lambda_n$, then these integers describe an element $m = m(\lambda) \in M_0$ which can be written as linear combination of $m_1 = m_1(\lambda)$, $m_2 = m_2(\lambda), \ldots$:

$$m = \sum_{p=1}^q \alpha_p m_{k_p}.$$ In this case the probability distribution of the random variables $\theta(\lambda) = \arg \Phi(\lambda)$, $\lambda = \lambda_1, \ldots, \lambda_n$ will be degenerate and concentrated on the $(n-q)$-dimensional surface of the n-dimensional torus T^n defined by the system of equations

$$\left.\begin{array}{c} \sum_\lambda m_{k_1}(\lambda)\,\theta(\lambda) \equiv \theta_{k_1}\,(\mathrm{mod}\,2\pi), \\ \cdots\cdots\cdots\cdots\cdots\cdots\cdots\cdots \\ \sum_\lambda m_{k_q}(\lambda)\,\theta(\lambda) \equiv \theta_{k_q}\,(\mathrm{mod}\,2\pi). \end{array}\right\}$$

The probability is uniformly distributed on this surface. Recall that by an n-dimensional torus T^n we mean the set of all points $\theta = \theta(\lambda)$, $\lambda = \lambda_1, \ldots, \lambda_n$ whose components are real numbers $\theta(\lambda)$ which are identified $\mathrm{mod}\,2\pi$ with the numbers of the interval $[-\pi, \pi]$. In the case of incommensurable points $\lambda_1, \ldots, \lambda_n$ which do not satisfy the condition (2.1) for any $m(\lambda)$ the random variables $\theta(\lambda) = \arg \Phi(\lambda)$, $\lambda = \lambda_1, \ldots, \lambda_n$ are uniformly distributed on T^n; this is equivalent to the fact that these variables $\theta(\lambda_1), \ldots, \theta(\lambda_n)$ are independent and each of them is uniformly distributed in the interval $[-\pi, \pi]$.

Stationary Processes of the Class $\Phi^{(2n)}$. Suppose that $\xi = \xi(t)$ is a strict sense stationary random process of the class $\Phi^{(2n)}$. The unitary operators U_t in $L^2(\Omega)$ which correspond to the process $\xi = \xi(t)$ operate on the elements $\Phi^{(k,l)}(\Delta)$, that is, on the values of the stochastic spectral measure $\Phi^{(k,l)}$, according to the following law:

$$U_t \, \Phi^{(k,l)}(\Delta) = \int_\Delta \exp\left\{ it \left(\sum_{p=1}^k \lambda_p - \sum_{q=1}^t \mu_q \right) \right\} \Phi^{(k,l)}(d\lambda \, d\mu).$$

The subspace $L^{(k,l)}$ described by the equation

$$\lambda_1 + \cdots + \lambda_k - \mu_1 - \cdots - \mu_l = 0$$

has the property that for any measurable set Δ the variable $\Phi^{(k,l)}(\Delta \cap L^{(k,l)})$ is invariant, and in the case of an ergodic process the relation $\Phi^{(k,l)}(\Delta \cap L^{(k,l)}) = \mathcal{M}^{(k,l)}(\Delta \cap L^{(k,l)})$ holds (see § 1.7) of this Chapter). Moreover, if $\Delta_1 \supseteq \Delta_2 \supseteq \cdots$ is a monotone sequence of sets such that $\Delta = \bigcap_k \Delta_k \subseteq L^{(k,l)}$, then we have

$$\lim_{n \to \infty} \Phi^{(k,l)}(\Delta_n) = \mathcal{M}^{(k,l)}(\Delta).$$

A particular manifestation of this fact is that for any ergodic stationary process $\xi = \xi(t)$ with $\mathbb{M}|\xi(t)|^2 < \infty$ the asymptotic relation

$$\lim_{n \to \infty} \sum_{k=1}^n |\Phi(\delta_{kn})|^2 = F(\delta)$$

holds where we are dealing with a partition of the arbitrary interval $\delta = (\lambda_1, \lambda_2)$ into n intervals δ_{kn} whose lengths converge uniformly to zero if $n \to \infty$, and $F(d\lambda) = \mathbb{M}|\Phi(d\lambda)|^2$ is the spectral measure of the stationary process $\xi = \xi(t)$.

The spectral moments $\mathcal{M}^{(k,l)} = \mathcal{M}^{(k,l)}(\Delta)$ of the stationary process $\xi = \xi(t)$ of the class $\Phi^{(2n)}$ have the property that for any measurable set Δ of the $(k+l)$-dimensional space $E^{(k+l)}$ the equation

$$\mathcal{M}^{(k,l)}(\Delta) = \mathcal{M}^{(k,l)}(\Delta \cap L^{(k,l)})$$

holds, that is, the subspace $L^{(k,l)}$ "carries" the measure $\mathcal{M}^{(k,l)}(d\lambda \, d\mu)$.

In the case of an ergodic process $\xi = \xi(t)$ the spectral moments $\mathcal{M}^{(k,l)}$ have additional properties which may be characterized in short as follows. Let k_1 and l_1 be arbitrary integers such that $0 \leq k_1 \leq k, 0 \leq l_1 \leq l$, $k_2 = k - k_1$ and $l_2 = l - l_1$. We denote by $L^{(k_1, l_1)}$ and $L^{(k_2, l_2)}$ the subspaces described by the equations $\lambda_1 + \cdots + \lambda_{k_1} = \mu_1 + \cdots + \mu_{l_1}$ and $\mu_{k_1+1} + \cdots + \lambda_k$ $= \mu_{l_1+1} + \cdots + \mu_l$. Then the equation

$$\mathcal{M}^{(k,l)}(\Delta_1 \times \Delta_2) = \mathcal{M}^{(k_1, l_1)}(\Delta_1)\, \mathcal{M}^{(k_2, l_2)}(\Delta_2),$$

holds for any measurable sets $\Delta_1 \subseteq L^{(k_1, l_1)}$ and $\Delta_2 \subseteq L^{(k_2, l_2)}$, that is, the spectral moment $\mathcal{M}^{(k,l)}$ on the subspace $L^{(k_1, l_1)} \times L^{(k_2, l_2)}$ equals the product of the spectral moments $\mathcal{M}^{(k_1, l_1)}$ and $\mathcal{M}^{(k_2, l_2)}$ in the sense of a product of measures on the product of the spaces $L^{(k_1, l_1)}$ and $L^{(k_2, l_2)}$. If $\xi = \xi(t)$ is a stationary process of the class $\Phi^{(\infty)}$, that is, $\xi = \xi(t)$ belongs to $\Phi^{(2n)}$ for $n = 1, 2, \ldots$, and hence its finite-dimensional distributions are uniquely determined by the moments $M^{(k,l)} = M^{(k,l)}(s, t)$ (see § 1.7 of this Chapter), then the relations stated before are not only necessary but also sufficient [69] for the ergodicity of $\xi = \xi(t)$.

The class $\Phi^{(\infty)}$ includes many important processes. For example, $\Phi^{(\infty)}$ contains all Gaussian stationary processes. A necessary and sufficient condition for the ergodicity of a Gaussian stationary process $\xi = \xi(t)$ is that its spectral measure $F = F(\Delta)$ is continuous, that is, $F(\lambda) = 0$ for any "one-point" set λ.

§ 3. Stationary Gaussian Processes

1. Some Properties of the Trajectories

Continuity. A stationary Gaussian process $\xi = \xi(t)$ is either continuous with probability 1 or has almost surely unbounded trajectories in every interval. A separable stationary Gaussian process $\xi = \xi(t)$ is continuous with probability 1 if

$$B(0) - B(h) \leq \frac{1}{\|\log |h|\|^2} \qquad (\alpha > 1)$$

for sufficiently small h or if

$$\int_{-\infty}^{\infty} [\log(1 + |\lambda|)]^\alpha\, F(d\lambda) < \infty \qquad (\alpha > 1).$$

Assume that in a sufficiently small neighborhood of the point $t = 0$ the correlation function $B = B(t)$ is convex from below. Then under the condition

$$B(0) - B(h) \geq c\, \frac{1}{\|\log |h|\|}$$

---

[69] *Shiryaev, A. N.,* On ergodicity conditions for stationary processes in terms of moments of higher orders. Teor. veroyat. i primen. VIII, **4** (1963), 470—473 (Russian).

almost all trajectories $\xi(\omega, t)$ are unbounded in any interval Δ: in fact with probability 1, given any N, there exist points $t_1 = t_1(\omega)$ and $t_2 = t_2(\omega)$ such that $t_1, t_2 \in \Delta$ and

$$\xi(\omega, t_1) \leq -N, \qquad \xi(\omega, t_2) \geq N.$$

Assume that the correlation function $B = B(t)$ of the separable stationary Gaussian process $\xi = \xi(t)$ satisfies the inequality

$$B(0) - B(h) \leq \frac{h^{2\alpha}}{|\log|h||}$$

or

$$\int_{-\infty}^{\infty} |\lambda|^{2\alpha} \log(1 + |\lambda|) \, F(d\lambda) < \infty \qquad (\alpha > 0).$$

Then its trajectories satisfy with probability 1 the condition

$$|\xi(\omega, t + h) - \xi(\omega, t)| \leq \sqrt{C} \, \frac{2^{2\alpha + 1}}{2^{\alpha} - 1} \, |h|^{\alpha}$$

in any interval $-\tau \leq t \leq \tau$ for sufficiently small h.

If the correlation function $B = B(t)$ is convex from below in some neighborhood of $t = 0$ and

$$B(0) - B(h) \geq c \, \frac{h^{2\alpha}}{|\log|h||}$$

with some $c > 0$, then the inequality [70]

$$\overline{\lim_{n \to \infty}} \, |\xi(\omega, t + h) - \xi(\omega, t)| \, h^{-\alpha} \geq \sqrt{c}$$

holds with probability 1.

Bilinear Forms of Infinitely Small Increments. The peculiar properties of the trajectories of a stationary Gaussian process $\xi = \xi(t)$ find their expression in the behavior of the functionals

$$V_{pq}(t_0) = \frac{1}{n} \sum_{k=1}^{n} [\Delta_h^p \, \xi(k h)] \, [\Delta_h^q \, \xi(t_0 + k h)]$$

where Δ_h is the difference operator

$$\Delta_h \, \xi(t) = \xi(t + h) - \xi(t), \qquad h = \frac{1}{n} (\tau - t_0),$$

associated with a partition of the intervals $0 \leq t \leq \tau - t_0$ and $t_0 \leq t \leq \tau$. We assume that for any $\varepsilon > 0$ we can find a finite system of intervals I_ε whose number may depend on ε with a total length not larger than ε

[70] Belyaev, Yu. K., Local properties of sample functions of a stationary Gaussian process. Teor. veroyat. i primen. V, 1 (1960), 128—131 (Russian).

such that we have

$$\Delta_h^p \, \Delta_{-h}^p \, B(t) = o(\Delta_h^p \, \Delta_{-h}^p \, B) \qquad (h \to 0)$$

uniformly for all t, $-\tau < t < \tau$ outside of I_ε. Here, Δ_h^p stands for the p-th power of the operator Δ_h, and

$$\Delta_h^p \, \Delta_{-h}^p \, B = \Delta_h^p \, \Delta_{-h}^p \, B(0) \, .$$

This will be the case, for example, if the $(2p)$-th derivative $B^{(2p)}(t)$ of the correlation function $B(t)$ exists and is continuous except a finite number of points and except the point $t = 0$ where a discontinuity occurs. Under the condition stated above there exists the mean square limit

$$\lim_{h \to 0} (\Delta_h^p \, \Delta_{-h}^p \, B)^{-1} \, V_{pp}(0) = 1 \, .$$

We remark that

$$\mathbb{M} \, V_{pp}(0) = \Delta_h^p \, \Delta_{-h}^p \, B \, ,$$

$$\mathbb{D} \, V_{pp}(0) = \frac{2}{n^2} \sum_{k,j} [\Delta_h^p \, \Delta_{-h}^p \, B(k-j) \, h]^2 \, .$$

Consider the functional $V_{11}(t_0)$ of the non-differentiable stationary process $\xi = \xi(t)$ where the derivative $B'(t)$ of the correlation function can have discontinuities. We assume that for some sequence $\{h_j\}$, $h_j > 0$, $h_j \to 0$ there exist the one-sided limits $B'(t_0 - 0) = \lim_{h \to 0} B'(t_0 - h_j)$ and $B'(t_0 + 0) = \lim B'(t_0 + h_j)$. Assume that

$$\Delta_h B = o\{\sqrt{h}\}$$

for $h \to 0$ and that, as a rule,

$$\frac{1}{n^2} \sum_{k,j=1}^{n} [\Delta_h \Delta_{-h} B(k-j) \, h]^2 = O\{h(\Delta_h B)^2\}$$

is always satisfied. Then there exists the mean square limit [71]

$$\lim_{h_j \to 0} [h_j^{-1} \, V_{11}(t_0)] = B'(t_0 - 0) - B'(t_0 + 0) \, .$$

An analogous relation holds for the functional $V_{21}(t_0)$ provided that

$$\Delta_h B = o\{h\sqrt{h}\}$$

and that, consequently, the first derivate $B'(t)$ is continuous. In fact,

$$\lim_{h_j \to 0} [h_j^{-1} \, V_{21}(t_0)] = B''(t_0 - 0) - B''(t_0 + 0) \, .$$

If the sequences $\{h_j\}$ decrease sufficiently fast, these asymptotic relations hold also with probability 1.

---

[71] Rozanov, Yu. A., On probabilistic measures in functional spaces corresponding to stationary Gaussian processes. Teor. veroyat. i primen. IX, 3 (1964), 448—465 (Russian).

2. Exits of a Stationary Gaussian Process Beyond a Given Level

Let $\xi = \xi(t)$ be a stationary Gaussian process which has with probability 1 a continuous derivative $\xi' = \xi'(t)$. Then with probability 1 this process crosses an arbitrary level a during any finite period of time only a finite number of times. Moreover, the derivative $\xi'(t)$ preserves a definite sign in some neighborhood of the crossing time τ so that the trajectory of the process $\xi(t)$ either increases or decreases monotonically in this neighborhood; $\xi'(t)$ is positive if a is crossed from below in an upward direction, and negative if a is crossed from above in a downward direction. We remark that if the stationary Gaussian process has no continuous derivative, then its trajectories are monotone on no interval no matter how small.

We introduce the following notations. τ_1^- is the instant of the first upward crossing of a after some fixed time $t = t_0$, τ_1^+ denotes the instant of the first downward crossing of a after τ_1^-, τ_2^- the instant of the second crossing of a in upward direction, τ_2^+ the instant of the second crossing of a in downward direction etc.; $v^-(t_0, t)$ is the number of upward crossings of a within the period of time (t_0, t), $v^+(t_0, t)$ the number of downward crossings, and $v(t_0, t)$ the total number of all crossings.

The number of crossings during any finite interval is not only bounded with probability 1 but also has a finite expectation:

$$\mathbb{M} v^-(t_0, t) = \lambda(t - t_0), \qquad \mathbb{M} v^+(t_0, t) = \lambda(t - t_0),$$
$$\mathbb{M} v(t_0, t) = 2\lambda(t - t_0),$$

where the parameter λ is the average number of crossings during one unit of time, and can be obtained by the formula

$$\lambda = \frac{1}{2\pi} \sqrt{\frac{B''(0)}{B(0)}} \exp\left\{-\frac{a^2}{2B(0)}\right\};$$

here $B = B(t)$ denotes the correlation function of the Gaussian process $\xi = \xi(t)$ under consideration.

Let us consider the upward crossings of a level a; the results about the opposite crossings are completely analogous. We remark that for $h \to 0$

$$\mathbb{P}\{v^-(t_0, t_0 + h) > 1\} = o(h)$$

and that moreover,

$$\lim_{h \to 0} h^{-1} \mathbb{P}\{v^-(t_0, t_0 + h) = 1\} = \lambda.$$

There exists the conditional probability distribution of the periods of "*ejections*" $\tau_1^+ - \tau_1^-$, $\tau_2^+ - \tau_2^-$ of the process $\xi(t)$ from the level a given that an exit time $\tau_k^- = t_k$ of the trajectory of $\xi(t)$ from a is fixed; we set

$$F(t) = \mathbb{P}\{\tau_k^+ - \tau_k^- \leq t \,|\, \tau_k^- = t_k\}\,.$$

The distribution function $F = F(t)$ is the same for all k and t_k, and can be determined from the following asymptotic relation:

$$F(t) = \lim_{h \to 0} \frac{\mathbb{P}\{v^-(-h, 0) = 1, v^+(0, t) \geq 1\}}{\mathbb{P}\{v^-(-h, 0) = 1\}}$$

The conditional distribution of the "ejection" is closely connected with the function

$$G(t) = \mathbb{P}\{\xi(s) \geq a,\ 0 \leq s \leq t\}\,.$$

In fact,

$$F(t) = 1 + \frac{1}{\lambda}\, G'(t+0)\,.$$

We have the following

Comparison Theorem[72]. *If $B(t)$ and $\tilde{B}(t)$ are the correlation functions of a stationary Gaussian process $\xi = \xi(t)$ with zero mean corresponding to probability distributions $\mathbb{P}$ and $\tilde{\mathbb{P}}$, respectively, such that*

$$B(s) \geq \tilde{B}(s)$$

for all s, $0 \leq s \leq t$, then

$$\mathbb{P}\{\xi(s) \geq 0, 0 \leq s \leq t\} \geq \tilde{\mathbb{P}}\{\xi(s) \geq 0, 0 \leq s \leq t\}\,.$$

The average duration of the "ejection" $\Delta = \int\limits_0^\infty t \, dF(t)$ can be computed by the formula

$$\Delta = \frac{1}{\lambda}\, \mathbb{P}\{\xi(t) \geq a\} = \sqrt{\frac{2\pi}{B''(0)}} \int\limits_a^\infty \exp\left\{-\frac{1}{2B(0)}(x^2 - a^2)\right\} dx\,.$$

Ergodic Properties. Suppose that the stationary process $\xi = \xi(t)$ under consideration is ergodic. Then with probability 1

$$\lim_{T \to \infty} \frac{1}{T}\, v^-(0, T) = \lambda\,,$$

$$\lim_{T \to \infty} \frac{v_t^-(0, T)}{v^-(0, T)} = F(t)\,,$$

where $v_t^-(0, T)$ is the number of "ejections" starting at moments τ^- from the interval $(0, T)$, and with a duration not exceeding t.

---

[72] Slepian, D., The one-side barrier problem for Gaussian noise. Bell System Techn. J. **41**, 2 (1962), 463—501.

Limit Distributions. We state some asymptotic formulas for the probability distributions of the number of crossings and the duration of single "ejections" if the level a increases beyond all bounds. Let $\xi = \xi(t)$ be a completely regular Gaussian process whose exponent $r(t)$ satisfies the condition.

$$r(t) = O\{t^{-\varepsilon}\} \quad (\varepsilon > 0)$$

(see § 2.2, Chapter II and § 1.2, Chapter VI).

The average number of crossings of a within a unit of time decreases extremely fast if $a \to \infty$. It is convenient to introduce a new time scale setting $t^* = \lambda^{-1} t$. Then the asymptotic relation

$$\lim_{a \to \infty} \mathbb{P}\{v^-(s_1^*, t_1^*) = k_1, \ldots, v^-(s_n^*, t_n^*) = k_n\} = \prod_{i=1}^{n} \frac{(t_i - s_i)^{k_i}}{k_i!} e^{-(t_i - s_i)}$$

holds for any disjoint intervals (s_i, t_i), $s_i = \lambda s_i^*$, $t_i = \lambda t_i^*$, $i = 1, \ldots, n$.

The average duration Δ of a single ejection from a satisfies

$$\lim_{a \to \infty} \Delta = \frac{B(0)}{a} \sqrt{-\frac{2\pi}{B''(0)}}.$$

For the distribution function $F = F(t)$ of the duration of an ejection we have the asymptotic relation

$$\lim_{a \to \infty} F\left(t \frac{B(0)}{a} \sqrt{-\frac{2\pi}{B''(0)}}\right) = 1 - \exp\left\{-\frac{\pi t^2}{4}\right\} \quad (t \geq 0).$$

We denote by $\tau(0, t)$ the time spent by the process $\xi(t)$ above the level a within the period from 0 to t. Let $V = V(s)$ be the probability distribution function with the characteristic function

$$\varphi(u) = \exp\left\{t\left[e^{-\frac{u^2}{\pi}}(1 + iu) - 1\right]\right\};$$

thus $V = V(s)$ represents the probability distribution of a sum of a random number v of independent variables which have the same probability distribution $1 - \exp\{-\pi t^2/4\}$, where v does not depend on these variables and has a Poisson distribution with mean t. Then the asymptotic relation

$$\lim_{a \to \infty} \mathbb{P}\left\{\tau(0, t^*) \frac{B(0)}{a} \sqrt{-\frac{2\pi}{B''(0)}} \leq s\right\} = V(s)$$

holds [73].

[73] *Volkonsky, V. A.*, and *Yu. A. Rozanov*, Some limit theorems for random functionals. Teor. veroyat. i primen. VI, 2 (1961), 202—215 (Russian).

Behavior of the Maximum. The distribution of the maximum of $\xi = \xi(t)$ on the interval $0 \leq t \leq T$ is closely associated with the distribution of the number $v(0, T)$ of crossings of a. In fact, we have

$$\mathbb{P}\left\{\max_{0 \leq t \leq T} \xi(t) \leq a\right\} + \mathbb{P}\left\{\min_{0 \leq t \leq T} \xi(t) \geq a\right\} = \mathbb{P}\{v(0, T) = 0\}.$$

Under the regularity conditions described above with $r(t) = O\{t^{-\varepsilon}\}$ we obtain

$$\lim_{T \to \infty} P\left\{\max_{0 \leq t \leq T} \xi(t) \leq a\right\} = \lim_{T \to \infty} \mathbb{P}\{v(0, T) = 0\} = e^{-y}$$

$$\left(T = \frac{y}{\lambda}\right)$$

where y is some fixed number and λ the average number of crossings of a which equals

$$\frac{1}{2\pi} \sqrt{-\frac{B''(0)}{B(0)}} \exp\left\{-\frac{a^2}{2B(0)}\right\}.$$

If the maximum of the process under consideration is written in the form

$$\max_{0 \leq t \leq T} \xi(t) = \sqrt{\frac{B(0)}{2 \log T}}\left(\log \frac{T^2 \sqrt{-B''(0)}}{2\pi} + \zeta_T\right),$$

then the random variable ζ_T defined by this relation satisfies the following limit theorem:

$$\lim_{T \to \infty} \mathbb{P}\{\zeta_T \leq z\} = e^{-y} \quad \text{where} \quad y = e^{-z}.$$

Thus

$$\max_{0 \leq t \leq T} \xi(t) \sim \sqrt{2B(0) \log T}.$$

3. Equivalence of Probability Distributions of Stationary Gaussian Processes

Equivalence conditions for general distributions were given in § 2.2, Chapter III. An application of the spectral decomposition permits to write these conditions in a spectral form. This opens a fairly efficient way of finding the densities (likelihood ratios) of equivalent distributions.

Equivalence on an Infinite Interval. Let $\mathbb{P} = \mathbb{P}(A)$ and $\tilde{\mathbb{P}} = \tilde{\mathbb{P}}(A)$ be two probability distributions of a stationary Gaussian process $\xi = \xi(t)$, $-\infty < t < \infty$, and $B = B(t)$, $\tilde{B} = \tilde{B}(t)$ and $F = F(\Delta)$, $\tilde{F} = \tilde{F}(\Delta)$ the corresponding correlation functions and spectral measures. The equivalence condition for the distributions $\mathbb{P}$ and $\tilde{\mathbb{P}}$ on the σ-algebra $\mathfrak{A}(-\infty, \infty)$ consists in the following. First, the set of points λ for which $F(\lambda) > 0$ coincides with the set of points for which $\tilde{F}(\lambda) > 0$, and with these points $\lambda_1, \lambda_2, \ldots$ the relation

$$\sum_k \left[1 - \frac{\tilde{F}(\lambda_k)}{F(\lambda_k)} \right]^2 < \infty$$

must be satisfied.

Secondly, the continuous parts of the spectral measures F and $\tilde{F}$ must coincide:

$$F(\Delta) = \tilde{F}(\Delta)$$

for any measurable set which does not contain points λ of positive measure. In particular, in the ergodic case the distributions $\mathbb{P}$ and $\tilde{\mathbb{P}}$ are equivalent if and only if they coincide.

The Equivalence of Distributions with Different Mean. Let $\mathbb{P}$ be the probability distribution of the stationary Gaussian process

$$\xi(t) = \int_{-\infty}^{\infty} e^{i\lambda t} \, \Phi(d\lambda)$$

with expectation zero and spectral measure F. Suppose that the probability distribution $\tilde{\mathbb{P}}$ differs from $\mathbb{P}$ only in the mean values $\tilde{A}(t) = \mathbb{M}\,\xi(t)$, $t \in T$ on some set T of the real line $-\infty < t \leq \infty$. Then a necessary and sufficient condition for the equivalence of $\mathbb{P}$ and $\tilde{\mathbb{P}}$ is that the function $a = \tilde{A}(t)$ can be represented in the form

$$a(t) = \int e^{-i\lambda t} \varphi(\lambda) F(d\lambda) \qquad (t \in T) \tag{3.1}$$

where $\varphi(\lambda)$ is a function in the space L_T^2, that is,

$$\int_{-\infty}^{\infty} |\varphi(\lambda)|^2 F(d\lambda) < \infty,$$

$$\inf_{c_k; t_k \in T} \int_{-\infty}^{\infty} \left| \varphi(\lambda) - \sum_k c_k e^{i\lambda t_k} \right|^2 F(d\lambda) = 0.$$

The corresponding density $p(\omega) = \dfrac{\tilde{\mathbb{P}}(d\omega)}{\mathbb{P}(d\omega)}$ can be expressed in the following form:

$$p(\omega) = D \exp \left\{ \int_{-\infty}^{\infty} \varphi(\lambda) \, \Phi(d\lambda) \right\}$$

where the constant factor D is determined from the condition $\mathbb{M}\,p(\omega) = 1$. In the case considered here we have

$$D = \exp \left\{ -\frac{1}{2} \int_{-\infty}^{\infty} |\varphi(\lambda)|^2 F(d\lambda) \right\}.$$

The relation (3.1) is an integral equation for the unknown function $\varphi \in L_T^2$.

Suppose that the set T is an interval of the form $[0, \tau]$. If the spectral measure F has the property

$$\lim_{\lambda \to \infty} \lambda^{2n} \frac{F(d\lambda)}{d\lambda} > 0 \tag{3.2}$$

for some n, then every function $a(t)$ with an $(n-1)$-st absolutely continuous derivative $a^{(n-1)}(t)$ satisfying

$$\int_0^\tau |a^{(n)}(t)|^2 \, dt < \infty$$

can be represented in the form (3.1). If, however, F decreases very fast for $\lambda \to \infty$, for example

$$\lim_{\lambda \to \infty} e^{\lambda \delta} \frac{F(d\lambda)}{d\lambda} = 0 \quad (\delta > 0),$$

then even the function $a(t)$ which is identically constant cannot be represented in the form (3.1). If besides (3.2) we have

$$\overline{\lim_{\lambda \to \infty}} \lambda^{2n} \frac{F(d\lambda)}{d\lambda} < \infty,$$

then in order to represent the function $a(t)$ in the form (3.1) it is necessary that it have $n-1$ absolutely continuous derivatives and the square of the n-th derivative $[a^{(n)}(t)]^2$ be integrable on the interval $0 \leq t \leq \tau$ under consideration.

The Equivalence of Distributions with Different Correlation Functions. Let $\mathbb{P}$ and $\tilde{\mathbb{P}}$ be probability distributions of a stationary Gaussian process with expectation zero and correlation functions

$$B(t) = \int e^{i\lambda t} F(d\lambda), \qquad \tilde{B}(t) = \int e^{i\lambda t} \tilde{F}(d\lambda).$$

A necessary and sufficient condition for the equivalence of $\mathbb{P}$ and $\tilde{\mathbb{P}}$ on the σ-algebra $\mathfrak{A}(T)$ where T denotes an arbitrary set on the real line is that the difference of the corresponding correlation functions $b(s, t) = B(s, t) - \tilde{B}(s, t)$ can be represented in the form

$$b(s, t) = \iint e^{-i(\lambda s - \mu t)} \varphi(\lambda, \mu) F(d\lambda) \tilde{F}(d\mu) \quad (s, t \in T) \tag{3.3}$$

where $\varphi(\lambda, \mu)$ is a function in the space $L^2(F, \tilde{F})$, this space being defined as the set of all functions φ which satisfy the conditions

$$\iint |\varphi(\lambda, \mu)|^2 F(d\lambda) \tilde{F}(d\mu) < \infty,$$

$$\inf_{c_{kj}; s_k, t_j \in T} \iint \left| \varphi(\lambda, \mu) - \sum_{k, j} c_{kj} e^{i(\lambda s_k - \mu t_j)} \right|^2 F(d\lambda) \tilde{F}(d\mu) = 0.$$

The corresponding density $p(\omega) = \dfrac{\tilde{\mathbb{P}}(d\omega)}{\mathbb{P}(d\omega)}$ can be expressed by the formula

$$p(\omega) = D \exp\left\{-\frac{1}{2}\lim_{n\to\infty}\left[\iint_{|\varphi|\leq m} \varphi(\lambda, \mu)\,\Phi(d\lambda)\,\Phi(d\mu) - \int_{|\varphi|<n} \varphi(\lambda, \lambda)\,F(d\lambda)\right]\right\}$$

where the constant factor D is obtained from the condition $\mathbb{M}\,p(\omega) = 1$.

The relation (3.3) is an integral equation for the function $\varphi \in L_T^2(F, \tilde{F})$. Let T be an interval of the form $[0, \tau]$. If

$$0 < \varliminf_{\lambda\to\infty} \lambda^\alpha\,\frac{F(d\lambda)}{d\lambda} \leq \varlimsup_{\lambda\to\infty} \lambda^\alpha\,\frac{F(d\lambda)}{d\lambda} < \infty,$$

then for $\alpha = 2n$ the function $b(s, t)$ can be written in the form (3.2) if and only if it has absolutely continuous partial derivatives $\dfrac{\partial^{2n-1} b(s, t)}{\partial s^{n-1}\,\partial t^n}$ and $\dfrac{\partial^{2n-1} b(s, t)}{\partial s^n\,\partial t^{n-1}}$, and

$$\int_0^\tau\int_0^\tau \left|\frac{\partial^{2n} b(s, t)}{\partial s^n\,\partial t^n}\right|^2 ds\,dt < \infty.$$

If the spectral measures F and $\tilde{F}$ have densities $f = f(\lambda)$ and $\tilde{f} = \tilde{f}(\lambda)$, respectively, then in the case of rational $f(\lambda)$ and $\tilde{f}(\lambda)$ the distributions $\mathbb{P}$ and $\tilde{\mathbb{P}}$ are equivalent if and only if

$$\lim_{\lambda\to\infty} \frac{\tilde{f}(\lambda)}{f(\lambda)} = 1.$$

If the spectral density $\tilde{f}(\lambda)$ satisfies

$$\lim_{\lambda\to\infty} \lambda^\beta[\tilde{f}(\lambda) - f(\lambda)] = 0$$

for some $\beta > \alpha + 1/2$, then the distributions $\mathbb{P}$ and $\tilde{\mathbb{P}}$ are equivalent. If, however, $\tilde{f}(\lambda) \geq f(\lambda)$ and

$$\varlimsup_{\lambda\to\infty} \lambda^\beta[\tilde{f}(\lambda) - f(\lambda)] > 0$$

for $\beta = \alpha + 1/2$, then the distributions $\mathbb{P}$ and $\tilde{\mathbb{P}}$ will be *perpendicular*.

Example. Suppose that the correlation functions are given by

$$B(t) = \sigma^2 e^{-a|t|}, \quad \tilde{B}(t) = \begin{cases} 1 - |t| & \text{for } |t| \leq 1, \\ 0 & \text{for } |t| \geq 1. \end{cases}$$

Then the corresponding spectral densities have the form

$$f(\lambda) = \frac{\sigma^2}{\pi}\cdot\frac{a}{\lambda^2 + a^2}, \quad \tilde{f}(\lambda) = \frac{1}{\pi}\cdot\frac{1 - \cos\lambda}{\lambda^2}.$$

If $\sigma^2 a = 1$, then the distributions $\mathbb{P}$ and $\tilde{\mathbb{P}}$ are equivalent for arbitrary $\tau \leq 1$. If $\sigma^2 a \neq 1$ or $\tau > 1$, then the probabilities $\mathbb{P}$ and $\tilde{\mathbb{P}}$ are perpendicular.

Example. Let $\mathbb{P}$ and $\tilde{\mathbb{P}}$ be probability distributions of a stationary Gaussian process corresponding to the expectation zero and the correlation functions

$$B(t) = \sigma^2 e^{-\alpha|t|} \quad \text{and} \quad \tilde{B}(t) = \sigma^2 e^{-\tilde{\alpha}|t|}.$$

In this case the formula for the density $p(\omega) = \dfrac{\tilde{\mathbb{P}}(d\omega)}{\mathbb{P}(d\omega)}$ looks like this:

$$p(\omega) = \frac{\tilde{\alpha}}{\alpha} \exp\left\{ \frac{\tilde{\alpha} - \alpha}{\tau} - \frac{1}{2}(\tilde{\alpha}^2 - \alpha^2) \int_0^\tau [\xi(\omega, t)]^2 \, dt \right.$$
$$\left. - \frac{1}{2}(\tilde{\alpha} - \alpha) [[\xi(\omega, 0)]^2 + [\xi(\omega, \tau)]^2] \right\}.$$

§ 4. Elements of the Mathematical Theory of the Transmission of Information through Stationary Communication Channels

1. Fundamental Results on the Possibility of Transmitting Informations

Communication Channels. A mathematical model of a communication channel is described by a set X_1 of elements x_1, the so-called *input signals*, a set X_2 of elements x_2 called *output signals*, and conditional probability distributions $\mathbb{P}_2 = \mathbb{P}_2(A_2 | x_1)$ on the space X_2 of the output signals x_2. If the input signal x_1 is sent, then with probability $\mathbb{P}_2(A_2 | x_1)$ we will receive at the end of the channel a signal x_2 from the set $A_2 \subseteq X_2$; thus the conditional distributions describe the probabilities of the various distortions of x_1.

A communication channel is intended for the transmission of messages. We denote by X_0 the set of all possible messages. It is assumed that each message $x_0 \in X_0$ occurs with a certain probability, more precisely, there is given a certain probability distribution $\mathbb{P}_0 = \mathbb{P}_0(A_0)$ on the space X_0.

The messages x_0 cannot be transmitted directly through the communication channel since for a transmission we can only use signals $x_1 \in X_1$. The "encoding" of the messages x_0 into signals x_1 is described by a conditional probability distribution $\mathbb{P}_1 = \mathbb{P}_1(A_1 | x_0)$. If the message x_0 occurs, then with probability $\mathbb{P}_1(A_1 | x_0)$ a signal x_1 of the set $A_1 \subset X_1$ will be sent; thus the conditional probability distributions $\mathbb{P}_1(A_1 | x_0)$

allow for possible distortions during the encoding of the messages. In an analogous way we can describe the "decoding" of the received signals x_2 into messages x_3: it is given by conditional probability distribution $\mathbb{P}_3 = \mathbb{P}_3(A_3|x_2)$ on the space X_3 of messages x_3 received at the end of the communication channel.

The transmission scheme looks as follows. A random message ξ_0 is fed into the communication channel with the probability distribution $\mathbb{P}_0 = \mathbb{P}_0(A_0)$. Then a signal ξ_1 is transmitted whose probability distribution is determined by the "encoding rule" $\mathbb{P}_1 = \mathbb{P}_1(A_1|\xi_0)$:

$$\mathbb{P}\{\xi_1 \in A_1|\xi_0\} = P_1(A_1|\xi_0).$$

As the result of the transmission of the input signal ξ_1 we obtain the signal ξ_2:

$$\mathbb{P}\{\xi_2 \in A_2|\xi_0, \xi_1\} = \mathbb{P}_2(A_2|\xi_1).$$

Finally, the signal ξ_2 received is decoded, and as a result we obtain a message ξ_3:

$$\mathbb{P}\{\xi_3 \in A_3|\xi_0, \xi_1, \xi_2\} = \mathbb{P}_3(A_3|\xi_2).$$

The sequence $\xi_0 \to \xi_1 \to \xi_2 \to \xi_3$ is Markovian. For any encoding and decoding of the type described above the following inequality holds:

$$I(\xi_0, \xi_3) \leqq I(\xi_1, \xi_2)$$

where $I(\xi_0, \xi_3)$ is the *amount of information* about ξ_0 contained in the message ξ_3, and $I(\xi_1, \xi_2)$ the amount of information about ξ_1 carried by the signal ξ_2.

The Shannon Theorem. Assume that the probability distribution of the input signal ξ_1 is not arbitrary but is subject to certain restrictions, like being contained in a certain class W. The number

$$C = \sup I(\xi_1, \xi_2)$$

where the least upper bound is taken with respect to all possible distributions $\mathbb{P}_1 \in W$, is *called the capacity* of the channel and characterizes the *maximal amount of informations* which can be transmitted through the given communication channel.

We impose further on the transmission of the messages $\xi_0 \to \xi_3$ certain correctness requirements expressed by the condition that the joint probability distributions $\mathbb{P}_{\xi_0 \xi_3}$ of the transmitted and received messages ξ_0 and ξ_3 must belong to a certain class V. The number

$$H = \inf I(\xi_0, \xi_3)$$

where the greatest lower bound is taken with respect to all possible distributions $\mathbb{P}_{\xi_0 \xi_3} \in V$, characterizes the minimal amount of informations about ξ_0 carried by ξ_3 and compatible with the given correctness requirement. It is called the *entropy* of the source of messages.

Suppose that a transmission $\xi_0 \to \xi_1 \to \xi_2 \to \xi_3$ satisfying the requirements V and W is possible, that is, the corresponding methods of encoding and decoding exist; in other words, there exist the conditional probability distributions $\mathbb{P}_1$, $\mathbb{P}_2$ and $\mathbb{P}_3$. Then

$$H \leq C.$$

If this inequality is satisfied, then in some sense a transmission will be possible; there we are thinking of a transmission of successive messages $\xi_0^{(1)}, \xi_0^{(2)}, \ldots, \xi_0^{(n)}$.

Assume that the set X_0 of all possible messages x_0 is discrete, that is, we are given a countable number of different messages x_0 which occur with probabilities $\mathbb{P}_0(x_0)$, $x_0 \in X_0$, and assume that the condition V of an exact transmission consists in the requirement that the message ξ_3 received simply coincides with the message ξ_0 transmitted, in other words, $\xi_3 = \xi_0$ with probability 1. Then

$$H = - \sum_{x_0} \mathbb{P}_0(x_0) \log \mathbb{P}_0(x_0) = - \mathbb{M} \log \mathbb{P}_0(\xi_0).$$

We assume further that there exists only a finite number N of different input signals x_1, and that no restrictions are imposed on the probabilities $\mathbb{P}\{\xi_1 = x_1\}$, $x_1 \in X_1$. Moreover, we assume that the transmitted signals are received without distortion, that is, we have $\xi_2 = \xi_1$ with probability 1. Then the capacity of the channel is given by

$$C = \log_2 N,$$

that is, the transmitted amount of information $I(\xi_1, \xi_2)$ is maximal if the signals $x_1 \in X_1$ are equally probable.

If the messages $\xi_0^{(1)}, \xi_0^{(2)}, \ldots, \xi_0^{(n)}$ occur independently from each other, then the amount of information carried by the group of messages $\boldsymbol{\xi}_{0n} = (\xi_0^{(1)}, \xi_0^{(2)}, \ldots, \xi_0^{(n)})$ equals

$$H_n = - \sum_{x_{0n}} \mathbb{P}(x_{0n}) \log \mathbb{P}(x_{0n}) = - \mathbb{M} \log \mathbb{P}(\boldsymbol{\xi}_{0n}) = nH$$

where $x_{0n} = (x_0^{(1)}, \ldots, x_0^{(n)})$ is a group of messages to be encoded with probability $\mathbb{P}(x_{0n}) = \mathbb{P}_0(x_0^{(1)}) \mathbb{P}_0(x_0^{(2)}) \ldots \mathbb{P}_0(x_0^{(n)})$.

Assume that $H < C$. We set $\delta = 1/2(C - H)$. According to the law of large numbers applied to the sequence of independent and identically distributed random variables $\log \mathbb{P}_0(\xi_0^{(k)})$ $(k = 1, 2, \ldots)$ with expectation $\mathbb{M} \log \mathbb{P}_0(\xi_0^{(k)}) = - H$ there exists for any $\varepsilon > 0$ an $n(\varepsilon)$ such that

$$\mathbb{P}\left\{-H - \delta \leq \frac{1}{n} \log \mathbb{P}(\boldsymbol{\xi}_{0n}) \leq H + \delta\right\} \geq 1 - \varepsilon,$$

for $n \geq n(\varepsilon)$ where

$$\log \mathbb{P}(\xi_{0n}) = \sum_{k=1}^{n} \log \mathbb{P}_0(\xi_0^{(k)}).$$

This inequality entails that we can divide the set of all groups of messages x_{0n} into two classes. The first class contains the "highly probable" messages x_{0n} for which $\mathbb{P}(x_{0n}) \geq 2^{-n(H+\delta)}$; their number M_n does not exceed $2^{n(H+\delta)}$:

$$M_n \leq 2^{n(H+\delta)}.$$

The second class comprises the remaining "little probable" messages $x_{0n} : \mathbb{P}\{\xi_{0n} \in X_{0n}^2\} \leq \varepsilon.$

In principle we can transmit each group of the highly probable messages x_{0n} by encoding it into a corresponding combination of signals $x_{1n} = (x_1^{(1)}, \ldots, x_1^{(n)})$. The number of all possible combinations of this form is given by $N_n = 2^{nC}$ and we see that $M_n < N_n$. Thus there exist N_n different signals x_{1n} by means of which all of the M_n highly probable messages $x_{0n} \in X_{0n}^1$ can be correctly encoded and transmitted. To complete the procedure we transmit in the case of the occurrence of a little probable message $x_{0n} \in X_{0n}^2$ one and the same signal x_{1n}^0 which is different from the signals by means of which the highly probable messages $x_{0n} \in X_{0n}^1$ are transmitted. Then with a probability not smaller than $1 - \varepsilon$ we receive at the end of the communication channel a sequence $\xi_3^{(1)}, \xi_3^{(2)}, \ldots, \xi_3^{(n)}$ which coincides with the transmitted sequence $\xi_0^{(1)}, \xi_0^{(2)}, \ldots, \xi_0^{(n)}$, that is,

$$\mathbb{P}\{\xi_3^{(1)} = \xi_0^{(1)}, \xi_3^{(2)} = \xi_0^{(2)}, \ldots, \xi_3^{(n)} = \xi_0^{(n)}\} \geq 1 - \varepsilon.$$

Hence if the inequality $H < C$ is satisfied, a transmission of sufficiently long messages $\xi_0^{(1)}, \ldots, \xi_0^{(n)}$ will be possible provided that we allow an error with probability ε where ε may be any small positive number given in advance. Actually we are dealing with an entire family of communication channels and sources of messages depending on a parameter n.

Information Density. The amount of information $I(\xi_0, \xi_3)$ for abstract random variables in the spaces X_0 and X_3 can be written like this:

$$I(\xi_0, \xi_3) = \mathbb{M} i(\xi_0, \xi_3)$$

where

$$i(x_0, x_3) = \frac{\mathbb{P}_{\xi_0 \xi_3}(dx_0 \, dx_3)}{\mathbb{P}(dx_0) \, \mathbb{P}_3(dx_3)}$$

is the so-called *information density*. A sequence of pairs (ξ_{0n}, ξ_{3n}) is called *stable in information* if for $n \to \infty$ we have $I(\xi_{0n}, \xi_{3n}) \to \infty$ and $\dfrac{i(\xi_{0n}, \xi_{3n})}{I(\xi_{0n}, \xi_{3n})} \to 1$ in probability.

The sequence (ξ_{0n}, ξ_{3n}); $\xi_{3n} = \xi_{0n}$ of messages $\xi_{0n} = (\xi_0^{(1)}, \xi_0^{(2)}, \ldots, \xi_0^{(n)})$ considered above has the property of stability in information which after all also accounted for the possibility of a correct transmission of ξ_{0n} up to ε. This fact can be vastly generalized. In fact, if C_n denotes the capacity of the channel $\xi_{1n} \to \xi_{2n}$, if H_n is the minimal amount of information necessary to guarantee a transmission $\xi_{0n} \to \xi_{3n}$ with the required correctness, if, moreoever,

$$\varlimsup_{n \to \infty} \frac{H_n}{C_n} < 1 \, ,$$

and if, finally, there exist sequences of pairs (ξ_{0n}, ξ_{3n}) and (ξ_{1n}, ξ_{2n}) which are stable in information and such that we have simultaneously

$$\frac{1}{H_n} I(\xi_{0n}, \xi_{3n}) \to 1 \quad \text{and} \quad \frac{1}{C_n} I(\xi_{1n}, \xi_{2n}) \to 1 \, ,$$

then under rather weak assumptions there exists for any $\varepsilon > 0$ an $n(\varepsilon)$ with the property that through all communication channels with a parameter $n \geq n(\varepsilon)$ a transmission up to ε is possible [74].

Communication Channels with Changing States. As stated above a channel is characterized by the conditional probability distribution $\mathbb{P}_2$ which defines the probabilities of distortions of the various input signals x_1. We now modify the scheme of a communication channel a bit by assuming that we are given some set Z of possible states z of the communication channel and that if the channel is in some state z and x_1 is the input signal, then the channel independently of other previous facts enters the new state z_1. This transition depends on chance and is described by a conditional probability distribution $\mathbb{P}(C \mid x_1, z)$; here $\mathbb{P}(C \mid x_1, z)$ stands for the probability that the new state z_1 belongs to the set $C \subset Z$. Moreover we assume that the output signal x_2 is uniquely determined by the state of the channel z_1, that is, there exists a function $\varphi = \varphi(z)$ on the space Z of all possible states with the property that $x_2 = \varphi(z_1)$. By means of this more generalized scheme we are able to take into account changes which in principle may occur in the channel in connection with its operation.

Stationary Channels. Consider a communication channel under stationary working conditions and assume that the signals $\ldots, \xi_1(-1), \xi_1(0), \xi_1(1), \ldots$ transmitted successively, the corresponding states of the channel $\ldots, \zeta(-1), \zeta(0), \zeta(1), \ldots$ and the output signals $\ldots, \xi_2(-1), \xi_2(0), \xi_2(1), \ldots$ determined by them form stationary and

[74] *Dobrushin, R. L.*, A general formulation of Shannon's fundamental theorem in the theory of information. Uspehi Matem. Nauk XIV, (1959), 3—104 (Russian). (German translation in: Arbeiten zur Informationstheorie IV. Berlin: VEB Deutscher Verlag der Wissenschaften 1963.

stationarily connected random sequences. The number

$$\mathscr{C} = \sup \mathscr{I}(\xi_1, \xi_2)$$

where $\mathscr{I}(\xi_1, \xi_2)$ denotes the *speed of transmission of information* about the stationary sequence $\{\xi_1(n)\}$ by the sequence $\{\xi_2(n)\}$ (see the following section), and the least upper bound is taken with respect to all admissible probability distributions of the input sequence $\{\xi_1(n)\}$ is called the *transmission capacity* of the communication channel.

Assume that the input messages $\{\xi_0(n)\}$, $n = \ldots, -1, 0, 1, \ldots$ form a stationary random sequence. An encoding rule will be considered to be given if for all k, m and $k_1, \ldots, k_m \geq k$ we have defined the conditional probabilities

$$\mathbb{P}\{\xi_1(k_1) \in B_1, \ldots, \xi_1(k_m) \in B_m | \xi_0(-\infty, k)\}$$

that, whenever the sequence of messages

$$\xi_0(-\infty, k) = \ldots, \xi_0(k-1), \xi_0(k)$$

occurs, signals $\xi_1(k_1), \ldots, \xi_1(k_m)$ belonging to the sets $B_1, \ldots, B_m$ will be transmitted at the corresponding places. These probabilities are assumed to be stationary in the sense that they do not change if at the same time for any integer l the terms k and $k_1, \ldots, k_m$ are replaced by $k+l$ and $k_1 + l, \ldots, k_m + l$. The decoding rule is determined by analogous probabilities $\mathbb{P}\{\xi_3(k_1) \in D_1, \ldots, \xi_3(k_m) \in D_m | \xi_2(-\infty, k)\}$.

Define a number $\mathscr{H}$ by the formula

$$\mathscr{H} = \inf \mathscr{I}(\xi_0, \xi_3)$$

where $\mathscr{I}(\xi_0, \xi_3)$ is the speed of transmission of information about the stationary sequence $\{\xi_0(n)\}$ by the sequence $\{\xi_3(n)\}$, $n = \ldots, -1, 0, 1, \ldots$ (these sequences are assumed to be stationarily connected), and the lower bound is taken with respect to all admissible probability distributions satisfying the correctness requirements of the transmission $\{\xi_0(n)\} \to \{\xi_3(n)\}$. The inequality

$$\mathscr{H} \leq \mathscr{C}$$

is a necessary condition in order that the transmission

$$\{\xi_0(n)\} \to \{\xi_1(n)\} \to \{\xi_2(n)\} \to \{\xi_3(n)\}$$

be possible.

Recall that every message $\xi_0(k)$ is an element x_0 of X_0. We can interpret X_0 as some alphabet consisting of symbol letters x_0. Assume that this alphabet X_0 is finite, and that the correctness requirement of the transmission consists in an error-free reproduction of the transmitted symbols:

$$\mathbb{P}\{\xi_3(k) = \xi_0(k)\} = 1 \quad \text{for any integer } k.$$

Assume further that there is only a finite number of input signals x_1 and of states z of the channel. We denote these by the integers $1, 2, \ldots, N$. Let $p(k, x_1, j)$ be the corresponding transition probabilities from the state k to the state j for the input signal x_1:

$$p(k, x_1, j) = \mathbb{P}\{\zeta(n+1) = j \mid \zeta(n) = k, \xi_1(n+1) = x_1\}.$$

Besides this we assume that any products of the form

$$p(k_0, x_1(1), k_1)\, p(k_1, x_1(2), k_2) \ldots p(k_{n-1}, x_1(n), k_n)$$

are stochastic matrices generating ergodic Markov chains. This condition will be satisfied, for example, if each transition matrix $\{p(k, x_1, j)\}$ has a positive coefficient of ergodicity. Then if the inequality $\mathscr{H} < \mathscr{C}$ is satisfied and the stationary sequence of messages $\{\xi_0(n)\}$ fulfills the ergodicity condition, the input message can be transmitted correctly up to $\varepsilon > 0$, that is, by appropriate methods of encoding and decoding the received sequence of message $\{\xi_3(n)\}$ will have the property that

$$\mathbb{P}\{\xi_3(k) \neq \xi_0(k)\} < \varepsilon \quad \text{for any integer } k.$$

2. Formulas for the Amount of Information

The Amount of Information About Gaussian Variables, Let $\xi_1 = \{\xi(t), t \in T_1\}$ and $\xi_2 = \{\xi(t), t \in T_2\}$ be two families of random variables with a joint Gaussian probability distribution, and let H_1 and H_2 be the closed linear spaces generated by the variables $\xi(t), t \in T_1$ and $\xi(t), t \in T_2$, in the Hilbert space $L^2(\Omega)$. Denote the projection operators on the subspaces H_1 and H_2 by P_1 and P_2 and set $P^{(1)} = P_1 P_2 P_1$, $P^{(2)} = P_2 P_1 P_2$. The amount of information $I(\xi_1, \xi_2)$ on the family of variables ξ_1 contained in the family ξ_2 is finite if and only if one of the operators $P^{(1)}$ or $P^{(2)}$ is nuclear, that is, the sequence $\lambda_1, \lambda_2, \ldots$ of its eigenvalues (they are all non-negative) satisfies the condition $\sum_k \lambda_k < \infty$. We then have

$$I(\xi_1, \xi_2) = -\frac{1}{2} \sum_k \log(1 - \lambda_k).$$

If ξ_1 and ξ_2 are formed by a finite number of Gaussian variables:

$$\xi_1 = \{\xi(1), \ldots, \xi(m)\}, \qquad \xi_2 = \{\xi(m+1), \ldots, \xi(m+n)\}$$

where the correlation matrix B of the total set $\xi(1), \ldots, \xi(m+n)$ is non-degenerate, the amount of information $I(\xi_1, \xi_2)$ can be written as follows:

$$I(\xi_1, \xi_2) = \frac{1}{2} \log \frac{(\det B_1)(\det B_2)}{\det B}$$

where B_1 and B_2 are the correlation matrices of the corresponding families ξ_1 and ξ_2.

ε-*entropy.* Let $\xi = (\xi_1, \ldots, \xi_n)$ and $\eta = (\eta_1, \ldots, \eta_n)$ be random vector variables in the n-dimensional Euclidean space X, and $\varrho(x, y)$ some non-negative function, which defines a concept of nearness of the variables ξ and η by means of the following relation:

$$\mathsf{M}\varrho(\xi, \eta) \leq \varepsilon .$$

The number $H = H_\varepsilon$ defined by

$$H_\varepsilon = \inf I(\xi, \eta)$$

where the lower bound is taken with respect to all random variables η which are ε-near to ξ in the sense defined above, is usually called the ε-entropy of the random variable ξ.

Suppose that $\varrho(x, y) = \varrho(|x - y|)$, and that the derivative $\varrho'(0)$, $0 < \varrho'(0) < \infty$ exists. Then an asymptotic formula holds for $\varepsilon \to 0$, logarithms being taken with respect to the base e:

$$H_\varepsilon = n \log \frac{1}{\varepsilon} + h(\xi) + \log \frac{\Gamma(n/2)\,[n \cdot \varrho'(0)]^n}{(2\pi)^{n/2}(n-1)!\,e^n} + O(1)$$

where $\Gamma(\cdot)$ is the Gamma-function and $h(\xi)$ the so-called *differential entropy* of ξ:

$$h(\xi) = - \int\limits_x p_\xi(x) \log p_\xi(x)\, dx ;$$

the probability density $p_\xi(x)$ is subject to rather broad conditions only, which are satisfied, for example, if $p_\xi(x)$ is bounded and $h(\xi) > -\infty$.

Let

$$\varrho(x, y) = \left(\frac{1}{n} \sum_{k=1}^n |x_k - y_k|^\alpha \right)^\beta \qquad (\alpha, \beta > 0) .$$

Then

$$H_\varepsilon = \frac{n}{\alpha\beta} \log \frac{1}{\varepsilon} + h(\xi) - \log \left\{ \left(\frac{\alpha\beta e}{n} \right)^{\frac{n}{\alpha\beta}} \left[\frac{2}{\alpha} \Gamma\left(\frac{1}{\alpha} \right) \right]^n \frac{\Gamma\left(\dfrac{n}{\alpha\beta} \right)}{\beta \Gamma\left(\dfrac{n}{\alpha} \right)} \right\} + O(1).$$

In particular for $\alpha = 2$, $\beta = 1$ we have the asymptotic formula [75]

$$H_\varepsilon = \frac{n}{2} \log \frac{1}{\varepsilon} + h(\xi) - n \log \sqrt{2\pi e} + O(1) .$$

---

[75] *Linkov, Yu. N.,* Computation of the ε-entropy of random variables for small ε. Problemy peredači informacii, I, 2 (1965), 18—27.

The Speed of Transmission of Information. Suppose that the pair of random processes $(\xi_1(t), \xi_2(t))$ is stationary in the strict sense, let $\xi^{[u, v]}$ be the set of all values $\xi(t)$, $u \leq t \leq v$, and let

$$I\{\xi_1, \xi_2^{[t_0, t]} \,|\, \xi_2^{[-\infty, t_0]}\}$$

be the conditional amount of information about the process $\xi_1 = \xi_1^{[-\infty, \infty]}$ contained in the section $\xi_2^{[t_0, t]}$ of the process ξ_2. The average amount of this information is a linearly increasing function of t:

$$\mathbf{M}\, I\{\xi_1, \xi_2^{[t_0, t]} \,|\, \xi_2^{[-\infty, t_0]}\} = (t - t_0)\,\mathscr{I}(\xi_1, \xi_2).$$

The number $\mathscr{I}(\xi_1, \xi_2)$ appearing here is called the average speed of transmission of information about the stationary process ξ_1 by the stationary process ξ_2, or for short the *speed of transmission of information.*

The speed of transmission of information $\mathscr{I}(\xi_1, \xi_2)$ has many properties which are analogous to those of the amount of information. In addition, however, there are specific properties. For example, the equation

$$\mathscr{I}(\xi_1, \xi_2) = 0$$

holds for any singular random process ξ_2, that is, a process whose values $\xi_2(t)$ are functions of the family of variables $\xi_2^{[-\infty, t_0]}$ where t_0 may be chosen arbitrarily. For every regular random process ξ_2, however, the equation $\mathscr{I}(\xi_1, \xi_2) = 0$ holds if and only if the random process ξ_1 does not depend on ξ_2. This entails, in particular, that in some cases $\mathscr{I}(\xi_1, \xi_2) \neq \mathscr{I}(\xi_2, \xi_1)$.

Under additional regularity conditions the speed of transmission of information $\mathscr{I}(\xi_1, \xi_2)$ coincides with the limit

$$\mathscr{I}(\xi_1, \xi_2) = \lim_{t - t_0 \to \infty} \frac{1}{t - t_0}\, I(\xi_1^{[t_0, t]}, \xi_2^{[t_0, t]})$$

where $I(\xi_1^{[t_0, t]}, \xi_2^{[t_0, t_1]})$ is the amount of information about the section of the process $\xi_1^{[t_0, t]}$ contained in $\xi_2^{[t_0, t]}$. This will be true, for example, when the time t is discrete, and the individual variables $\xi_1(t)$ and $\xi_2(t)$ can take only a finite number of different values or the probability distribution of the process ξ_1 and ξ_2 is Gaussian. In the case of a continuous time, the same holds for Gaussian processes if the spectral density $f(\lambda)$ of the processes $\xi_2(t)$ satisfies the condition

$$0 < c \leq \lambda^{2n} f(\lambda) \leq C < \infty.$$

Example. Let the stationary process $\xi = \xi(t)$ be a sequence of variables where each variable takes values from an "alphabet" X consisting of a finite number of "symbols" $x_1, x_2, \ldots, x_N$. Assume that the probability p_i for a specific symbol x_i to appear at a fixed place is given and that the probability p_{ij} for the symbol x_j to appear next does not depend on the preceding values x_i:

$$\mathbb{P}\{\xi(t) = x_i\} = p_i, \quad \mathbb{P}\{\xi(t+1) = x_j | \xi(t) = x_i, \, \xi(t-1), ...\} = p_{ij}.$$

In other words, $\xi = \xi(t)$ is a Markov chain with transition probabilities $\{p_{ij}\}$ and a stationary distribution $\{p_i\}$. Then the speed of transmission of information by means of the stationary process $\xi(t)$ equals

$$\mathscr{I}(\xi, \xi) = -\sum_{i,j} -p_i p_{ij} \log p_{ij}.$$

In particular, if $\xi = \xi(t)$ is a sequence of independent variables and hence $p_{ij} = p_j$, we have

$$\mathscr{I}(\xi, \xi) = -\sum_j p_j \log p_j.$$

The Speed of Transmission of Information in the Case of a Stationary Gaussian Process. Let $\xi_1 = \xi_1(t)$ and $\xi_2 = \xi_2(t)$ be a stationary Gaussian process with the spectral densities $f_{11}(\lambda)$, $f_{22}(\lambda)$ and the joint spectral density $f_{12}(\lambda)$, and assume that $\xi_2 = \xi_2(t)$ is regular. Then

$$\mathscr{I}(\xi_1, \xi_2) = -\frac{1}{4\pi} \int \log \left[1 - \frac{|f_{12}(\lambda)|^2}{f_{11}(\lambda) f_{22}(\lambda)} \right] d\lambda.$$

Consider the following condition of nearness of the stationary Gaussian processes $\xi_1(t)$ and $\xi_2(t)$:

$$\mathbb{M}|\xi_1(t) - \xi_2(t)|^2 \leq \delta^2.$$

The minimal speed of transmission of information

$$H = \inf \mathscr{I}(\xi_1, \xi_2)$$

compatible with the requirement of "δ-correctness" mentioned above is given by the following formula

$$H = \frac{1}{4\pi} \int_{f_{11}(\lambda) \geq \theta^2} \log \frac{f_{11}(\lambda)}{\theta^2} d\lambda = -\frac{1}{4\pi} \int \log \left[1 - \frac{|f_{12}(\lambda)|^2}{f_{11}(\lambda) f_{22}(\lambda)} \right] d\lambda$$

where

$$f_{22}(\lambda) = \begin{cases} f_{11}(\lambda) - \theta & \text{for} \quad f_{11}(\lambda) \geq \theta^2, \\ 0 & \text{for} \quad f_{11}(\lambda) < \theta^2, \end{cases} \quad f_{12}(\lambda) = f_{22}(\lambda),$$

and the parameter θ^2 is determined by the equation

$$\int [f(\lambda) - f_{22}(\lambda)] \, d\lambda = \delta^2.$$

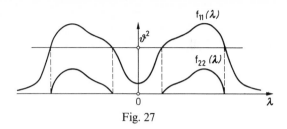

Fig. 27

This formula shows the type of spectral density $f_{22}(\lambda)$ a stationary process $\xi_2(t)$ must have when carrying minimal information $\mathscr{I}(\xi_1, \xi_2) \approx H$ about $\xi_1(t)$ (Fig. 27). In the case of discrete t, if $f_{11}(\lambda) \geq \theta^2$ for all λ, $-\pi \leq \lambda \leq \pi$, the lower bound H of the speed of transmission is attained for a process $\xi_2(t)$ with a spectral density $f_{22}(\lambda)$ given by the formula above which is connected with $\xi_1(t)$ by the relation

$$\xi_1(t) = \xi_2(t) + \zeta(t)$$

where $\zeta(t)$ is a stationary Gaussian noise independent of $\xi_2(t)$; in the general case the formula for $f_{22}(\lambda)$ represents the corresponding density of the *regular* process $\xi_2(t)$ asymptotically.

If the spectral density $f_{11}(\lambda)$ is approximately given by

$$f_{11}(\lambda) \approx \begin{cases} \dfrac{\sigma^2}{2w} & \text{for} \quad |\lambda \pm \lambda_0| \leq \dfrac{1}{2}w, \\ 0 & \text{for the remaining } \lambda \end{cases}$$

(Fig. 28), then the corresponding minimal speed of transmission of information $\mathscr{H}$ can be computed by an approximate formula of the form

$$H \approx \frac{w}{2\pi} \log \frac{\sigma^2}{\delta^2},$$

$$\sigma^2 = \mathbb{M}[\xi(t)]^2.$$

The symmetric channel without memory. Consider a symmetric channel without memory and with a finite number of input signals x_1, where the

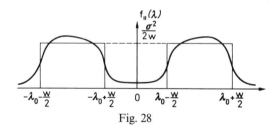

Fig. 28

signal x_1 transmitted is received correctly at the end of the channel x_1 with probability $1 - p$, and distorted with probability p. Then all possible distortions have the equal probability, that is, an output signal x_2 will be received with probability $\dfrac{p}{N-1}$ for any $x_2 \neq x_1$ where N stands for the total number of signals. For such a communication channel the capacity

$$\mathscr{C} = \sup \mathscr{I}(\xi_1, \xi_2)$$

is attained in the case of a sequence of independent and identically distributed input signals $\dots, \xi_1(-1), \xi_1(0), \xi_1(1), \dots$; this capacity is given by the formula

$$\mathscr{C} = \log_2 N - (1 - p) \log_2 (1 - p) - p \log_2 \frac{p}{N-1}.$$

The Capacity in the Presence of Gaussian Noises. Consider a communication channel whose input signals form a stationary process $\xi_1 = \xi_1(t)$, $\mathrm{M}[\xi_1(t)]^2 < \infty$. Assume that during the transmission the signal $\xi_1 = \xi_1(t)$ undergoes a linear transformation A_φ with the spectral characteristic $\varphi(\lambda)$, and moreover that an additive stationary Gaussian noise $\zeta = \zeta(t)$ is superimposed. In this way we have at the end of the channel a random process $\xi_2(t)$ of the form

$$\xi_2(t) = A_\varphi \xi_1(t) + \zeta(t).$$

Assume further that the restrictions on the input process consist in the inequality

$$\mathrm{M}[\xi_1(t)]^2 \leq \varDelta^2,$$

that is, the constant $\varDelta^2$ bounds the energy of the input signal. The capacity of this channel can be computed by means of the formula

$$
\begin{aligned}
\mathscr{C} &= \frac{1}{4\pi} \int\limits_{|\varphi(\lambda)|^2 \theta^2 \geq f_{\zeta\zeta}(\lambda)} \log \frac{|\varphi(\lambda)|^2 \theta^2}{f_{\zeta\zeta}(\lambda)} \, d\lambda \\
&= -\frac{1}{4\pi} \int \log \left[1 - \frac{|\varphi(\lambda)|^2 f(\lambda)}{|\varphi(\lambda)|^2 f(\lambda) + f_{\zeta\zeta}(\lambda)} \right] d\lambda \,;
\end{aligned}
$$

in the latter expression we integrate within the limits $-\pi \leq \lambda \leq \pi$ for discrete t, and within the limits $-\infty < \lambda < \infty$ for continuous t, $f_{\zeta\zeta}(\lambda)$ is the spectral density of the Gaussian process $\zeta(t)$, the function $f(\lambda)$ has the form

$$f(\lambda) = \begin{cases} \theta^2 - f_{\zeta\zeta}(\lambda) |\varphi(\lambda)|^{-2} & \text{for} \quad \theta^2 \geq f_{\zeta\zeta}(\lambda) |\varphi(\lambda)|^{-2}, \\ 0 & \text{in the opposite case}, \end{cases}$$

and the parameter θ^2 is obtained from the equation

$$\int f(\lambda)\,d\lambda = \Delta^2 \, .$$

It seems necessary to remark that if $f(\lambda)$ is the spectral density of a *regular* stationary Gaussian process $\xi_1(t)$, then this process considered as the input signal guarantees a transmission of information with minimal speed $\mathscr{I}(\xi_1,\xi_2)=\mathscr{C}$. In the most interesting cases, however, if t is continuous, the function $f(\lambda)$ vanishes on the intervals of frequencies λ where the intensity of the noise is comparatively strong; the non-vanishing values $f(\lambda)$ are mainly concentrated on frequency intervals λ where the intensity of the noise is comparatively small. Hence $f(\lambda)$ cannot be

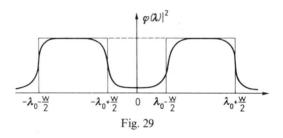

Fig. 29

the spectral density of a regular process. Moreover, if we choose as the input signal a process $\xi_1(t)$ with such a spectral density $f(\lambda)$, then this signal will be singular and the speed of transmission of information $\mathscr{I}(\xi_1,\xi_2)$ equals zero, and not the greatest possible value $\mathscr{C}$ defined above.

Nevertheless the expressions introduced above are useful since they enable us to represent approximately the kind of spectral densities $f(\lambda)$ of regular input signal $\xi_1(t)$ which guarantee a speed of transmission $\mathscr{I}(\xi_1,\xi_2)$ close to $\mathscr{C}$. From the practical point of view the most interesting case arises when the band w of the non-absorbed frequencies in the communication channel is bounded, that is, when the spectral characteristic φ is approximately given by

$$|\varphi(\lambda)|^2 \approx \begin{cases} 1 & \text{for} \quad |\lambda \pm \lambda_0| \leq \dfrac{1}{2}\,W, \\ 0 & \text{for the remaining } \lambda \end{cases}$$

(Fig. 29), and the noise passing through the channel has a uniform spectrum

$$f_{\zeta\zeta}(\lambda) \approx \begin{cases} \dfrac{\sigma^2}{2\,W} & \text{for} \quad |\lambda \pm \lambda_0| \leq \dfrac{1}{2}\,W, \\ 0 & \text{for the remaining } \lambda \, . \end{cases}$$

In this case the capacity can be computed by means of the approximate formula

$$\mathscr{C} \approx \frac{W}{2\pi} \log\left(1 + \frac{\varDelta^2}{\sigma^2}\right).$$

Moreover the input signal which leads to a speed of transmission $\mathscr{I}(\xi_1, \xi_2)$ close to the maximal speed is a stationary Gaussian process with the spectral density $f(\lambda)$ of the form

$$f(\lambda) \approx \begin{cases} \dfrac{\varDelta^2}{2W} & \text{for} \quad |\lambda \pm \lambda_0| \leq \dfrac{1}{2}W, \\ 0 & \text{for the remaining } \lambda, \end{cases}$$

and hence the parameter $\varDelta^2$ and σ^2 have the following physical interpretation:

$$\varDelta^2 = \mathbb{M}|\xi_1(t)|^2 \quad \text{is the energy level of the input signal,}$$
$$\sigma^2 = \mathbb{M}|\zeta(t)|^2 \quad \text{is the energy level of the noise.}$$

Bibliography

Aitchison, J., and J. A. C. Brown: The lognormal distribution. Cambridge: Univ. Press 1957.

Anderson, T. W.: An introduction to multivariate statistical analysis. New York: Wiley 1958.

Andreev, N. I.: Correlation theory of statistical optimal systems. Moscow: Nauka 1966 (Russian).

Arley, N., and K. R. Buch: Introduction to the theory of probability and statistics. New York: Wiley 1950.

Ash, B. B.: Information theory. New York: Wiley 1966.

Bailey, N. T.: The elements of stochastic processes with applications to the natural sciences. New York: Wiley 1965.

Barlow, R., and F. Proschan: Mathematical theory of reliability. New York: Wiley 1965.

Bartlett, M. S.: An introduction to stochastic processes. Cambridge: University Press 1955.

Bellman, R.: Dynamic programming. Princeton, N. J.: University Press 1957.

— Adaptive control processes. Princeton, N. J.: University Press 1966.

—, and *S. Dreyfus:* Applied dynamic programming. Princeton, N. J.: University Press 1962.

Bendat, D.: Principles and applications of random noise theory. New York: John Wiley 1958.

Bendat, J. S., and A. G. Piersol: Measurement and analysis of random data. New York: Wiley 1966.

Berge, C.: Théorie générale des jeux à *n* personnes. Paris: Gauthier-Villars 1957.

Bernstein, S. N.: Probability theory. 4th ed. Moscow-Leningrad: Gostechizdat 1946 (Russian).

— Collection of his works. Vol. IV. Moscow: Nauka 1964.

Bharucha-Reid, A. T.: Elements of the theory of Markov processes and their applications. New York: McGraw-Hill 1960.

Billingsley, P.: Ergodic theory and information. New York: Wiley 1965.

Blackwell, D., and M. A. Girshick: Theory of games and statistical decisions. New York: Wiley 1954.

Blanc-Lapierre, A., and R. Fortet: Théorie des fonctions aléatoires. Paris: Masson 1953.

Blumenthal, R. M., and R. K. Getoor: Markov processes and potential theory. New York and London: Academic Press 1968.

Bochner, S.: Harmonic analysis and the theory of probability. Berkeley, Los Angeles: University Press 1955.

Borel, E.: Probabilité, certitude et application aux nombres premiers. Paris: Gauthier-Villars 1952.

Brioullin, L.: Science and information theory. New York: Academic Press 1956.

Bunimovič, V. I.: Fluctuation processes in radio-receivers. Moscow: Sovetskoje radio 1951 (Russian).

Bush, A., and *F. Mosteller:* Stochastic models for learning. New York: Wiley 1955.

Buslenko, N. P., and others: Method of statistical studies (Monte-Carlo method). Moscow: Fismatgiz 1962 (Russian).

Chernoff, G., and *L. E. Moses:* Elementary decision theory. New York: Wiley 1959.

Chung, K. L.: Markov chains with stationary transition probabilities. Berlin-Göttingen-Heidelberg: Springer 1960.

Cox, D., and *U. Smith:* Queues. London: Methuen and Co. 1961.

Cramér, H.: Random variables and probability distribution. Cambridge Tracts in Mathematics, Nr. 36. London: Cambridge University Press 1937.

— Mathematical methods of statistics. Princeton, N. J.: University Press 1946.

Davenport, W. B., and *W. L. Root:* An introduction to the theory of random signals and noise. New York: McGraw-Hill 1958.

Deutsch, R.: Non-linear transformations of random processes. Englewood Cliffs, N. J.: Prentice-Hall, Inc., 1962.

Doob, D. L.: Stochastic processes. New York: Wiley 1953.

Dubins, L. E., and *L. J. Savage:* How to gamble if you must. Inequalities for stochastic processes. New York: McGraw-Hill 1965.

Eisenschütz, R.: Statistical theory of irreversible processes. London: Oxford University Press 1958.

Fano, R. M.: Transmission of information. New York: Wiley 1961.

Feinstein, A.: Foundation of information theory. New York: McGraw-Hill 1958.

Feldbaum, A. A.: Principles of the theory of optimal automatical systems. 2nd ed. Moscow: Nauka 1966 (Russian).

Feller, W.: Introduction to probability theory and its applications. 3rd ed. New York: Wiley 1968.

— An introduction to probability theory and its applications. Vol. II. New York: Wiley 1966.

Ficher, R. A.: Statistical methods and scientific inference. New York: Hafner 1956.

Finney, D. J.: An introduction to the theory of experimental design. Chicago: University Press 1960.

Fraser, D. A. S.: Non-parametric methods in statistics. New York: Wiley; London: Chapman and Hall 1957.

Furstenberg, H.: Stationary processes and prediction theory. Ann. of Math. Studies, no. 44. Princeton: PrincetonUniversity Press 1960.

Gichman, J. J., and *A. V. Skorochod:* Introduction to the theory of random processes. Moscow: Nauka 1965 (Russian).

Gnedenko, B. V.: Lehrbuch der Wahrscheinlichkeitstheorie. Berlin: Akademie-Verlag 1957.

—, *Yu. K. Belyaev,* and *A. D. Sobolev:* Mathematical methods in the theory of reliability. Moscow: Nauka 1965 (Russian).

—, and *A. Ya. Hinčin:* An elementary introduction to the theory of probability. 6th ed. Moscow: Nauka 1964 (Russian).

Godwin, H.: Inequalities on distribution functions. London: Griffin 1964.

Goldmann, S.: Information theory. New York: Prentice-Hall 1954.

Grenander, U.: Stochastic processes and statistical inference. Ark. Mat. 1, 195—277 (1950).

— Probabilities on algebraic structures. London: Wiley 1963.

—, and *G. Szegö:* Toeplitz forms and their applications. Berkeley, Los Angeles: University of California Press 1958.

Grenander, U., and *M. Rosenblatt:* Statistical analysis of stationary time series. Stockholm: Almquist and Wiksell 1956.

Gumbel, E. J.: Statistics of extremes. New York: Columbia University Press 1958.

Hald, A.: Statistical theory with engineering applications. New York: Wiley 1952.

Hamilton, W. C.: Statistics in physical science. Estimation, hypothesis, testing and least squares. New York: Bonald Press 1964.

Hammersley, J., and D. C. Handscomb: Monte Carlo methods. London: Methuen; New York: Wiley 1964.

Hannan, E.: Time series analysis. Methuen's Monographs in Applied Probabilities and Statistics 1960.

Hanssmann, F.: Operations research in production and inventory control. New York: Wiley 1962.

Harkevič, A. A.: Spectra and analysis. 4th ed. Moscow: Fizmatgiz 1962 (Russian).

Harman, H. H.: Modern factor analysis. Chicago: University Press 1960.

Harris, T.: Theory of branching processes. Berlin-Göttingen-Heidelberg: Springer 1963.

Herdan, G.: The advanced theory of language as choice and chance. Bd. 4: Kommunikation und Kybernetik in Einzeldarstellung. Berlin-Heidelberg-New York: Springer 1965.

Hinčin, A. Y.: Asymptotic laws in probability theory. Moscow-Leningrad: GONTI 1936 (Russian).

— Asymptotic laws fro sums of independent random variables. Moscow-Leningrad: GONTI 1938.

— On the mathematical theory of a multi-service system. Moscow: Fizmatgiz 1963.

Howard, R. A.: Dynamic programming and Markov processes. New York: Wiley 1960.

Hunt, G. A.: Markov processes and potentials. Proc. Nat. Acad. Sci. U.S. **42**, 414—418 (1956).

— Martingales et processus de Markov. Paris: Dunod 1966.

Ibragimov, I. A., and *Yu. V. Linnik:* Independent stationarily connected variables. Moscow: Nauka 1965 (Russian).

Ito, K.: On stochastic processes. I. Jap. J. Math. **18**, 261—301 (1942).

— On stochastic processes. II. Proc. Imp. Acad. Tokyo **20**, 519—524 (1944).

—, and *H. McKean:* Diffusion processes and their sample paths. Berlin-Heidelberg-New York: Springer 1965.

Johnson, N. L., and *F. S. Leone:* Statistics and experimental design in engineering and the physical sciences. New York: Wiley 1964.

Kac, M.: Statistical independence in probability, analysis and number theory. Carus, Math. Monographs 12. New York: Wiley 1959.

— Probability and related topics in physical sciences. London-New York: Interscience Publisher 1959.

Karlin, S.: A first course in stochastic processes. New York: Academic Press 1965.

Kaufman, A., and *R. Cruon:* Temps d'attente dans une file avec arivées suivant la loi de Poisson par «grappes». Chiffres **4**, 135—142 (1961).

Keilson, J.: Green's function methods in probability theory. London: Griffin 1965.

Kelly, T. L.: Fundamentals of statistics. Cambridge, Mass.: Harvard University Press 1947.

Kemeny, J. G., J. L., Snell, A. W. Knapp: Denumerable Markov chains. Princeton-New York-Toronto: Van Nostrand 1966.

Kempermann, J. H. B.: The passage problem for a stationary Markov chain. Chicago: University Press 1961.

Kendall, M. G., and *A. Buchland:* A dictionary of statistics terms. Edinburgh-London: Griffin 1957.

—, and *A. G. Diig:* Bibliography of statistical literature (1940—1949). New York: Hafner 1965.

—, and *A. Stuart:* The advanced theory of statistics (in three Vol.). London: Griffin 1963.

Klepikov, N. P., and *S. N. Sokolov:* Analysis and planning of experiments by the method of maximal likelihood. Moscow: Nauka 1964 (Russian).

Klimov, G. P.: Stochastic service systems. Moscow: Nauka 1966 (Russian).

Kolmogorov, A. N.: Foundations of the theory of probability. New York: Chelsea Press 1950.

Kotz, S. (with collaboration of *W. Hoeffding*): Russian-English dictionary of statistical terms and expressions. Oxford: University Press 1964.

Krickeberg, K.: Probability theory. Reading, Mass.: Addison-Wesley.

Kubilius, I. P.: Probabilistic methods in number theory. Vilnius: Gospolitnaučizdat 1959 (Russian).

Lanning, J. H., and *R. H. Battin:* Random processes in automatic control. New York: Mc Graw-Hill 1956.

Lebedev, V. L.: Random processes in electrical and mechanical systems. Moscow: Fizmatgiz 1958 (Russian).

Lehmann, E. L.: Testing statistical hypothesis. New York: Wiley 1959.

Leonov, V. P.: Some applications of leading semi-invariants to the theory of stationary stochastic processes. Moscow: Nauka 1964 (Russian).

Levin, B. R.: Theory of random processes and its application in radiotechnics. Moscow: Sovetskoje radio 1960 (Russian).

— Theoretical fundamentals of statistical radiotechnics. Moscow: Sovetskoje radio 1966 (Russian).

L *évy, P.:* Théorie de l'addition des variables aléatoires. Paris: Gauthiers-Villars 1937.

— Processus stochastiques et mouvement brownien, 2. ed. Paris: Gauthiers-Villars 1965.

— Le mouvement brownien. Paris: Gauthiers-Villars 1954.

Lifšic, N. A., and *V. S. Pugačev:* A probabilistic analysis of systems of automatic control. Moscow: Sovetskoje radio 1963 (Russian).

Lindley, D.: Introduction to probability and statistics from a Bayesian viewpoint. Cambridge: University Press 1965.

Linnik, Yu. V.: Decomposition of probabilistic measures. Ed. by Leningrad University, Leningrad 1960.

Lloyd, D. K., and *M. Lipow:* Reliability: Management, methods, and mathematics. Englewood Cliffs, N. J.: Prentice-Hall, Inc. 1962.

Lukacs, E., and *R. C. Laha:* Applications of characteristic functions. London: Griffin 1964.

Massey, J.: Threshhold decoding. Massachusetts Institute of Technology, Techn. Rep. 410, Cambridge Mass. 1963.

Meyer, P. A.: Probability and potentials. Waltham, Mass.-Toronto-London: Blaisdell Publishing Company 1966.

Mitropolsky, A. K.: Techniques of statistical computation. Moscow: Fizmatgiz 1961 (Russian).

Monin, A. S., and *A. M. Yaglom:* Statistical hydromechanics. Moskow: Nauka 1965 (Russian).

Morgenstern, D.: Einführung in die Wahrscheinlichkeitsrechnung und mathematische Statistik. Berlin-Göttingen-Heidelberg-New York: Springer 1964.

Morse, Ph. M., and *G. E. Kimball:* Methods of operations research. New York: Wiley 1951.

Neveu, J.: Bases mathématiques du calcul des probabilités. Paris: Masson et Cie 1964.

Parzen, E.: Modern probability theory and its applications. New York-London: Wiley 1960.

— Stochastic processes. San Francisco: Holden-Day 1962.

Pinsker, M. S.: Information and informational stability of random variables and processes. San Francisco: Holden-Day 1964.

Postnikov, A. G.: Arithmetic modelling of random processes. Published by Akad. Nauk SSSR 1960 (Russian).

Quenouille, M. H.: The analysis of multiple timeseries. London: Griffin 1957.

Rao, C.: Advanced statistical methods in biometric research. New York: Wiley; London: Chapman and Hall 1952.

Rényi, A.: Wahrscheinlichkeitsrechnung mit einem Anhang über Informationstheory. Berlin: Deutscher Verlag d. Wissenschaften 1962

Riordan, J.: Stochastic service systems. New York: Wiley 1962.

Romanovsky, V. I.: Discrete Markov chains. Moscow-Leningrad: Gostechizdat 1949 (Russian).

— Selected papers. Tashkent: Nauka 1964 (Russian).

Rosenblatt, M.: Random processes. New York-Oxford: University Press 1962.

Rozanov, Yu. A.: Stationary random processes. Moscow: Fizmatgiz 1963 (Russian).

Saaty, T. L.: Mathematical methods of operations research. New York: McGraw-Hill 1959.

— Elements of queueing theory with applications. New York: McGraw-Hill 1959.

Sarymsakov, T. A.: Fundamentals of the theory of Markov processes. Moscow: Gostechizdat 1954 (Russian).

Savage, L. J.: The foundation of statistics. New York: Wiley; London: Chapman and Hall 1954.

Scheffé, H.: The analysis of variance. New York: Wiley 1959.

Selin, I.: Detection theory. Princeton, N. J.: University Press 1965.

Serebrennikov, M. G., and *A. A. Pervozvansky:* The appearance of latent periodicities. Moscow: Nauka 1965 (Russian).

Shannon, C. E.: The mathematical theory of communication. 9th ed. Urbana: University of Illinois Press 1962

Siraždinov, S. Ch.: Limit theorems for homogeneous Markov chains. Published by Akad. Nauk UdSSR, Tashkent 1955 (Russian).

Skorochod, A. V.: Studies in the theory of random processes. Cambridge: Addison Wesley 1965.

Slutsky, E. E.: Selected papers. Published by Akad. Nauk SSSR, Moscow 1960 (Russian).

Smirnov, N. V., and *I. V. Dunin-Barkovsky:* Probability theory and mathematical statistics for technical applications. 2nd ed. Moscow: Nauka 1965 (Russian).

Solodovnikov, V. V.: Introduction to statistical dynamics of systems with automatical control. Moscow-Leningrad: Gostechizdat 1952 (Russian).

Spitzer, F.: Principles of random walk. New York-Toronto-London: Van Nostrand 1964.

Storm, R.: Wahrscheinlichkeitsrechnung, mathematische Statistik und statistische Qualitätskontrolle. Leipzig: Fachbuchverlag 1965.

Stratonovič, R. L.: Conditional Markov processes and their application to the theory of optimal control. Ed. by Moscow University, 1966 (Russian).

Sveshnikov, A. A.: Applied methods of the theory of random functions. Published by SP, Leningrad 1961 (Russian).

Takacs, L.: Introduction to the theory of queues. New York-Oxford: University Press 1962.

Tortrat, A.: Principes de statistique mathématique. Paris: Dunod 1961.

Uspensky, J. V.: Introduction to mathematical probability. New York-London: McGraw-Hill 1937.

Van der Waerden, B. L.: Mathematische Statistik. Berlin-Göttingen-Heidelberg: Springer 1957.

Wald, A.: Sequential analysis. London: Wiley 1947.

— Statistical decision functions. New York: Wiley; London: Chapman and Hall 1950.

Walsh, J. E.: Handbook of nonparametric statistics. I. New Jersey: Van Nostrand 1962.

— Handbook of nonparametric statistics. II. New York-Toronto-London: Van Nostrand 1965.

Wentzel, E. S.: Theory of probability. Moscow: Fizmatgiz 1958 (Russian).

Whittle, P.: Prediction and regulation by linear least-square methods. London: University Press 1963.

Wiener, N.: Cybernetics. New York: Wiley 1948.

— Non-linear problems in random theory. The Technology Press of the Massachusetts Institute of Technology and New York: Wiley 1958.

Wolfowitz, J.: Coding theorems of information theory. Berlin-Göttingen-Heidelberg-New York: Springer 1964.

Woodward, P. M.: Probability and information theory with application to radar. New York: McGraw-Hill 1953.

Wozencraft, J. M.: Sequential decoding. Massachusetts Institute of Technology 1957.

Yaglom, A. M., and *I. M. Yaglom:* Wahrscheinlichkeit und Information. 2. ed. Berlin: VEB Deutscher Verlag der Wissenschaften 1965.

Yule, G., and *M. D. Kendall:* An introduction to the theory of statistics 14th. ed. New York: Hafner Publ. Comp. 1950.

Subject Index

Brühlsche Universitätsdruckerei Gießen

Die Grundlehren der mathematischen Wissenschaften in Einzeldarstellungen mit besonderer Berücksichtigung der Anwendungsgebiete